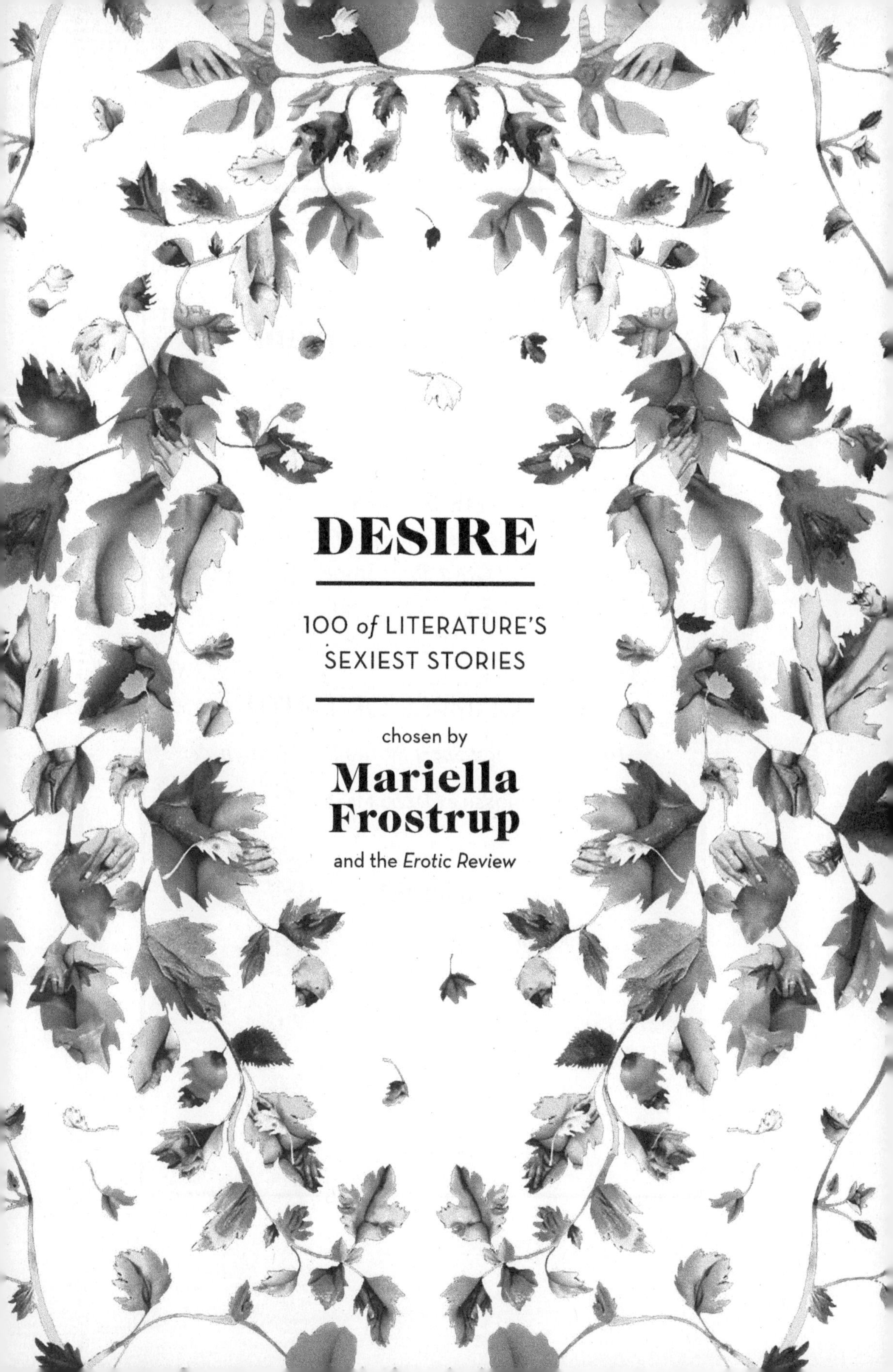

DESIRE

100 *of* LITERATURE'S SEXIEST STORIES

chosen by

Mariella Frostrup

and the *Erotic Review*

Also available from

HEAD *of* ZEUS

THE STORY

Love, Loss and the Lives of Women
100 Great Short Stories

Chosen by Victoria Hislop

THAT GLIMPSE OF TRUTH

100 of the Finest Short Stories Ever Written

Chosen by David Miller

GHOST

100 Stories to Read with the Lights On

Chosen by Louise Welsh

DESIRE

100 *of* LITERATURE'S
SEXIEST STORIES

chosen by

Mariella Frostrup

and the *Erotic Review*

HEAD of ZEUS

First published in the UK in 2016 by Head of Zeus Ltd.

9 7 5 3 2 4 6 8

A catalogue record for this book is available from the British Library.

ISBN (HB) 9781784975449
ISBN (E) 9781784975432

Typeset by PDQ, Bungay, Suffolk

Printed and bound in Germany by CPI Books GmbH

Head of Zeus Ltd
Clerkenwell House
45–47 Clerkenwell Green
London EC1R 0HT
WWW.HEADOFZEUS.COM

DESIRE

Contents

Foreword xiii

Introduction xxi

Awakening Desire

Anonymous	from *Eveline*	3
Rudyard Kipling	*First Dawn*	9
Kate Chopin	*A Respectable Woman*	15
Anonymous	from *A Night in a Moorish Harem*	19
Bram Stoker	from *Dracula*	31
D. H. Lawrence	from *Lady Chatterley's Lover*	35
John Fowles	from *The Magus*	45
Angela Carter	*The Bloody Chamber*	53
Angela Carter	*The Company of Wolves*	81
Patricia Highsmith	from *Carol*	89
Alice Munro	*Bardon Bus*	93
Luke Jennings	*Serena*	107
Henri Breton	*The Disappearing Island*	111
Justine Dubois	*San Sebastian*	119

Justine Dubois	*Torn Lace*	123
Rebecca Chance	*Gluttony*	129
Roger Moineau	*Coming Swimmingly*	131
Alessandra Rivalta	*The Perfect Italian Wife*	137
Harriet Warner	*A Bed for the Night*	143
Diana Gabaldon	*Revelations of the Bridal Chamber*	147
John Gibb	*Blind Love*	163
John Gibb	*Green*	167
Francis Dean	*The Elegant Duchess*	171
Adnan Mahmutović	*Fatima*	177
Paullina Simons	from *The Bronze Horseman*	185
Edward Field	*Forbidden Arias*	197
Primula Bond	from *The Silver Chain*	203
Emma Donoghue	*The Tale of the Rose*	221
Jodi Ellen Malpas	from *This Man*	227
Ali May	*When it Gets Hot in Tehran*	239
John Gibb	*Four in Hand*	243
Nina Gibb	*On the Beach*	249
Ruby McNally	*The Midwesterners*	253
Anna Maconochie	*What Have I to Do With You?*	263
Veronica Cancio De Grandy	*Pears and Silk*	265
Laurence Klavan	*The Witness*	269

Burning Desire

John Cleland	from *Fanny Hill*	279
Kate Percival	from *The Life and Amours of the Beautiful, Gay and Dashing Kate Percival, the Belle of the Delaware*	293
James Joyce	from *Ulysses*	301
Henry Miller	from *Quiet Days in Clichy*	335
Roald Dahl	*The Great Switcheroo*	341
Anne Rice	from *The Claiming of Sleeping Beauty*	359
Roberta Latow	from *Three Rivers*	367
Alan Hollinghurst	from *The Swimming-Pool Library*	375
Anaïs Nin	*A Model*	381
Luke Jennings	*Small Talk*	397
Elizabeth Speller	*Thought Waves*	399
Louise Welsh	*The Worm on the Bud*	403
Louise Black	*Grammar Lessons*	407
Justine Dubois	*Dorchester Evening*	409
Nikki Gemmell	from *The Bride Stripped Bare*	415
Helen Cross	*Pull*	421
Andrew Crumey	*Vox Vulva*	425
Michel Faber	*Bed & Breakfast*	431

Nikki Gemmell	*Nevertire*	441
Louise Welsh	*Belle and Sylvie*	447
Katie Kelly	*Summer*	453
Alex Chambers	*The Selfish Giantess*	459
Garry Stewart	*Off the Road*	463
Nnenna Marcia	*House Keeping*	469
Nnenna Marcia	*Mrs Salad Woman*	475
Malachi O'Doherty	*Love Me, Love My Wife*	483
LaShonda Katrice Burnett	*The Art of Losing*	493
Kass Goldsworthy	*Commute*	497
Kass Goldsworthy	*This Is What It's Like*	505
Charlotte Stein	from *Intrusion*	509
Neville Elder	*The Red House*	523
Arlene Heyman	*The Loves of Her Life*	531

Darkest Desire

Marquis de Sade	from *Justine*	547
Guillaume Apollinaire	from *Memoirs of a Young Rakehill*	555
Georges Bataille	*The Antique Wardrobe*	559
Pauline Réage	from *Story of O*	563
Sebastion Gray	from *The Slit*	567

Alina Reyes	from *Behind Closed Doors*	577
Michel Houellebecq	from *Atomised*	583
Henri Breton	*The Devil's Whisper*	587
Michel Faber	*The Perfect W*	593
Lucy Golden	*Hannah's Tale – Flat*	599
Geoff Nicholson	*Glove Story*	605
Christine Pountney	*Mean Streak*	609
Christine Pountney	*The Cat that Got the Cream*	613
David Henry Sterry	*The Snow Leopard*	617
Mitzi Szereto	*Moonburn*	621
Harriet Warner	*Burning Desire*	627
Anne Billson	*Dead Girls*	631
Angelica Jacob	*This Year at Marienbad*	635
Geoff Nicholson	*California Streamin'*	639
D. B. C. Pierre	*Lust*	643
Helen Walsh	*Men and Motors*	647
Helen Walsh	*You've Been Framed*	651
Lucy Golden	*Finny's Tale – The Creature in the Garden*	655
Katie Kelly	*Let's Put This to Bed*	669
A. F. Harrold	*The Boys*	673
Nicholson Baker	*Shandee Finds Dave's Arm*	679
Fulani	*The Phenomenology of the Whip (Porn Mix)*	683

Danielle Schloss	*Park Antics*	687
Ortensia Visconti	*Tokyo*	691
Tiffany Reisz	from *The Saint*	705
Jo Mazelis	*Rose Madder and the Silken Robe*	711
Christopher Peachment	*The Man Also Rises*	717

Extended Copyright 721

About the Artwork 735

Foreword

In a world saturated with sexual imagery a new anthology of erotic stories might appear superfluous. With real sex in every manifestation available at the click of a mouse on the World Wide Web, who would bother reading (itself considered a prehistoric activity in some quarters) fictional descriptions of other people's sexual adventures? Perhaps I'm just one of a tiny minority; for me it's rather like asking if you have real sex, why you'd bother wasting your thoughts on sexual fantasies?

My first introduction to the erotic world was the proverbial fumble behind the bike shed, but that furtive initiation arrived in tandem with stories I'd unearthed among my parents seemingly dreary tomes at home – illicit material beyond my wildest imaginings. Back in the 1970's, long before

you could log on and find every variety of sexual act performed by the poor and downtrodden, the desperate and the dispossessed, sex was available predominately on the page.

The obscenity trial for Lady Chatterley had taken place just two years before I was born, and so, only fifteen years later, I turned to D. H. Lawrence and his hirsute, brooding heroes with their overwhelming desires to try and unlock the secrets of the sensual universe. It was in my father's smoke-filled study that I happened upon *The Virgin and the Gypsy* as a precocious thirteen year old, and devoured descriptions of the flighty Yvette's passion for the eponymous gypsy, loping past on 'flexible hips'. I knew exactly what he was getting at when he described 'the curious dark, suave purity of all his body, outlined in the green jersey: a purity like a living sneer'. I'd already met a boy just like that. Every single Lawrencium syllable suggested a sexual tryst of a dangerous, convention-defying variety.

Next came Anaïs Nin, purloined from my mother's bedside table, whose *Delta of Venus* transported me to a world long passed and physical sensations I was only just discovering. I luxuriated in her conjured world of sex, oblivion and depravity, and still occasionally enjoy an imaginative flight to the same territory. A pioneer of early female erotic writing (of which there is still nowhere near enough), Nin's racy

Parisian literary life, passionate affair with Henry Miller and need to make a buck or two, led to her penning prolific amounts of page-turning, pitch-perfect, purple prose. Her sensual world, suffused with the heady scent of 1920's opium dens, delved into very dark territory, including incest and paedophilia – topics wholly unpalatable in today's more enlightened society, but her prose remains sublime. Where Lawrence alluded to sex and class, power and subjugation, Nin described, in great physical detail, how all those elements were brought into play in our expressions of sexuality.

These two writers formed my early sexual education, revealing the power of the mind to transport you to places, situations and stimulations that you might avoid in real life, but can safely embrace cerebrally. As human beings, our ability to imagine things we refrain from doing is more impressive than our capacity for doing things we can't imagine. The state of human arousal is far more closely connected to a world we conjure than the one in which we spend our daily lives. The best sex, even while you're physically engaged in doing it, involves an ability to rise above the mechanics. Or is this just a woman's point of view?

Our engagement with, and attitude to, physical passion can seem the one area where men and women really do come from different planets. The

products of the contemporary, male-dominated porn industry, with its relentless pounding and abusing of female bodies via every orifice and in positions even the *Kamasutra* failed to dream up, suggests so. This century's visual pornography, featuring sex as gymnastics with extra lashings of masochism, sadism, or both, seems to have evolved little from the last century, apart from in its abundance. Pornography may do the trick, but through a criminal lack of imagination it renders sex as just another physical activity, like jogging with benefits.

Over the course of my lifetime, the place of sex in our lives has changed immeasurably; once obscured behind closed doors and quivering net curtains, it has become a ubiquitous driving force of the commercial world. Sex sells, and its omnipresence in everything from perfume adverts to pop songs feels close to saturation. Yet is the world a sexier place? Are more of us having sex? Or are we so busy on our smartphones, working twenty-hour days and keeping up with social media, that sex has slipped to the bottom of our to do lists – and even then it is, increasingly, relegated to an online spectator sport.

If conversations with friends and the wider correspondence I receive for my *Observer* 'Dear Mariella' column can be counted as evidence, the prolificacy of pornography is actually becoming a turn off for the over-exposed. Once, as teenagers ourselves, the

scent of sex, the possibility of passion, the longing for love, suffused every moment of our waking lives. Now, we watch our children step gingerly into that seductive, all-consuming period of their lives, and the sex they'll encounter if, like the majority of their generation they seek illumination online, will be graphic, often violent and leave little to the imagination. That for me is the tragedy of their introduction into the world of Eros. Rather than rummaging through their parents' books to find mention of anything even vaguely reflecting the fires they start to feel burning, they're given a full frontal view from day one.

Not that literature necessarily provides a softer way in – the stories collected here can't be regarded as tame, or a young person's guide. This collection is strictly for adults only, though I confess to employing a degree of censorship. With sexual violence so predominant in our news bulletins, I was eager to keep this an abuse- and crime-free zone, despite my belief that dark fantasies can be an outlet for hidden demons, not a trigger for creating real-life monsters. We all have fantasies we'd be ashamed to admit and are reluctant to entertain, but also the capacity for restraint and self-analysis. Hopefully, the stories you'll encounter in this anthology will be shocking, but also entertaining, immersive, seductive and downright dirty.

These are tall tales penned by writers skilled in the art of evoking sexual desire in all its visceral and varied glory. Personally, I'm not particularly interested in watching other people have sex, but I've always enjoyed imagining it. We sit on trains and imagine sex with strangers, catch someone's eye across a room and feel a frisson that sets our imaginative juices flowing. We imagine actors in movies, liberated from the confines of the story entering an adventure of our own creation and lie in bed during the bleak mid-winter thinking about sun-kissed sex on tropical beaches. The minute we stop imagining sex, our ability to enjoy it is, surely, also diminished.

Increasingly, behavioural links are being drawn between teenagers and adults at midlife and, for me, one of the most compelling examples of this connection is when it comes to sex. For decades we are busy doing it and nursing the products of our procreative impulses, and then, as in adolescence, sex either becomes a rarity or returns to occupy the imagination as it did during our prepubescent days.

In my lifetime the world has grown into an endlessly literal place; everything is available, exposure is graphic and nothing is left to our imaginations. That's where erotica has an important role to play. Stories with a beginning, a middle and a climax have existed since human beings first learnt to express

themselves in words. This diverse collection of such stories, old and new, runs the gamut from romantic to bizarre, the amusingly old-fashioned to the futuristic. In these stories, a woman is ravaged at a fancy dress party by two guests in gorilla suits; a married couple perform for onlookers by a Scottish loch; a frustrated housewife seduces her driver on a scorching road trip through the Australian desert; a tennis lesson descends into chaotic coupling. Servants will be ravished in anonymous tales from the 19th century; lesbians will be reluctantly unfaithful; men will suffer the agonies of their enormous erections. We will be exposed to frotting on an Iranian bus, an African maid stepping in for her mistress and a wealthy west London couple getting more than they bargained for when they fork out for a garden statue.

In the course of editing this anthology I've become adept at reading graphic sex in the company of total strangers and leaving them none the wiser. It's quite a challenge to keep your expression neutral, commuting on Great Western Railways, reading about an eight inch 'succubus' pleasuring his power-dressing corporate mistress. Contained here are laughs and shocks, filthy talk and funny scenarios and, hopefully, like the promise of a multiplex pick 'n' mix, something for everyone.

Selecting these stories reminded me of the all-consuming passion of my teenage years, returned me to a heady erotic world I'd become somewhat estranged from and reawakened my interest in this intimate and ancient form of literary pleasure. I hope those of you reading will be similarly seduced.

Mariella Frostrup
October 2016

Introduction

It has been said that 'one man's erotica is another's pornography'. Really? Today, post-*Fifty Shades of Grey* and *YouPorn.com*, this can no longer hold true: whether we hate it or love it, whether we are inured to it or not, pornography has lost pretty much all of its power to shock. Now, for many readers, Julie Burchill's long-standing contempt for 'erotica' has been vindicated: the word has finally acquired a genteel, middle-class patina. Moreover, had we paid any heed to this old saw whilst selecting stories for *Desire: 100 of Literature's Sexiest Stories,* it would have introduced some unwelcome inhibitions. So, significantly, the word 'erotic' is absent from the title. Instead, we've used the word 'sexy'. Though perhaps a little pedestrian, I still find this a more honest and inclusive adjective, and I'm content to

leave the debate of what is erotic and what is pornographic to the people who so love to take issue with those words.

In our selection I wanted the stories to be of a certain literary standard, while still earning the epithet of sexy, libidinous, titillating, erotic and, yes, even pornographic. Of course it's true that, to some degree, this will depend on the reader's perspective. But first and foremost, the stories in this book had to be entertaining in a way that was broadly appropriate for the genre.

Our final choice reflects as wide a range as the category will allow. For some 'sexy' might mean a bit of harmless slap and tickle. For the more deviant and gimp-mask-oriented, it could imply a good deal more 'slap': the sort the Marquis de Sade or Pauline Réage felt so compelled to write about. This anthology, however varied its contents and from whatever century or country its stories hail, has a common goal and, quite frequently, a common destination: namely, to fire up the reader's erotic imagination and – without frightening the horses too much – to set them on the enjoyable path of both mental and physical arousal.

It's reasonable to argue that the creation of the Obscene Publications Act, passed just over a hundred and fifty years ago, has had a lingering effect upon the way we write sex today. One fateful day

in 1857, those of their lordships still awake in the Upper Chamber were listening with half an ear to one of their company droning on about the sale of dangerous poisons. To the amazement of some, and amusement of others, they saw the elderly Chief Justice Lord Campbell leap (uncharacteristically) to his feet in order to deliver an impassioned speech:

'There are far greater dangers to society,' fulminated the Scottish church minister's son, 'than those caused by the misuse of poisons. I have learned with horror and alarm that a sale of poison more deadly than prussic acid, strychnine or arsenic – the sale of obscene publications and indecent books – is openly going on.'

The septuagenarian Campbell was referring to London's infamous Holywell Street, where every sort of pornographic picture, book, guide or manual was on sale. His emotional outburst was particularly surprising to his noble colleagues, since he was better known as 'a learned and industrious gentleman who made up for his lack of sparkle by his glum determination'. Among the murmurs of approval there were equally cries of derision from their lordships, but eventually, despite a rough ride in the Commons, this ageing advocate had the last laugh: his moral outrage was transmogrified into an Act of Parliament that blighted Britain's libido in ways that are still being counted today.

Thus, for the next hundred years, Eros slept. Thanks to Campbell's obsession with porn, a law was created that told us what we could and couldn't publish and what sort of literature the British public were permitted to read; a moral climate was engendered that impeded our access to great authors (as evidenced by the imprisonment of the respected publisher Henry Vizetelly for his translation of Émile Zola's *La Terre* in 1889); and the creation and publishing of any explicit literature was driven deep underground. This erotic winter lasted until, finally, an ordinary jury's common sense prevailed at the infamous Lady Chatterley trial in 1960.

Since then things have changed, to the extent that nowadays the idea of an author being jailed for writing or publishing something salacious is outrageous – at least in this country. In the wider world, at the time of writing, an unpleasant echo of those proscriptive times rings out: the author Ahmed Naji has recently been sentenced to two years' imprisonment by an Egyptian court for violating public modesty after a chapter from his novel, *The Use of Life*, appeared in the state-run literary review *Akhbar al-Adab*.

*

The connection between the *Erotic Review* and erotic literature is a close one: early in our existence we published a limited edition facsimile set of Aubrey Beardsley's illustrations to *Lysistrata*. Upon reading Aristophanes' play, first performed circa 411 BC, it came as a surprise to us how very early sex started to feature in literature. And not just as some coy or veiled reference; sexual frustration is one of the play's central themes: gigantic, painfully unassuaged erections play a prominent part in its stage directions. Sex was as important then as it is now, and it's hard not to speculate whether the Athenian audience found the play not only side-splittingly funny, but shocking and erotic, too.

Although the Athenians regarded sex as completely natural, there remained some inhibitions – though these were social, rather than moral. Aristophanes knew well enough that, when dealing with sexual content, he needed to call upon humour as a useful collaborator in ridding his audience of any hang-ups they might possess; consequently this particular collusion has been popular for a very long time indeed. Lucius Apuleius uses it in his brilliant, farcical *The Golden Ass*, which he wrote more than five hundred years later in the Roman province of what is now Morocco. There is a direct link between Aristophanes and contemporary writers, such as Nicholson Baker, with his rude and extremely

funny *House of Holes,* Christopher Peachment's 'The Man Also Rises' and Luke Jennings' 'Small Talk'. Sandwiched between them are Chaucer's bawdy 'Miller's Tale', the endless raunchy innuendos of Shakespeare's sonnets and plays, Rochester's libertine *Sodom* and Cleland's archly lustful *Fanny Hill.*

*

And what of our collection of short stories that form *Desire*? Where are we now? Has the democratisation and ubiquity of porn via the Internet, the relentless sexualisation of the media, the new gender and identity politics and the blurring of conventional male and female boundaries started a gender fragmentation process?

Certainly, since Lord Campbell's day, there has been a paradigm shift in the way the sexes view sex: over the last few decades birth control, feminism, even a greater anatomical awareness, have forever changed the way we approach each other for sex and the way we enjoy it together. But down the centuries has any real transformation taken place? While the dance steps may change, the rhythm does not: the sexual act, in all its visceral, messy, sweaty, orgasmic glory, seems quite incapable of evolution.

And here is the problem when writing about

sex: there is something so basic and bestial about the way in which we copulate, and yet so uniquely human in the way we blend strong emotions with sexual desire, that occasionally prose can seem like an inadequate form of expression. It's as if there simply aren't enough words to describe the experience. And so it becomes blindingly clear that the context of fucking is far more important than the fucking itself.

This doesn't seem to stop authors regularly trying – and often failing – to 'write sex'. The *Literary Review* gives a prize every year to the author guiltiest of poorly written, perfunctory or redundant passages of sexual description in their novel, but 'the prize is not intended to cover pornographic or expressly erotic literature'. So apprehensive are authors of being crowned with this particular set of withered laurels, that its presenters may have ended up competing with Lord Campbell; it's a different kind of censorship, but few writers care to take the risk of being nominated for the notorious Bad Sex in Fiction Award.

And it's not as if there weren't enough problems already. Writing for the *Erotic Review*, Malachi O'Doherty has observed that, 'Perhaps we feel that in writing about sex we disclose our personal knowledge of naked intimacy. We implicate ourselves. And we don't want to do that. It is no secret

that everyone masturbates, but it is a secret that you or I do. . . And since sex is private and is conducted inside pairings, mostly, where two people together have their private language of gestures and noises, and even subliminally of smells and reflexes, no writer describing a sexual grapple for a wide audience can trust to being understood in the same way by all readers.'

Writing sex, writing an erotic or a pornographic (if you must distinguish) story may cause your work to be relegated to the literary status of 'genre'. But it is a great genre, one that transcends all others for, unlike those that deal with office romances, faster-than-light space travel or the 87th Precinct, it concerns itself with that primal intimacy that is such a crucial component of the human condition.

So here are one hundred reasons to celebrate stories whose authors, in different ways, might regard sex thus. Authors such as Nnenna Marcia, John Gibb, or Geoff Nicholson, who are simply great storytellers; or those, like Nikki Gemmell, Michel Faber or Lucy Golden, who describe the act of sex with such elegant confidence. And there are those who we have come to regard as the classic authors of this genre: John Cleland, Georges Bataille, Anaïs Nin and Henry Miller.

Desire salutes the bravery, the persistence and the sheer chutzpah of all those writers who have,

for millennia, written sex. It applauds the risks of imprisonment, or worse, that they took and their refusal to bow to the cultural conventions of their time. Erotic heroes all, to a woman and a man!

Jamie Maclean, Erotic Review
October 2016
www.ermagazine.com

Awakening Desire

From EVELINE

Anonymous

The author of the preface to the 1904 edition of *Eveline* makes a case for the adventurous and independent Eveline being some sort of sexual psychopath, or as he puts it, 'inheriting an absence of moral perceptions so far as it relates to the sexual instinct'. A common attitude, perhaps, when stout Edwardian gentlemen, in complete denial of their own satyriasic condition, viewed any sort of female sexual independence with alarm. If they could not control an erotic situation, it was aberrant. Today's women might view Eveline's progress with a certain degree of admiration.

I determined to run up to town. I went by an early train, alone. I entered the station some fifteen minutes before the train started. On the platform was a gentlemanly-looking man in a tweed suit. I thought I had seen his face before. I could not recall where. We passed each other. He looked pointedly at me. Certainly I knew his features. I never forget, if I take an interest in a man's appearance. I liked the look of this tall, well-built fellow in tweeds. He appeared to be about thirty-five to forty years of age – hale and hearty. I gave him one of my glances as he passed me.

"This way, miss. First class – no corridors on this train. You will be all right here. You're all alone at present."

"Thank you, guard. Does the train go up without stopping?"

"Stops at Lewes, miss. That's all – then right up."

I saw my tall friend pass the carriage. Another glance. He stopped – hesitated – then opened the door and got in. He took a seat opposite me. The newspaper appeared to engross his attention until the whistle sounded. We were off.

"Would you object to my lowering the window? These carriages are stuffy. The morning is so warm."

I made no objection, but smilingly gave consent. "How calm and beautiful the sea looks! It seems a pity to leave it."

"Indeed I think so – especially for London."

"You are going up to London? How odd! So am I!"

I could not be mistaken. I had seen him somewhere before.

"I shall miss the sea very much. We have no sea baths in Manchester. I love my morning dip."

It struck me like a flash. I remembered him now.

"You must have enjoyed it very much, coming from an inland city."

"Well, yes, you see I had a good time. They looked after me well. Always had my machine ready."

"I have no doubt of that."

"No. 33. A new one – capital people – very fine machine."

I suppose I smiled a little. He laughed in reply as if he read my thought. Then he folded up his paper. I arranged my small reticule. It unfortunately dropped from my hand. He picked it up and presented it to me. His foot touched mine. We conversed. He told me he lived near Manchester. He had been to Eastbourne for rest. His business had been too much for him, but he was all right now. His gaze was constantly upon me. I kept thinking of his appearance all naked on the platform of the bathing machine as old David Jones rowed me past. We stopped at Lewes. My companion put his head out of the window. He prevented the entry of an old lady by abusing the newspaper boy for his want of activity. The train started again.

"I think Eastbourne is one of the best bathing places on the coast. You know where the gentlemen's machines are?"

"I think I know where they keep them."

"Well, I was going to say – but – well – what a funny girl you are! Why are you laughing?"

"Because a funny idea struck me. I was thinking of a friend."

His foot was pushed a little closer – very perceptible was the touch. He never ceased gloating on my person. My gloves evidently had an especial attraction for him. Meanwhile, I looked him well over. He was certainly a fine man. He roused my emotions. I permitted his foot to remain in contact with my boot. I even moved it past his, so that my ankle touched his. His face worked nervously. Poor man, no wonder! He gave me a searching look. Our glances met. He pressed my leg between his own. His fingers were trembling with that undefined longing for contact with the object of desire I so well understood. I smiled.

"You seem very fond of the ladies."

I said it boldly, with a familiar meaning he could not fail to understand. I glanced at his leather bag in the rack above.

"I cannot deny the soft impeachment. I am. Especially when they are young and beautiful."

"Oh, you men! You are dreadfully wicked. What would Mrs Turner say to that?"

I laughed. He stared with evident alarm. It was a bold stroke. I risked it. Either way I lost nothing.

"How do you know I am married?" My shaft had gone home. He had actually missed the first evident fact. He picked it up, however, quickly, before I could reply. "It appears you know me? You know my name?"

"Well, yes. You see I am not blind."

I pointed to the label on the bag above his head. It was his turn to laugh.

"Ah! You have me there! What a terribly observant young lady you must be!"

He seized my hand before I could regain my attitude. He pressed it in both his own.

"You will not like me any the less – will you? I thought we were going to be so friendly."

"On the contrary – they say married men are the best."

Up to this point, my effrontery had led him on. He must have felt he was on safe ground. My last remark was hardly even equivocal. He evidently took it as it was intended. I was equally excited. The man and the opportunity tempted me on. I wanted him. I was delighted with his embarrassment – with his fast increasing assurance. I made no attempt to withdraw my hand. He crossed over. He occupied the seat beside me. My gloved hand remained in his.

"I am so glad you think so. You do not know how charming I think you. Married men ought to be good judges, you know."

"I suppose so. I rather prefer them."

I looked in his face and laughed as I uttered the words. He brought his very close. He passed his left arm round my waist. I made no resistance. The carriage gave a sympathetic jerk as it rushed along. Our faces touched. His lips were in contact with mine. It was quite accidental, of course, the line is so badly laid. We kissed.

"Oh, you *are* nice! How pretty you are!"

He pressed his hot lips again to mine. I thought of the sight I had seen on the bathing machine. My blood boiled. I half closed my eyes. I let him keep his mouth upon mine. He pressed me to him. He drew my light form to his stout and well-built frame as in a vice.

I put my right foot up on the opposite seat. He glared at the pretty tight little kid boot. He was evidently much agitated.

"Ah! What a lovely foot!"

He touched it with his hand. His fingers ran over the soft pale cream-coloured leather. I wore a pair of papa's prime favourites. He did not stop there. The trembling hand passed on to my stocking, advancing by stealthy degrees. It was then he tried to push forward the tip of his tongue.

"How beautiful you are and how gentle and kind!"

His arm enfolded me still closer, my bosom pressed his shoulder. His hand pressed further and further up my stocking. I closed my knees resolutely. I gave a hurried glance around.

"Are we quite safe here, do you think?"

"Quite safe, and, as you see, quite alone."

Our lips met again. This time I kissed him boldly. The tip of his active tongue inserted itself between my moist lips.

"Ah! How lovely you are! How gloriously pretty!"

"Hush! They might hear us in the next carriage. I am frightened."

"You are deliciously sweet. I long for you dreadfully."

Mr Turner's hand continued its efforts towards my knees. I relaxed my pressure a little. He reached my garters above them. In doing so he uncovered my ankles. He feasted his eyes on my calves daintily set off in openwork stockings of a delicate shade of pale brown.

"Oh, you are too bad, really! I ought not to let you do that – no, really! Pray do not do so – oh!"

It was a delicious game of seduction. I enjoyed his lecherous touches. He was constantly becoming more confident of his sudden and uncontrollable passion. He strained me to him. His breath came quick and sweet upon my face. I lusted for this man's embrace beyond all power of language to convey. His warm hand reached my plump thigh. I made pretence to prevent his advance.

"Pray – oh, pray do not do that! Oh!"

A sudden jerk as we apparently sped over some points. I relaxed my resistance a trifle. He took instant advantage of the movement. His finger was on the most sensitive part of my private parts. It pressed upon my clitoris. I felt the little thing stiffen, swell and throb under the touch of a man's hand. His excitement increased. He drew me even closer. He pressed my warm body to his. His kisses, hot and voluptuous, covered my face and neck.

"How divinely sweet you are! The perfume of your lovely breath is so rapturously nice. Do let me – do – do! I love you so!"

He held me tight with his left arm. He had withdrawn his right. I was conscious he was undoing his trousers. He had left my skirts in disorder. I saw him pull aside his protruding shirt. I secretly watched his movements out of a corner of my eye while he kept my face close to his. Then appeared all that I had seen on the bathing machine, but standing fiercely erect, red-headed and formidable – a huge limb. He thrust it into full view.

"My darling! My beauty! See this! See! See to what a state you have driven me. You will let me – won't you?"

"Oh, for shame! Let me go – pray do not do that – you must not. Your finger hurts. Don't – pray don't! Oh, dear! Oh! Oh!"

The jolting of the carriage favoured his operations. His hand was again between my thighs. His second finger pressed my throbbing button. My parts were bedewed with the fluid begotten by desire. He was inspecting the premises before taking possession. I only hoped he would not find the accommodation insufficient for so large a tenant.

"Oh, pray don't! Oh, goodness! What a man you are!"

With a sudden movement, he slipped round upon his knees, passing one of my legs over his left arm and thus thrust me back on the soft sprung seat of the carriage. He threw up my clothes. He was between my thighs. My belly and private parts were exposed to his lascivious operations. I looked over my dress as I attempted to right myself. I saw him kneeling before me in the most indelicate position. His trousers were open. His huge privates stood menacingly before my eyes. He had so far loosened his clothing that his testicles were out. His belly was covered with crisp black hair. I saw all in that quick feverish glance. I saw the dull red head of his big limb drawn downward by the little string as it faced me, and the slit-like opening through which the men spurt their white venom.

He audaciously took my hand, gloved as it was, and placed it upon his member. It was hard and rigid as wood.

"Feel that – dear girl! Do not be frightened. I will not hurt you. Feel – feel my prick!"

He drew me forward. I felt him as requested. I had ceased all resistance. My willing little hand clasped the immense instrument he called his "prick".

"Now put it there yourself, little girl. It is longing to be into you."

"Oh – my good heavens! It will never go in! You will kill me!"

Nevertheless I assisted him to his enjoyment. I put the nut between the nether lips. He pushed while firmly holding me by both hips. My parts relaxed – my vagina adapted itself as I had been told it could without injury to the most

formidable of male organs. The huge thing entered me. He thrust in fierce earnest. He got it fairly in.

"Oh! My God! I'm into you now! Oh! Oh! How delicious! Hold tight! Let me pull you down to me – so – oh! My God! How nice! How soft! How exquisite!"

I passed my left arm through the strap. My right clutched him round the neck. He put down his hand. He parted the strained lips round his huge intruding weapon. Then he seized me by the buttocks. He strained me towards him as he pushed. My head fell back – my lips parted. I felt his testicles rubbing close up between my legs. He was into me to the quick!

"Oh, dear! Dear! You are too rough! You hurt – you push too hard! My goodness me! How you are tearing me. Oh! Oh! Ah! It is too much! You darling man! Push! Push! Oh!"

It was too much pleasure. I threw my head back again. I grasped the cushions on either side. I could not speak. I could only gasp and whine now. I moved my head from side to side as he lay down on my belly and enjoyed me. His thing – stiff as a staff – worked up and down my vagina. I could feel the big plum-like gland pushed forcibly against my womb. I spent over and over again. I was in heaven.

He ground his teeth. He hissed. He lolled his head. He kissed me on the lips. He breathed hard and fast. His pleasure was delicious to witness.

"Oh! Oh! Hold tight, love. I am in an agony of pleasure. I – I – can't tell you! I – never – tasted – such delicious poking! Oh! Ugh!"

"Oh, dear! Oh, dear! You are so large! So strong!"

"Don't move! Don't pinch my prick more than you can help, darling girl. Let us go on as long as possible. You are coming again. I can feel you squeezing me! Oh! Wait a moment – so – hold still!"

"Oh! I can feel it at my womb – you are up to my waist! Oh, dear! Oh! Oh! You are so stiff!"

"I cannot hold much longer. I must spend soon!"

Bang! Bang! ! Bang! ! !

The train was passing over the points at Reigate. The alarm was sufficient to retard our climax. It acted as a check to his wild excitement – to the coming climax.

"Hold quite still, you sweet little beauty. We do not stop. The speed is quickening again. Now push! Push! Push! Is that nice? Do you like my big prick? Does it stir you up? You are right, my sweet. I can feel your little womb with the tip."

He assisted me to throw my legs up over his shoulders. He seemed to enter me further than ever.

"Oh! You're so large! Oh! Good Lord! Go on slowly – don't finish me yet! It's so – so – so nice! You're making me come again. Oh my!"

"No, dear, I won't finish you before I can help it. You are so nice to poke slowly! Do you like being finished? Do you – oh, my God! There, push! Push! Do you like to feel a man come?"

"Oh! Not so hard! There! Oh, my! Must – must I tell you – I – I love to feel – to feel a man spend – all the sweet sperm!"

"You'll feel mine very – very soon, you beautiful little angel. Oh! I shall swim

you in it! There! My prick is in now up to the balls – Oh! Oh! How you nip it – oh!"

He gave some exquisite short stabs with his loins. His thing, as hard as wood, was up my belly as far as its great length could reach. He sank his head on my shoulder.

"Hold still – I'm spending! Oh, my God! How luscious!"

I felt a great gush come from him. It flowed from him in quick hot jets. He groaned in his ecstasy. I opened my legs. I raised up my loins to receive it. I clutched right and left at anything and everything – I spent furiously. He gave me a quantity. I was swimming in it. At length he desisted and released me.

A few minutes sufficed in which to rearrange ourselves decently. Mr Turner asked me many questions. I fenced some – I answered others. I let him believe I was professionally employed in a provincial company. I told him I had been unwell and had been resting a short time at Eastbourne. He was delicate enough not to press for particulars, but he asked for an address. I gave him a country post office. In a few minutes more we stopped on the river bridge to deliver up tickets.

The train rolled into the station. My new friend made his *adieux*. He dexterously slipped two sovereigns into my glove as he squeezed my hand. I was glad. It proved the complete success of my precautions.

I hailed a hansom and drove direct to Swan and Edgar's. Outside the station, my cab stopped in the crowd. A poor woman thrust a skinny arm and hand towards me with an offer of a box of matches. I took them and substituted one of the sovereigns. As I alighted in Piccadilly, a ragged little urchin made a dash to turn back the door of my cab. He looked half starved.

"Have you a mother? How many brothers and sisters?"

"Six of us, lydy; muvver's out o' work."

"Take that home as quick as you can."

"Blimy! A thick 'un! There ain't no ruddy copper lookin' to pinch it off me! Muvver'll plant it away, so as 'ow favver won't have no cause to bash her for it."

He had never been taught to say "thank you". He took one hasty glance in either direction and darted away in the throng.

I discharged the cab. I made quite sure I was not followed.

Meanwhile my late companion was no doubt speeding on towards Manchester where he said he must dine that evening with Mrs Turner. I hope the good lady was reasonable with her spouse.

FIRST DAWN

Rudyard Kipling

Rudyard Kipling was a British writer of short stories, a novelist, a poet and a journalist. He was born in Bombay and died in London at the age of seventy. He is famous for *The Jungle Book*, *Just So Stories*, *Kim*, 'If…', 'Gunga Din' and 'The White Man's Burden'. He was awarded the Nobel Prize in literature in 1907. He declined several offers of both a knighthood and the Poet Laureateship. George Orwell hailed him as a 'prophet of British Imperialism'.

To-night God knows what thing shall tide,
The Earth is racked and faint
Expectant, sleepless, open-eyed;
And we, who from the Earth were made,
Thrill with our Mother's pain.
In Durance.

No man will ever know the exact truth of this story; though women may sometimes whisper it to one another after a dance, when they are putting up their hair for the night and comparing lists of victims. A man, of course, cannot assist at these functions. So the tale must be told from the outside – in the dark – all wrong.

Never praise a sister to a sister, in the hope of your compliments reaching the proper ears, and so preparing the way for you later on. Sisters are women first, and sisters afterwards; and you will find that you do yourself harm.

Saumarez knew this when he made up his mind to propose to the elder Miss Copleigh. Saumarez was a strange man, with few merits, so far as men could see, though he was popular with women, and carried enough conceit to stock a Viceroy's Council and leave a little over for the Commander-in-Chief's Staff. He was a Civilian. Very many women took an interest in Saumarez, perhaps, because his manner to them was offensive. If you hit a pony over the nose at the outset of your acquaintance, he may not love you, but he will take a deep interest in your movements ever afterwards. The elder Miss Copleigh was nice, plump, winning and pretty. The younger was not so pretty, and, from men disregarding the hint set forth above, her style was repellent and unattractive. Both girls had, practically, the same figure, and there was a strong likeness between them in look and voice; though no one could doubt for an instant which was the nicer of the two.

Saumarez made up his mind, as soon as they came into the station from Behar, to marry the elder one. At least, we all made sure that he would, which comes

to the same thing. She was two and twenty, and he was thirty-three, with pay and allowances of nearly fourteen hundred rupees a month. So the match, as we arranged it, was in every way a good one. Saumarez was his name, and summary was his nature, as a man once said. Having drafted his Resolution, he formed a Select Committee of One to sit upon it, and resolved to take his time. In our unpleasant slang, the Copleigh girls 'hunted in couples'. That is to say, you could do nothing with one without the other. They were very loving sisters; but their mutual affection was sometimes inconvenient. Saumarez held the balance-hair true between them, and none but himself could have said to which side his heart inclined, though every one guessed. He rode with them a good deal and danced with them, but he never succeeded in detaching them from each other for any length of time.

Women said that the two girls kept together through deep mistrust, each fearing that the other would steal a march on her. But that has nothing to do with a man. Saumarez was silent for good or bad, and as business-likely attentive as he could be, having due regard to his work and his polo. Beyond doubt both girls were fond of him.

As the hot weather drew nearer, and Saumarez made no sign, women said that you could see their trouble in the eyes of the girls – that they were looking strained, anxious, and irritable. Men are quite blind in these matters unless they have more of the woman than the man in their composition, in which case it does not matter what they say or think. I maintain it was the hot April days that took the colour out of the Copleigh girls' cheeks. They should have been sent to the Hills early. No one – man or woman – feels an angel when the hot weather is approaching. The younger sister grew more cynical, not to say acid, in her ways; and the winningness of the elder wore thin. There was effort in it.

Now the Station wherein all these things happened was, though not a little one, off the line of rail, and suffered through want of attention. There were no gardens or bands or amusements worth speaking of, and it was nearly a day's journey to come into Lahore for a dance. People were grateful for small things to interest them.

About the beginning of May, and just before the final exodus of Hill-goers, when the weather was very hot and there were not more than twenty people in the Station, Saumarez gave a moonlight riding-picnic at an old tomb, six miles away, near the bed of the river. It was a 'Noah's Ark' picnic; and there was to be the usual arrangement of quarter-mile intervals between each couple, on account of the dust. Six couples came altogether, including chaperones. Moonlight picnics are useful just at the very end of the season, before all the girls go away to the Hills. They lead to understandings, and should be encouraged by chaperones; especially those whose girls look sweetest in riding habits. I knew a case once. But that is another story. That picnic was called the 'Great Pop Picnic', because every one knew Saumarez would propose then to the eldest Miss Copleigh; and, beside his affair, there was another which might possibly come to happiness.

The social atmosphere was heavily charged and wanted clearing.

We met at the parade ground at ten: the night was fearfully hot. The horses sweated even at walking-pace, but anything was better than sitting still in our own dark houses. When we moved off under the full moon we were four couples,

one triplet, and Me. Saumarez rode with the Copleigh girls, and I loitered at the tail of the procession, wondering with whom Saumarez would ride home. Every one was happy and contented; but we all felt that things were going to happen. We rode slowly; and it was nearly midnight before we reached the old tomb, facing the ruined tank, in the decayed gardens where we were going to eat and drink. I was late in coming up; and, before I went into the garden, I saw that the horizon to the north carried a faint, dun-coloured feather. But no one would have thanked me for spoiling so well-managed an entertainment as this picnic – and a dust-storm, more or less, does no great harm.

We gathered by the tank. Some one had brought out a banjo – which is a most sentimental instrument – and three or four of us sang.

You must not laugh at this. Our amusements in out-of-the-way Stations are very few indeed. Then we talked in groups or together, lying under the trees, with the sun-baked roses dropping their petals on our feet, until supper was ready. It was a beautiful supper, as cold and as iced as you could wish; and we stayed long over it.

I had felt that the air was growing hotter and hotter; but nobody seemed to notice it until the moon went out and a burning hot wind began lashing the orange-trees with a sound like the noise of the sea. Before we knew where we were the dust-storm was on us, and everything was roaring, whirling darkness. The supper-table was blown bodily into the tank. We were afraid of staying anywhere near the old tomb for fear it might be blown down. So we felt our way to the orange-trees where the horses were picketed and waited for the storm to blow over. Then the little light that was left vanished, and you could not see your hand before your face. The air was heavy with dust and sand from the bed of the river, that filled boots and pockets, and drifted down necks and coated eyebrows and moustaches. It was one of the worst dust-storms of the year.

We were all huddled together close to the trembling horses, with the thunder chattering overhead, and the lightning spurting like water from a sluice, all ways at once. There was no danger, of course, unless the horses broke loose. I was standing with my head downwind and my hands over my mouth, hearing the trees thrashing each other. I could not see who was next me till the flashes came.

Then I found that I was packed near Saumarez and the eldest Miss Copleigh, with my own horse just in front of me. I recognized the eldest Miss Copleigh, because she had a pagri round her helmet, and the younger had not. All the electricity in the air had gone into my body, and I was quivering and tingling from head to foot – exactly as a corn shoots and tingles before rain. It was a grand storm.

The wind seemed to be picking up the earth and pitching it to leeward in great heaps; and the heat beat up from the ground like the heat of the Day of Judgment.

The storm lulled slightly after the first half-hour, and I heard a despairing little voice close to my ear, saying to itself, quietly and softly, as if some lost soul were flying about with the wind: "O my God!" Then the younger Miss Copleigh stumbled into my arms, saying: "Where is my horse? Get my horse. I want to go home. I want to go home. Take me home."

I thought that the lightning and the black darkness had frightened her; so I said there was no danger, but she must wait till the storm blew over. She an-

swered: "It is not that! It is not that! I want to go home! Oh, take me away from here!"

I said that she could not go till the light came; but I felt her brush past me and go away. It was too dark to see where. Then the whole sky was split open with one tremendous flash, as if the end of the world were coming, and all the women shrieked.

Almost directly after this, I felt a man's hand on my shoulder and heard Saumarez bellowing in my ear. Through the rattling of the trees and howling of the wind I did not catch his words at once, but at last I heard him say: "I've proposed to the wrong one! What shall I do?" Saumarez had no occasion to make this confidence to me. I was never a friend of his, nor am I now; but I fancy neither of us were ourselves just then. He was shaking as he stood with excitement, and I was feeling queer all over with the electricity.

I could not think of anything to say except, "More fool you for proposing in a dust-storm." But I did not see how that would improve the mistake.

Then he shouted: "Where's Edith – Edith Copleigh?" Edith was the younger sister. I answered out of my astonishment, "What do you want with her?" For the next two minutes, he and I were shouting at each other like maniacs – he vowing that it was the younger sister he had meant to propose to all along, and I telling him, till my throat was hoarse, that he must have made a mistake! I can't account for this except, again, by the fact that we were neither of us ourselves. Everything seemed to me like a bad dream – from the stamping of the horses in the darkness to Saumarez telling me the story of his loving Edith Copleigh from the first. He was still clawing my shoulder and begging me to tell him where Edith Copleigh was, when another lull came and brought light with it, and we saw the dust-cloud forming on the plain in front of us. So we knew the worst was over. The moon was low down, and there was just the glimmer of the false dawn that comes about an hour before the real one. But the light was very faint, and the dun cloud roared like a bull. I wondered where Edith Copleigh had gone; and as I was wondering I saw three things together: First Maud Copleigh's face come smiling out of the darkness and move towards Saumarez, who was standing by me. I heard the girl whisper, "George," and slide her arm through the arm that was not clawing my shoulder, and I saw that look on her face which only comes once or twice in a lifetime – when a woman is perfectly happy and the air is full of trumpets and gorgeously-coloured fire, and the Earth turns into cloud because she loves and is loved. At the same time, I saw Saumarez's face as he heard Maud Copleigh's voice, and fifty yards away from the clump of orange-trees I saw a brown holland habit getting upon a horse.

It must have been my state of over-excitement that made me so ready to meddle with what did not concern me. Saumarez was moving off to the habit; but I pushed him back and said, "Stop here and explain. I'll fetch her back!" And I ran out to get at my own horse. I had a perfectly unnecessary notion that everything must be done decently and in order, and that Saumarez's first care was to wipe the happy look out of Maud Copleigh's face. All the time I was linking up the curb-chain I wondered how he would do it.

I cantered after Edith Copleigh, thinking to bring her back slowly on some pretence or another. But she galloped away as soon as she saw me, and I was

forced to ride after her in earnest. She called back over her shoulder – "Go away! I'm going home. Oh, go away!" two or three times; but my business was to catch her first, and argue later. The ride fitted in with the rest of the evil dream. The ground was very rough, and now and again we rushed through the whirling, choking 'dust-devils' in the skirts of the flying storm. There was a burning hot wind blowing that brought up a stench of stale brick-kilns with it; and through the half light and through the dust-devils, across that desolate plain, flickered the brown holland habit on the grey horse. She headed for the Station at first. Then she wheeled round and set off for the river through beds of burnt down jungle-grass, bad even to ride a pig over. In cold blood I should never have dreamed of going over such a country at night, but it seemed quite right and natural with the lightning crackling overhead, and a reek like the smell of the Pit in my nostrils. I rode and shouted, and she bent forward and lashed her horse, and the aftermath of the dust-storm came up and caught us both, and drove us downwind like pieces of paper.

I don't know how far we rode; but the drumming of the horse-hoofs and the roar of the wind and the race of the faint blood-red moon through the yellow mist seemed to have gone on for years and years, and I was literally drenched with sweat from my helmet to my gaiters when the grey stumbled, recovered himself, and pulled up dead lame. My brute was used up altogether. Edith Copleigh was bare headed, plastered with dust, and crying bitterly. "Why can't you let me alone?" she said. "I only wanted to get away and go home. Oh, please let me go!"

"You have got to come back with me, Miss Copleigh. Saumarez has something to say to you."

It was a foolish way of putting it; but I hardly knew Miss Copleigh, and, though I was playing Providence at the cost of my horse, I could not tell her in as many words what Saumarez had told me. I thought he could do that better himself. All her pretence about being tired and wanting to go home broke down, and she rocked herself to and fro in the saddle as she sobbed, and the hot wind blew her black hair to leeward. I am not going to repeat what she said, because she was utterly unstrung.

This, if you please, was the cynical Miss Copleigh. Here was I, almost an utter stranger to her, trying to tell her that Saumarez loved her, and she was to come back to hear him say so. I believe I made myself understood, for she gathered the grey together and made him hobble somehow, and we set off for the tomb, while the storm went thundering down to Umballa and a few big drops of warm rain fell. I found out that she had been standing close to Saumarez when he proposed to her sister, and had wanted to go home to cry in peace, as an English girl should. She dabbled her eyes with her pocket-handkerchief as we went along, and babbled to me out of sheer lightness of heart and hysteria. That was perfectly unnatural; and yet, it seemed all right at the time and in the place. All the world was only the two Copleigh girls, Saumarez and I, ringed in with the lightning and the dark; and the guidance of this misguided world seemed to lie in my hands.

When we returned to the tomb in the deep, dead stillness that followed the storm, the dawn was just breaking and nobody had gone away. They were wait-

ing for our return. Saumarez most of all. His face was white and drawn. As Miss Copleigh and I limped up, he came forward to meet us, and, when he helped her down from her saddle, he kissed her before all at the picnic. It was like a scene in a theatre, and the likeness was heightened by all the dust-white, ghostly-looking men and women under the orange-trees, clapping their hands – as if they were watching a play – at Saumarez's choice. I never knew anything so un-English in my life.

Lastly, Saumarez said we must all go home or the Station would come out to look for us, and would I be good enough to ride home with Maud Copleigh? Nothing would give me greater pleasure, I said.

So we formed up, six couples in all, and went back two by two; Saumarez walking at the side of Edith Copleigh, who was riding his horse. Maud Copleigh did not talk to me at any length.

The air was cleared; and, little by little, as the sun rose, I felt we were all dropping back again into ordinary men and women, and that the 'Great Pop Picnic' was a thing altogether apart and out of the world – never to happen again. It had gone with the dust-storm and the tingle in the hot air.

I felt tired and limp, and a good deal ashamed of myself as I went in for a bath and some sleep.

There is a woman's version of this story, but it will never be written… unless Maud Copleigh cares to try.

A RESPECTABLE WOMAN

Kate Chopin

Kate Chopin, born Katherine O'Flaherty, was a American author of short stories and novels. Her short stories were well received on publication the 1890s and were featured in some of America's most prestigious magazines – *Vogue*, *The Atlantic Monthly*, *Harper's Young People* and the *Century*. Chopin's work was mostly forgotten after her death, but, beginning in the 1950s, scholars rediscovered it and praised it for its truthful depictions of women's lives.

Mrs Baroda was a little provoked to learn that her husband expected his friend, Gouvernail, up to spend a week or two on the plantation. They had entertained a good deal during the winter; much of the time had also been passed in New Orleans in various forms of mild dissipation. She was looking forward to a period of unbroken rest, now, and undisturbed tête-à-tête with her husband, when he informed her that Gouvernail was coming up to stay a week or two.

This was a man she had heard much of but never seen. He had been her husband's college friend; was now a journalist, and in no sense a society man or "a man about town," which were, perhaps, some of the reasons she had never met him. But she had unconsciously formed an image of him in her mind. She pictured him tall, slim, cynical; with eye-glasses, and his hands in his pockets; and she did not like him. Gouvernail was slim enough, but he wasn't very tall nor very cynical; neither did he wear eyeglasses or carry his hands in his pockets. And she rather liked him when he first presented himself.

But why she liked him she could not explain satisfactorily to herself when she partly attempted to do so. She could discover in him none of those brilliant and promising traits which Gaston, her husband, had often assured her that he possessed. On the contrary, he sat rather mute and receptive before her chatty eagerness to make him feel at home, and in face of Gaston's frank and wordy hospitality. His manner was as courteous toward her as the most exacting woman could require; but he made no direct appeal to her approval or even esteem.

Once settled at the plantation he seemed to like to sit upon the wide portico in the shade of one of the big Corinthian pillars, smoking his cigar lazily and listening attentively to Gaston's experience as a sugar planter.

"This is what I call living," he would utter with deep satisfaction, as the air that swept across the sugar field caressed him with its warm and scented velvety touch. It pleased him also to get on familiar terms with the big dogs that came about him, rubbing themselves sociably against his legs. He did not care to fish,

and displayed no eagerness to go out and kill gros becs when Gaston proposed doing so.

Gouvernail's personality puzzled Mrs Baroda, but she liked him. Indeed, he was a lovable, inoffensive fellow. After a few days, when she could understand him no better than at first, she gave over being puzzled and remained piqued. In this mood she left her husband and her guest, for the most part, alone together. Then finding that Gouvernail took no manner of exception to her action, she imposed her society upon him, accompanying him in his idle strolls to the mill and walks along the batture. She persistently sought to penetrate the reserve in which he had unconsciously enveloped himself.

"When is he going – your friend?" she one day asked her husband. "For my part, he tires me frightfully."

"Not for a week yet, dear. I can't understand; he gives you no trouble."

"No. I should like him better if he did; if he were more like others, and I had to plan somewhat for his comfort and enjoyment."

Gaston took his wife's pretty face between his hands and looked tenderly and laughingly into her troubled eyes.

They were making a bit of toilet sociably together in Mrs Baroda's dressing-room.

"You are full of surprises, ma belle," he said to her. "Even I can never count upon how you are going to act under given conditions." He kissed her and turned to fasten his cravat before the mirror.

"Here you are," he went on, "taking poor Gouvernail seriously and making a commotion over him, the last thing he would desire or expect."

"Commotion!" she hotly resented. "Nonsense! How can you say such a thing? Commotion, indeed! But, you know, you said he was clever."

"So he is. But the poor fellow is run down by overwork now. That's why I asked him here to take a rest."

"You used to say he was a man of ideas," she retorted, unconciliated. "I expected him to be interesting, at least. I'm going to the city in the morning to have my spring gowns fitted. Let me know when Mr Gouvernail is gone; I shall be at my Aunt Octavie's."

That night she went and sat alone upon a bench that stood beneath a live oak tree at the edge of the gravel walk.

She had never known her thoughts or her intentions to be so confused. She could gather nothing from them but the feeling of a distinct necessity to quit her home in the morning.

Mrs Baroda heard footsteps crunching the gravel; but could discern in the darkness only the approaching red point of a lighted cigar. She knew it was Gouvernail, for her husband did not smoke. She hoped to remain unnoticed, but her white gown revealed her to him. He threw away his cigar and seated himself upon the bench beside her; without a suspicion that she might object to his presence.

"Your husband told me to bring this to you, Mrs Baroda," he said, handing her a filmy, white scarf with which she sometimes enveloped her head and shoulders. She accepted the scarf from him with a murmur of thanks, and let it lie in her lap.

He made some commonplace observation upon the baneful effect of the night air at the season. Then as his gaze reached out into the darkness, he murmured, half to himself:

"'Night of south winds – night of the large few stars! Still nodding night—'"

She made no reply to this apostrophe to the night, which, indeed, was not addressed to her.

Gouvernail was in no sense a diffident man, for he was not a self-conscious one. His periods of reserve were not constitutional, but the result of moods. Sitting there beside Mrs. Baroda, his silence melted for the time.

He talked freely and intimately in a low, hesitating drawl that was not unpleasant to hear. He talked of the old college days when he and Gaston had been a good deal to each other; of the days of keen and blind ambitions and large intentions. Now there was left with him, at least, a philosophic acquiescence to the existing order – only a desire to be permitted to exist, with now and then a little whiff of genuine life, such as he was breathing now.

Her mind only vaguely grasped what he was saying. Her physical being was for the moment predominant. She was not thinking of his words, only drinking in the tones of his voice. She wanted to reach out her hand in the darkness and touch him with the sensitive tips of her fingers upon the face or the lips. She wanted to draw close to him and whisper against his cheek – she did not care what – as she might have done if she had not been a respectable woman.

The stronger the impulse grew to bring herself near him, the further, in fact, did she draw away from him. As soon as she could do so without an appearance of too great rudeness, she rose and left him there alone.

Before she reached the house, Gouvernail had lighted a fresh cigar and ended his apostrophe to the night.

Mrs Baroda was greatly tempted that night to tell her husband – who was also her friend – of this folly that had seized her. But she did not yield to the temptation. Beside being a respectable woman she was a very sensible one; and she knew there are some battles in life which a human being must fight alone.

When Gaston arose in the morning, his wife had already departed. She had taken an early morning train to the city. She did not return till Gouvernail was gone from under her roof.

There was some talk of having him back during the summer that followed. That is, Gaston greatly desired it; but this desire yielded to his wife's strenuous opposition.

However, before the year ended, she proposed, wholly from herself, to have Gouvernail visit them again. Her husband was surprised and delighted with the suggestion coming from her.

"I am glad, chère amie, to know that you have finally overcome your dislike for him; truly he did not deserve it."

"Oh," she told him, laughingly, after pressing a long, tender kiss upon his lips, "I have overcome everything! You will see. This time I shall be very nice to him."

From A NIGHT IN A MOORISH HAREM

Anonymous

A Night in a Moorish Harem first appeared in Paris in the late 1890s. Redolent with orientalist mystery and exoticism, its antecedent can be traced to a much earlier novel, *The Lustful Turk* (1828), a tale of youthful English maidenhood being ravished by the 'stiff insertions' and 'horrid practices' of the randy Ottoman. To redress the balance, the *Moorish Harem*'s hero, Lord George Herbert, with the confident swagger of an aristocratic young naval officer, shows these Mediterranean girls just how passionate, virile and enduring a Briton can be.

Lord George Herbert is universally acknowledged to be the handsomest man in English nobility. His form is tall and muscular, but of a perfect symmetry. His features are handsome, but manly, and of a ruddy bronze colour, acquired at sea.

His short and curly brown hair shades a broad and white forehead, beneath which sparkle large blue eyes. He wears a heavy beard and moustache, but they are not able to conceal his handsome mouth.

His courage and talent, together with the influence of his family, had procured for him at the early age of twenty-three the command of one of the finest ships in the English navy. The following strange but true narrative is from his pen, and it may be imagined that he did not intend to have it copied.

But he left it in the possession of a fair and frail lady who thought it too good to keep secret, and so the reader has the benefit of it.

Abdallah Pasha's Seraglio

Her British Majesty's ship *Antler*, of which I was in command, lay becalmed one afternoon off the coast of Morocco. I did not allow the steam to be raised, for I knew the evening breeze would soon make toward the land. Retiring to my cabin, I threw myself upon the sofa. I could not sleep, for my thoughts kept wandering back to the beautiful women of London, and the favours which some of them had granted me when last on shore. Months had gone since then and months more would elapse before I could again hope to quench, in the laps of beauty, the hot desire which now coursed through my veins and distended my genitals. To divert my mind from thoughts at present so unprofitable, I resolved to take a bath.

Beneath the stern windows which lighted my cabin lay a small boat, into which I got by sliding down a rope which held it to the ship. Then I undressed and plunged into the cool waves. After bathing I dressed and, reclining in the boat, fell asleep.

When I awoke it was dark and I was floating alone near the shore with the ship miles away. The rope which held the boat must have slipped when the breeze sprung up, and the people on the ship, being busy getting under way, had not noticed me.

I had no oars and dared not use the sail for fear the Moorish vessels in sight would discover me.

I drifted toward a large building which was the only one to be seen; it rose from the water's edge. The approach to the place on which it stood seemed to be from the land side, and all the windows which I could see were high above the ground. The keel of my boat soon grated on the sand and I hastened to pull it among the rocks for concealment, or it was quite possible I might be seized and sold into slavery if discovered; my plan was to wait for the land breeze just before dawn and escape to sea.

At this moment I heard a whispered call from above. I looked up and saw two ladies looking down at me from one of the windows, and behind them were gathered several others whom I could just see in the gloom. "We have been watching you," said one of the ladies, "and will try to assist you; wait where you are." She spoke French, which is the common medium of communication among the different nations inhabiting the shores of the Mediterranean, and which had become familiar to me. I now thought this isolated building was a seraglio, and I resolved to trust the ladies who ran even more risk than myself in case of discovery. After waiting some time a rope of shawls was let down from the window and the same voice bade me climb. My discipline when a midshipman made this easy for me to do.

I rose hand over hand and safely reached the window, through which I was assisted by the ladies into the perfumed air of an elegant apartment, richly furnished and brilliantly lighted. My first duty was to kiss the hands which had aided me, and then I explained the accident which brought me among them and the plan which I had formed for escape before dawn. I then gave them my name and rank.

While doing this, I had an opportunity to observe the ladies. There were nine of them, and any one of them would have anywhere been remarked for her beauty. Each one of them differed from all the others in the style of her charms. Some were large and some were small, some slender and some plump, some blonde and some brunette; but all were bewitchingly beautiful. Each, too, was the most lovely type of a different nationality; for war and shipwrecks and piracy enable the Moorish pashas to choose their darlings from all the flags that float on the Mediterranean. A lady whom they called Inez, and whom, therefore, I took to be a Spaniard, answered me by bidding me in the name of all of them the warmest welcome.

"You are," she said, "in the seraglio of Abdallah, pasha of the district, who is not expected until tomorrow, and who will never be the wiser if his ladies seize the opportunity to entertain a gentleman during his absence. We have no secrets or jealousies among ourselves," smiling very significantly.

"That is very unusual," I remarked. "How can any of you know whether she has any secrets with the one he happens to be alone with?"

"But none of us are ever alone with him," replied Inez.

The blank look of consternation I wore set them all to laughing. They were brimful of mischief, and evidently bent on making the most of the unexpected company of a young man.

Inez put her hand on my sleeve. "How wet you are," said she. "It would not be hospitable to allow you to keep on such wet clothes."

My clothes were perfectly dry, but the winks and smiles which the young ladies exchanged as they began to disrobe me led me to submit cheerfully while they proceeded to divest me of every article of clothing. When at length my shirt was suddenly jerked off they gave little screams and peeped through their fingers at my shaft, which by this time was of most towering dimensions.

I had snatched a hearty kiss from one and all of them as they had gathered round to undress me.

Inez now handed me a scarf which she had taken from her own fair shoulders. "We can none of us bear to leave you," she said, "but you can only kiss one at a time; please throw this to the lady you prefer."

Good heavens! Then it was true that all of these beautiful ladies had been accustomed to be present when one of them was embraced.

"Ladies," said I, "you are unfair; you have stripped me, but you leave those charms concealed which you offer my preference. I am sure none of you have any imperfections which you wish to keep covered."

The ladies looked at one another, blushed a little, nodded and laughed and then began undressing. Velvet vests, skirts of lawn and silken trousers were rapidly flung to the floor; lastly, as if it were a given signal, every dainty chemise was stripped off, and nine of the most lovely forms that ever floated throughout a sculptor's dream stood naked before me. Was I dreaming, or had I suddenly been transported to the seventh heaven?

For a while I stood entranced, gazing at the charming spectacle. "Ladies," said I, "at least it would be immodest in me to give preference when all are so ravishingly lovely. Please keep the scarf, fair Inez, and when I have paid a tribute to your fair charms pass it yourself to another, until all have been gratified."

"Did he say all?" asked a little brunette.

"All indeed!" cried the rest in chorus bursting into laughter.

"Everyone," said I, "or I will perish in the attempt."

Inez was standing directly in front of me. She was about nineteen and of that rarest type of Spanish beauty, partly derived from Flemish blood.

Her eyes were sparkling brown, but her long hair was blonde. It was braided and coiled around the top of her head like a crown, which added to her queenly appearance, for she was about the ordinary stature; her plump and well-rounded form harmonized with her height. Her complexion had the slight yellow tinge of rich cream, which was set off by the rosy nipples that tipped her full breasts and the still deeper hue of her lips and mouth. She happened to be standing on one of the silken cushions which, singly and in piles, lay scattered about the room in profusion. It made her height just equal to my own. As soon as I had made the speech last recorded, I advanced and folded her in my embrace. Her soft

arms were wound around me in response, and our lips met in a delicious and prolonged kiss, during which my shaft was imprisoned against her warm smooth belly. Then she raised herself on tiptoes, which brought its crest among the short thick hair where the belly terminated. With one hand I guided my shaft to the entrance, which welcomed it; with my other I held her plump buttocks toward me.

Then she gradually settled on her feet again and, as she did so, the entrance was slowly and delightfully effected in her moist, hot and swollen sheath.

When she was on her feet again, I could feel her throbbing womb resting on my shaft.

The other ladies gathered around us, their kisses rained on my neck and shoulders, and the pressure of their bosoms was against my back and sides; indeed, they so completely sustained Inez and myself that I seemed about to mingle my being with them all at once. I had stirred the being of Inez with but a few thrusts when the rosy cheeks took on a deeper dye; her eyes swam, her lips parted and I felt a delicious baptism of moisture on my shaft.

Then her head sank on my shoulder and the gathered sperm of months gushed from my crest so profusely that I seemed completely transferred with the waves of rapture into the beautiful Spanish girl.

Her sighs of pleasure were not only echoed by mine, but by all the ladies in sympathy gathered around us. They gently lowered us from their sustaining embrace to a pile of cushions. As they did so with hardly any aid on our part, my diminished shaft was drawn out of Inez and with some of my tributary sperm, which splashed on the floor.

"It was bad of you, Inez, to take more than you could keep," said one of the others. She said it in such a pitiful tone it convulsed us all with laughter.

As for me, I now realized the rashness of the promise I had made them all. They gaily joined hands around Inez and myself and began a circling dance.

Their round, white limbs and plump bosoms floated in the lamp-light as they moved in cadence to a Moorish love song in which they all joined.

With my cheeks pillowed against the soft, full breasts of Inez, I watched the charming circle, which was like a scene from fairyland. Bracelets and anklets of heavy gold glittered on their arms and legs; rings, necklaces and earrings of diamonds and rubies, which they had in profusion, glittered at every moment. Each one had her hair elaborately dressed in the style most becoming to her, and there were no envious garments to conceal a single charm. I urged them to prolong the bewitching spectacle again and again, which they obligingly did. Then they gathered around me, reclining to rest on the cushion as near as they could get in attitudes which were picturesque and voluptuous.

While we were thus resting I frequently exchanged a kiss or caress with my fair companions, which I took care to do impartially. Then it occurred to me that I would like to hear from the lips of each the most interesting and voluptuous passage from their lives. Again these interesting ladies, after a little urging, consented to my wishes. Inez commenced.

The Spanish Lady's Story

We lived in Seville. At the age of sixteen my parents promised me in marriage to a gentleman whom I had never seen but twice and did not admire. My love was

already given to Carlos, a handsome young officer who had just been promoted for his bravery. He was elegantly formed; his hair and eyes were as dark as night, and he could dance to perfection. But it was for his gentle, winning smile that I loved him. On the evening of the day my parents had announced their determination to me I had gone to be alone in the orange grove in the farthest part of our garden, there to sorrow over my hard fate. In the midst of my grief I heard the voice of Carlos calling me. Could it be he who had been banished from the house and whom I never expected to see again? He sprang down from the garden wall, folded me in his embrace and covered my hair with kisses, for I had hidden my blushing face on his bosom. Then we talked of our sad lot. Carlos was poor and it would be impossible to marry without the consent of my parents. We could only mingle our tears and regrets. He led me to a grassy bank concealed by orange trees and rose bushes. Then he drew me on his lap and kissed my lips and cheeks and eyes. I did not chide him, for it must be our last meeting, but I did not return his kisses with passion. I had never felt a wanton desire in my life, much less when I was so sad. His passionate kisses were no longer confined to my face, but were showered on my neck, and at length my dress was parted and revealed my little bosoms to his ardent lips. I was startled and made an attempt to stop him in what I considered an impropriety, but he did not stop there. I felt my skirts raised, and a mingled sensation of alarm and shame accused me to try to prevent it, but it was impossible. I loved him too much to struggle long against him, and he was soon lying between my naked thighs. "Inez," he said, "if you love me be my wife these few minutes before we part." I could not resist the appeal.

I offered my lips to his kisses without any feeling save innocent love, and lay passive while I felt him guide a stiff, warm object between my thighs. It entered where nothing had ever gone before, and no sooner had it done so than he gave me a fierce thrust which seemed to tear my vitals with a cruel pain; then he gave a deep sigh and sank heavily on my bosom. I kissed him repeatedly for I supposed it had hurt him as much as it did me, little thinking that his pleasure was as exquisite as my suffering.

Just at that moment the harsh voice of my duenna resounded through the garden, calling, "Inez! Inez!"

Exchanging with my seducer a lingering, hearty kiss, I extracted myself from his embrace and answered the call. My duenna eyed me sharply as I approached her. "Why do you straddle your legs so far apart when you walk?" she asked as I came closer. "Why is the bosom of your dress so disordered, and why are your cheeks so flushed?" I made some excuse about climbing to get an orange and hurried to my room. I locked the door and prepared to go to bed, that I might think uninterruptedly of Carlos, whom I now loved more than ever. When I took off my petticoat I found it all stained with blood.

I folded it up and placed it beneath my pillow to dream upon, under the fond delusion that Carlos' blood was mingled with my own. For a few weeks afterwards I was so closely watched that I could not see Carlos. On the evening preceding my marriage I went to vespers with my duenna. While we were kneeling in the cathedral a large woman, closely veiled, came and knelt beside me. She attracted my attention by pulling my dress. As I turned to her, she momentarily

lifted the corner of her mantilla, and I saw it was Carlos in disguise. I was now on the alert, and a small package was slipped into my hand. I had just time to conceal it in my bosom when my duenna arose and we left the church. As soon as I regained the privacy of my room I tore open the package and found it contained a silken rope-ladder and a letter from Carlos requesting me to suspend it from my window that night after the family was at rest. The note was full of love.

There was much more to tell, it said, if I would grant the interview by means of the ladder. Of course I was determined to see him. I was ignorant of what most girls learn from each other, for I had no companion. I supposed when a woman was embraced as I had been she necessarily got with child and that such embraces therefore occurred at intervals of a year or so. I expected consequently nothing of the kind at the coming interview. I wanted to learn of Carlos if the child I supposed to be in my womb would be born so soon as to betray our secret to my husband. When the family retired I went to my room and dressed myself elaborately, braiding my hair and putting on all of my jewellery.

I then fastened one end of the rope-ladder to the bed-post and lowered the other end out of the window. It was at once strained by the ascending step of Carlos. My eyes were soon feasted with the sight of my lover, and then we were locked in each other's arms. Again and again we alternately devoured each other with our eyes and pressed each other to our hearts. Words did not seem to be of any use; our kisses and caresses became more passionate and for the first time in my life I felt a wanton emotion. The lips between my thighs became moistened and torrid with coursing blood; I could feel my cheeks burn under the ardent gaze of my lover; I could no longer meet his eyes; my own dropped in shame. He began to undress me rapidly and his hands trembled with eagerness. Could it be he wanted to pierce my loins so soon again, as he had done in the orange garden? An hour ago I would have dreaded it; now the thought caused throbs of welcome just where the pain had been sharpest. Stripped to my chemise, and even that unbuttoned by the eager hand of my lover, I darted from his arms and concealed my confusion beneath the covers.

He soon undressed and followed me; one kiss on my cheeks and one on each of my naked bosoms, then he opened my thighs and parted the little curls between. Again I felt the stiff, warm object entering; it went in slowly on account of the lightness, but every inch of its progress inward became more and more pleasant. When it had fully entered I was in a rapture of delight, yet something was wanting. I dropped my arms around my lover and responded passionately to his kisses. I was almost tempted to respond to his thrusts by a wanton motion of my loins. My maidenhead was gone and the tender virgin wound completely healed, but I still had a remnant of maidenly shame. For a moment he lay still and then he gave me half a dozen deep thrusts, each one giving me more and more pleasure. It culminated at last in a thrill so exquisite that my frame seemed to melt; nothing more was wanting! I gave a sigh of deep gratification and my arms fell helpless to my sides! But I received with passionate pleasure two or three more thrusts, which Carlos gave me. At each of them my sheath was penetrated by a copious gush that soothed and bathed its heated membranes.

For a long time we lay perfectly still; the stiff shaft, which had completely filled me, had diminished in size until it slipped completely out. Carlos at last

relieved me of his weight by lying by my side, but our legs were still entwined. We now had time to converse; my lover explained to me all the sexual mysteries, which remained for me to know. Then we formed plans which after marriage would enable us to meet often. These explanations and plans were mingled so freely with caresses that before my lover had left me we had melted five times in each other's arms.

I had barely strength to draw up the rope-ladder after he had departed. The day had now begun to dawn and I fell into a dreamless sleep. Being awakened by my duenna pounding on the door and calling that it was nearly ten o'clock, and that I was to be married at eleven. I was in no hurry, but they got me to church in time; during the whole ceremony I felt my lover's sperm trickling down my thighs.

We all applauded as she thus finished her story. While Inez was telling her story, one of the ladies, whom I had noticed to be the most fleshy of the number, cuddled up close to my side and suffered me to explore all of her charms with my hand. During the description of the scene in the orange garden my fingers toyed with the curls between her thighs, and as the story went on, I parted the curls and felt the lips beneath. She was partly on her belly against me, so that this by-play was not observed; my fingers were encouraged by the lady's hand until two of them made an entrance and were completely enclosed in the hot, moist tissue.

The little protuberance all women have within the orifice, and which is the principal seat of sensation, was in her remarkably developed. It was as large as the end of my little finger. I played with it and squeezed it and plunged my two fingers past it again and again. She manifested her delight by kissing me on the neck where she had hidden her face.

When Inez described her first thrill in the bedroom scene, my fingers were doing all in their power to complete the other lady's gratification, and this, too, with success, for they were suddenly bathed with moisture and the lady drew a deep sigh, which was not noticed, for all supposed it to be in sympathy with Inez's story. Then she withdrew my hand and lay perfectly still. Inez was about to give her her scarf, but she lay so motionless that she handed it to another. "This," said Inez, "is Helene, a Grecian lady; she will tell you a story and then she will do anything you wish." My head was still pillowed on Inez's breast. Helene smiled and then stooped and kissed me. She was about medium height; very slender, but graceful and well-rounded, and her skin was alabaster. Her features were of the perfect antique mould and were lighted with fine grey eyes. Her glossy black hair was all brushed back to a knot just below the back of her neck, from which but a single curl escaped on either side and toyed with her firm and finely rounded bosoms.

The deep vermilion of her lips compensated for the faint colour of her cheeks, whose tinge was scarcely deeper than that of the hard little nipples that tipped her bosoms or that of her small and finely cut ears. She was about twenty–two, and ripe to yield a charming embrace. I drew her down to a seat on my loins and begged her to begin her story.

The Grecian Lady's Story

I entered the bridal bed a virgin. When the bridesmaids left me I trembled with apprehension and covered up my head in the bed clothing; it was because I had heard so many stories of the trials and hardships of a virgin on her wedding night and not because I had any antipathy for my husband; on the contrary, I liked him. His courtship had been short, for he was a busy man in the diplomatic service of the Greek government. He was no longer young, but he was good-looking and manly, and I was proud that he had selected me from the other Athenian girls. He came to the side of my bed, and turning down the clothes from my head he saw how I was agitated. My heart beat still more violently when he entered. He simply kissed my hand and then went to the other side of the room to undress; this conduct somewhat reassured me. When he got into bed and took me in his arms my back was turned toward him. He took no liberties with any part of my person, but began to converse with me about the incidents of the wedding. I was soon so calm that I suffered him to turn me with my face toward him and kiss me first on the forehead and then on the lips. After a while he begged me to return his kisses, saying that if I did not it would prove that I disliked him. Thus encouraged, I returned his kisses.

When I had been so long in his arms that I began to feel at home, he turned me upon my back, unfastened the bosom of my chemise, and kissed and fondled my breasts. This set my heart to beating wildly again, but I kept exchanging kisses till he suddenly lifted the skirt of my chemise and lay between my thighs. Then I covered my face with my hands for shame, but he was so kind and gentle I soon got accustomed to the situation. I suffered him to remove my hands and fasten his mouth to mine in a passionate kiss; as he did so I felt something pushing between my thighs. It entered amid the curls and touched the naked lips beneath.

I felt my face grow hot with shame and I lay perfectly passive. He must have been in bed with me two hours before he ventured so far. He had his reward, for a soft desire began to grow in my brain; the blood centred in my loins and I longed for the connection, which was so imminent. I returned him a kiss as passionate as he gave; it was the signal for which he had been waiting. I felt a pressure on the virgin membrane, not hard enough however to be painful. The pressure slackened and then pushed again and again. By this time I was wanton with desire, and not only returned the passionate kisses, but wound my arms around him. Then came that fatal thrust, tearing away the obstruction and reaching to the very depths of my loins. I gave a cry of mingled bliss and agony, which I could not help repeating at each of three deep thrusts that followed. Then all was still and an effusion like balm filled my sheath in place of the organ that had so disturbed it. A delightful languor stole over my frame and I went to sleep in my husband's arms.

In less than six months circumstances compelled me to deceive him. After we had been married a while our position required us to go a great deal in company. Card playing was very fashionable and the stakes got very high. One night the luck was terribly against me. I proposed for the party to double. My husband had gone on a journey a few days before and had left a large sum of money in my charge; it was nearly all his fortune. A portion of this money I now staked, thinking that the luck could not possibly go against me again. But it did.

I was rendered desperate; again I proposed to double, it would take all I had left if I lost. The ladies who were playing withdrew; the gentlemen were too polite to do so. The cards were against me; I felt myself grow deadly pale. The French ambassador, Count Henri, who was sitting beside me, was disposed to conceal my terrible embarrassment; he was very stalwart. His manners were very engaging; he kept up a stream of small talk till the others had dispersed to other parts of the room; then he offered to bring me on the morrow the amount I had lost. I turned as crimson as I had before been pale; I knew too well the price of such assistance. I made him no reply. My eyes dropped to the floor and I begged him to leave me, which he politely did.

All the next day I was nearly distracted. I hoped Count Henri would not come, my cheeks would burn as on the evening before, and the blood all rushed back to my heart. At three o'clock he came, the valet showed him to the parlour, closed the door and retired. Count Henri must have known he was expected, for I was elegantly dressed in blue silk and my shoulders were set off with heavy lace; I was so agitated I could not rise from the sofa to greet him.

"May I have the happiness of being your confidant?" he asked, as he seated himself beside me, holding in one hand a well-filled purse and dropping the other about my waist. I could not reject the purse; if I kept it I could not ask him to remove his arm; I was giddy with contending emotions. "For God's sake spare me!" I murmured. My head drooped and he pressed it to his heart; I fainted away. When I became conscious I was lying on my back upon the sofa, in the arms of the count, the lace at my bosom was parted, my heavy skirts all turned up from my naked thighs, and he was in the very ecstasy of filling my sheath with sperm. It was this exquisite sensation which restored me to consciousness, but I was too late to join in the ecstasy. His shaft became limper and small, and I was left hopelessly in the lurch. Then I beseeched him to go as it was no time or place for this. "Will you receive me in your bedroom tonight?" asked he, kissing my bare bosoms. He had so excited my passions that I no longer hesitated. "The front door will be unfastened all night," I replied, "and my room is directly over this one." Then he allowed me to rise; I adjusted my disordered dress as quickly as possible, but it was not quick enough; the valet opened the door to bring the card of a visitor, he saw enough to put me in his power. When the count had gone I found the purse in my bosom; it contained more than I had lost, but my thoughts were not of money; my lips had tasted the forbidden fruit. I was no longer the same woman, my excitement had culminated in lascivious desire, I could hardly wait for night to come.

When finally the house was still I unfastened the front door, retired to my room, undressed and was standing in my chemise, with my nightgown in my hand ready to put on, when the door of my room opened and Alex, the valet, stood before me with a finger on his lips. He was a fine-looking youth of seventeen. A Hungarian of a reduced family, who acted half in the capacity of secretary and half in that of valet for my husband. I could not help giving a faint scream, while I concealed my person as much as possible with the nightgown.

"My lady," said he, "I know all. But I shall be discreet; I only ask you to give me the sweetest proof of your confidence." There was no help for it; with a murmur for shame I sprang into bed and hid under the bed clothes; he quickly

undressed and followed; my object was to dismiss him before the Count came. I therefore suffered him to make rapid progress. He took me in his arms and kissed my lips and bosoms, and as he raised my chemise our naked thighs met. He was more agitated than myself; I had been anticipating a paramour all afternoon, while he could not have known what reception would be accorded him; he could hardly guide his shaft to the lips that welcomed it; as for myself, I began where I had left off with the Count. My sheath with wanton greediness devoured every inch that entered it, and at the very first thrust I melted with an adulterous rapture never felt in my husband's embrace.

Just at that moment I heard the front door softly open and shut. I pushed Alex away with a force that drew his stiff shaft completely out of me.

"Gather up your clothes quickly and get into the closet," I said. Madly eager as he must have been to finish, he hurried with his clothes into the closet, the door of which just shut as the Count entered.

The Count came up and kissed me. I pretended to be asleep; he undressed hastily, got into bed and took me in his arms. But I delayed his progress as much as possible; I made him tell me everything that had been said about my losses at cards; I used every artifice to keep him at bay until his efforts should arouse my passions; then he mounted me; his stalwart shaft distended and penetrated me so much deeper than that of young Alex that it was more exquisite than before. Again the wild, adulterous thrill penetrated every part of my body. I fairly groaned with ecstasy. At that moment the front door loudly opened. It must be my husband unexpectedly returning. "Good heavens, Count!" I cried, "under the bed with you." He pulled his great stiff shaft out of me with a curse of disappointment that he could not finish, and scrambled under the bed, dragging his clothes with him. My husband came in all beaming with delight that he had been able to return so soon.

I received him with much demonstration. "How it flushes your cheeks to see me," he said. When he undressed and came to bed I returned his caresses with so much ardour that he soon entered where Alex and the Count had so hastily withdrawn. It was pleasant, but I feigned much more rapture than I felt. To console the Count I dropped one of my hands down alongside of the bed and he was so polite as to kiss it; as my husband's face was buried in my neck, and he was making rapid thrusts, I kissed my other hand to Alex, who was peering out of the closet. Then I gave motion to my loins, which sent my husband spending, and repeated it till I had extracted from him the most copious gushes; it was too soon for me to melt with another thrill; my object was to fix him for a sound sleep, but the balmy sperm was so grateful to my sheath after the two fierce preceding encounters that I felt rewarded for my troubles. He soon fell asleep. I then motioned for the Count to go. With his clothes in one hand and his stiff shaft in the other he glided out. Soon after I heard the front door shut, and the disconsolate Alex came forth, his clothes under his arm and both hands holding his rigid staff; he, too, disappeared.

Here Helene finished. During her story I lay on my back, resting on Inez's bosom. Helene sat astride of my loins with her face toward me, which gave me a fair view of her most secret beauties. She had carelessly let the scarf fall over

our laps, and under its protecting cover her little tapering fingers began to play with my limper shaft. As the story proceeded, it began to stiffen, and as she was describing the bedchamber scene she contrived to slip it into the crevice so directly above it. It rose until it was almost rigid, vivified as it was by the close retreat in which it was hidden. She kept undulating her loins as the story went on until, just as she finished, I was nearly ready; at the same moment I felt my shaft moistened by the libation of the Greek girl, and she fell fainting into the arms of a lady close by. My shaft drew out of her with a sucking noise that set all to laughing. She hurriedly gave the scarf to the lady in whose arms she lay and in whose bosom she had her face. "It is with you, Zuleika," they all cried in chorus. Zuleika looked very much embarrassed.

About eighteen years of age, she was formed very much like Inez, whom she equalled in height, but she was more muscular, and her skin was of deep bronze. Her large, white lustrous eyes were dark as night; as was her curly hair, which was set off by a snowy turban, on which gleamed a crescent of burnished silver. The colour deepened in her dusky cheeks as she drew close to me and timidly began her story.

From DRACULA

Bram Stoker

Bram Stoker was born in Dublin, Ireland. In 1879, he published his first literary work, *The Duties of Clerks of Petty Sessions in Ireland*, a handbook in legal administration. Turning to fiction later in life, Stoker published his masterpiece, *Dracula*, in 1897. Deemed a classic horror novel not long after its release, *Dracula* has continued to garner acclaim for more than a century, inspiring the creation of hundreds of film, theatrical and literary adaptations. In addition to *Dracula*, Stoker published more than a dozen novels before his death.

Later: the Morning of 16 May. – God preserve my sanity, for to this I am reduced. Safety and the assurance of safety are things of the past. Whilst I live on here there is but one thing to hope for: that I may not go mad, if, indeed, I be not mad already. If I be sane, then surely it is maddening to think that of all the foul things that lurk in this hateful place the Count is the least dreadful to me; that to him alone I can look for safety, even though this be only whilst I can serve his purpose. Great God! merciful God! Let me be calm, for out of that way lies madness indeed. I begin to get new lights on certain things which have puzzled me. Up to now I never quite knew what Shakespeare meant when he made Hamlet say: –

My tablets! quick, my tablets!
'Tis meet that I put it down, etc.,

for now, feeling as though my own brain were unhinged or as if the shock had come which must end in its undoing, I turn to my diary for repose. The habit of entering accurately must help to soothe me.

The Count's mysterious warning frightened me at the time; it frightens me more now when I think of it, for in future he has a fearful hold upon me. I shall fear to doubt what he may say!

When I had written in my diary and had fortunately replaced the book and pen in my pocket I felt sleepy. The Count's warning came into my mind, but I took a pleasure in disobeying it. The sense of sleep was upon me, and with it the obstinacy which sleep brings as outrider. The soft moonlight soothed, and the wide expanse without gave a sense of freedom which refreshed me. I determined not to return tonight to the gloom-haunted rooms, but to sleep here, where of old ladies had sat and sung and lived sweet lives whilst their gentle breasts were sad for their menfolk away in the midst of remorseless wars. I drew a great couch

out of its place near the corner, so that, as I lay, I could look at the lovely view to east and south, and unthinking of and uncaring for the dust, composed myself for sleep.

I suppose I must have fallen asleep; I hope so, but I fear, for all that followed was startlingly real – so real that now, sitting here in the broad, full sunlight of the morning, I cannot in the least believe that it was all sleep.

I was not alone. The room was the same, unchanged in any way since I came into it; I could see along the floor, in the brilliant moonlight, my own footsteps marked where I had disturbed the long accumulation of dust. In the moonlight opposite me were three young women, ladies by their dress and manner. I thought at the time that I must be dreaming when I saw them, for, though the moonlight was behind them, they threw no shadow on the floor. They came close to me and looked at me for some time, and then whispered together. Two were dark, and had high aquiline noses, like the Count, and great dark, piercing eyes, that seemed to be almost red when contrasted with the pale yellow moon. The other was fair, as fair as can be, with great, wavy masses of golden hair and eyes like pale sapphires. I seemed somehow to know her face, and to know it in connection with some dreamy fear, but I could not recollect at the moment how or where. All three had brilliant white teeth, that shone like pearls against the ruby of their voluptuous lips. There was something about them that made me uneasy, some longing and at the same time some deadly fear. I felt in my heart a wicked, burning desire that they would kiss me with those red lips. It is not good to note this down, lest some day it should meet Mina's eyes and cause her pain; but it is the truth. They whispered together, and then they all three laughed – such a silvery, musical laugh, but as hard as though the sound never could have come through the softness of human lips. It was like the intolerable, tingling sweetness of water-glasses[14] when played on by a cunning hand. The fair girl shook her head coquettishly, and the other two urged her on. One said: –

"Go on! You are first, and we shall follow; yours is the right to begin." The other added: –

"He is young and strong; there are kisses for us all." I lay quiet, looking out under my eyelashes in an agony of delightful anticipation. The fair girl advanced and bent over me till I could feel the movement of her breath upon me. Sweet it was in one sense, honey-sweet, and sent the same tingling through the nerves as her voice, but with a bitter underlying the sweet, a bitter offensiveness, as one smells in blood.

I was afraid to raise my eyelids, but looked out and saw perfectly under the lashes. The fair girl went on her knees, and bent over me, fairly gloating. There was a deliberate voluptuousness which was both thrilling and repulsive, and as she arched her neck she actually licked her lips like an animal, till I could see in the moonlight the moisture shining on the scarlet lips and on the red tongue as it lapped the white sharp teeth. Lower and lower went her head as the lips went below the range of my mouth and chin and seemed about to fasten on my throat. Then she paused, and I could hear the churning sound of her tongue as it licked her teeth and lips, and could feel the hot breath on my neck. Then the skin of my throat began to tingle as one's flesh does when the hand that is to tickle it approaches nearer – nearer. I could feel the soft, shivering touch of the lips on

the supersensitive skin of my throat, and the hard dents of two sharp teeth, just touching and pausing there. I closed my eyes in a languorous ecstacy and waited – waited with beating heart.

But at that instant another sensation swept through me as quick as lightning. I was conscious of the presence of the Count, and of his being as if lapped in a storm of fury. As my eyes opened involuntarily I saw his strong hand grasp the slender neck of the fair woman and with giant's power draw it back, the blue eyes transformed with fury, the white teeth champing with rage, and the fair cheeks blazing red with passion. But the Count! Never did I imagine such wrath and fury, even to the demons of the pit. His eyes were positively blazing. The red light in them was lurid, as if the flames of hell-fire blazed behind them. His face was deathly pale, and the lines of it were hard like drawn wires; the thick eyebrows that met over the nose now seemed like a heaving bar of white-hot metal. With a fierce sweep of his arm, he hurled the woman from him, and then motioned to the others, as though he were beating them back; it was the same imperious gesture that I had seen used to the wolves. In a voice which, though low and almost in a whisper, seemed to cut through the air and then ring round the room as he said: –

"How dare you touch him, any of you? How dare you cast eyes on him when I had forbidden it? Back, I tell you all! This man belongs to me! Beware how you meddle with him, or you'll have to deal with me." The fair girl, with a laugh of ribald coquetry, turned to answer him: –

"You yourself never loved; you never love!" On this the other women joined, and such a mirthless, hard, soulless laughter rang through the room that it almost made me faint to hear; it seemed like the pleasure of fiends. Then the Count turned, after looking at my face attentively, and said in a soft whisper: –

"Yes, I too can love; you yourselves can tell it from the past. Is it not so? Well, now I promise you that when I am done with him you shall kiss him at your will. Now go! go! I must awaken him, for there is work to be done."

"Are we to have nothing tonight?" said one of them, with a low laugh, as she pointed to the bag which he had thrown upon the floor, and which moved as though there were some living thing within it. For answer he nodded his head. One of the women jumped forward and opened it. If my ears did not deceive me there was a gasp and a low wail, as of a half-smothered child. The women closed round, whilst I was aghast with horror; but as I looked they disappeared, and with them the dreadful bag. There was no door near them, and they could not have passed me without my noticing. They simply seemed to fade into the rays of the moonlight and pass out through the window, for I could see outside the dim, shadowy forms for a moment before they entirely faded away.

Then the horror overcame me, and I sank down unconscious.

From LADY CHATTERLEY'S LOVER

D. H. Lawrence

David Herbert Lawrence was born in Eastwood, Nottinghamshire, the son of Arthur Lawrence and Lydia Beardsall. A prolific writer of poetry, novels, short stories, plays, essays, and criticism, Lawrence's works are heavily autobiographical and the experiences of his early years continued to exert a profound influence throughout his life. He is best known for *Sons and Lovers* (1913); *The Rainbow* (1915); *Women in Love* (1920) and *Lady Chatterley's Lover* (1928). He died on 2 March 1930 at Vence in the south of France.

Connie went to the wood directly after lunch. It was really a lovely day, the first dandelions making suns, the first daisies so white. The hazel thicket was a lace-work, of half-open leaves, and the last dusty perpendicular of the catkins. Yellow celandines now were in crowds, flat open, pressed back in urgency, and the yellow glitter of themselves. It was the yellow, the powerful yellow of early summer. And primroses were broad, and full of pale abandon, thick-clustered primroses no longer shy. The lush, dark green of hyacinths was a sea, with buds rising like pale corn, while in the riding the forget-me-nots were fluffing up, and columbines were unfolding their ink-purple riches, and there were bits of blue bird's eggshell under a bush. Everywhere the bud-knots and the leap of life!

The keeper was not at the hut. Everything was serene, brown chickens running lustily. Connie walked on towards the cottage, because she wanted to find him.

The cottage stood in the sun, off the wood's edge. In the little garden the double daffodils rose in tufts, near the wide-open door, and red double daisies made a border to the path. There was the bark of a dog, and Flossie came running.

The wide-open door! so he was at home. And the sunlight falling on the red-brick floor! As she went up the path, she saw him through the window, sitting at the table in his shirt-sleeves, eating. The dog wuffed softly, slowly wagging her tail.

He rose, and came to the door, wiping his mouth with a red handkerchief still chewing.

"May I come in?" she said.

"Come in!"

The sun shone into the bare room, which still smelled of a mutton chop, done in a dutch oven before the fire, because the dutch oven still stood on the fender, with the black potato-saucepan on a piece of paper, beside it on the white hearth. The fire was red, rather low, the bar dropped, the kettle singing.

On the table was his plate, with potatoes and the remains of the chop; also bread in a basket, salt, and a blue mug with beer. The table-cloth was white oil-cloth, he stood in the shade.

"You are very late," she said. "Do go on eating!"

She sat down on a wooden chair, in the sunlight by the door.

"I had to go to Uthwaite," he said, sitting down at the table but not eating.

"Do eat," she said. But he did not touch the food.

"Shall y'ave something?" he asked her. "Shall y'ave a cup of tea? t' kettle's on t' boil" – he half rose again from his chair.

"If you'll let me make it myself," she said, rising. He seemed sad, and she felt she was bothering him.

"Well, tea-pot's in there" – he pointed to a little, drab corner cupboard; "an' cups. An' tea's on t' mantel ower yer 'ead."

She got the black tea-pot, and the tin of tea from the mantel-shelf. She rinsed the tea-pot with hot water, and stood a moment wondering where to empty it.

"Throw it out," he said, aware of her. "It's clean."

She went to the door and threw the drop of water down the path. How lovely it was here, so still, so really woodland. The oaks were putting out ochre yellow leaves: in the garden the red daisies were like red plush buttons. She glanced at the big, hollow sandstone slab of the threshold, now crossed by so few feet.

"But it's lovely here," she said. "Such a beautiful stillness, everything alive and still."

He was eating again, rather slowly and unwillingly, and she could feel he was discouraged. She made the tea in silence, and set the tea-pot on the hob, as she knew the people did. He pushed his plate aside and went to the back place; she heard a latch click, then he came back with cheese on a plate, and butter.

She set the two cups on the table; there were only two. "Will you have a cup of tea?" she said.

"If you like. Sugar's in th' cupboard, an' there's a little cream jug. Milk's in a jug in th' pantry."

"Shall I take your plate away?" she asked him. He looked up at her with a faint ironical smile.

"Why . . . if you like," he said, slowly eating bread and cheese. She went to the back, into the pent-house scullery, where the pump was. On the left was a door, no doubt the pantry door. She unlatched it, and almost smiled at the place he called a pantry; a long narrow white-washed slip of a cupboard. But it managed to contain a little barrel of beer, as well as a few dishes and bits of food. She took a little milk from the yellow jug.

"How do you get your milk?" she asked him, when she came back to the table.

"Flints! They leave me a bottle at the warren end. You know, where I met you!"

But he was discouraged. She poured out the tea, poising the cream-jug.

"No milk," he said; then he seemed to hear a noise, and looked keenly through the doorway.

"'Appen we'd better shut," he said.

"It seems a pity," she replied. "Nobody will come, will they?"

"Not unless it's one time in a thousand, but you never know."

"And even then it's no matter," she said. "It's only a cup of tea."

"Where are the spoons?"

He reached over, and pulled open the table drawer. Connie sat at the table in the sunshine of the doorway.

"Flossie!" he said to the dog, who was lying on a little mat at the stair foot. "Go an' hark, hark!"

He lifted his finger, and his "hark!" was very vivid. The dog trotted out to reconnoitre.

"Are you sad today?" she asked him.

He turned his blue eyes quickly, and gazed direct on her.

"Sad! no, bored! I had to go getting summonses for two poachers I caught, and, oh well, I don't like people."

He spoke cold, good English, and there was anger in his voice. "Do you hate being a game-keeper?" she asked.

"Being a game-keeper, no! So long as I'm left alone. But when I have to go messing around at the police-station, and various other places, and waiting for a lot of fools to attend to me . . . oh well, I get mad . . ." and he smiled, with a certain faint humour.

"Couldn't you be really independent?" she asked.

"Me? I suppose I could, if you mean manage to exist on my pension. I could! But I've got to work, or I should die. That is, I've got to have something that keeps me occupied. And I'm not in a good enough temper to work for myself. It's got to be a sort of job for somebody else, or I should throw it up in a month, out of bad temper. So altogether I'm very well off here, especially lately . . ."

He laughed at her again, with mocking humour.

"But why are you in a bad temper?" she asked. "Do you mean you are *always* in a bad temper?"

"Pretty well," he said, laughing. "I don't quite digest my bile."

"But what bile?" she said.

"Bile!" he said. "Don't you know what that is?" She was silent, and disappointed. He was taking no notice of her.

"I'm going away for a while next month," she said.

"You are! Where to?"

"Venice!"

"With Sir Clifford? For how long?"

"For a month or so," she replied. "Clifford won't go."

"He'll stay here?" he asked.

"Yes! He hates to travel as he is."

"Ay, poor devil!" he said, with sympathy. There was a pause.

"You won't forget me when I'm gone, will you?" she asked. Again he lifted his eyes and looked full at her.

"Forget?" he said. "You know nobody forgets. It's not a question of memory!"

She wanted to say: "When then?" but she didn't. Instead, she said in a mute kind of voice: "I told Clifford I might have a child."

Now he really looked at her, intense and searching.

"You did?" he said at last. "And what did he say?"

"Oh, he wouldn't mind. He'd be glad, really, so long as it seemed to be his." She dared not look up at him.

He was silent a long time, then he gazed again on her face.

"No mention of *me*, of course?" he said.

"No. No mention of you," she said.

"No, he'd hardly swallow me as a substitute breeder. Then where are you supposed to be getting the child?"

"I might have a love-affair in Venice," she said.

"You might," he replied slowly. "So that's why you're going?"

"Not to have the love-affair," she said, looking up at him, pleading.

"Just the appearance of one," he said.

There was silence. He sat staring out the window, with a faint grin, half mockery, half bitterness, on his face. She hated his grin.

"You've not taken any precautions against having a child then?" he asked her suddenly. "Because I haven't."

"No," she said faintly. "I should hate that."

He looked at her, then again with the peculiar subtle grin out of the window. There was a tense silence.

At last he turned his head and said satirically:

"That was why you wanted me, then, to get a child?"

She hung her head.

"No. Not really," she said.

"What then, *really*?" he asked rather bitingly.

She looked up at him reproachfully, saying: "I don't know."

He broke into a laugh.

"Then I'm damned if I do," he said.

There was a long pause of silence, a cold silence.

"Well," he said at last. "It's as your Ladyship likes. If you get the baby, Sir Clifford's welcome to it. I shan't have lost anything. On the contrary, I've had a very nice experience, very nice indeed!" – and he stretched in a half-suppressed sort of yawn. "If you've made use of me," he said, "it's not the first time I've been made use of; and I don't suppose it's ever been as pleasant as this time; though of course one can't feel tremendously dignified about it." – He stretched again, curiously, his muscles quivering, and his jaw oddly set.

"But I didn't make use of you," she said, pleading.

"At your Ladyship's service," he replied.

"No," she said. "I liked your body."

"Did you?" he replied, and he laughed. "Well, then, we're quits, because I liked yours."

He looked at her with queer darkened eyes.

"Would you like to go upstairs now?" he asked her, in a strangled sort of voice.

"No, not here. Not now!" she said heavily, though if he had used any power

over her, she would have gone, for she had no strength against him.

He turned his face away again, and seemed to forget her. "I want to touch you like you touch me," she said. "I've never really touched your body."

He looked at her, and smiled again. "Now?" he said.

"No! No! Not here! At the hut. Would you mind?"

"How do I touch you?" he asked.

"When you feel me."

He looked at her, and met her heavy, anxious eyes.

"And do you like it when I feel you?" he asked, laughing at her still.

"Yes, do you?" she said.

"Oh, me!" Then he changed his tone. "Yes," he said. "You know without asking." Which was true.

She rose and picked up her hat. "I must go," she said.

"Will you go?" he replied politely.

She wanted him to touch her, to say something to her, but he said nothing, only waited politely.

"Thank you for the tea," she said.

"I haven't thanked your Ladyship for doing me the honours of my tea-pot," he said.

She went down the path, and he stood in the doorway, faintly grinning. Flossie came running with her tail lifted. And Connie had to plod dumbly across into the wood, knowing he was standing there watching her, with that incomprehensible grin on his face.

She walked home very much downcast and annoyed. She didn't at all like his saying he had been made use of because, in a sense, it was true. But he oughtn't to have said it. Therefore, again, she was divided between two feelings: resentment against him, and a desire to make it up with him.

She passed a very uneasy and irritated tea-time, and at once went up to her room. But when she was there it was no good; she could neither sit nor stand. She would have to do something about it. She would have to go back to the hut; if he was not there, well and good.

She slipped out of the side door, and took her way direct and a little sullen. When she came to the clearing she was terribly uneasy. But there he was again, in his shirt-sleeves, stooping, letting the hens out of the coops, among the chicks that were now growing a little gawky, but were much more trim than hen-chickens.

She went straight across to him. "You see I've come!" she said.

"Ay, I see it!" he said, straightening his back, and looking at her with a faint amusement.

"Do you let the hens out now?" she asked.

"Yes, they've sat themselves to skin and bone," he said. "An' now they're not all that anxious to come out an' feed. There's no self in a sitting hen; she's all in the eggs or the chicks."

The poor mother-hens; such blind devotion! Even to eggs not their own! Connie looked at them in compassion. A helpless silence fell between the man and the woman.

"Shall us go i' th' 'ut?" he asked.

"Do you want me?" she asked, in a sort of mistrust.

"Ay, if you want to come."

She was silent.

"Come then!" he said.

And she went with him to the hut. It was quite dark when he had shut the door, so he made a small light in the lantern, as before.

"Have you left your underthings off?" he asked her.

"Yes!"

"Ay, well, then I'll take my things off too."

He spread the blankets, putting one at the side for a coverlet. She took off her hat, and shook her hair. He sat down, taking off his shoes and gaiters, and undoing his cord breeches.

"Lie down then!" he said, when he stood in his shirt. She obeyed in silence, and he lay beside her, and pulled the blanket over them both.

"There!" he said.

And he lifted her dress right back, till he came even to her breasts. He kissed them softly, taking the nipples in his lips in tiny caresses.

"Eh, but tha'rt nice, tha'rt nice!" he said, suddenly rubbing his face with a snuggling movement against her warm belly.

And she put her arms round him under his shirt, but she was afraid, afraid of his thin, smooth, naked body, that seemed so powerful, afraid of the violent muscles. She shrank, afraid.

And when he said, with a sort of little sigh: "Eh, tha'rt nice!" something in her quivered, and something in her spirit stiffened in resistance: stiffened from the terribly physical intimacy, and from the peculiar haste of his possession. And this time the sharp ecstasy of her own passion did not overcome her; she lay with her ends inert on his striving body, and do what she might, her spirit seemed to look on from the top of her head, and the butting of his haunches seemed ridiculous to her, and the sort of anxiety of his penis to come to its little evacuating crisis seemed farcical. Yes, this was love, this ridiculous bouncing of the buttocks, and the wilting of the poor, insignificant, moist little penis. This was the divine love! After all, the moderns were right when they felt contempt for the performance; for it was a performance. It was quite true, as some poets said, that the God who created man must have had a sinister sense of humour, creating him a reasonable being, yet forcing him to take this ridiculous posture, and driving him with blind craving for this ridiculous performance. Even a Maupassant found it a humiliating anticlimax. Men despised the intercourse act, and yet did it.

Cold and derisive her queer female mind stood apart, and though she lay perfectly still, her impulse was to heave her loins, and throw the man out, escape his ugly grip, and the butting over-riding of his absurd haunches. His body was a foolish, impudent, imperfect thing, a little disgusting in its unfinished clumsiness. For surely a complete evolution would eliminate this performance, this "function".

And yet when he had finished, soon over, and lay very very still, receding into silence, and a strange motionless distance, far, farther than the horizon of her awareness, her heart began to weep. She could feel him ebbing away, ebbing away, leaving her there like a stone on a shore. He was withdrawing, his spirit was leaving her. He knew.

And in real grief, tormented by her own double consciousness and reaction, she began to weep. He took no notice, or did not even know. The storm of weeping swelled and shook her, and shook him.

"Ay!" he said. "It was no good that time. You wasn't there." – So he knew! Her sobs became violent.

"But what's amiss?" he said. "It's once in a while that way."

"I . . . I can't love you," she sobbed, suddenly feeling her heart breaking.

"Canna ter? Well, dunna fret! There's no law says as tha's got to. Ta'e it for what it is."

He still lay with his hand on her breast. But she had drawn both her hands from him.

His words were small comfort. She sobbed aloud.

"Nay, nay!" he said. "Ta'e the thick wi' th' thin. This wor a bit o' thin for once."

She wept bitterly, sobbing. "But I want to love you, and I can't. It only seems horrid."

He laughed a little, half bitter, half amused.

"It isna horrid," he said, "even if tha thinks it is. An' tha canna ma'e it horrid. Dunna fret thysen about lovin' me. Tha'lt niver force thysen to 't. There's sure to be a bad nut in a basketful. Tha mun ta'e th' rough wi' th' smooth."

He took his hand away from her breast, not touching her. And now she was untouched she took an almost perverse satisfaction in it. She hated the dialect: the *thee* and the *tha* and the *thysen*. He could get up if he liked, and stand there, above her, buttoning down those absurd corduroy breeches, straight in front of her. After all, Michaelis had had the decency to turn away. This man was so assured in himself he didn't know what a clown other people found him, a half-bred fellow.

Yet, as he was drawing away, to rise silently and leave her, she clung to him in terror.

"Don't! Don't go! Don't leave me! Don't be cross with me! Hold me! Hold me fast!" she whispered in blind frenzy, not even knowing what she said, and clinging to him with uncanny force. It was from herself she wanted to be saved, from her own inward anger and resistance. Yet how powerful was that inward resistance that possessed her!

He took her in his arms again and drew her to him, and suddenly she became small in his arms, small and nestling. It was gone, the resistance was gone, and she began to melt in a marvellous peace. And as she melted small and wonderful in his arms, she became infinitely desirable to him, all his blood-vessels seemed to scald with intense yet tender desire, for her, for her softness, for the penetrating beauty of her in his arms, passing into his blood. And softly, with that marvellous swoon-like caress of his hand in pure soft desire, softly he stroked the silky slope of her loins, down, down between her soft warm buttocks, coming nearer and nearer to the very quick of her. And she felt him like a flame of desire, yet tender, and she felt herself melting in the flame. She let herself go. She felt his penis risen against her with silent amazing force and assertion and she let herself go to him. She yielded with a quiver that was like death, she went all open to him. And oh, if he were not tender to her now, how cruel, for she was all open to him and helpless!

She quivered again at the potent inexorable entry inside her, so strange and terrible. It might come with the thrust of a sword in her softly-opened body, and that would be death. She clung in a sudden anguish of terror. But it came with a strange slow thrust of peace, the dark thrust of peace and a ponderous, primordial tenderness, such as made the world in the beginning. And her terror subsided in her breast, her breast dared to be gone in peace, she held nothing. She dared to let go everything, all herself and be gone in the flood.

And it seemed she was like the sea, nothing but dark waves rising and heaving, heaving with a great swell, so that slowly her whole darkness was in motion, and she was Ocean rolling its dark, dumb mass. Oh, and far down inside her the deeps parted and rolled asunder, in long, fair-travelling billows, and ever, at the quick of her, the depths parted and rolled asunder, from the centre of soft plunging, as the plunger went deeper and deeper, touching lower, and she was deeper and deeper and deeper disclosed, the heavier the billows of her rolled away to some shore, uncovering her, and closer and closer plunged the palpable unknown, and further and further rolled the waves of herself away from herself leaving her, till suddenly, in a soft, shuddering convulsion, the quick of all her plasm was touched, she knew herself touched, the consummation was upon her, and she was gone. She was gone, she was not, and she was born: a woman.

Ah, too lovely, too lovely! In the ebbing she realized all the loveliness. Now all her body clung with tender love to the unknown man, and blindly to the wilting penis, as it so tenderly, frailly, unknowingly withdrew, after the fierce thrust of its potency. As it drew out and left her body, the secret, sensitive thing, she gave an unconscious cry of pure loss, and she tried to put it back. It had been so perfect! And she loved it so!

And only now she became aware of the small, bud-like reticence and tenderness of the penis, and a little cry of wonder and poignancy escaped her again, her woman's heart crying out over the tender frailty of that which had been the power.

"It was so lovely!" she moaned. "It was so lovely!" But he said nothing, only softly kissed her, lying still above her. And she moaned with a sort of bliss, as a sacrifice, and a newborn thing.

And now in her heart the queer wonder of him was awakened.

A man! The strange potency of manhood upon her! Her hands strayed over him, still a little afraid. Afraid of that strange, hostile, slightly repulsive thing that he had been to her, a man. And now she touched him, and it was the sons of god with the daughters of men. How beautiful he felt, how pure in tissue! How lovely, how lovely, strong, and yet pure and delicate, such stillness of the sensitive body! Such utter stillness of potency and delicate flesh. How beautiful! How beautiful! Her hands came timorously down his back, to the soft, smallish globes of the buttocks. Beauty! What beauty! a sudden little flame of new awareness went through her. How was it possible, this beauty here, where she had previously only been repelled? The unspeakable beauty to the touch of the warm, living buttocks! The life within life, the sheer warm, potent loveliness. And the strange weight of the balls between his legs! What a mystery! What a strange heavy weight of mystery, that could lie soft and heavy in one's hand! The roots, root of all that is lovely, the primeval root of all full beauty.

She clung to him, with a hiss of wonder that was almost awe, terror. He held her close, but he said nothing. He would never say anything. She crept nearer to him, nearer, only to be near to the sensual wonder of him. And out of his utter, incomprehensible stillness, she felt again the slow momentous, surging rise of the phallus again, the other power. And her heart melted out with a kind of awe.

And this time his being within her was all soft and iridescent, purely soft and iridescent, such as no consciousness could seize. Her whole self quivered unconscious and alive, like plasm. She could not know what it was. She could not remember what it had been. Only that it had been more lovely than anything ever could be. Only that. And afterwards she was utterly still, utterly unknowing, she was not aware for how long. And he was still with her, in an unfathomable silence along with her. And of this, they would never speak.

When awareness of the outside began to come back, she clung to his breast, murmuring "My love! My love!" And he held her silently. And she curled on his breast, perfect.

But his silence was fathomless. His hands held her like flowers, so still and strange. "Where are you?" she whispered to him.

"Where are you? Speak to me! Say something to me!"

He kissed her softly, murmuring: "Ay, my lass!"

But she did not know what he meant, she did not know where he was. In his silence he seemed lost to her.

"You love me, don't you?" she murmured.

"Ay, tha knows!" he said.

"But tell me!" she pleaded.

"Ay! Ay! 'asn't ter felt it?" he said dimly, but softly and surely. And she clung close to him, closer. He was so much more peaceful in love than she was, and she wanted him to reassure her.

"You do love me!" she whispered, assertive. And his hands stroked her softly, as if she were a flower, without the quiver of desire, but with delicate nearness. And still there haunted her a restless necessity to get a grip on love.

"Say you'll always love me!" she pleaded.

"Ay!" he said, abstractedly. And she felt her questions driving him away from her.

"Mustn't we get up?" he said at last.

"No!" she said.

But she could feel his consciousness straying, listening to the noises outside.

"It'll be nearly dark," he said. And she heard the pressure of circumstances in his voice. She kissed him, with a woman's grief at yielding up her hour.

He rose, and turned up the lantern, then began to pull on his clothes, quickly disappearing inside them. Then he stood there, above her, fastening his breeches and looking down at her with dark, wide-eyes, his face a little flushed and his hair ruffled, curiously warm and still and beautiful in the dim light of the lantern, so beautiful, she would never tell him how beautiful. It made her want to cling fast to him, to hold him, for there was a warm, half-sleepy remoteness in his beauty that made her want to cry out and clutch him, to have him. She would never have him. So she lay on the blanket with curved, soft naked haunches, and he had no idea what she was thinking, but

to him too she was beautiful, the soft, marvellous thing he could go into, beyond everything.

"I love thee that I can go into thee," he said.

"Do you like me?" she said, her heart beating.

"It heals it all up, that I can go into thee. I love thee that tha opened to me. I love thee that I came into thee like that."

He bent down and kissed her soft flank, rubbed his cheek against it, then covered it up.

"And will you never leave me?" she said.

"Dunna ask them things," he said.

"But you do believe I love you?" she said.

"Tha loved me just now, wider than iver tha thout tha would. But who knows what'll 'appen, once tha starts thinkin' about it!"

"No, don't say those things! – And you don't really think that I wanted to make use of you, do you?"

"How?"

"To have a child – ?"

"Now anybody can 'ave any childt i' th' world," he said, as he sat down fastening on his leggings.

"Ah no!" she cried. "You don't mean it?"

"Eh well!" he said, looking at her under his brows. "This wor t' best."

She lay still. He softly opened the door. The sky was dark blue, with crystalline, turquoise rim. He went out, to shut up the hens, speaking softly to his dog. And she lay and wondered at the wonder of life, and of being.

When he came back she was still lying there, glowing like a gipsy. He sat on the stool by her.

"Tha mun come one naight ter th' cottage, afore tha goos; sholl ter?" he asked, lifting his eyebrows as he looked at her, his hands dangling between his knees.

"Sholl ter?" she echoed, teasing.

He smiled. "Ay, sholl ter?" he repeated.

"Ay!" she said, imitating the dialect sound.

"Yi!" he said.

"Yi!" she repeated.

"An' slaip wi' me," he said. "It needs that. When sholt come?"

"When sholl I?" she said.

"Nay," he said, "tha canna do't. When sholt come then?"

"'Appen Sunday," she said.

"'Appen a' Sunday! Ay!"

He laughed at her quickly.

"Nay, tha canna," he protested.

"Why canna I?" she said.

From THE MAGUS

John Fowles

John Fowles was born in Bedford. After graduating from Oxford University, where he studied French, he went on to teach in France, and then for several years on a Greek island, the setting for his novel *The Magus* (1965). *The Magus* is considered to be a masterpiece of contemporary literature. It is about a young Englishman, Nicholas Urfe, who accepts a teaching position on a Greek island, where his friendship with the mysterious and reclusive owner of a magnificent estate on the island leads him into a nightmare. As reality and fantasy are deliberately blurred by staged deaths, erotic encounters, and terrifying violence, Urfe becomes a desperate man fighting for his sanity and his life.

As we approached the colonnade, a barelegged figure in a brick-red shirt stood from the steps in the sun where she had been sitting.

"I nearly started without you. I'm hungry."

The shirt was unbuttoned, and underneath I could see a dark blue bikini. The word, like the fashion, was very new then: in fact it was the first bikini I had ever seen outside a newspaper photograph and it gave me something of a shock . . . the bare navel, the slender legs, brown-gold skin, a pair of amusedly questioning eyes. I caught Julie wrinkling her nose at this young Mediterranean goddess, who only widened her smile. As we followed her to the table set back in the shade beneath the arches, I remembered the story of *Three Hearts* . . . but banned the thought before it grew. June went to the corner of the colonnade and called for Maria, then turned to her sister.

"She's been trying to tell me something about the yacht. I couldn't work it out."

We sat, and Maria appeared. She spoke to Julie. I followed well enough. The yacht was arriving at five, to take the girls away. Hermes was coming to take Maria herself back to the village for a night. She had to see the dentist there. The "young gentleman" must return to the school, as the house would be locked up. I heard Julie ask where the yacht was going. *Then xero, despoina.* I don't know, miss. She repeated, as if that was the nub of her message. At five o'clock? Then she bobbed in her usual way, and disappeared back to her cottage.

Julie translated for June's benefit.

I said, "This wasn't planned?"

"I thought we were staying here." She looked doubtfully at her sister, who in turn eyed me, then drily queried Julie back.

"Do we trust him? Does he trust us?"

"Yes."

June gave me a little grin. "Then welcome, Pip."

I looked to Julie for help. She murmured, "I thought you claimed to have read English at Oxford."

There was suddenly a shadow of reawakened suspicion between us. Then I woke up, and took a breath. "All these literary references." I smiled. "Miss Havisham rides again?"

"And Estella."

I looked from one to the other. "You're not serious?"

"Just our little joke."

Julie regarded her sister. "*Your* little joke."

June spoke to me. "Which I've tried to get Maurice to share. With total unsuccess." She leant her elbows on the table. "But come on. Tell me what great conclusions you've reached."

"Nicholas has told me something extraordinary."

I was given one more chance to test a reaction; and found myself once more convinced, though June seemed more outraged than amused by the new evidence of the old man's duplicity. As we went over it all again, I discovered (and might have already deduced from their names) that in terms of delivery June was the older twin. She also seemed it in other ways. I detected a protectiveness in her towards Julie, which sprang from a more open personality, greater experience of men. There was a shadow of reality in the casting of the masque: a more normal and a less normal sister, or one more assertive, the other more fragile. I sat between them, facing the sea, keeping an eye open for the hidden watcher – though he stayed hidden, if he was still spying on us. The girls started questioning me, my own background and past.

So we talked about Nicholas: his family, his ambitions, his failings. The third person is apt, because I presented a sort of fictional self to them, a victim of circumstances, a mixture of attractive raffishness and essential inner decency. Alison came up again briefly. I put the main blame there on hazard, on fate, on elective affinity, one's knowing one sought more; and let them feel, copying Julie, that I didn't want to talk in detail about all that. It was over and done with, pale and sour beside the present.

Something about that long lunch, the enjoyable food and the *retsina*, all the debating and speculating, the questions they asked, the being between the two of them, the dressed and the near-naked, feeling closer to them both all the time – we got on to their father, their having lived their childhood in the shadow of a boys' boarding-school, then their mother, they kept capping each other's affectionate stories about her silliness . . . it was like entering a deliciously warm room after a long, cold journey; an erotically warm room, as well. Towards the end of the meal June slipped out of her shirt. In return Julie slipped out a sisterly tongue, which was met by an impervious little smile. I began to have trouble keeping my eyes off that body. The bikini top barely covered the breasts; and the bottom half was tied at the hips by white laces that let the skin show through. I knew I was being visually teased a little, innocently flirted with . . . some small revenge, perhaps, on June's part for

having been kept so long in the wings. If human beings could purr, I should have done so then.

About half past two we decided to go out of Bourani and down to Moutsa to swim – partly to see whether we should be allowed to. If Joe blocked our way, I promised not to challenge him. The girls seemed to share my own view of his physical strength. So we strolled down the track, expecting to be stopped, as June had been once. But there was no one there; only the pines, the heat, the racket of the cicadas. We installed ourselves halfway down the beach, near the little chapel in the trees. I spread two rugs where the needled earth ran into the shingle. Julie, who had disappeared for a minute before we left the house, peeled off her schoolgirl stockings, then pulled her dress over her head. She was wearing a white one-piece bare-backed costume underneath, and she managed to look shyly ashamed at the weakness of her own tan.

Her sister grinned. "If only Maurice could provide the seven dwarfs as well."

"Shut up. It's not fair. I'll never catch up now." She gave me what was almost a scowl. "Honestly I've been sitting on that wretched yacht under an awning while all she does is . . ." she turned away and folded her dress.

They both did up their hair, we went down the burning shingle and into the water, and swam a little way out. I looked down the beach towards Bourani, but saw no one. We were alone in the world, in the cool blue water, three heads; and again I felt a near-absolute happiness, a being poised, not sure how all this would turn out, but also not wanting to know, totally identified with the moment: with Greece, this lost place, these two real-life nymphs. We came back ashore, dried, lay on the rugs; myself beside Julie on one of them, she was anointing herself with sun-tan oil; June on the far side on the other rug, flat on her stomach, her head couched on her hands and turned towards us. I thought of the school, its repressed boys and sour masters, the unendurable lack of femininity and natural sexuality in its life. We began to talk about Maurice again. Julie put on sun-glasses, lay on her back, while I still lay propped on an elbow.

There came in the end a little silence; the wine at lunch, the soporific sun. June reached back and undid the hook at the back of her bikini top, then stretched up and eased it away to dry on the stones beside her. I glimpsed her bare breasts as she reached an arm to do it; and the long golden back, divided by the taut little strip of dark blue from the long golden legs. There was no white bar on her skin, the breasts were the same colour as the rest; she must have tanned a lot like that. It had been done casually and naturally, but I made sure my eyes were looking out to sea when she lay flat again, turned towards us as before. Once more I was shocked: this was not just the latest clothes fashion, but behaviour years ahead of its time. I was also uncomfortably aware that she was staring at me, that a comparison was being invited – or a reaction, observed. After a few moments she shifted a little and moved her head to face the other way. I looked at her brown figure, then down at Julie; then lay on my back myself and felt for the hand of the girl beside me. Her fingers curled through mine, played, contracted. I closed my eyes. Darkness, both; the old wickedness of Greece.

But I was soon punished for my day-dreaming. Out of nowhere, a minute or two later, there was an abrupt approaching roar. For a wild first second I thought it was something to do with Bourani. Then I realized it was a sound I had not

heard since I had been on the island: a low-flying plane, a fighter by the sound of it. Julie and I sat up, June leant round on an elbow, her back to us. The plane was very low. It shot out from behind the Bourani cape, some four hundred yards to sea of it, and scorched like an angry hornet over the water towards the Peloponnesus. In a few seconds it had passed out of sight behind the headland to the west; but not before we had seen the American markings – or at least I had. Julie seemed more interested in her sister's bare back.

June said, "What a cheek."

"He'll probably be back, now he's seen you like that."

"Don't be such a prude."

"Nicholas is perfectly well aware of what beautiful bodies we both have."

June turned to us then, on her elbows, a small pendant breast visible past the nearer bent arm. She was biting her lips. "I didn't realize things had gone that far."

Julie stared fixedly out to sea. "We are not amused."

"Nicholas seems to be."

"You're showing off."

"Since he's already had the divine good luck to see me – "

"*June.*"

Through all this little spat Julie hadn't looked at me. But now she did, and made it clear whose side I was to be on. It was delicious: she was both embarrassed and piqued, like still water ruffled. She surveyed me reproachfully, as if it was all my fault.

"Let's go and look at the chapel."

I glanced at June as I obediently stood, and received a sarcastic and impudent little cast skywards of her eyes. Now I had to bite my lips. Julie and I strolled away into the trees, the shade, in bare feet. There was a charming pinkness about her cheeks, and a setness of mouth.

"She's only teasing you."

"I could scratch her eyes out sometimes."

"A classicist shouldn't be shocked by nakedness in Greece."

"I'm not a classicist at the moment. Just a girl who feels at a disadvantage."

I leant and kissed the side of her head. I was pushed away, but without force.

We came to the whitewashed chapel. I thought it would be locked, as it had been when I had tried to get in before. But the primitive wooden latch gave – someone must have been there, and forgotten to relock the place. There was no window, only the light from the door. It was bare of chairs; an iron candle-holder with one or two ancient stumps on its spikes, a naïvely painted iconostasis spanning the far end, a very faint aroma of incense. We went and looked at the crudely figured saints on the worm-eaten wall of wood, but I knew we were both less aware of them than of the darkness and seclusion of the little place. I put an arm round her shoulders. A moment later she had turned and we were kissing. She twisted her mouth away and turned her cheek against my shoulder. I looked at the open door, then drew her back towards it; pushed it to, leant against the wall on the hinge side and coaxed her to me. I began to kiss her throat, her shoulder, then reached up to the straps of her costume.

"No. You mustn't."

But her voice had that peculiar feminine tone that invites you to go on as much as to stop. I gently eased the straps off her shoulders, then down, till she was bare to the waist; caressed the waist, then up, slowly, to the firm small breasts, still a little damp from the seawater, but warm, excited. I bent and licked the salt from the nipples. Her hands began to stroke down my back, in my hair. I let my own wander down to the waist again, to where the costume hung, but then her hands were abruptly on mine.

She whispered. "Please. Not yet."

I brushed my lips against her mouth. "I want you so much."

"I know."

"You're so beautiful."

"But we can't. Not here."

I moved my hands up to her breasts.

"Do you want me to?"

"You know I do. But not now."

Her arms slipped round my neck and we kissed again, crushing each other. I slid a hand down her back, slipped the fingers inside the edge of the costume, appled a curved cheek, pulled her closer still, against the hardness in my loins, made sure she could feel it and know she was wanted. Our mouths twisted, our tongues explored wildly, she began to rock against me and I could sense she was losing control, that this nakedness, darkness, pent-up emotion, repressed need . . .

There was a sound. It was minute, and gave no indication of what had caused it. But it came beyond any doubt from the far end of, and inside, the chapel. We clung in petrified horror for a long second. Julie's head twisted round to look where I was looking, but the few glints of light through the sides of the closed door made it difficult to see. Instinctively we both reached for her costume and slipped it back on over her arms. Then I gripped her hand, moved her against the wall beside me, and reached for the door. I jerked it open, light flooded in. The iconostasis stared at us, the black iron candlestand in front of it. There was nothing else. But I could see that the iconostasis, as in all such Greek chapels, stood some three or four feet off the back wall; and there was a narrow door at one end. Suddenly Julie was in front of me, mutely but violently shaking her head – she must have seen my instinct was to rush down there. I had guessed at once who it was: that accursed Negro. He could have sneaked in easily enough when we were swimming, and had probably assumed we would not leave the beach and the sea.

Julie pulled my hand urgently, casting a quick look back at the far end. I hesitated, then let her drag me out into the open air. I slammed the door shut, then looked at her.

"The bastard."

"He can't have known we were going in there."

"But he could damn well have warned us earlier."

We spoke in whispers. She made me walk a few steps away. Beyond, in the sun, I could see June with her head raised, looking at us. She must have heard the sharp bang of the door.

Julie said, "Maurice will know for sure now."

"That no longer worries me. It's about bloody time he did."

June called. "Is something wrong?"

Julie raised a finger to her mouth. Her sister turned, sat up, put her bikini top on, then came to meet us.

"Joe's in there. Hidden."

June looked past us at the white walls of the chapel, then at our faces – no longer teasing, but concerned.

Julie said, "I'm going to have it out with Maurice. Either Joe goes, or we do."

"I suggested that weeks ago."

"I know."

"Were you talking? Did he hear anything?"

Julie looked down. "It's not that." Her cheeks were flushed. June gave me a sympathetic little smile, but had the grace to look down as well.

I said, "I'm only too happy to go in there and . . ."

But they were firmly against that. We walked back to our things and talked it over for a few minutes, covertly watching the chapel door. It stayed as it was, but somehow the place was spoilt now. That invisible black presence in the little building seeped into the landscape, the sunlight, the whole afternoon. I also felt a violent sexual frustration . . . but there was nothing now to be done about that. We decided to go back to the house.

There we found Maria sitting impassively outside her cottage, talking to the donkeyman, Hermes. She said tea was waiting for us, on the table. The two peasants stared at us from their wooden chairs, as if we were so remote from their simple world, so foreign, that all communication was impossible. But then Maria pointed mysteriously out to sea and said two or three words in Greek that I didn't understand. We looked, but saw nothing.

Julie said, "She says a fleet of warships."

We went to the edge of the gravel to the south of the house; and there, almost hull down, a line of grey ships steamed east across the Aegean between Malea and Skyli: a carrier, a cruiser, four destroyers, another ship, intent on some new Troy. The harsh irruption of the fighter plane into our peace was explained.

June said, "Perhaps it's Maurice's last trick. To bombard us to death."

We laughed, but were held by those cloud-grey shapes on the world's blue rim. Death machines holding thousands of gum-chewing, contraceptive-carrying men, for some reason more thirty years away than thirty miles; as if we were looking into the future, not the south; into a world where there were no more Prosperos, no private domaines, no poetries, fantasies, tender sexual promises . . . I stood between the two girls and felt acutely the fragility not only of the old man's extraordinary enterprise, but of time itself. I knew I would never have another adventure like this. I would have sacrificed all the rest of my days to have this one afternoon endless, endlessly repeated, a closed circle, instead of what it was: a brief and tiny step that could never be retraced.

My previous euphoria waned further over the tea. The girls had gone indoors, then re-appeared in their dresses of that morning. The yacht was due so soon, and there was a hurried confusion over all we said. They were in two minds over what they should do; there was even a moment when we talked of their coming back with me to the other side of the island – they could put up

at the hotel. But in the end we decided to give Conchis one more chance, one last week-end to declare himself. We were still discussing that when something else out to sea caught my eye. It came round the headland from the direction of Nauplia.

They had told me about the yacht, how luxurious it was, how much proof, if any more were needed, that one thing the old man must be was rich. It still took my breath away a little. We all went again to the edge of the gravel, where we could see better. A two-master, it was moving very slowly, under engine power, its sails furled; a long white hull, cabins rising out of the deck both fore and aft. The Greek flag hung lazily at a small mast at the stern. I saw half a dozen blue and white figures, presumably the crew. It was too far out, nearly half a mile, to distinguish a face.

I said, "Well. As prisons go . . ."

June said, "You should see below decks. There are eight brands of French scent on our cabin table."

The yacht almost ceased to move. Three men were at a davit, getting ready to lower a small boat. A siren moaned, to be sure we knew of the arrival. I felt, in characteristic Engish fashion, both a stab of envy and a contempt. The yacht itself was not vulgar, but I smelt something vulgar about owning it. I also saw myself aboard it one day. Nothing in my life before had taken me into the world of the very rich – I had had one or two rich acquaintances at Oxford, people like Billie Whyte, but had never experienced their home backgrounds. I did envy the two girls then; it was easier for them, good looks were the only passports they needed to enter that world. Money-getting was a male thing, sublimated virility. Perhaps Julie sensed all this. At any rate, when we went back to the colonnade for them to collect their things, she suddenly caught my hand and drew me indoors out of June's sight and hearing.

"It's only a few days."

"Which are going to seem like a few years."

"And for me."

I said, "I've been waiting to meet you all my life."

She looked down, we were standing very close. "I know."

"Do you feel the same?"

"I don't know what I feel, Nicholas. Except that I want you to feel like that."

"If you come back, could you get away one evening during the week?"

She glanced round through the open doors, then into my eyes. "It's not that I wouldn't love to, but – "

"I could make Wednesday. We could meet down by the chapel." I added, "Not in it."

She appealed for understanding. "We may not even be here."

"I'll come anyway. After dark. I'll wait till midnight. It'll be better than biting my fingernails in that damned school."

"I will try. If I possibly can. If we're here."

We kissed, but there was something torn, already too late, about it.

We went outside. June waited by the tea-table and immediately nodded across the gravel. There, standing on the path that led down to the private beach, was the Negro. He was in black trousers and a polo-necked jumper, and he wore

dark glasses; waiting. The yacht's siren moaned again. I could hear the sound of a small outboard engine coming fast ashore.

June reached out a hand, and I wished them both good luck. Then I stood watching them walk across the gravel, in their pink dresses and blue stockings, baskets in hand. The Negro turned long before they reached him and started to walk down the path, as if he was too sure they would follow him to bother any more. When their heads had disappeared, I went to the top of the path. The power dinghy entered the little cove and came alongside the jetty. A minute later, the black figure, with the two pale pink ones of the girls just behind, walked down it. There was a sailor in the boat, white shorts, a dark blue shortsleeved singlet with a name in red across the breast. I couldn't read it at that range, but it was obviously *Arethusa.* The sailor helped the two girls into the boat, then the Negro got in. I noticed he sat in the bows, behind their backs. They started out to sea. After a few yards, they must have seen me standing up above, the girls waved; then again, when they left the cove and began to head faster towards the waiting yacht.

The afternoon sea stretched down to Crete, ninety miles away. The fleet had almost disappeared. The black shadow of a cypress halfway down the cliff stabbed across a patch of parched red-grey earth, already lengthening. The day died. I felt both sexually and socially deprived, I did not expect we should be able to meet during the week; but yet a deep excitement buoyed me on, a knowledge like that of the poker-player who needs only one more card to have an unbeatable hand.

I turned back to the house, where Maria was now waiting to lock up. I didn't try to pump her, I knew it was useless, but went up to my bedroom and packed my things in the duffel-bag. When I came down again, the small boat was already being hauled inboard and the huge yacht was under way. It began a long turn, then held course towards the southern end of the Peloponnesus. I was tempted to watch it out of sight; but then, knowing I was probably being watched as well from out there, decided that I did not want to play the wistful marooned man.

A few moments later I set off back to my dull, daily penal colony on the far side of the dream; as Adam left the Garden of Eden, perhaps . . . except that I knew there were no gods, and nothing was going to bar my return.

THE BLOODY CHAMBER

Angela Carter

Angela Carter is best known for her novels, *Nights at the Circus* and *Wise Children*, but might be better known for her journalism, criticism and her short stories. Perhaps her finest work in fiction were her re-tellings of tales told before, especially *The Bloody Chamber* and her two Virago books of fairy tales. Fearsomely intelligent – 'a day without an argument is like an egg without salt' – and wickedly funny, she died, aged fifty-two from cancer. She said, 'Reading a book is like re-writing it for yourself. You bring to a novel, anthing you read, all your experience of the world. You bring your history and you read it in your own terms.'

I remember how, that night, I lay awake in the wagon-lit in a tender, delicious ecstasy of excitement, my burning cheek pressed against the impeccable linen of the pillow and the pounding of my heart mimicking that of the great pistons ceaselessly thrusting the train that bore me through the night, away from Paris, away from girlhood, away from the white, enclosed quietude of my mother's apartment, into the unguessable country of marriage.

And I remember I tenderly imagined how, at this very moment, my mother would be moving slowly about the narrow bedroom I had left behind for ever, folding up and putting away all my little relics, the tumbled garments I would not need any more, the scores for which there had been no room in my trunks, the concert programmes I'd abandoned; she would linger over this torn ribbon and that faded photograph with all the half-joyous, half-sorrowful emotions of a woman on her daughter's wedding day. And, in the midst of my bridal triumph, I felt a pang of loss as if, when he put the gold band on my finger, I had, in some way, ceased to be her child in becoming his wife.

Are you sure, she'd said when they delivered the gigantic box that held the wedding dress he'd bought me, wrapped up in tissue paper and red ribbon like a Christmas gift of crystallized fruit. Are you sure you love him? There was a dress for her, too; black silk, with the dull, prismatic sheen of oil on water, finer than anything she'd worn since that adventurous girlhood in Indo-China, daughter of a rich tea planter. My eagle-featured, indomitable mother; what other student at the Conservatoire could boast that her mother had outfaced a junkful of Chinese pirates, nursed a village through a visitation of the plague, shot a man-eating tiger with her own hand and all before she was as old as I?

"Are you sure you love him?"

"I'm sure I want to marry him," I said.

And would say no more. She sighed, as if it was with reluctance that she might

at last banish the spectre of poverty from its habitual place at our meagre table. For my mother herself had gladly, scandalously, defiantly beggared herself for love; and, one fine day, her gallant soldier never returned from the wars, leaving his wife and child a legacy of tears that never quite dried, a cigar box full of medals and the antique service revolver that my mother, grown magnificently eccentric in hardship, kept always in her reticule, in case – how I teased her – she was surprised by footpads on her way home from the grocer's shop.

Now and then a starburst of lights spattered the drawn blinds as if the railway company had lit up all the stations through which we passed in celebration of the bride. My satin nightdress had just been shaken from its wrappings; it had slipped over my young girl's pointed breasts and shoulders, supple as a garment of heavy water, and now teasingly caressed me, egregious, insinuating, nudging between my thighs as I shifted restlessly in my narrow berth. His kiss, his kiss with tongue and teeth in it and a rasp of beard, had hinted to me, though with the same exquisite tact as this nightdress he'd given me, of the wedding night, which would be voluptuously deferred until we lay in his great ancestral bed in the sea-girt, pinnacled domain that lay, still, beyond the grasp of my imagination . . . that magic place, the fairy castle whose walls were made of foam, that legendary habitation in which he had been born. To which, one day, I might bear an heir. Our destination, my destiny.

Above the syncopated roar of the train, I could hear his even, steady breathing. Only the communicating door kept me from my husband and it stood open. If I rose up on my elbow, I could see the dark, leonine shape of his head and my nostrils caught a whiff of the opulent male scent of leather and spices that always accompanied him and sometimes, during his courtship, had been the only hint he gave me that he had come into my mother's sitting room, for, though he was a big man, he moved as softly as if all his shoes had soles of velvet, as if his footfall turned the carpet into snow.

He had loved to surprise me in my abstracted solitude at the piano. He would tell them not to announce him, then soundlessly open the door and softly creep up behind me with his bouquet of hot-house flowers or his box of marrons glacés, lay his offering upon the keys and clasp his hands over my eyes as I was lost in a Debussy prelude. But that perfume of spiced leather always betrayed him; after my first shock, I was forced always to mimic surprise, so that he would not be disappointed.

He was older than I. He was much older than I; there were streaks of pure silver in his dark mane. But his strange, heavy, almost waxen face was not lined by experience. Rather, experience seemed to have washed it perfectly smooth, like a stone on a beach whose fissures have been eroded by successive tides. And sometimes that face, in stillness when he listened to me playing, with the heavy eyelids folded over eyes that always disturbed me by their absolute absence of light, seemed to me like a mask, as if his real face, the face that truly reflected all the life he had led in the world before he met me, before, even, I was born, as though that face lay underneath this mask. Or else, elsewhere. As though he had laid by the face in which he had lived for so long in order to offer my youth a face unsigned by the years.

And, elsewhere, I might see him plain. Elsewhere. But, where?

In, perhaps, that castle to which the train now took us, that marvellous castle in which he had been born.

Even when he asked me to marry him, and I said: "Yes," still he did not lose that heavy, fleshy composure of his. I know it must seem a curious analogy, a man with a flower, but sometimes he seemed to me like a lily. Yes. A lily. Possessed of that strange, ominous calm of a sentient vegetable, like one of those cobra-headed, funereal lilies whose white sheaths are curled out of a flesh as thick and tensely yielding to the touch as vellum. When I said that I would marry him, not one muscle in his face stirred, but he let out a long, extinguished sigh. I thought: Oh! how he must want me! And it was as though the imponderable weight of his desire was a force I might not withstand, not by virtue of its violence but because of its very gravity.

He had the ring ready in a leather box lined with crimson velvet, a fire opal the size of a pigeon's egg set in a complicated circle of dark antique gold. My old nurse, who still lived with my mother and me, squinted at the ring askance; opals are bad luck, she said. But this opal had been his own mother's ring, and his grandmother's, and her mother's before that, given to an ancestor by Catherine de Medici . . . every bride that came to the castle wore it, time out of mind. And did he give it to his other wives and have it back from them? asked the old woman rudely; yet she was a snob. She hid her incredulous joy at my marital coup – her little Marquise – behind a façade of fault-finding. But, here, she touched me. I shrugged and turned my back pettishly on her. I did not want to remember how he had loved other women before me, but the knowledge often teased me in the threadbare self-confidence of the small hours.

I was seventeen and knew nothing of the world; my Marquis had been married before, more than once, and I remained a little bemused that, after those others, he should now have chosen me. Indeed, was he not still in mourning for his last wife? Tsk, tsk, went my old nurse. And even my mother had been reluctant to see her girl whisked off by a man so recently bereaved. A Romanian countess, a lady of high fashion. Dead just three short months before I met him, a boating accident, at his home, in Brittany. They never found her body but I rummaged through the back copies of the society magazines my old nanny kept in a trunk under her bed and tracked down her photograph. The sharp muzzle of a pretty, witty, naughty monkey; such potent and bizarre charm, of a dark, bright, wild yet worldly thing whose natural habitat must have been some luxurious interior decorator's jungle filled with potted palms and tame, squawking parakeets.

Before that? *Her* face is common property; everyone painted her but the Redon engraving I liked best, *The Evening Star Walking on the Rim of Night*. To see her skeletal, enigmatic grace, you would never think she had been a barmaid in a café in Montmartre until Puvis de Chavannes saw her and had her expose her flat breasts and elongated thighs to his brush. And yet it was the absinthe doomed her, or so they said.

The first of all his ladies? That sumptuous diva; I had heard her sing Isolde, precociously musical child that I was, taken to the opera for a birthday treat. My first opera; I had heard her sing Isolde. With what white-hot passion had she burned from the stage! So that you could tell she would die young. We sat high up, halfway to heaven in the gods, yet she half-blinded me. And my father, still

alive (oh, so long ago), took hold of my sticky little hand, to comfort me, in the last act, yet all I heard was the glory of her voice.

Married three times within my own brief lifetime to three different graces, now, as if to demonstrate the eclecticism of his taste, he had invited me to join this gallery of beautiful women, I, the poor widow's child with my mouse-coloured hair that still bore the kinks of the plaits from which it had so recently been freed, my bony hips, my nervous, pianist's fingers.

He was rich as Croesus. The night before our wedding – a simple affair, at the Mairie, because his countess was so recently gone – he took my mother and me, curious coincidence, to see *Tristan.* And, do you know, my heart swelled and ached so during the Liebestod that I thought I must truly love him. Yes. I did. On his arm, all eyes were upon me. The whispering crowd in the foyer parted like the Red Sea to let us through. My skin crisped at his touch.

How my circumstances had changed since the first time I heard those voluptuous chords that carry such a charge of deathly passion in them! Now, we sat in a loge, in red velvet armchairs, and a braided, bewigged flunkey brought us a silver bucket of iced champagne in the interval. The froth spilled over the rim of my glass and drenched my hands, I thought: My cup runneth over. And I had on a Poiret dress. He had prevailed upon my reluctant mother to let him buy my trousseau; what would I have gone to him in, otherwise? Twice-darned underwear, faded gingham, serge skirts, hand-me-downs. So, for the opera, I wore a sinuous shift of white muslin tied with a silk string under the breasts. And everyone stared at me. And at his wedding gift.

His wedding gift, clasped round my throat. A choker of rubies, two inches wide, like an extraordinarily precious slit throat.

After the Terror, in the early days of the Directory, the aristos who'd escaped the guillotine had an ironic fad of tying a red ribbon round their necks at just the point where the blade would have sliced it through, a red ribbon like the memory of a wound. And his grandmother, taken with the notion, had her ribbon made up in rubies; such a gesture of luxurious defiance! That night at the opera comes back to me even now . . . the white dress; the frail child within it; and the flashing crimson jewels round her throat, bright as arterial blood.

I saw him watching me in the gilded mirrors with the assessing eye of a connoisseur inspecting horseflesh, or even of a housewife in the market, inspecting cuts on the slab. I'd never seen, or else had never acknowledged, that regard of his before, the sheer carnal avarice of it; and it was strangely magnified by the monocle lodged in his left eye. When I saw him look at me with lust, I dropped my eyes but, in glancing away from him, I caught sight of myself in the mirror. And I saw myself, suddenly, as he saw me, my pale face, the way the muscles in my neck stuck out like thin wire. I saw how much that cruel necklace became me. And, for the first time in my innocent and confined life, I sensed in myself a potentiality for corruption that took my breath away.

The next day, we were married.

The train slowed, shuddered to a halt. Lights; clank of metal; a voice declaring the name of an unknown, never-to-be visited station; silence of the night; the rhythm of his breathing, that I should sleep with, now, for the rest of my life. And

I could not sleep. I stealthily sat up, raised the blind a little and huddled against the cold window that misted over with the warmth of my breathing, gazing out at the dark platform towards those rectangles of domestic lamplight that promised warmth, company, a supper of sausages hissing in a pan on the stove for the station master, his children tucked up in bed asleep in the brick house with the painted shutters . . . all the paraphernalia of the everyday world from which I, with my stunning marriage, had exiled myself.

Into marriage, into exile; I sensed it, I knew it – that, henceforth, I would always be lonely. Yet that was part of the already familiar weight of the fire opal that glimmered like a gypsy's magic ball, so that I could not take my eyes off it when I played the piano. This ring, the bloody bandage of rubies, the wardrobe of clothes from Poiret and Worth, his scent of Russian leather – all had conspired to seduce me so utterly that I could not say I felt one single twinge of regret for the world of tartines and maman that now receded from me as if drawn away on a string, like a child's toy, as the train began to throb again as if in delighted anticipation of the distance it would take me.

The first grey streamers of the dawn now flew in the sky and an eldritch half-light seeped into the railway carriage. I heard no change in his breathing but my heightened, excited senses told me he was awake and gazing at me. A huge man, an enormous man, and his eyes, dark and motionless as those eyes the ancient Egyptians painted upon their sarcophagi, fixed upon me. I felt a certain tension in the pit of my stomach, to be so watched, in such silence. A match struck. He was igniting a Romeo y Julieta fat as a baby's arm.

"Soon," he said in his resonant voice that was like the tolling of a bell and I felt, all at once, a sharp premonition of dread that lasted only as long as the match flared and I could see his white, broad face as if it were hovering, disembodied, above the sheets, illuminated from below like a grotesque carnival head. Then the flame died, the cigar glowed and filled the compartment with a remembered fragrance that made me think of my father, how he would hug me in a warm fug of Havana, when I was a little girl, before he kissed me and left me and died.

As soon as my husband handed me down from the high step of the train, I smelled the amniotic salinity of the ocean. It was November; the trees, stunted by the Atlantic gales, were bare and the lonely halt was deserted but for his leather-gaitered chauffeur waiting meekly beside the sleek black motor car. It was cold; I drew my furs about me, a wrap of white and black, broad stripes of ermine and sable, with a collar from which my head rose like the calyx of a wild-flower. (I swear to you, I had never been vain until I met him.) The bell clanged; the straining train leapt its leash and left us at that lonely wayside halt where only he and I had descended. Oh, the wonder of it; how all that might of iron and steam had paused only to suit his convenience. The richest man in France.

"Madame."

The chauffeur eyed me; was he comparing me, invidiously, to the countess, the artist's model, the opera singer? I hid behind my furs as if they were a system of soft shields. My husband liked me to wear my opal over my kid glove, a showy, theatrical trick – but the moment the ironic chauffeur glimpsed its simmering

flash he smiled, as though it was proof positive I was his master's wife. And we drove towards the widening dawn, that now streaked half the sky with a wintry bouquet of pink of roses, orange of tiger-lilies, as if my husband had ordered me a sky from a florist. The day broke around me like a cool dream.

Sea; sand; a sky that melts into the sea – a landscape of misty pastels with a look about it of being continuously on the point of melting. A landscape with all the deliquescent harmonies of Debussy, of the études I played for him, the reverie I'd been playing that afternoon in the salon of the princess where I'd first met him, among the teacups and the little cakes, I, the orphan, hired out of charity to give them their digestive of music.

And, ah! his castle. The faery solitude of the place; with its turrets of misty blue, its courtyard, its spiked gate, his castle that lay on the very bosom of the sea with seabirds mewing about its attics, the casements opening on to the green and purple, evanescent departures of the ocean, cut off by the tide from land for half a day . . . that castle, at home neither on the land nor on the water, a mysterious, amphibious place, contravening the materiality of both earth and the waves, with the melancholy of a mermaiden who perches on her rock and waits, endlessly, for a lover who had drowned far away, long ago. That lovely, sad, sea-siren of a place!

The tide was low; at this hour, so early in the morning, the causeway rose up out of the sea. As the car turned on to the wet cobbles between the slow margins of water, he reached out for my hand that had his sultry, witchy ring on it, pressed my fingers, kissed my palm with extraordinary tenderness. His face was as still as ever I'd seen it, still as a pond iced thickly over, yet his lips, that always looked so strangely red and naked between the black fringes of his beard, now curved a little. He smiled; he welcomed his bride home.

No room, no corridor that did not rustle with the sound of the sea and all the ceilings, the walls on which his ancestors in the stern regalia of rank lined up with their dark eyes and white faces, were stippled with refracted light from the waves which were always in motion; that luminous, murmurous castle of which I was the châtelaine, I, the little music student whose mother had sold all her jewellery, even her wedding ring, to pay the fees at the Conservatoire.

First of all, there was the small ordeal of my initial interview with the housekeeper, who kept this extraordinary machine, this anchored, castellated ocean liner, in smooth running order no matter who stood on the bridge; how tenuous, I thought, might be my authority here! She had a bland, pale, impassive, dislikeable face beneath the impeccably starched white linen headdress of the region. Her greeting, correct but lifeless, chilled me; daydreaming, I dared presume too much on my status . . . briefly wondered how I might install my old nurse, so much loved, however cosily incompetent, in her place. Ill-considered schemings! He told me this one had been his foster mother; was bound to his family in the utmost feudal complicity, "as much part of the house as I am, my dear". Now her thin lips offered me a proud little smile. She would be my ally as long as I was his. And with that, I must be content.

But, here, it would be easy to be content. In the turret suite he had given me for my very own, I could gaze out over the tumultuous Atlantic and imagine myself the Queen of the Sea. There was a Bechstein for me in the music room

and, on the wall, another wedding present – an early Flemish primitive of Saint Cecilia at her celestial organ. In the prim charm of this saint, with her plump, sallow cheeks and crinkled brown hair, I saw myself as I could have wished to be. I warmed to a loving sensitivity I had not hitherto suspected in him. Then he led me up a delicate spiral staircase to my bedroom; before she discreetly vanished, the housekeeper set him chuckling with some, I dare say, lewd blessing for newlyweds in her native Breton. That I did not understand. That he, smiling, refused to interpret.

And there lay the grand, hereditary matrimonial bed, itself the size, almost, of my little room at home, with the gargoyles carved on its surfaces of ebony, vermilion lacquer, gold leaf; and its white gauze curtains, billowing in the sea breeze. Our bed. And surrounded by so many mirrors! Mirrors on all the walls, in stately frames of contorted gold, that reflected more white lilies than I'd ever seen in my life before. He'd filled the room with them, to greet the bride, the young bride. The young bride, who had become that multitude of girls I saw in the mirrors, identical in their chic navy blue tailor-mades, for travelling, madame, or walking. A maid had dealt with the furs. Henceforth, a maid would deal with everything.

"See," he said, gesturing towards those elegant girls. "I have acquired a whole harem for myself!"

I found that I was trembling. My breath came thickly. I could not meet his eye and turned my head away, out of pride, out of shyness, and watched a dozen husbands approach me in a dozen mirrors and slowly, methodically, teasingly, unfasten the buttons of my jacket and slip it from my shoulders. Enough! No; more! Off comes the skirt; and, next, the blouse of apricot linen that cost more than the dress I had for first communion. The play of the waves outside in the cold sun glittered on his monocle; his movements seemed to me deliberately coarse, vulgar. The blood rushed to my face again, and stayed there.

And yet, you see, I guessed it might be so – that we should have a formal disrobing of the bride, a ritual from the brothel. Sheltered as my life had been, how could I have failed, even in the world of prim bohemia in which I lived, to have heard hints of *his* world?

He stripped me, gourmand that he was, as if he were stripping the leaves off an artichoke – but do not imagine much finesse about it; this artichoke was no particular treat for the diner nor was he yet in any greedy haste. He approached his familiar treat with a weary appetite. And when nothing but my scarlet, palpitating core remained, I saw, in the mirror, the living image of an etching by Rops from the collection he had shown me when our engagement permitted us to be alone together . . . the child with her sticklike limbs, naked but for her button boots, her gloves, shielding her face with her hand as though her face were the last repository of her modesty; and the old, monocled lecher who examined her, limb by limb. He in his London tailoring; she, bare as a lamb chop. Most pornographic of all confrontations. And so my purchaser unwrapped his bargain. And, as at the opera, when I had first seen my flesh in his eyes, I was aghast to feel myself stirring.

At once he closed my legs like a book and I saw again the rare movement of his lips that meant he smiled.

Not yet. Later. Anticipation is the greater part of pleasure, my little love.

And I began to shudder, like a racehorse before a race, yet also with a kind of fear, for I felt both a strange, impersonal arousal at the thought of love and at the same time a repugnance I could not stifle for his white, heavy flesh that had too much in common with the armfuls of arum lilies that filled my bedroom in great glass jars, those undertakers' lilies with the heavy pollen that powders your fingers as if you had dipped them in turmeric. The lilies I always associate with him; that are white. And stain you.

This scene from a voluptuary's life was now abruptly terminated. It turns out he has business to attend to; his estates, his companies – even on your honeymoon? Even then, said the red lips that kissed me before he left me alone with my bewildered senses – a wet, silken brush from his beard; a hint of the pointed tip of the tongue. Disgruntled, I wrapped a négligé of antique lace around me to sip the little breakfast of hot chocolate the maid brought me; after that, since it was second nature to me, there was nowhere to go but the music room and soon I settled down at my piano.

Yet only a series of subtle discords flowed from beneath my fingers: out of tune . . . only a little out of tune; but I'd been blessed with perfect pitch and could not bear to play any more. Sea breezes are bad for pianos; we shall need a resident piano-tuner on the premises if I'm to continue with my studies! I flung down the lid in a little fury of disappointment; what should I do now, how shall I pass the long, sea-lit hours until my husband beds me?

I shivered to think of *that.*

His library seemed the source of his habitual odour of Russian leather. Row upon row of calf-bound volumes, brown and olive, with gilt lettering on their spines, the octavo in brilliant scarlet morocco. A deep-buttoned leather sofa to recline on. A lectern, carved like a spread eagle, that held open upon it an edition of Huysmans's *Là-bas*, from some over-exquisite private press; it had been bound like a missal, in brass, with gems of coloured glass. The rugs on the floor, deep, pulsing blues of heaven and red of the heart's dearest blood, came from Isfahan and Bokhara; the dark panelling gleamed; there was the lulling music of the sea and a fire of apple logs. The flames flickered along the spines inside a glass-fronted case that held books still crisp and new. Eliphas Levy; the name meant nothing to me. I squinted at a title or two: *The Initiation*, *The Key of Mysteries*, *The Secret of Pandora's Box*, and yawned. Nothing, here, to detain a seventeen-year-old girl waiting for her first embrace. I should have liked, best of all, a novel in yellow paper; I wanted to curl up on the rug before the blazing fire, lose myself in a cheap novel, munch sticky liqueur chocolates. If I rang for them, a maid would bring me chocolates.

Nevertheless, I opened the doors of that bookcase idly to browse. And I think I knew, I knew by some tingling of the fingertips, even before I opened that slim volume with no title at all on the spine, what I should find inside it. When he showed me the Rops, newly bought, dearly prized, had he not hinted that he was a connoisseur of such things? Yet I had not bargained for this, the girl with tears hanging on her cheeks like stuck pearls, her cunt a split fig below the great globes of her buttocks on which the knotted tails of the cat were about to descend, while a man in a black mask fingered with his free hand his prick, that curved upwards like the scimitar he held. The picture had a caption: "Reproof of curiosity". My

mother, with all the precision of her eccentricity, had told me what it was that lovers did; I was innocent but not naïve. *The Adventures of Eulalie at the Harem of the Grand Turk* had been printed, according to the flyleaf, in Amsterdam in 1748, a rare collector's piece. Had some ancestor brought it back himself from that northern city? Or had my husband bought it for himself, from one of those dusty little bookshops on the Left Bank where an old man peers at you through spectacles an inch thick, daring you to inspect his wares . . . I turned the pages in the anticipation of fear; the print was rusty. Here was another steel engraving: "Immolation of the wives of the Sultan". I knew enough for what I saw in that book to make me gasp.

There was a pungent intensification of the odour of leather that suffused his library; his shadow fell across the massacre.

"My little nun has found the prayerbooks, has she?" he demanded, with a curious mixture of mockery and relish; then, seeing my painful, furious bewilderment, he laughed at me aloud, snatched the book from my hands and put it down on the sofa.

"Have the nasty pictures scared Baby? Baby mustn't play with grown-ups' toys until she's learned how to handle them, must she?"

Then he kissed me. And with, this time, no reticence. He kissed me and laid his hand imperatively upon my breast, beneath the sheath of ancient lace. I stumbled on the winding stair that led to the bedroom, to the carved, gilded bed on which he had been conceived. I stammered foolishly: We've not taken luncheon yet; and, besides, it is broad daylight . . .

All the better to see you.

He made me put on my choker, the family heirloom of one woman who had escaped the blade. With trembling fingers, I fastened the thing about my neck. It was cold as ice and chilled me. He twined my hair into a rope and lifted it off my shoulders so that he could the better kiss the downy furrows below my ears; that made me shudder. And he kissed those blazing rubies, too. He kissed them before he kissed my mouth. Rapt, he intoned: "Of her apparel she retains/Only her sonorous jewellery."

A dozen husbands impaled a dozen brides while the mewing gulls swung on invisible trapezes in the empty air outside.

I was brought to my senses by the insistent shrilling of the telephone. He lay beside me, felled like an oak, breathing stertorously, as if he had been fighting with me. In the course of that one-sided struggle, I had seen his deathly composure shatter like a porcelain vase flung against a wall; I had heard him shriek and blaspheme at the orgasm; I had bled. And perhaps I had seen his face without its mask; and perhaps I had not. Yet I had been infinitely dishevelled by the loss of my virginity.

I gathered myself together, reached into the cloisonné cupboard beside the bed that concealed the telephone and addressed the mouthpiece. His agent in New York. Urgent.

I shook him awake and rolled over on my side, cradling my spent body in my arms. His voice buzzed like a hive of distant bees. My husband. My husband, who, with so much love, filled my bedroom with lilies until it looked like an

embalming parlour. Those somnolent lilies, that wave their heavy heads, distributing their lush, insolent incense reminiscent of pampered flesh.

When he'd finished with the agent, he turned to me and stroked the ruby necklace that bit into my neck, but with such tenderness now, that I ceased flinching and he caressed my breasts. My dear one, my little love, my child, did it hurt her? He's so sorry for it, such impetuousness, he could not help himself; you see, he loves her so . . . and this lover's recitative of his brought my tears in a flood. I clung to him as though only the one who had inflicted the pain could comfort me for suffering it. For a while, he murmured to me in a voice I'd never heard before, a voice like the soft consolations of the sea. But then he unwound the tendrils of my hair from the buttons of his smoking jacket, kissed my cheek briskly and told me the agent from New York had called with such urgent business that he must leave as soon as the tide was low enough. Leave the castle? Leave France! And would be away for at least six weeks.

"But it is our honeymoon!"

A deal, an enterprise of hazard and chance involving several millions, lay in the balance, he said. He drew away from me into that wax-works stillness of his; I was only a little girl, I did not understand. And, he said unspoken to my wounded vanity, I have had too many honeymoons to find them in the least pressing commitments. I know quite well that this child I've bought with a handful of coloured stones and the pelts of dead beasts won't run away. But, after he'd called his Paris agent to book a passage for the States next day – just one tiny call, my little one – we should have time for dinner together.

And I had to be content with that.

A Mexican dish of pheasant with hazelnuts and chocolate; salad; white, voluptuous cheese; a sorbet of muscat grapes and Asti spumante. A celebration of Krug exploded festively. And then acrid black coffee in precious little cups so fine it shadowed the birds with which they were painted. I had Cointreau, he had cognac in the library, with the purple velvet curtains drawn against the night, where he took me to perch on his knee in a leather armchair beside the flickering log fire. He had made me change into that chaste little Poiret shift of white muslin; he seemed especially fond of it, my breasts showed through the flimsy stuff, he said, like little soft white doves that sleep, each one, with a pink eye open. But he would not let me take off my ruby choker, although it was growing very uncomfortable, nor fasten up my descending hair, the sign of a virginity so recently ruptured that still remained a wounded presence between us. He twined his fingers in my hair until I winced; I said, I remember, very little.

"The maid will have changed our sheets already," he said. "We do not hang the bloody sheets out of the window to prove to the whole of Brittany you are a virgin, not in these civilized times. But I should tell you it would have been the first time in all my married lives I could have shown my interested tenants such a flag."

Then I realized, with a shock of surprise, how it must have been my innocence that captivated him – the silent music, he said, of my unknowingness, like *La Terrasse des audiences au clair de lune* played upon a piano with keys of ether. You must remember how ill at ease I was in that luxurious place, how unease

had been my constant companion during the whole length of my courtship by this grave satyr who now gently martyrized my hair. To know that my naïvety gave him some pleasure made me take heart. Courage! I shall act the fine lady to the manner born one day, if only by virtue of default.

Then, slowly yet teasingly, as if he were giving a child a great, mysterious treat, he took out a bunch of keys from some interior hidey-hole in his jacket – key after key, a key, he said, for every lock in the house. Keys of all kinds – huge, ancient things of black iron; others slender, delicate, almost baroque; wafer-thin Yale keys for safes and boxes. And, during his absence, it was I who must take care of them all.

I eyed the heavy bunch with circumspection. Until that moment, I had not given a single thought to the practical aspects of marriage with a great house, great wealth, a great man, whose key ring was as crowded as that of a prison warder. Here were the clumsy and archaic keys for the dungeons, for dungeons we had in plenty although they had been converted to cellars for his wines; the dusty bottles inhabited in racks all those deep holes of pain in the rock on which the castle was built. These are the keys to the kitchens, this is the key to the picture gallery, a treasure house filled by five centuries of avid collectors – ah! he foresaw I would spend hours there.

He had amply indulged his taste for the Symbolists, he told me with a glint of greed. There was Moreau's great portrait of his first wife, the famous *Sacrificial Victim* with the imprint of the lacelike chains on her pellucid skin. Did I know the story of the painting of that picture? How, when she took off her clothes for him for the first time, she fresh from her bar in Montmartre, she had robed herself involuntarily in a blush that reddened her breasts, her shoulders, her arms, her whole body? He had thought of that story, of that dear girl, when first he had undressed me . . . Ensor, the great Ensor, his monolithic canvas: *The Foolish Virgins*. Two or three late Gauguins, his special favourite the one of the tranced brown girl in the deserted house which was called: *Out of the Night We Come, Into the Night We* Go. And, besides the additions he had made himself, his marvellous inheritance of Watteaus, Poussins and a pair of very special Fragonards, commissioned for a licentious ancestor who, it was said, had posed for the master's brush himself with his own two daughters . . . He broke off his catalogue of treasures abruptly.

Your thin white face, chérie; he said, as if he saw it for the first time. Your thin white face, with its promise of debauchery only a connoisseur could detect.

A log fell in the fire, instigating a shower of sparks; the opal on my finger spurted green flame. I felt as giddy as if I were on the edge of a precipice; I was afraid, not so much of him, of his monstrous presence, heavy as if he had been gifted at birth with more specific *gravity* than the rest of us, the presence that, even when I thought myself most in love with him, always subtly oppressed me . . . No. I was not afraid of him; but of myself. I seemed reborn in his unreflective eyes, reborn in unfamiliar shapes. I hardly recognized myself from his descriptions of me and yet, and yet – might there not be a grain of beastly truth in them? And, in the red firelight, I blushed again, unnoticed, to think he might have chosen me because, in my innocence, he sensed a rare talent for corruption.

Here is the key to the china cabinet – don't laugh, my darling; there's a king's

ransom in Sèvres in that closet, and a queen's ransom in Limoges. And a key to the locked, barred room where five generations of plate were kept.

Keys, keys, keys. He would trust me with the keys to his office, although I was only a baby; and the keys to his safes, where he kept the jewels I should wear, he promised me, when we returned to Paris. Such jewels! Why, I would be able to change my earrings and necklaces three times a day, just as the Empress Josephine used to change her underwear. He doubted, he said, with that hollow, knocking sound that served him for a chuckle, I would be quite so interested in his share certificates although they, of course, were worth infinitely more.

Outside our firelit privacy, I could hear the sound of the tide drawing back from the pebbles of the foreshore; it was nearly time for him to leave me. One single key remained unaccounted for on the ring and he hesitated over it; for a moment, I thought he was going to unfasten it from its brothers, slip it back into his pocket and take it away with him.

"What is *that* key?" I demanded, for his chaffing had made me bold. "The key to your heart? Give it me!"

He dangled the key tantalizingly above my head, out of reach of my straining fingers; those bare red lips of his cracked sidelong in a smile.

"Ah, no," he said. "Not the key to my heart. Rather, the key to my enfer."

He left it on the ring, fastened the ring together, shook it musically, like a carillon. Then threw the keys in a jingling heap in my lap. I could feel the cold metal chilling my thighs through my thin muslin frock. He bent over me to drop a beard-masked kiss on my forehead.

"Every man must have one secret, even if only one, from his wife," he said. "Promise me this, my whey-faced piano-player; promise me you'll use all the keys on the ring except that last little one I showed you. Play with anything you find, jewels, silver plate; make toy boats of my share certificates, if it pleases you, and send them sailing off to America after me. All is yours, everywhere is open to you – except the lock that this single key fits. Yet all it is is the key to a little room at the foot of the west tower, behind the still-room, at the end of a dark little corridor full of horrid cobwebs that would get into your hair and frighten you if you ventured there. Oh, and you'd find it such a dull little room! But you must promise me, if you love me, to leave it well alone. It is only a private study, a hideaway, a 'den', as the English say, where I can go, sometimes, on those infrequent yet inevitable occasions when the yoke of marriage seems to weigh too heavily on my shoulders. There I can go, you understand, to savour the rare pleasure of imagining myself wifeless."

There was a little thin starlight in the courtyard as, wrapped in my furs, I saw him to his car. His last words were, that he had telephoned the mainland and taken a piano-tuner on to the staff; this man would arrive to take up his duties the next day. He pressed me to his vicuña breast, once, and then drove away.

I had drowsed away that afternoon and now I could not sleep. I lay tossing and turning in his ancestral bed until another daybreak discoloured the dozen mirrors that were iridescent with the reflections of the sea. The perfume of the lilies weighed on my senses; when I thought that, henceforth, I would always share these sheets with a man whose skin, as theirs did, contained that toad-like,

clammy hint of moisture, I felt a vague desolation that within me, now my female wound had healed, there had awoken a certain queasy craving like the cravings of pregnant women for the taste of coal or chalk or tainted food, for the renewal of his caresses. Had he not hinted to me, in his flesh as in his speech and looks, of the thousand, thousand baroque intersections of flesh upon flesh? I lay in our wide bed accompanied by a sleepless companion, my dark newborn curiosity.

I lay in bed alone. And I longed for him. And he disgusted me.

Were there jewels enough in all his safes to recompense me for this predicament? Did all that castle hold enough riches to recompense me for the company of the libertine with whom I must share it? And what, precisely, was the nature of my desirous dread for this mysterious being who, to show his mastery over me, had abandoned me on my wedding night?

Then I sat straight up in bed, under the sardonic masks of the gargoyles carved above me, riven by a wild surmise. Might he have left me, not for Wall Street but for an importunate mistress tucked away God knows where who knew how to pleasure him far better than a girl whose fingers had been exercised, hitherto, only by the practice of scales and arpeggios? And, slowly, soothed, I sank back on to the heaping pillows; I acknowledged that the jealous scare I'd just given myself was not unmixed with a little tincture of relief.

At last I drifted into slumber, as daylight filled the room and chased bad dreams away. But the last thing I remembered, before I slept, was the tall jar of lilies beside the bed, how the thick glass distorted their fat stems so they looked like arms, dismembered arms, drifting drowned in greenish water.

Coffee and croissants to console this bridal, solitary waking. Delicious. Honey, too, in a section of comb on a glass saucer. The maid squeezed the aromatic juice from an orange into a chilled goblet while I watched her as I lay in the lazy, midday bed of the rich. Yet nothing, this morning, gave me more than a fleeting pleasure except to hear that the piano-tuner had been at work already. When the maid told me that, I sprang out of bed and pulled on my old serge skirt and flannel blouse, costume of a student, in which I felt far more at ease with myself than in any of my fine new clothes.

After my three hours of practice, I called the piano-tuner in, to thank him. He was blind, of course; but young, with a gentle mouth and grey eyes that fixed upon me although they could not see me. He was a blacksmith's son from the village across the causeway; a chorister in the church whom the good priest had taught a trade so that he could make a living. All most satisfactory. Yes. He thought he would be happy here. And if, he added shyly, he might sometimes be allowed to hear me play . . . for, you see, he loved music. Yes. Of course, I said. Certainly. He seemed to know that I had smiled.

After I dismissed him, even though I'd woken so late, it was still barely time for my "five o'clock". The housekeeper, who, thoughtfully forewarned by my husband, had restrained herself from interrupting my music, now made me a solemn visitation with a lengthy menu for a late luncheon. When I told her I did not need it, she looked at me obliquely, along her nose. I understood at once that one of my principal functions as châtelaine was to provide work for the staff. But, all the same, I asserted myself and said I would wait until dinner-time, although I looked forward nervously to the solitary meal. Then I found I had to

tell her what I would like to have prepared for me; my imagination, still that of a schoolgirl, ran riot. A fowl in cream – or should I anticipate Christmas with a varnished turkey? No; I have decided. Avocado and shrimp, lots of it, followed by no entrée at all. But surprise me for dessert with every ice-cream in the ice box. She noted all down but sniffed; I'd shocked her. Such tastes! Child that I was, I giggled when she left me.

But, now . . . what shall I do, now?

I could have spent a happy hour unpacking the trunks that contained my trousseau but the maid had done that already, the dresses, the tailor-mades hung in the wardrobe in my dressing room, the hats on wooden heads to keep their shape, the shoes on wooden feet as if all these inanimate objects were imitating the appearance of life, to mock me. I did not like to linger in my overcrowded dressing room, nor in my lugubriously lily-scented bedroom. How shall I pass the time?

I shall take a bath in my own bathroom! And found the taps were little dolphins made of gold, with chips of turquoise for eyes. And there was a tank of goldfish, who swam in and out of moving fronds of weeds, as bored, I thought, as I was. How I wished he had not left me. How I wished it were possible to chat with, say, a maid; or, the piano-tuner . . . but I knew already my new rank forbade overtures of friendship to the staff.

I had been hoping to defer the call as long as I could, so that I should have something to look forward to in the dead waste of time I foresaw before me, after my dinner was done with, but, at a quarter before seven, when darkness already surrounded the castle, I could contain myself no longer. I telephoned my mother. And astonished myself by bursting into tears when I heard her voice.

No, nothing was the matter. Mother, I have gold bath taps.

I said, gold bath taps!

No; I suppose that's nothing to cry about, Mother.

The line was bad, I could hardly make out her congratulations, her questions, her concern, but I was a little comforted when I put the receiver down.

Yet there still remained one whole hour to dinner and the whole, unimaginable desert of the rest of the evening.

The bunch of keys lay, where he had left them, on the rug before the library fire which had warmed their metal so that they no longer felt cold to the touch but warm, almost, as my own skin. How careless I was; a maid, tending the logs, eyed me reproachfully as if I'd set a trap for her as I picked up the clinking bundle of keys, the keys to the interior doors of this lovely prison of which I was both the inmate and the mistress and had scarcely seen. When I remembered that, I felt the exhilaration of the explorer.

Lights! More lights!

At the touch of a switch, the dreaming library was brilliantly illuminated. I ran crazily about the castle, switching on every light I could find – I ordered the servants to light up all their quarters, too, so the castle would shine like a seaborne birthday cake lit with a thousand candles, one for every year of its life, and everybody on shore would wonder at it. When everything was lit as brightly as the café in the Gare du Nord, the significance of the possessions implied by that bunch of keys no longer intimidated me, for I was determined, now, to search through them all for evidence of my husband's true nature.

His office first, evidently.

A mahogany desk half a mile wide, with an impeccable blotter and a bank of telephones. I allowed myself the luxury of opening the safe that contained the jewellery and delved sufficiently among the leather boxes to find out how my marriage had given me access to a jinn's treasury – parures, bracelets, rings . . . While I was thus surrounded by diamonds, a maid knocked on the door and entered before I spoke; a subtle discourtesy. I would speak to my husband about it. She eyed my serge skirt superciliously; did madame plan to dress for dinner?

She made a moue of disdain when I laughed to hear that, she was far more the lady than I. But, imagine – to dress up in one of my Poiret extravaganzas, with the jewelled turban and aigrette on my head, roped with pearl to the navel, to sit down all alone in the baronial dining hall at the head of that massive board at which King Mark was reputed to have fed his knights . . . I grew calmer under the cold eye of her disapproval.

I adopted the crisp inflections of an officer's daughter. No, I would not dress for dinner. Furthermore, I was not hungry enough for dinner itself. She must tell the housekeeper to cancel the dormitory feast I'd ordered. Could they leave me sandwiches and a flask of coffee in my music room? And would they all dismiss for the night?

Mais oui, madame.

I knew by her bereft intonation I had let them down again but I did not care; I was armed against them by the brilliance of his hoard. But I would not find his heart amongst the glittering stones; as soon as she had gone, I began a systematic search of the drawers of his desk.

All was in order, so I found nothing. Not a random doodle on an old envelope, nor the faded photograph of a woman. Only the files of business correspondence, the bills from the home farms, the invoices from tailors, the billets-doux from international financiers. Nothing. And this absence of the evidence of his real life began to impress me strangely; there must, I thought, be a great deal to conceal if he takes such pains to hide it.

His office was a singularly impersonal room, facing inwards, on to the courtyard, as though he wanted to turn his back on the siren sea in order to keep a clear head while he bankrupted a small businessman in Amsterdam or – I noticed with a thrill of distaste – engaged in some business in Laos that must, from certain cryptic references to his amateur botanist's enthusiasm for rare poppies, be to do with opium. Was he not rich enough to do without crime? Or was the crime itself his profit? And yet I saw enough to appreciate his zeal for secrecy.

Now I had ransacked his desk, I must spend a cool-headed quarter of an hour putting every last letter back where I had found it, and, as I covered the traces of my visit, by some chance, as I reached inside a little drawer that had stuck fast, I must have touched a hidden spring, for a secret drawer flew open within that drawer itself; and this secret drawer contained – at last! – a file marked: *Personal*.

I was alone, but for my reflection in the uncurtained window.

I had the brief notion that his heart, pressed flat as a flower, crimson and thin as tissue paper, lay in this file. It was a very thin one.

I could have wished, perhaps, I had not found that touching, ill-spelt note, on a paper napkin marked *La Coupole*, that began: "My darling, I cannot wait

for the moment when you may make me yours completely." The diva had sent him a page of the score of *Tristan*, the Liebestod, with the single, cryptic word: "Until . . ." scrawled across it. But the strangest of all these love letters was a postcard with a view of a village graveyard, among mountains, where some black-coated ghoul enthusiastically dug at a grave; this little scene, executed with the lurid exuberance of Grand Guignol, was captioned: "Typical Transylvanian Scene – Midnight, All Hallows." And, on the other side, the message: "On the occasion of this marriage to the descendant of Dracula – always remember, 'the supreme and unique pleasure of love is the certainty that one is doing evil'. Toutes amitiés, C."

A joke. A joke in the worst possible taste; for had he not been married to a Romanian countess? And then I remembered her pretty, witty face, and her name – Carmilla. My most recent predecessor in this castle had been, it would seem, the most sophisticated.

I put away the file, sobered. Nothing in my life of family love and music had prepared me for these grown-up games and yet these were clues to his self that showed me, at least, how much he had been loved, even if they did not reveal any good reason for it. But I wanted to know still more; and, as I closed the office door and locked it, the means to discover more fell in my way.

Fell, indeed; and with the clatter of a dropped canteen of cutlery, for, as I turned the slick Yale lock, I contrived, somehow, to open up the key ring itself, so that all the keys tumbled loose on the floor. And the very first key I picked out of that pile was, as luck or ill fortune had it, the key to the room he had forbidden me, the room he would keep for his own so that he could go there when he wished to feel himself once more a bachelor.

I made my decision to explore it before I felt a faint resurgence of my ill-defined fear of his waxen stillness. Perhaps I half-imagined, then, that I might find his real self in his den, waiting there to see if indeed I had obeyed him; that he had sent a moving figure of himself to New York, the enigmatic, self-sustaining carapace of his public person, while the real man, whose face I had glimpsed in the storm of orgasm, occupied himself with pressing private business in the study at the foot of the west tower, behind the still-room. Yet, if that were so, it was imperative that I should find him, should know him; and I was too deluded by his apparent taste for me to think my disobedience might truly offend him.

I took the forbidden key from the heap and left the others lying there.

It was now very late and the castle was adrift, as far as it could go from the land, in the middle of the silent ocean where, at my orders, it floated, like a garland of light. And all silent, all still, but for the murmuring of the waves.

I felt no fear, no intimation of dread. Now I walked as firmly as I had done in my mother's house.

Not a narrow, dusty little passage at all; why had he lied to me? But an ill-lit one, certainly; the electricity, for some reason, did not extend here, so I retreated to the still-room and found a bundle of waxed tapers in a cupboard, stored there with matches to light the oak board at grand dinners. I put a match to my little taper and advanced with it in my hand, like a penitent, along the corridor hung with heavy, I think Venetian, tapestries. The flame picked out, here, the head of

a man, there, the rich breast of a woman spilling through a rent in her dress – the Rape of the Sabines, perhaps? The naked swords and immolated horses suggested some grisly mythological subject. The corridor wound downwards; there was an almost imperceptible ramp to the thickly carpeted floor. The heavy hangings on the wall muffled my footsteps, even my breathing. For some reason, it grew very warm; the sweat sprang out in beads on my brow. I could no longer hear the sound of the sea.

A long, a winding corridor, as if I were in the viscera of the castle; and this corridor led to a door of worm-eaten oak, low, round-topped, barred with black iron.

And still I felt no fear, no raising of the hairs on the back of the neck, no prickling of the thumbs.

The key slid into the new lock as easily as a hot knife into butter.

No fear; but a hesitation, a holding of the spiritual breath.

If I had found some traces of his heart in a file marked: *Personal*, perhaps, here, in his subterranean privacy, I might find a little of his soul. It was the consciousness of the possibility of such a discovery, of its possible strangeness, that kept me for a moment motionless, before, in the foolhardiness of my already subtly tainted innocence, I turned the key and the door creaked slowly back.

"There is a striking resemblance between the act of love and the ministrations of a torturer," opined my husband's favourite poet; I had learned something of the nature of that similarity on my marriage bed. And now my taper showed me the outlines of a rack. There was also a great wheel, like the ones I had seen in woodcuts of the martyrdoms of the saints, in my old nurse's little store of holy books. And – just one glimpse of it before my little flame caved in and I was left in absolute darkness – a metal figure, hinged at the side, which I knew to be spiked on the inside and to have the name: the Iron Maiden.

Absolute darkness. And, about me, the instruments of mutilation.

Until that moment, this spoiled child did not know she had inherited nerves and a will from the mother who had defied the yellow outlaws of Indo-China. My mother's spirit drove me on, into that dreadful place, in a cold ecstasy to know the very worst. I fumbled for the matches in my pocket; what a dim, lugubrious light they gave! And yet, enough, oh, more than enough, to see a room designed for desecration and some dark night of unimaginable lovers whose embraces were annihilation.

The walls of this stark torture chamber were the naked rock; they gleamed as if they were sweating with fright. At the four corners of the room were funerary urns, of great antiquity, Etruscan, perhaps, and, on three-legged ebony stands, the bowls of incense he had left burning which filled the room with a sacerdotal reek. Wheel, rack and Iron Maiden were, I saw, displayed as grandly as if they were items of statuary and I was almost consoled, then, and almost persuaded myself that I might have stumbled only upon a little museum of his perversity, that he had installed these monstrous items here only for contemplation.

Yet at the centre of the room lay a catafalque, a doomed, ominous bier of Renaissance workmanship, surrounded by long white candles and, at its foot, an armful of the same lilies with which he had filled my bedroom, stowed in a four-foot-high jar glazed with a sombre Chinese red. I scarcely dared examine this catafalque and its occupant more closely; yet I knew I must.

Each time I struck a match to light those candles round her bed, it seemed a garment of that innocence of mine for which he had lusted fell away from me.

The opera singer lay, quite naked, under a thin sheet of very rare and precious linen, such as the princes of Italy used to shroud those whom they had poisoned. I touched her, very gently, on the white breast; she was cool, he had embalmed her. On her throat I could see the blue imprint of his strangler's fingers. The cool, sad flame of the candles flickered on her white, closed eyelids. The worst thing was, the dead lips smiled.

Beyond the catafalque, in the middle of the shadows, a white, nacreous glimmer; as my eyes accustomed themselves to the gathering darkness, I at last – oh, horrors! – made out a skull; yes, a skull, so utterly denuded, now, of flesh, that it scarcely seemed possible the stark bone had once been richly upholstered with life. And this skull was strung up by a system of unseen cords, so that it appeared to hang, disembodied, in the still, heavy air, and it had been crowned with a wreath of white roses, and a veil of lace, the final image of his bride.

Yet the skull was still so beautiful, had shaped with its sheer planes so imperiously the face that had once existed above it, that I recognized her the moment I saw her; face of the evening star walking on the rim of night. One false step, oh, my poor, dear girl, next in the fated sisterhood of his wives; one false step and into the abyss of the dark you stumbled.

And where was she, the latest dead, the Romanian countess who might have thought her blood would survive his depredations? I knew she must be here, in the place that had wound me through the castle towards it on a spool of inexorability. But, at first, I could see no sign of her. Then, for some reason – perhaps some change of atmosphere wrought by my presence – the metal shell of the Iron Maiden emitted a ghostly twang; my feverish imagination might have guessed its occupant was trying to clamber out, though, even in the midst of my rising hysteria, I knew she must be dead to find a home there.

With trembling fingers, I prised open the front of the upright coffin, with its sculpted face caught in a rictus of pain. Then, overcome, I dropped the key I still held in my other hand. It dropped into the forming pool of her blood.

She was pierced, not by one but by a hundred spikes, this child of the land of the vampires who seemed so newly dead, so full of blood . . . oh God! how recently had he become a widower? How long had he kept her in this obscene cell? Had it been all the time he had courted me, in the clear light of Paris?

I closed the lid of her coffin very gently and burst into a tumult of sobbing that contained both pity for his other victims and also a dreadful anguish to know I, too, was one of them.

The candles flared, as if in a draught from a door to elsewhere. The light caught the fire opal on my hand so that it flashed, once, with a baleful light, as if to tell me the eye of God – his eye – was upon me. My first thought, when I saw the ring for which I had sold myself to this fate, was, how to escape it.

I retained sufficient presence of mind to snuff out the candles round the bier with my fingers, to gather up my taper, to look around, although shuddering, to ensure I had left behind me no traces of my visit.

I retrieved the key from the pool of blood, wrapped it in my handkerchief to keep my hands clean, and fled the room, slamming the door behind me.

It crashed to with a juddering reverberation, like the door of hell.

I could not take refuge in my bedroom, for that retained the memory of his presence trapped in the fathomless silvering of his mirrors. My music room seemed the safest place, although I looked at the picture of Saint Cecilia with a faint dread; what had been the nature of her martyrdom? My mind was in a tumult; schemes for flight jostled with one another . . . as soon as the tide receded from the causeway, I would make for the mainland – on foot, running, stumbling; I did not trust that leather-clad chauffeur, nor the well-behaved housekeeper, and I dared not take any of the pale, ghostly maids into my confidence, either, since they were his creatures, all. Once at the village, I would fling myself directly on the mercy of the gendarmerie.

But – could I trust them, either? His forefathers had ruled this coast for eight centuries, from this castle whose moat was the Atlantic. Might not the police, the advocates, even the judge, all be in his service, turning a common blind eye to his vices since he was milord whose word must be obeyed? Who, on this distant coast, would believe the white-faced girl from Paris who came running to them with a shuddering tale of blood, of fear, of the ogre murmuring in the shadows? Or, rather, they would immediately know it to be true. But were all honour-bound to let me carry it no further.

Assistance. My mother. I ran to the telephone; and the line, of course, was dead.

Dead as his wives.

A thick darkness, unlit by any star, still glazed the windows. Every lamp in my room burned, to keep the dark outside, yet it seemed still to encroach on me, to be present beside me but as if masked by my lights, the night like a permeable substance that could seep into my skin. I looked at the precious little clock made from hypocritically innocent flowers long ago, in Dresden; the hands had scarcely moved one single hour forward from when I first descended to that private slaughterhouse of his. Time was his servant, too; it would trap me, here, in a night that would last until he came back to me, like a black sun on a hopeless morning.

And yet the time might still be my friend; at that hour, that very hour, he set sail for New York.

To know that, in a few moments, my husband would have left France calmed my agitation a little. My reason told me I had nothing to fear; the tide that would take him away to the New World would let me out of the imprisonment of the castle. Surely I could easily evade the servants. Anybody can buy a ticket at a railway station. Yet I was still filled with unease. I opened the lid of the piano; perhaps I thought my own particular magic might help me, now, that I could create a pentacle out of music that would keep me from harm for, if my music had first ensnared him, then might it not also give me the power to free myself from him?

Mechanically, I began to play but my fingers were stiff and shaking. At first, I could manage nothing better than the exercises of Czerny but simply the act of playing soothed me and, for solace, for the sake of the harmonious rationality of its sublime mathematics, I searched among his scores until I found *The Well-Tempered Clavier.* I set myself the therapeutic task of playing all Bach's equations, every one, and, I told myself, if I played them all through without a single mistake – then the morning would find me once more a virgin.

Crash of a dropped stick.

His silver-headed cane! What else? Sly, cunning, he had returned; he was waiting for me outside the door!

I rose to my feet; fear gave me strength. I flung back my head defiantly.

"Come in!" My voice astonished me by its firmness, its clarity.

The door slowly, nervously opened and I saw, not the massive, irredeemable bulk of my husband but the slight, stooping figure of the piano-tuner, and he looked far more terrified of me than my mother's daughter would have been of the Devil himself. In the torture chamber, it seemed to me that I would never laugh again; now, helplessly, laugh I did, with relief, and, after a moment's hesitation, the boy's face softened and he smiled a little, almost in shame. Though they were blind, his eyes were singularly sweet.

"Forgive me," said Jean-Yves. "I know I've given you grounds for dismissing me, that I should be crouching outside your door at midnight . . . but I heard you walking about, up and down – I sleep in a room at the foot of the west tower – and some intuition told me you could not sleep and might, perhaps, pass the insomniac hours at your piano. And I could not resist that. Besides, I stumbled over these –"

And he displayed the ring of keys I'd dropped outside my husband's office door, the ring from which one key was missing. I took them from him, looked round for a place to stow them, fixed on the piano stool as if to hide them would protect me. Still he stood smiling at me. How hard it was to make everyday conversation.

"It's perfect," I said. "The piano. Perfectly in tune."

But he was full of the loquacity of embarrassment, as though I would only forgive him for his impudence if he explained the cause of it thoroughly.

"When I heard you play this afternoon, I thought I'd never heard such a touch. Such technique. A treat for me, to hear a virtuoso! So I crept up to your door now, humbly as a little dog might, madame, and put my ear to the keyhole and listened, and listened – until my stick fell to the floor through a momentary clumsiness of mine, and I was discovered."

He had the most touchingly ingenuous smile.

"Perfectly in tune," I repeated. To my surprise, now I had said it, I found I could not say anything else. I could only repeat: "In tune . . . perfect . . . in tune," over and over again. I saw a dawning surprise in his face. My head throbbed. To see him, in his lovely, blind humanity, seemed to hurt me very piercingly, somewhere inside my breast; his figure blurred, the room swayed about me. After the dreadful revelation of that bloody chamber, it was his tender look that made me faint.

When I recovered consciousness, I found I was lying in the piano-tuner's arms and he was tucking the satin cushion from the piano-stool under my head.

"You are in some great distress," he said. "No bride should suffer so much, so early in her marriage."

His speech had the rhythms of the countryside, the rhythms of the tides.

"Any bride brought to this castle should come ready dressed in mourning, should bring a priest and a coffin with her," I said.

"What's this?"

It was too late to keep silent; and if he, too, were one of my husband's creatures, then at least he had been kind to me. So I told him everything, the keys, the interdiction, my disobedience, the room, the rack, the skull, the corpses, the blood.

"I can scarcely believe it," he said, wondering. "That man . . . so rich; so well born."

"Here's proof," I said and tumbled the fatal key out of my handkerchief on to the silken rug.

"Oh God," he said. "I can smell the blood."

He took my hand; he pressed his arms about me. Although he was scarcely more than a boy, I felt a great strength flow into me from his touch.

"We whisper all manner of strange tales up and down the coast," he said. "There was a Marquis, once, who used to hunt young girls on the mainland; he hunted them with dogs, as though they were foxes. My grandfather had it from his grandfather, how the Marquis pulled a head out of his saddle bag and showed it to the blacksmith while the man was shoeing his horse. 'A fine specimen of the genus, brunette, eh, Guillaume?' And it was the head of the blacksmith's wife."

But, in these more democratic times, my husband must travel as far as Paris to do his hunting in the salons. Jean-Yves knew the moment I shuddered.

"Oh, madame! I thought all these were old wives' tales, chattering of fools, spooks to scare bad children into good behaviour! Yet how could you know, a stranger, that the old name for this place is the Castle of Murder?"

How could I know, indeed? Except that, in my heart, I'd always known its lord would be the death of me.

"Hark!' said my friend suddenly. "The sea has changed key; it must be near morning, the tide is going down."

He helped me up. I looked from the window, towards the mainland, along the causeway where the stones gleamed wetly in the thin light of the end of the night and, with an almost unimaginable horror, a horror the intensity of which I cannot transmit to you, I saw, in the distance, still far away yet drawing moment by moment inexorably nearer, the twin headlamps of his great black car, gouging tunnels through the shifting mist.

My husband had indeed returned; this time, it was no fancy.

"The key!" said Jean-Yves. "It must go back on the ring, with the others. As though nothing had happened."

But the key was still caked with wet blood and I ran to my bathroom and held it under the hot tap. Crimson water swirled down the basin but, as if the key itself were hurt, the bloody token stuck. The turquoise eyes of the dolphin taps winked at me derisively; they knew my husband had been too clever for me! I scrubbed the stain with my nail brush but still it would not budge. I thought how the car would be rolling silently towards the closed courtyard

gate; the more I scrubbed the key, the more vivid grew the stain.

The bell in the gatehouse would jangle. The porter's drowsy son would push back the patchwork quilt, yawning, pull the shirt over his head, thrust his feet into his sabots . . . slowly, slowly; open the door for your master as slowly as you can . . .

And still the bloodstain mocked the fresh water that spilled from the mouth of the leering dolphin.

"You have no more time," said Jean-Yves. "He is here. I know it. I must stay with you."

"You shall not!" I said. "Go back to your room, now. Please."

He hesitated. I put an edge of steel in my voice, for I knew I must meet my lord alone.

"Leave me!"

As soon as he had gone, I dealt with the keys and went to my bedroom. The causeway was empty; Jean-Yves was correct, my husband had already entered the castle. I pulled the curtains close, stripped off my clothes and pulled the bedcurtain around me as a pungent aroma of Russian leather assured me my husband was once again beside me.

"Dearest!"

With the most treacherous, lascivious tenderness, he kissed my eyes, and, mimicking the new bride newly wakened, I flung my arms around him, for on my seeming acquiescence depended my salvation.

"Da Silva of Rio outwitted me," he said wryly. "My New York agent telegraphed Le Havre and saved me a wasted journey. So we may resume our interrupted pleasures, my love."

I did not believe one word of it. I knew I had behaved exactly according to his desires; had he not bought me so that I should do so? I had been tricked into my own betrayal to that illimitable darkness whose source I had been compelled to seek in his absence and, now that I had met that shadowed reality of his that came to life only in the presence of its own atrocities, I must pay the price of my new knowledge. The secret of Pandora's box; but he had given me the box, himself, knowing I must learn the secret. I had played a game in which every move was governed by a destiny as oppressive and omnipotent as himself, since that destiny was himself; and I had lost. Lost at that charade of innocence and vice in which he had engaged me. Lost, as the victim loses to the executioner.

His hand brushed my breast, beneath the sheet. I strained my nerves yet could not help but flinch from the intimate touch, for it made me think of the piercing embrace of the Iron Maiden and of his lost lovers in the vault. When he saw my reluctance, his eyes veiled over and yet his appetite did not diminish. His tongue ran over red lips already wet. Silent, mysterious, he moved away from me to draw off his jacket. He took the gold watch from his waistcoat and laid it on the dressing table, like a good bourgeois; scooped out his rattling loose change and now – oh God! – makes a great play of patting his pockets officiously, puzzled lips pursed, searching for something that has been mislaid. Then turns to me with a ghastly, a triumphant smile.

"But of course! I gave the keys to you!"

"Your keys? Why, of course. Here, they're under the pillow; wait a mo-

ment – what – Ah! No . . . now, where can I have left them? I was whiling away the evening without you at the piano, I remember. Of course! The music room!"

Brusquely he flung my négligé of antique lace on the bed.

"Go and get them."

"Now? This moment? Can't it wait until morning, my darling?"

I forced myself to be seductive. I saw myself, pale, pliant as a plant that begs to be trampled underfoot, a dozen vulnerable, appealing girls reflected in as many mirrors, and I saw how he almost failed to resist me. If he had come to me in bed, I would have strangled him, then.

But he half-snarled: "No. It won't wait. Now."

The unearthly light of dawn filled the room; had only one previous dawn broken upon me in that vile place? And there was nothing for it but to go and fetch the keys from the music stool and pray he would not examine them too closely, pray to God his eyes would fail him, that he might be struck blind.

When I came back into the bedroom carrying the bunch of keys that jangled at every step like a curious musical instrument, he was sitting on the bed in his immaculate shirtsleeves, his head sunk in his hands.

And it seemed to me he was in despair.

Strange. In spite of my fear of him, that made me whiter than my wrap, I felt there emanate from him, at that moment, a stench of absolute despair, rank and ghastly, as if the lilies that surrounded him had all at once begun to fester, or the Russian leather of his scent were reverting to the elements of flayed hide and excrement of which it was composed. The chthonic gravity of his presence exerted a tremendous pressure on the room, so that the blood pounded in my ears as if we had been precipitated to the bottom of the sea, beneath the waves that pounded against the shore.

I held my life in my hands amongst those keys and, in a moment, would place it between his well-manicured fingers. The evidence of that bloody chamber had showed me I could expect no mercy. Yet, when he raised his head and stared at me with his blind, shuttered eyes as though he did not recognize me, I felt a terrified pity for him, for this man who lived in such strange, secret places that, if I loved him enough to follow him, I should have to die.

The atrocious loneliness of that monster!

The monocle had fallen from his face. His curling mane was disordered, as if he had run his hands through it in his distraction. I saw how he had lost his impassivity and was now filled with suppressed excitement. The hand he stretched out for those counters in his game of love and death shook a little; the face that turned towards me contained a sombre delirium that seemed to me compounded of a ghastly, yes, shame but also of a terrible, guilty joy as he slowly ascertained how I had sinned.

That tell-tale stain had resolved itself into a mark the shape and brilliance of the heart on a playing card. He disengaged the key from the ring and looked at it for a while, solitary, brooding.

"It is the key that leads to the kingdom of the unimaginable," he said. His voice was low and had in it the timbre of certain great cathedral organs that seem, when they are played, to be conversing with God.

I could not restrain a sob.

"Oh, my love, my little love who brought me a white gift of music," he said, almost as if grieving. "My little love, you'll never know how much I hate daylight!"

Then he sharply ordered: "Kneel!"

I knelt before him and he pressed the key lightly to my forehead, held it there for a moment. I felt a faint tingling of the skin and, when I involuntarily glanced at myself in the mirror, I saw the heart-shaped stain had transferred itself to my forehead, to the space between the eyebrows, like the caste mark of a brahmin woman. Or the mark of Cain. And now the key gleamed as freshly as if it had just been cut. He clipped it back on the ring, emitting that same, heavy sigh as he had done when I said that I would marry him.

"My virgin of the arpeggios, prepare yourself for martyrdom."

"What form shall it take?" I said.

"Decapitation," he whispered, almost voluptuously. "Go and bathe yourself; put on that white dress you wore to hear *Tristan* and the necklace that prefigures your end. And I shall take myself off to the armoury, my dear, to sharpen my great-grandfather's ceremonial sword."

"The servants?"

"We shall have absolute privacy for our last rites; I have already dismissed them. If you look out of the window you can see them going to the mainland."

It was now the full, pale light of morning; the weather was grey, indeterminate, the sea had an oily, sinister look, a gloomy day on which to die. Along the causeway I could see trooping every maid and scullion, every pot-boy and pan-scourer, valet, laundress and vassal who worked in that great house, most on foot, a few on bicycles. The faceless housekeeper trudged along with a great basket in which, I guessed, she'd stowed as much as she could ransack from the larder. The Marquis must have given the chauffeur leave to borrow the motor for the day, for it went last of all, at a stately pace, as though the procession were a cortège and the car already bore my coffin to the mainland for burial.

But I knew no good Breton earth would cover me, like a last, faithful lover; I had another fate.

"I have given them all a day's holiday, to celebrate our wedding," he said. And smiled.

However hard I stared at the receding company, I could see no sign of Jean-Yves, our latest servant, hired but the preceding morning.

"Go, now. Bathe yourself; dress yourself. The lustratory ritual and the ceremonial robing; after that, the sacrifice. Wait in the music room until I telephone for you. No, my dear!" And he smiled, as I started, recalling the line was dead. "One may call inside the castle just as much as one pleases; but, outside – never."

I scrubbed my forehead with the nail brush as I had scrubbed the key but this red mark would not go away, either, no matter what I did, and I knew I should wear it until I died, though that would not be long. Then I went to my dressing room and put on that white muslin shift, costume of a victim of an auto-da-fé, he had bought me to listen to the Liebestod in. Twelve young women combed out twelve listless sheaves of brown hair in the mirrors; soon, there would be none. The mass of lilies that surrounded me exhaled, now, the odour of their withering. They looked like the trumpets of the angels of death.

On the dressing table, coiled like a snake about to strike, lay the ruby choker.

Already almost lifeless, cold at heart, I descended the spiral staircase to the music room but there I found I had not been abandoned.

"I can be of some comfort to you," the boy said. "Though not much use."

We pushed the piano stool in front of the open window so that, for as long as I could, I would be able to smell the ancient, reconciling smell of the sea that, in time, will cleanse everything, scour the old bones white, wash away all the stains. The last little chambermaid had trotted along the causeway long ago and now the tide, fated as I, came tumbling in, the crisp wavelets splashing on the old stones.

"You do not deserve this," he said.

"Who can say what I deserve or no?" I said. "I've done nothing; but that may be sufficient reason for condemning me."

"You disobeyed him," he said. "That is sufficient reason for him to punish you."

"I only did what he knew I would."

"Like Eve," he said.

The telephone rang a shrill imperative. Let it ring. But my lover lifted me up and set me on my feet; I knew I must answer it. The receiver felt heavy as earth.

"The courtyard. Immediately."

My lover kissed me, he took my hand. He would come with me if I would lead him. Courage. When I thought of courage, I thought of my mother. Then I saw a muscle in my lover's face quiver.

"Hoofbeats!" he said.

I cast one last, desperate glance from the window and, like a miracle, I saw a horse and rider galloping at a vertiginous speed along the causeway, though the waves crashed, now, high as the horse's fetlocks. A rider, her black skirts tucked up around her waist so she could ride hard and fast, a crazy, magnificent horsewoman in widow's weeds.

As the telephone rang again.

"Am I to wait all morning?"

Every moment, my mother drew nearer.

"She will be too late," Jean-Yves said and yet he could not restrain a note of hope that, though it must be so, yet it might not be so.

The third, intransigent call.

"Shall I come up to heaven to fetch you down, Saint Cecilia? You wicked woman, do you wish me to compound my crimes by desecrating the marriage bed?"

So I must go to the courtyard where my husband waited in his London-tailored trousers and the shirt from Turnbull and Asser, beside the mounting block, with, in his hand, the sword which his great-grandfather had presented to the little corporal, in token of surrender to the Republic, before he shot himself. The heavy sword, unsheathed, grey as that November morning, sharp as childbirth, mortal.

When my husband saw my companion, he observed: "Let the blind lead the blind, eh? But does even a youth as besotted as you are think she was truly blind to her own desires when she took my ring? Give it me back, whore."

The fires in the opal had all died down. I gladly slipped it from my finger and, even in that dolorous place, my heart was lighter for the lack of it. My husband took it lovingly and lodged it on the tip of his little finger; it would go no further.

"It will serve me for a dozen more fiancées," he said. "To the block, woman. No – leave the boy; I shall deal with him later, utilizing a less exalted instrument than the one with which I do my wife the honour of her immolation, for do not fear that in death you will be divided."

Slowly, slowly, one foot before the other, I crossed the cobbles. The longer I dawdled over my execution, the more time it gave the avenging angel to descend . . .

"Don't loiter, girl! Do you think I shall lose appetite for the meal if you are so long about serving it? No; I shall grow hungrier, more ravenous with each moment, more cruel . . . Run to me, run! I have a place prepared for your exquisite corpse in my display of flesh!"

He raised the sword and cut bright segments from the air with it, but still I lingered although my hopes, so recently raised, now began to flag. If she is not here by now, her horse must have stumbled on the causeway, have plunged into the sea . . . One thing only made me glad; that my lover would not see me die.

My husband laid my branded forehead on the stone and, as he had done once before, twisted my hair into a rope and drew it away from my neck.

"Such a pretty neck," he said with what seemed to be a genuine, retrospective tenderness. "A neck like the stem of a young plant."

I felt the silken bristle of his beard and the wet touch of his lips as he kissed my nape. And, once again, of my apparel I must retain only my gems; the sharp blade ripped my dress in two and it fell from me. A little green moss, growing in the crevices of the mounting block, would be the last thing I should see in all the world.

The whizz of that heavy sword.

And – a great battering and pounding at the gate, the jangling of the bell, the frenzied neighing of a horse! The unholy silence of the place shattered in an instant. The blade did *not* descend, the necklace did *not* sever, my head did *not* roll. For, for an instant, the beast wavered in his stroke, a sufficient split second of astonished indecision to let me spring upright and dart to the assistance of my lover as he struggled sightlessly with the great bolts that kept her out.

The Marquis stood transfixed, utterly dazed, at a loss. It must have been as if he had been watching his beloved *Tristan* for the twelfth, the thirteenth time and Tristan stirred, then leapt from his bier in the last act, announced in a jaunty aria interposed from Verdi that bygones were bygones, crying over spilt milk did nobody any good and, as for himself, he proposed to live happily ever after. The puppet master, open-mouthed, wide-eyed, impotent at the last, saw his dolls break free of their strings, abandon the rituals he had ordained for them since time began and start to live for themselves; the king, aghast, witnesses the revolt of his pawns.

You never saw such a wild thing as my mother, her hat seized by the winds and blown out to sea so that her hair was her white mane, her black lisle legs exposed to the thigh, her skirts tucked round her waist, one hand on the reins of the rearing horse while the other clasped my father's service revolver and, behind her, the breakers of the savage, indifferent sea, like the witnesses of a furious

justice. And my husband stood stock-still, as if she had been Medusa, the sword still raised over his head as in those clockwork tableaux of Bluebeard that you see in glass cases at fairs.

And then it was as though a curious child pushed his centime into the slot and set all in motion. The heavy, bearded figure roared out aloud, braying with fury, and, wielding the honourable sword as if it were a matter of death or glory, charged us, all three.

On her eighteenth birthday, my mother had disposed of a man-eating tiger that had ravaged the villages in the hills north of Hanoi. Now, without a moment's hesitation, she raised my father's gun, took aim and put a single, irreproachable bullet through my husband's head.

We lead a quiet life, the three of us. I inherited, of course, enormous wealth but we have given most of it away to various charities. The castle is now a school for the blind, though I pray that the children who live there are not haunted by any sad ghosts looking for, crying for, the husband who will never return to the bloody chamber, the contents of which are buried or burned, the door sealed.

I felt I had a right to retain sufficient funds to start a little music school here, on the outskirts of Paris, and we do well enough. Sometimes we can even afford to go to the Opéra, though never to sit in a box, of course. We know we are the source of many whisperings and much gossip but the three of us know the truth of it and mere chatter can never harm us. I can only bless the – what shall I call it? – the *maternal telepathy* that sent my mother running headlong from the telephone to the station after I had called her, that night. I never heard you cry before, she said, by way of explanation. Not when you were happy. And who ever cried because of gold bath taps?

The night train, the one I had taken; she lay in her berth, sleepless as I had been. When she could not find a taxi at that lonely halt, she borrowed old Dobbin from a bemused farmer, for some internal urgency told her that she must reach me before the incoming tide sealed me away from her for ever. My poor old nurse, left scandalized at home – what? interrupt milord on his honeymoon? – she died soon after. She had taken so much secret pleasure in the fact that her little girl had become a marquise; and now here I was, scarcely a penny the richer, widowed at seventeen in the most dubious circumstances and busily engaged in setting up house with a piano-tuner. Poor thing, she passed away in a sorry state of disillusion! But I do believe my mother loves him as much as I do.

No paint nor powder, no matter how thick or white, can mask that red mark on my forehead; I am glad he cannot see it – not for fear of his revulsion, since I know he sees me clearly with his heart – but, because it spares my shame.

THE COMPANY OF WOLVES

Angela Carter

Angela Carter is best known for her novels, *Nights at the Circus* and *Wise Children*, but might be better known for her journalism, criticism and her short stories. Perhaps her finest work in fiction were her retellings of tales told before, especially *The Bloody Chamber* and her two Virago books of fairy tales. Fearsomely intelligent – 'a day without an argument is like an egg without salt' – and wickedly funny, she died, aged fifty-two from cancer. She said, 'Reading a book is like re-writing it for yourself. You bring to a novel, anthing you read, all your experience of the world. You bring your history and you read it in your own terms.'

One beast and only one howls in the woods by night.

The wolf is carnivore incarnate and he's as cunning as he is ferocious; once he's had a taste of flesh then nothing else will do.

At night, the eyes of wolves shine like candle flames, yellowish, reddish, but that is because the pupils of their eyes fatten on darkness and catch the light from your lantern to flash it back to you – red for danger; if a wolf's eyes reflect only moonlight, then they gleam a cold and unnatural green, a mineral, a piercing colour. If the benighted traveller spies those luminous, terrible sequins stitched suddenly on the black thickets, then he knows he must run, if fear has not struck him stock-still.

But those eyes are all you will be able to glimpse of the forest assassins as they cluster invisibly round your smell of meat as you go through the wood unwisely late. They will be like shadows, they will be like wraiths, grey members of a congregation of nightmare; hark! his long, wavering howl . . . an aria of fear made audible.

The wolfsong is the sound of the rending you will suffer, in itself a murdering.

It is winter and cold weather. In this region of mountain and forest, there is now nothing for the wolves to eat. Goats and sheep are locked up in the byre, the deer departed for the remaining pasturage on the southern slopes – wolves grow lean and famished. There is so little flesh on them that you could count the starveling ribs through their pelts, if they gave you time before they pounced. Those slavering jaws; the lolling tongue; the rime of saliva on the grizzled chops – of all the teeming perils of the night and the forest, ghosts, hobgoblins, ogres that grill babies upon gridirons, witches that fatten their captives in cages for

cannibal tables, the wolf is worst for he cannot listen to reason.

You are always in danger in the forest, where no people are. Step between the portals of the great pines where the shaggy branches tangle about you, trapping the unwary traveller in nets as if the vegetation itself were in a plot with the wolves who live there, as though the wicked trees go fishing on behalf of their friends – step between the gateposts of the forest with the greatest trepidation and infinite precautions, for if you stray from the path for one instant, the wolves will eat you. They are grey as famine, they are as unkind as plague.

The grave-eyed children of the sparse villages always carry knives with them when they go out to tend the little flocks of goats that provide the homesteads with acrid milk and rank, maggoty cheeses. Their knives are half as big as they are, the blades are sharpened daily.

But the wolves have ways of arriving at your own hearth-side. We try and try but sometimes we cannot keep them out. There is no winter's night the cottager does not fear to see a lean, grey, famished snout questing under the door, and there was a woman once bitten in her own kitchen as she was straining the macaroni.

Fear and flee the wolf; for, worst of all, the wolf may be more than he seems.

There was a hunter once, near here, that trapped a wolf in a pit. This wolf had massacred the sheep and goats; eaten up a mad old man who used to live by himself in a hut halfway up the mountain and sing to Jesus all day; pounced on a girl looking after the sheep, but she made such a commotion that men came with rifles and scared him away and tried to track him into the forest but he was cunning and easily gave them the slip. So this hunter dug a pit and put a duck in it, for bait, all alive-oh; and he covered the pit with straw smeared with wolf dung. Quack, quack! went the duck and a wolf came slinking out of the forest, a big one, a heavy one, he weighed as much as a grown man and the straw gave way beneath him – into the pit he tumbled. The hunter jumped down after him, slit his throat, cut off all his paws for a trophy.

And then no wolf at all lay in front of the hunter but the bloody trunk of a man, headless, footless, dying, dead.

A witch from up the valley once turned an entire wedding party into wolves because the groom had settled on another girl. She used to order them to visit her, at night, from spite, and they would sit and howl around her cottage for her, serenading her with their misery.

Not so very long ago, a young woman in our village married a man who vanished clean away on her wedding night. The bed was made with new sheets and the bride lay down in it; the groom said he was going out to relieve himself, insisted on it, for the sake of decency, and she drew the coverlet up to her chin and she lay there. And she waited and she waited and then she waited again – surely he's been gone a long time? Until she jumps up in bed and shrieks to hear a howling, coming on the wind from the forest.

That long-drawn, wavering howl has, for all its fearful resonance, some inherent sadness in it, as if the beasts would love to be less beastly if only they knew how and never cease to mourn their own condition. There is a vast melancholy in the canticles of the wolves, melancholy infinite as the forest, endless as these long nights of winter and yet that ghastly sadness, that mourning for their own,

irremediable appetites, can never move the heart for not one phrase in it hints at the possibility of redemption; grace could not come to the wolf from its own despair, only through some external mediator, so that, sometimes, the beast will look as if he half welcomes the knife that despatches him.

The young woman's brothers searched the outhouses and the hay-stacks but never found any remains so the sensible girl dried her eyes and found herself another husband not too shy to piss into a pot who spent the nights indoors. She gave him a pair of bonny babies and all went right as a trivet until, one freezing night, the night of the solstice, the hinge of the year when things do not fit together as well as they should, the longest night, her first good man came home again.

A great thump on the door announced him as she was stirring the soup for the father of her children and she knew him the moment she lifted the latch to him although it was years since she'd worn black for him and now he was in rags and his hair hung down his back and never saw a comb, alive with lice.

"Here I am again, missus," he said. "Get me my bowl of cabbage and be quick about it."

Then her second husband came in with wood for the fire and when the first one saw she'd slept with another man and, worse, clapped his red eyes on her little children who'd crept into the kitchen to see what all the din was about, he shouted: "I wish I were a wolf again, to teach this whore a lesson!" So a wolf he instantly became and tore off the eldest boy's left foot before he was chopped up with the hatchet they used for chopping logs. But when the wolf lay bleeding and gasping its last, the pelt peeled off again and he was just as he had been, years ago, when he ran away from his marriage bed, so that she wept and her second husband beat her.

They say there's an ointment the Devil gives you that turns you into a wolf the minute you rub it on. Or, that he was born feet first and had a wolf for his father and his torso is a man's but his legs and genitals are a wolf's. And he has a wolf's heart.

Seven years is a werewolf's natural span but if you burn his human clothing you condemn him to wolfishness for the rest of his life, so old wives hereabouts think it some protection to throw a hat or an apron at the werewolf, as if clothes made the man. Yet by the eyes, those phosphorescent eyes, you know him in all his shapes; the eyes alone unchanged by metamorphosis.

Before he can become a wolf, the lycanthrope strips stark naked. If you spy a naked man among the pines, you must run as if the Devil were after you.

It is midwinter and the robin, the friend of man, sits on the handle of the gardener's spade and sings. It is the worst time in all the year for wolves but this strong-minded child insists she will go off through the wood. She is quite sure the wild beasts cannot harm her although, well-warned, she lays a carving knife in the basket her mother has packed with cheeses. There is a bottle of harsh liquor distilled from brambles; a batch of flat oatcakes baked on the hearthstone; a pot or two of jam. The flaxen-haired girl will take these delicious gifts to a reclusive grandmother so old the burden of her years is crushing her to death. Granny lives two hours' trudge through the winter woods; the child wraps herself up in

her thick shawl, draws it over her head. She steps into her stout wooden shoes; she is dressed and ready and it is Christmas Eve. The malign door of the solstice still swings upon its hinges but she has been too much loved ever to feel scared.

Children do not stay young for long in this savage country. There are no toys for them to play with so they work hard and grow wise but this one, so pretty and the youngest of her family, a little late-comer, had been indulged by her mother and the grandmother who'd knitted her the red shawl that, today, has the ominous if brilliant look of blood on snow. Her breasts have just begun to swell; her hair is like lint, so fair it hardly makes a shadow on her pale forehead; her cheeks are an emblematic scarlet and white and she has just started her woman's bleeding, the clock inside her that will strike, henceforward, once a month.

She stands and moves within the invisible pentacle of her own virginity. She is an unbroken egg; she is a sealed vessel; she has inside her a magic space the entrance to which is shut tight with a plug of membrane; she is a closed system; she does not know how to shiver. She has her knife and she is afraid of nothing.

Her father might forbid her, if he were home, but he is away in the forest, gathering wood, and her mother cannot deny her.

The forest closed upon her like a pair of jaws.

There is always something to look at in the forest, even in the middle of winter – the huddled mounds of birds, succumbed to the lethargy of the season, heaped on the creaking boughs and too forlorn to sing; the bright frills of the winter fungi on the blotched trunks of the trees; the cuneiform slots of rabbits and deer, the herringbone tracks of the birds, a hare as lean as a rasher of bacon streaking across the path where the thin sunlight dapples the russet brakes of last year's bracken.

When she heard the freezing howl of a distant wolf, her practised hand sprang to the handle of her knife, but she saw no sign of a wolf at all, nor of a naked man, neither, but then she heard a clattering among the brushwood and there sprang on to the path a fully clothed one, a very handsome young one, in the green coat and wideawake hat of a hunter, laden with carcasses of game birds. She had her hand on her knife at the first rustle of twigs but he laughed with a flash of white teeth when he saw her and made her a comic yet flattering little bow; she'd never seen such a fine fellow before, not among the rustic clowns of her native village. So on they went together, through the thickening light of the afternoon.

Soon they were laughing and joking like old friends. When he offered to carry her basket, she gave it to him although her knife was in it because he told her his rifle would protect them. As the day darkened, it began to snow again; she felt the first flakes settle on her eyelashes but now there was only half a mile to go and there would be a fire, and hot tea, and a welcome, a warm one, surely, for the dashing huntsman as well as for herself.

This young man had a remarkable object in his pocket. It was a compass. She looked at the little round glass face in the palm of his hand and watched the wavering needle with a vague wonder. He assured her this compass had taken him safely through the wood on his hunting trip because the needle always told him with perfect accuracy where the north was. She did not believe it; she knew

she should never leave the path on the way through the wood or else she would be lost instantly. He laughed at her again; gleaming trails of spittle clung to his teeth. He said, if he plunged off the path into the forest that surrounded them, he could guarantee to arrive at her grandmother's house a good quarter of an hour before she did, plotting his way through the undergrowth with his compass, while she trudged the long way, along the winding path.

I don't believe you. Besides, aren't you afraid of the wolves?

He only tapped the gleaming butt of his rifle and grinned.

Is it a bet? he asked her. Shall we make a game of it? What will you give me if I get to your grandmother's house before you?

What would you like? she asked disingenuously.

A kiss.

Commonplaces of a rustic seduction; she lowered her eyes and blushed.

He went through the undergrowth and took her basket with him but she forgot to be afraid of the beasts, although now the moon was rising, for she wanted to dawdle on her way to make sure the handsome gentleman would win his wager.

Grandmother's house stood by itself a little way out of the village. The freshly falling snow blew in eddies about the kitchen garden and the young man stepped delicately up the snowy path to the door as if he were reluctant to get his feet wet, swinging his bundle of game and the girl's basket and humming a little tune to himself.

There is a faint trace of blood on his chin; he has been snacking on his catch.

He rapped upon the panels with his knuckles.

Aged and frail, granny is three-quarters succumbed to the mortality the ache in her bones promises her and almost ready to give in entirely. A boy came out from the village to build up her hearth for the night an hour ago and the kitchen crackles with busy firelight. She has her Bible for company, she is a pious old woman. She is propped up on several pillows in the bed set into the wall peasant-fashion, wrapped up in the patch-work quilt she made before she was married, more years ago than she cares to remember. Two china spaniels with liver-coloured blotches on their coats and black noses sit on either side of the fireplace. There is a bright rug of woven rags on the pantiles. The grandfather clock ticks away her eroding time.

We keep the wolves outside by living well.

He rapped upon the panels with his hairy knuckles.

It is your granddaughter, he mimicked in a high soprano.

Lift up the latch and walk in, my darling.

You can tell them by their eyes, eyes of a beast of prey, nocturnal, devastating eyes as red as a wound; you can hurl your Bible at him and your apron after, granny, you thought that was a sure prophylactic against these infernal vermin . . . now call on Christ and his mother and all the angels in heaven to protect you but it won't do you any good.

His feral muzzle is sharp as a knife; he drops his golden burden of gnawed pheasant on the table and puts down your dear girl's basket, too. Oh, my God, what have you done with her?

Off with his disguise, that coat of forest-coloured cloth, the hat with the

feather tucked into the ribbon; his matted hair streams down his white shirt and she can see the lice moving in it. The sticks in the hearth shift and hiss; night and the forest has come into the kitchen with darkness tangled in its hair.

He strips off his shirt. His skin is the colour and texture of vellum. A crisp stripe of hair runs down his belly, his nipples are ripe and dark as poison fruit but he's so thin you could count the ribs under his skin if only he gave you the time. He strips off his trousers and she can see how hairy his legs are. His genitals, huge. Ah! huge.

The last thing the old lady saw in all this world was a young man, eyes like cinders, naked as a stone, approaching her bed.

The wolf is carnivore incarnate.

When he had finished with her, he licked his chops and quickly dressed himself again, until he was just as he had been when he came through her door. He burned the inedible hair in the fireplace and wrapped the bones up in a napkin that he hid away under the bed in the wooden chest in which he found a clean pair of sheets. These he carefully put on the bed instead of the tell-tale stained ones he stowed away in the laundry basket. He plumped up the pillows and shook out the patch-work quilt, he picked up the Bible from the floor, closed it and laid it on the table. All was as it had been before except that grandmother was gone. The sticks twitched in the grate, the clock ticked and the young man sat patiently, deceitfully beside the bed in granny's nightcap.

Rat-a-tap-tap.

Who's there, he quavers in granny's antique falsetto.

Only your granddaughter.

So she came in, bringing with her a flurry of snow that melted in tears on the tiles, and perhaps she was a little disappointed to see only her grandmother sitting beside the fire. But then he flung off the blanket and sprang to the door, pressing his back against it so that she could not get out again.

The girl looked round the room and saw there was not even the indentation of a head on the smooth cheek of the pillow and how, for the first time she'd seen it so, the Bible lay closed on the table. The tick of the clock cracked like a whip. She wanted her knife from her basket but she did not dare reach for it because his eyes were fixed upon her – huge eyes that now seemed to shine with a unique, interior light, eyes the size of saucers, saucers full of Greek fire, diabolic phosphorescence.

What big eyes you have.

All the better to see you with.

No trace at all of the old woman except for a tuft of white hair that had caught in the bark of an unburned log. When the girl saw that, she knew she was in danger of death.

Where is my grandmother?

There's nobody here but we two, my darling.

Now a great howling rose up all around them, near, very near, as close as the kitchen garden, the howling of a multitude of wolves; she knew the worst wolves are hairy on the inside and she shivered, in spite of the scarlet shawl she pulled more closely round herself as if it could protect her although it was as red as the blood she must spill.

Who has come to sing us carols, she said.

Those are the voices of my brothers, darling; I love the company of wolves. Look out of the window and you'll see them.

Snow half-caked the lattice and she opened it to look into the garden. It was a white night of moon and snow; the blizzard whirled round the gaunt, grey beasts who squatted on their haunches among the rows of winter cabbage, pointing their sharp snouts to the moon and howling as if their hearts would break. Ten wolves; twenty wolves – so many wolves she could not count them, howling in concert as if demented or deranged. Their eyes reflected the light from the kitchen and shone like a hundred candles.

It is very cold, poor things, she said; no wonder they howl so.

She closed the window on the wolves' threnody and took off her scarlet shawl, the colour of poppies, the colour of sacrifices, the colour of her menses, and, since her fear did her no good, she ceased to be afraid.

What shall I do with my shawl?

Throw it on the fire, dear one. You won't need it again.

She bundled up her shawl and threw it on the blaze, which instantly consumed it. Then she drew her blouse over her head; her small breasts gleamed as if the snow had invaded the room.

What shall I do with my blouse?

Into the fire with it, too, my pet.

The thin muslin went flaring up the chimney like a magic bird and now off came her skirt, her woollen stockings, her shoes, and on to the fire they went, too, and were gone for good. The firelight shone through the edges of her skin; now she was clothed only in her untouched integument of flesh. This dazzling, naked she combed out her hair with her fingers; her hair looked white as the snow outside. Then went directly to the man with red eyes in whose unkempt mane the lice moved; she stood up on tiptoe and unbuttoned the collar of his shirt.

What big arms you have.

All the better to hug you with.

Every wolf in the world now howled a prothalamion outside the window as she freely gave the kiss she owed him.

What big teeth you have!

She saw how his jaw began to slaver and the room was full of the clamour of the forest's Liebestod but the wise child never flinched, even when he answered:

All the better to eat you with.

The girl burst out laughing; she knew she was nobody's meat. She laughed at him full in the face, she ripped off his shirt for him and flung it into the fire, in the fiery wake of her own discarded clothing. The flames danced like dead souls on Walpurgisnacht and the old bones under the bed set up a terrible clattering but she did not pay them any heed.

Carnivore incarnate, only immaculate flesh appeases him.

She will lay his fearful head on her lap and she will pick out the lice from his pelt and perhaps she will put the lice into her mouth and eat them, as he will bid her, as she would do in a savage marriage ceremony.

The blizzard will die down.

The blizzard died down, leaving the mountains as randomly covered with

snow as if a blind woman had thrown a sheet over them, the upper branches of the forest pines limed, creaking, swollen with the fall.

Snowlight, moonlight, a confusion of paw-prints.

All silent, all still.

Midnight; and the clock strikes. It is Christmas Day, the were-wolves' birthday, the door of the solstice stands wide open; let them all sink through.

See! sweet and sound she sleeps in granny's bed, between the paws of the tender wolf.

From CAROL

Patricia Highsmith

Patricia Highsmith was born in Fort Worth, Texas. She wrote more than twenty novels, short stories, essays and articles, and owes much of her fame to the five Ripley novels, featuring the murderer and anti-hero, Tom Ripley. Highsmith was fascinated with the psychology of her characters' relationships and the way in which they could degenerate into violence. *The Price of Salt*, which was later retitled *Carol*, was first published in 1952 under the pseudonym, Claire Morgan. Highsmith was wary of derailing her career, and it is thought she may have been uncomfortable with the book's exaltation of love. Nevertheless, when the viscerally romantic novel was first published, it garnered favorable reviews, and later went on to sell more than one million copies.

Late the next afternoon they left Chicago and drove in the direction of Rockford. Carol said she might have a letter from Abby there, but probably not, because Abby was a bad correspondent. Therese went to a shoe-repair shop to get a moccasin stitched, and when she came back, Carol was reading the letter in the car.

"What road do we take out?" Carol's face looked happier.

"Twenty, going west."

Carol turned on the radio and worked the dial until she found some music. "What's a good town for tonight on the way to Minneapolis?"

"Dubuque," Therese said, looking at the map. "Or Waterloo looks fairly big, but it's about two hundred miles away."

"We might make it."

They took Highway 20 towards Freeport and Galena, which was starred on the map as the home of Ulysses S. Grant.

"What did Abby say?"

"Nothing much. Just a very nice letter."

Carol said little to her in the car, or even in the café where they stopped later for coffee. Carol went over and stood in front of a juke box, dropping nickels slowly.

"You wish Abby'd come along, don't you?" Therese said.

"No," Carol said.

"You're so different since you got the letter from her."

Carol looked at her across the table. "Darling, it's just a silly letter. You can even read it if you want to." Carol reached for her handbag, but she did not get the letter out.

Some time that evening, Therese fell asleep in the car and woke up with the lights of a city on her face. Carol was resting both arms tiredly on the top of the wheel. They had stopped for a red light.

"Here's where we stay the night," Carol said.

Therese's sleep still clung to her as she walked across the hotel lobby. She rode up in an elevator and she was acutely conscious of Carol beside her, as if she dreamed a dream in which Carol was the subject and the only figure. In the room, she lifted her suitcase from the floor to a chair, unlatched it and left it, and stood by the writing table, watching Carol. As if her emotions had been in abeyance all the past hours, or days, they flooded her now as she watched Carol opening her suitcase, taking out, as she always did first, the leather kit that contained her toilet articles, dropping it on to the bed. She looked at Carol's hands, at the lock of hair that fell over the scarf tied around her head, at the scratch she had gotten days ago across the toe of her moccasin.

"What're you standing there for?" Carol asked. "Get to bed, sleepy-head."

"Carol, I love you."

Carol straightened up. Therese stared at her with intense, sleepy eyes. Then Carol finished taking her pyjamas from the suitcase and pulled the lid down. She came to Therese and put her hands on her shoulders. She squeezed her shoulders hard, as if she were exacting a promise from her, or perhaps searching her to see if what she had said were real. Then she kissed Therese on the lips, as if they had kissed a thousand times before.

"Don't you know I love you?" Carol said.

Carol took her pyjamas into the bathroom, and stood for a moment, looking down at the basin.

"I'm going out," Carol said. "But I'll be back right away."

Therese waited by the table while Carol was gone, while time passed indefinitely or maybe not at all, until the door opened and Carol came in again. She set a paper bag on the table, and Therese knew she had only gone to get a container of milk, as Carol or she herself did very often at night.

"Can I sleep with you?" Therese asked.

"Did you see the bed?"

It was a double bed. They sat up in their pyjamas, drinking milk and sharing an orange that Carol was too sleepy to finish. Then Therese set the container of milk on the floor and looked at Carol who was sleeping already, on her stomach, with one arm flung up as she always went to sleep. Therese pulled out the light. Then Carol slipped her arm under her neck, and all the length of their bodies touched, fitting as if something had prearranged it. Happiness was like a green vine spreading through her, stretching fine tendrils, bearing flowers through her flesh. She had a vision of a pale white flower, shimmering as if seen in darkness, or through water. Why did people talk of heaven, she wondered.

"Go to sleep," Carol said.

Therese hoped she would not. But when she felt Carol's hand move on her shoulder, she knew she had been asleep. It was dawn now. Carol's fingers tightened in her hair, Carol kissed her on the lips, and pleasure leaped in Therese again as if it were only a continuation of the moment when Carol had slipped her arm under her neck last night. I love you, Therese wanted to say again,

and then the words were erased by the tingling and terrifying pleasure that spread in waves from Carol's lips over her neck, her shoulders, that rushed suddenly the length of her body. Her arms were tight around Carol, and she was conscious of Carol and nothing else, of Carol's hand that slid along her ribs, Carol's hair that brushed her bare breasts, and then her body too seemed to vanish in widening circles that leaped further and further, beyond where thought could follow. While a thousand memories and moments, words, the first darling, the second time Carol had met her at the store, a thousand memories of Carol's face, her voice, moments of anger and laughter flashed like the tail of a comet across her brain. And now it was pale blue distance and space, an expanding space in which she took flight suddenly like a long arrow. The arrow seemed to cross an impossibly wide abyss with ease, seemed to arc on and on in space, and not quite to stop. Then she realized that she still clung to Carol, that she trembled violently, and the arrow was herself. She saw Carol's pale hair across her eyes, and now Carol's head was close against hers. And she did not have to ask if this was right, no one had to tell her, because this could not have been more right or perfect. She held Carol tighter against her, and felt Carol's mouth on her own smiling mouth. Therese lay still, looking at her, at Carol's face only inches away from her, the grey eyes calm as she had never seen them, as if they retained some of the space she had just emerged from. And it seemed strange that it was still Carol's face, with the freckles, the bending blonde eyebrow that she knew, the mouth now as calm as her eyes, as Therese had seen it many times before.

"My angel," Carol said. "Flung out of space."

Therese looked up at the corners of the room, that were much brighter now, at the bureau with the bulging front and the shield-shaped drawer pulls, at the frameless mirror with the bevelled edge, at the green-patterned curtains that hung straight at the windows, and the two grey tips of buildings that showed just above the sill. She would remember every detail of this room for ever.

"What town is this?" she asked.

Carol laughed. "This? This is Waterloo." She reached for a cigarette. "Isn't that awful."

Smiling, Therese raised up on her elbow. Carol put a cigarette between her lips. "There's a couple of Waterloos in every state," Therese said.

BARDON BUS

Alice Munro

Alice Munro was born and raised on a farm outside Wingham, Ontario. She attended the University of Western Ontario where she studied English and published her first short story in the university's literary magazine. Her first book of short stories was published in 1968, and since then she has published fifteen more. Her work frequently appears in magazines, including *The New Yorker*, *The Atlantic Monthly*, and *The Paris Review*. She divorced in 1972 and moved back to Ontario to take up a post as writer-in-residence at the University of Western Ontario, a position she later held at the University of British Columbia and at the University of Queensland. She was awarded the Nobel Prize in Literature and has recently announced her retirement from writing.

1

I think of being an old maid, in another generation. There were plenty of old maids in my family. I come of straitened people, madly secretive, tenacious, economical. Like them, I could make a little go a long way. A piece of Chinese silk folded in a drawer, worn by the touch of fingers in the dark. Or the one letter, hidden under maidenly garments, never needing to be opened or read because every word is known by heart, and a touch communicates the whole. Perhaps nothing so tangible, nothing but the memory of an ambiguous word, an intimate, casual tone of voice, a hard, helpless look. That could do. With no more than that I could manage, year after year as I scoured the milk pails, spit on the iron, followed the cows along the rough path among the alder and the black-eyed Susans, spread the clean wet overalls to dry on the fence, and the tea towels on the bushes. Who would the man be? He could be anybody. A soldier killed at the Somme or a farmer down the road with a rough-tongued wife and a crowd of children; a boy who went to Saskatchewan and promised to send for me, but never did, or the preacher who rouses me every Sunday with lashings of fear and promises of torment. No matter. I could fasten on any of them, in secret. A lifelong secret, lifelong dream-life. I could go round singing in the kitchen, polishing the stove, wiping the lamp chimneys, dipping water for the tea from the drinking-pail. The faintly sour smell of the scrubbed tin, the worn scrub-cloths. Upstairs my bed with the high headboard, the crocheted spread, and the rough, friendly-smelling flannelette sheets, the hot-water bottle to ease my cramps or be clenched between my legs. There I come back again and again to the center of my fantasy, to the moment when you give yourself up, give yourself over, to the assault which

is guaranteed to finish off everything you've been before. A stubborn virgin's belief, this belief in perfect mastery; any broken-down wife could tell you there is no such thing.

Dipping the dipper in the pail, lapped in my harmless craziness, I'd sing hymns, and nobody would wonder.

"He's the Lily of the Valley,
The Bright and Morning Star.
He's the Fairest of Ten Thousand to my Soul."

2

This summer I'm living in Toronto, in my friend Kay's apartment, finishing a book of family history which some rich people are paying me to write. Last spring, in connection with this book, I had to spend some time in Australia. There I met an anthropologist whom I had known slightly, years before, in Vancouver. He was then married to his first wife (he is now married to his third) and I was married to my first husband (I am now divorced). We both lived in Fort Camp, which was the married students' quarters, at the university.

The anthropologist had been investigating language groups in northern Queensland. He was going to spend a few weeks in the city, at a university, before joining his wife in India. She was there on a grant, studying Indian music. She is the new sort of wife with serious interests of her own. His first wife had been a girl with a job, who would help him get through the university, then stay home and have children.

We met at lunch on Saturday, and on Sunday we went up the river on an excursion boat, full of noisy families, to an animal preserve. There we looked at wombats curled up like blood puddings, and disgruntled, shoddy emus, and walked under an arbor of brilliant unfamiliar flowers and had our pictures taken with koala bears. We brought each other up-to-date on our lives, with jokes, sombre passages, buoyant sympathy. On the way back we drank gin from the bar on the boat, and kissed, and made a mild spectacle of ourselves. It was almost impossible to talk because of the noise of the engines, the crying babies, the children shrieking and chasing each other, but he said, "Please come and see my house. I've got a borrowed house. You'll like it. Please, I can't wait to ask you, please come and live with me in my house."

"Should I?"

"I'll get down on my knees," he said, and did.

"Get up, behave!" I said. "We're in a foreign country."

"That means we can do anything we like."

Some of the children had stopped their game to stare at us. They looked shocked and solemn.

3

I call him X, as if he were a character in an old-fashioned novel, that pretends to be true. X is a letter in his name, but I chose it also because it seems to suit

him. The letter X seems to me expansive and secretive. And using just the letter, not needing a name, is in line with a system I often employ these days. I say to myself, "Bardon Bus, No. 144," and I see a whole succession of scenes. I see them in detail; streets and houses. LaTrobe Terrace, Paddington. Schools like large, pleasant bungalows, betting shops, frangipani trees dropping their waxy, easily bruised, and highly scented flowers. It was on this bus that we rode downtown, four or five times in all, carrying our string bags, to shop for groceries at Woolworths, meat at Coles, licorice and chocolate ginger at the candy store. Much of the city is built on ridges between gullies, so there was a sense of coming down through populous but half-wild hill villages into the central part of town, with its muddy river and pleasant colonial shabbiness. In such a short time everything seemed remarkably familiar and yet not to be confused with anything we had known in the past. We felt we knew the lives of the housewives in sun-hats riding with us on the bus, we knew the insides of the shuttered, sun-blistered houses set up on wooden posts over the gullies, we knew the streets we couldn't see. This familiarity was not oppressive but delightful, and there was a slight strangeness to it, as if we had come by it in a way we didn't understand. We moved through a leisurely domesticity with a feeling of perfect security – a security we hadn't felt, or so we told each other, in any of our legal domestic arrangements, or in any of the places where we more properly belonged. We had a holiday of lightness of spirit without the holiday feeling of being at loose ends. Every day X went off to the university and I went downtown to the research library, to look at old newspapers on the microfilm reader.

One day I went to the Toowong Cemetery to look for some graves. The cemetery was more magnificent and ill-kempt than cemeteries are in Canada. The inscriptions on some of the splendid white stones had a surprising informality. "Our Wonderful Mum," and "A Fine Fellow." I wondered what this meant, about Australians, and then I thought how we are always wondering what things mean, in another country, and how I would talk this over with X.

The sexton came out of his little house, to help me. He was a young man in shorts, with a full-blown sailing ship tattooed on his chest. *Australia Felix* was its name. A harem girl on the underside of one arm, a painted warrior on top. The other arm decorated with dragons and banners. A map of Australia on the back of one hand; the Southern Cross on the back of the other. I didn't like to peer at his legs, but had an impression of complicated scenes like a vertical comic strip, and a chain of medallions wreathed in flowers, perhaps containing girls' names. I took care to get all these things straight, because of the pleasure of going home and telling X.

He too would bring things home: conversations on the bus; word derivations; connections he had found.

We were not afraid to use the word love. We lived without responsibility, without a future, in freedom, with generosity, in constant but not wearying celebration. We had no doubt that our happiness would last out the little time required. The only thing we reproached ourselves for was laziness. We wondered if we would later regret not going to the Botanical Gardens to see the lotus in bloom, not having seen one movie together; we were sure we would think of more things we wished we had told each other.

4

I dreamed that X wrote me a letter. It was all done in clumsy block printing and I thought, that's to disguise his handwriting, that's clever. But I had great trouble reading it. He said he wanted us to go on a trip to Cuba. He said the trip had been offered to him by a clergyman he met in a bar. I wondered if the clergyman might be a spy. He said we could go skiing in Vermont. He said he did not want to interfere with my life but he did want to shelter me. I loved that word. But the complications of the dream multiplied. The letter had been delayed. I tried to phone him and I couldn't get the telephone dial to work. Also it seemed I had the responsibility of a baby, asleep in a dresser drawer. Things got more and more tangled and dreary, until I woke. The word shelter was still in my head. I had to feel it shrivel. I was lying on a mattress on the floor of Kay's apartment at the corner of Queen and Bathurst streets at eight o'clock in the morning. The windows were open in the summer heat, the streets full of people going to work, the streetcars stopping and starting and creaking on the turn.

This is a cheap, pleasant apartment with high windows, white walls, unbleached cotton curtains, floorboards painted in a glossy gray. It has been a cheap temporary place for so long that nobody ever got around to changing it, so the wainscoting is still there, and the old-fashioned perforated screens over the radiators. Kay has some beautiful faded rugs, and the usual cushions and spreads, to make the mattresses on the floor look more like divans and less like mattresses. A worn-out set of bedsprings is leaning against the wall, covered with shawls and scarves and pinned-up charcoal sketches by Kay's former lover, the artist. Nobody can figure a way to get the springs out of here, or imagine how they got up here in the first place.

Kay makes her living as a botanical illustrator, doing meticulous drawings of plants for textbooks and government handbooks. She lives on a farm, in a household of adults and children who come and go and one day are gone for good. She keeps this place in Toronto, and comes down for a day or so every couple of weeks. She likes this stretch of Queen Street, with its taverns and secondhand stores and quiet derelicts. She doesn't stand much chance here of running into people who went to Branksome Hall with her, or danced at her wedding. When Kay married, her bridegroom wore a kilt, and his brother officers made an arch of swords. Her father was a brigadier-general; she made her debut at Government House. I often think that's why she never tires of a life of risk and improvisation, and isn't frightened by the sound of brawls late at night under these windows, or the drunks in the doorway downstairs. She doesn't feel the threat that I would feel, she never sees herself slipping under.

Kay doesn't own a kettle. She boils water in a saucepan. She is ten years younger than I am. Her hips are narrow, her hair long and straight and dark and streaked with gray. She usually wears a beret and charming, raggedy clothes from the secondhand stores. I have known her six or seven years and during that time she has often been in love. Her loves are daring, sometimes grotesque.

On the boat from Centre Island she met a paroled prisoner, a swarthy tall fellow with an embroidered headband, long gray-black hair blowing in the wind. He had been sent to jail for wrecking his ex-wife's house, or her lover's house; some crime of passion Kay boggled at, then forgave. He said he was part

Indian and when he had cleared up some business in Toronto he would take her to his native island off the coast of British Columbia, where they would ride horses along the beach. She began to take riding lessons.

During her break-up with him she was afraid for her life. She found threatening, amorous notes pinned to her nightgowns and underwear. She changed her locks, she went to the police, but she didn't give up on love. Soon she was in love with the artist, who had never wrecked a house but was ruled by signs from the spirit world. He had gotten a message about her before they met, knew what she was going to say before she said it, and often saw an ominous blue fire around her neck, a yoke or a ring. One day he disappeared, leaving those sketches, and a lavish horrible book on anatomy which showed real sliced cadavers, with innards, skin, and body hair in their natural colors, injected dyes of red or blue illuminating a jungle of blood vessels. On Kay's shelves you can read a history of her love affairs: books on prison riots, autobiographies of prisoners, from the period of the parolee; this book on anatomy and others on occult phenomena, from the period of the artist; books on caves, books by Albert Speer, from the time of the wealthy German importer who taught her the word *spelunker*; books on revolution which date from the West Indian.

She takes up a man and his story wholeheartedly. She learns his language, figuratively or literally. At first she may try to disguise her condition, pretending to be prudent or ironic. "Last week I met a peculiar character – " or, "I had a funny conversation with a man at a party, did I tell you?" Soon a tremor, a sly flutter, an apologetic but stubborn smile. "Actually I'm afraid I've fallen for him, isn't that terrible?" Next time you see her she'll be in deep, going to fortune-tellers, slipping his name into every other sentence; with this mention of the name there will be a mushy sound to her voice, a casting down of the eyes, an air of cherished helplessness, appalling to behold. Then comes the onset of gloom, the doubts and anguish, the struggle either to free herself or to keep him from freeing himself; the messages left with answering services. Once she disguised herself as an old woman, with a gray wig and a tattered fur coat; she walked up and down, in the cold, outside the house of the woman she thought to be her supplanter. She will talk coldly, sensibly, wittily, about her mistake, and tell discreditable things she has gleaned about her lover, then make desperate phone calls. She will get drunk, and sign up for rolfing, swim therapy, gymnastics.

In none of this is she so exceptional. She does what women do. Perhaps she does it more often, more openly, just a bit more ill-advisedly, and more fervently. Her powers of recovery, her faith, are never exhausted. I joke about her, everybody does, but I defend her too, saying that she is not condemned to living with reservations and withdrawals, long-drawn-out dissatisfactions, inarticulate wavering miseries. Her trust is total, her miseries are sharp, and she survives without visible damage. She doesn't allow for drift or stagnation and the spectacle of her life is not discouraging to me.

She is getting over someone now; the husband, the estranged husband, of another woman at the farm. His name is Roy; he too is an anthropologist.

"It's really a low ebb falling in love with somebody who's lived at the farm," she says. "Really low. Somebody you know all about."

I tell her I'm getting over somebody I met in Australia, and that I plan to be

over him just about when I get the book done, and then I'll go and look for another job, a place to live.

"No rush, take it easy," she says.

I think about the words "getting over." They have an encouraging, crisp, everyday sound. They are in tune with Kay's present mood. When love is fresh and on the rise she grows mystical, tentative; in the time of love's decline, and past the worst of it, she is brisk and entertaining, straightforward, analytical.

"It's nothing but the desire to see yourself reflected," she says. "Love always comes back to self-love. The idiocy. You don't want them, you want what you can get from them. Obsession and self-delusion. Did you every read those journals of Victor Hugo's daughter, I think that's who it was?"

"No."

"I never did either, but I read about them. The part I remember, the part I remember reading about, that struck me so, was where she goes out into the street after years and years of loving this man, obsessively loving him, and she meets him. She passes him in the street and she either doesn't recognize him or she does but she can't connect the real man any more with the person she loves, in her head. She can't connect him at all."

5

When I knew X in Vancouver he was a different person. A serious graduate student, still a Lutheran, stocky and resolute, rather a prig in some people's opinion. His wife was more scatterbrained; a physiotherapist named Mary, who liked sports and dancing. Of the two, you would have said she might be the one to run off. She had blond hair, big teeth; her gums showed. I watched her play baseball at a picnic. I had to go off and sit in the bushes, to nurse my baby. I was twenty-one, a simple-looking girl, a nursing mother. Fat and pink on the outside; dark judgements and strenuous ambitions within. Sex had not begun for me, at all.

X came around the bushes and gave me a bottle of beer.

"What are you doing back here?"

"I'm feeding the baby."

"Why do you have to do it here? Nobody would care."

"My husband would have a fit."

"Oh. Well, drink up. Beer's supposed to be good for your milk, isn't it?"

That was the only time I talked to him, so far as I can remember. There was something about the direct approach, the slightly clumsy but determined courtesy, my own unexpected, lightened feeling of gratitude, that did connect with his attentions to women later, and his effect on them. I am sure he was always patient, unalarming; successful, appreciative, sincere.

6

I met Dennis in the Toronto Reference Library and he asked me out to dinner.

Dennis is a friend of X's, who came to visit us in Australia. He is a tall, slight, stiff, and brightly smiling young man – not so young either, he must be thirty-five – who has an elaborately courteous and didactic style.

I go to meet him thinking he may have a message for me. Isn't it odd, otherwise, that he would want to have dinner with an older woman he has met only once before? I think he may tell me whether X is back in Canada. X told me that they would probably come back in July. Then he was going to spend a year writing his book. They might live in Nova Scotia during that year. They might live in Ontario.

When Dennis came to see us in Australia, I made a curry. I was pleased with the idea of having a guest and glad that he arrived in time to see the brief evening light on the gully. Our house like the others was built out on posts, and from the window where we ate we looked out over a gully like an oval bowl, ringed with small houses and filled with jacaranda, poinciana, frangipani, cypress, and palm trees. Leaves like fans, whips, feathers, plates; every bright, light, dark, dusty, glossy shade of green. Guinea fowl lived down there, and flocks of rackety kookaburras took to the sky at dusk. We had to scramble down a steep dirt bank under the house to get to the wash-hut, and peg the clothes on a revolving clothesline. There we encountered spider-webs draped like tent-tops, matched like lids and basins with one above and one below. We had to watch out for the one little spider that weaves a conical web and has a poison for which there is no antidote.

We showed Dennis the gully and told him this was a typical old Queensland house with the high tongue-and-groove walls and the ventilation panels over the doors filled with graceful carved vines. He did not look at anything with much interest, but talked about China, where he had just been. X said afterwards that Dennis always talked about the last place he'd been and the last people he'd seen, and never seemed to notice anything, but that he would probably be talking about us, and describing this place, to the next people he had dinner with, in the next city. He said that Dennis spent most of his life traveling, and talking about it, and that he knew a lot of people just well enough that when he showed up somewhere he had to be asked to dinner.

Dennis told us that he had seen the recently excavated Army Camp at Sian, in China. He described the rows of life-sized soldiers, each of them so realistic and unique, some still bearing traces of the paint which had once covered them and individualized them still further. Away at their backs, he said, was a wall of earth. The terra-cotta soldiers looked as if they were marching out of the earth.

He said it reminded him of X's women. Row on row and always a new one appearing at the end of the line.

"The Army marches on," he said.

"Dennis, for God's sake," said X.

"But do they really come out of the earth like that?" I said to Dennis. "Are they intact?"

"Are which intact?" said Dennis with his harsh smile. "The soldiers or the women? The women aren't intact. Or not for long."

"Could we get off the subject?" said X.

"Certainly. Now to answer your question," said Dennis, turning to me. "They are very seldom found as whole figures. Or so I understand. Their legs and torsos and heads have to be matched up, usually. They have to be put together and stood on their feet."

"It's a lot of work, I can tell you," said X, with a large sigh.

"But it's not that way with the women," I said to Dennis. I spoke with a special, social charm, almost flirtatiously, as I often do when I detect malice. "I think the comparison's a bit off. Nobody has to dig the women out and stand them on their feet. Nobody put them there. They came along and joined up of their own free will and some day they'll leave. They're not a standing army. Most of them are probably on their way to someplace else anyway."

"Bravo," said X.

When we were washing the dishes, late at night, he said, "You didn't mind Dennis saying that, did you? You didn't mind if I went along with him a little bit? He has to have his legends."

I laid my head against his back, between the shoulder blades.

"Does he? No. I thought it was funny."

"I bet you didn't know that soap was first described by Pliny and was used by the Gauls. I bet you didn't know they boiled goat's tallow with the lye from the wood ashes."

"No. I didn't know that."

7

Dennis hasn't said a word about X, or about Australia. I wouldn't have thought his asking me to dinner strange, if I had remembered him better. He asked me so he would have somebody to talk to. Since Australia, he has been to Iceland, and the Faeroe Islands. I ask him questions. I am interested, and surprised, even shocked, when necessary. I took trouble with my makeup and washed my hair. I hope that if he does see X, he will say that I was charming.

Besides his travels Dennis has his theories. He develops theories about art and literature, history, life.

"I have a new theory about the life of women. I used to feel it was so unfair the way things happened to them."

"What things?"

"The way they have to live, compared to men. Specifically with aging. Look at you. Think of the way your life would be, if you were a man. The choices you would have. I mean sexual choices. You could start all over. Men do. It's in all the novels and it's in life too. Men fall in love with younger women. Men want younger women. Men can get younger women. The new marriage, new babies, new families."

I wonder if he is going to tell me something about X's wife; perhaps that she is going to have a baby.

"It's such a coup for them, isn't it?" he says in his malicious, sympathetic way. "The fresh young wife, the new baby when other men their age are starting on grandchildren. All those men envying them and trying to figure out how to do the same. It's the style, isn't it? It must be hard to resist starting over and having that nice young mirror to look in, if you get the opportunity."

"I think I might resist it," I say cheerfully, not insistently. "I don't really think I'd want to have a baby, now."

"That's it, that's just it, though, you don't get the opportunity! You're a woman

and life only goes in one direction for a woman. All this business about younger lovers, that's just froth, isn't it? Do you want a younger lover?"

"I guess not," I say, and pick my dessert from a tray. I pick a rich creamy pudding with pureed chestnuts at the bottom of it and fresh raspberries on top. I purposely ate a light dinner, leaving plenty of room for dessert. I did that so I could have something to look forward to, while listening to Dennis.

"A woman your age can't compete," says Dennis urgently. "You can't compete with younger women. I used to think that was so rottenly unfair."

"It's probably biologically correct for men to go after younger women. There's no use whining about it."

"So the men have this way of renewing themselves, they get this refill of vitality, while the women are you might say removed from life. I used to think that was terrible. But now my thinking has undergone a complete reversal. Do you know what I think now? I think women are the lucky ones! Do you know why?"

"Why?"

"Because they are forced to live in the world of loss and death! Oh, I know, there's face-lifting, but how does that really help? The uterus dries up. The vagina dries up."

I feel him watching me. I continue eating my pudding.

"I've seen so many parts of the world and so many strange things and so much suffering. It's my conclusion now that you won't get any happiness by playing tricks on life. It's only by natural renunciation and by accepting deprivation, that we prepare for death and therefore that we get any happiness. Maybe my ideas seem strange to you?"

I can't think of anything to say.

8

Often I have a few lines of a poem going through my head, and I won't know what started it. It can be a poem or rhyme that I didn't even know I knew, and it needn't be anything that conforms to what I think is my taste. Sometimes I don't pay any attention to it, but if I do, I can usually see that the poem, or the bit of it I've got hold of, has some relation to what is going on in my life. And that may not be what seems to be going on.

For instance last spring, last autumn in Australia, when I was happy, the line that would go through my head, at a merry clip, was this:

"Even such is time, that takes in trust –"

I could not go on, though I knew trust rhymed with dust, and that there was something further along about "and in the dark and silent grave, shuts up the story of our days." I knew the poem was written by Sir Walter Raleigh on the eve of his execution. My mood did not accord with such a poem and I said it, in my head, as if it was something pretty and lighthearted. I did not stop to wonder what it was doing in my head in the first place.

And now that I'm trying to look at things soberly I should remember what we said when our bags were packed and we were waiting for the taxi. Inside the bags our clothes that had shared drawers and closet space, tumbled together in the wash, and been pegged together on the clothesline where the kookaburras

sat, were all sorted and separated and would not rub together any more.

"In a way I'm glad it's over and nothing spoiled it. Things are so often spoiled."

"I know."

"As it is, it's been perfect."

I said that. And that was a lie. I had cried once, thought I was ugly, thought he was bored.

But he said, "Perfect."

On the plane the words of the poem were going through my head again, and I was still happy. I went to sleep thinking the bulk of X was still beside me and when I woke I filled the space quickly with memories of his voice, looks, warmth, our scenes together.

I was swimming in memories, at first. Those detailed, repetitive scenes were what buoyed me up. I didn't try to escape them, didn't wish to. Later I did wish to. They had become a plague. All they did was stir up desire, and longing, and hopelessness, a trio of miserable caged wildcats that had been installed in me without my permission, or at least without my understanding how long they would live and how vicious they would be. The images, the language, of pornography and romance are alike; monotonous and mechanically seductive, quickly leading to despair. That was what my mind dealt in; that is what it still can deal in. I have tried vigilance and reading serious books but I can still slide deep into some scene before I know where I am.

On the bed a woman lies in a yellow nightgown which has not been torn but has been pulled off her shoulders and twisted up around her waist so that it covers no more of her than a crumpled scarf would. A man bends over her, naked, offering a drink of water. The woman, who has almost lost consciousness, whose legs are open, arms flung out, head twisted to the side as if she has been struck down in the course of some natural disaster – this woman rouses herself and tries to hold the glass in her shaky hands. She slops water over her breast, drinks, shudders, falls back. The man's hands are trembling, too. He drinks out of the same glass, looks at her, and laughs. His laugh is rueful, apologetic, and kind, but it is also amazed, and his amazement is not far from horror. How are we capable of all this? his laugh says, what is the meaning of it?

He says, "We almost finished each other off."

The room seems still full of echoes of the recent commotion, the cries, pleas, brutal promises, the climactic sharp announcements and the long subsiding spasms.

The room is brimming with gratitude and pleasure, a rich broth of love, a golden twilight of love. Yes, yes, you can drink the air.

You see the sort of thing I mean, that is my torment.

9

This is the time of year when women are tired of sundresses, prints, sandals. It is already fall in the stores. Thick sweaters and skirts are pinned up against black or plum-colored velvet. The young salesgirls are made up like courtesans. I've become feverishly preoccupied with clothes. All the conversations in the stores make sense to me.

"The neckline doesn't work. It's too stark. I need a flutter. Do you know what I mean?"

"Yes. I know what you mean."

"I want something very classy and very provocative. Do you know what I mean?"

"Yes. I know exactly what you mean."

For years I've been wearing bleached-out colors which I suddenly can't bear. I buy a deep-red satin blouse, a purple shawl, a dark-blue skirt. I get my hair cut and pluck my eyebrows and try a lilac lipstick, a brownish rouge. I'm appalled to think of the way I went around in Australia, in a faded wraparound cotton skirt and T-shirt, my legs bare because of the heat, my face bare too and sweating under a cotton hat. My legs with the lumps of veins showing. I'm half convinced that a more artful getup would have made a more powerful impression, more dramatic clothes might have made me less discardable. I have fancies of meeting X unexpectedly at a party or on a Toronto street, and giving him a shock, devastating him with my altered looks and late-blooming splendor. But I do think you have to watch out, even in these garish times; you have to watch out for the point at which the splendor collapses into absurdity. Maybe they are all watching out, all the old women I see on Queen Street: the fat woman with pink hair; the eighty-year-old with painted-on black eyebrows; they may all be thinking they haven't gone too far yet, not quite yet. Even the buttercup woman I saw a few days ago on the streetcar, the little, stout, sixtyish woman in a frilly yellow dress well above the knees, a straw hat with yellow ribbons, yellow pumps dyed-to-match on her little fat feet – even she doesn't aim for comedy. She sees a flower in the mirror: the generous petals, the lovely buttery light.

I go looking for earrings. All day looking for earrings which I can see so clearly in my mind. I want little filigree balls of silver, of diminishing size, dangling. I want old and slightly tarnished silver. It's a style I well remember; you'd think the secondhand stores would be sure to have them. But I can't find them, I can't find anything resembling them, and they seem more and more necessary. I go into a little shop on a side street near College and Spadina. The shop is all done up in black paper with cheap, spooky effects – for instance a bald, naked mannequin sitting on a stepladder, dangling some beads. A dress such as I wore in the fifties, a dance dress of pink net and sequins, terribly scratchy under the arms, is displayed against the black paper in a way that makes it look sinister, and desirable.

I look around for the tray of jewelry. The salesgirls are busy dressing a customer hidden from me by a three-way mirror. One salesgirl is fat and gypsyish with a face warmly colored as an apricot. The other is spiky and has a crest of white hair surrounded by black hair, like a skunk. They are shrieking with pleasure as they bring hats and beads for the customer to try. Finally everybody is satisfied and a beautiful young lady, who is not a young lady at all but a pretty boy dressed up as a lady, emerges from the shelter of the mirror. He is wearing a black velvet dress with long sleeves and a black lace yoke; black pumps and gloves; a little black hat with a dotted veil. He is daintily and discreetly made up; he has a fringe of brown curls; he is the prettiest and most ladylike person I have seen all day. His smiling face is tense and tremulous. I

remember how when I was ten or eleven years old I used to dress up as a bride in old curtains, or as a lady in rouge and a feathered hat. After all the effort and contriving and my own enchantment with the finished product there was a considerable letdown. What are you supposed to do now? Parade up and down on the sidewalk? There is a great fear and daring and disappointment in this kind of display.

He has a boyish, cracking voice. He is brash and timid.

"How do I look, momma?"

"You look very nice."

10

I am at a low point. I can recognize it. That must mean I will get past it.

I am at a low point, certainly. I cannot deal with all that assails me unless I get help and there is only one person I want help from and that is X. I can't continue to move my body along the streets unless I exist in his mind and in his eyes. People have this problem frequently, and we know it is their own fault and they have to change their way of thinking, that's all. It is not an honorable problem. Love is not serious though it may be fatal. I read that somewhere and I believe it. Thank God I don't know where he is. I can't telephone him, write letters to him, waylay him on the street.

A man I had broken with used to follow me. Finally he persuaded me to go into a café and have a cup of tea with him.

"I know what a spectacle I am," he said. "I know if you did have any love left for me this would destroy it."

I said nothing.

He beat the spoon against the sugar bowl.

"What do you think of, when you're with me?"

I meant to say, "I don't know," but instead I said, "I think of how much I want to get away."

He reared up trembling and dropped the spoon on the floor.

"You're free of me," he said in a choking voice.

This is the scene both comic and horrible, stagy and real. He was in desperate need, as I am now, and I didn't pity him, and I'm not sorry I didn't.

11

I have had a pleasant dream that seems far away from my waking state. X and I and some other people I didn't know or can't remember were wearing innocent athletic underwear outfits, which changed at some point into gauzy bright white clothes, and these turned out to be not just clothes but our substances, our flesh and bones and in a sense our souls. Embraces took place which started out with the usual urgency but were transformed, by the lightness and sweetness of our substance, into a rare state of content. I can't describe it very well, it sounds like a movie-dream of heaven, all banality and innocence. So I suppose it was. I can't apologize for the banality of my dreams.

12

I go along the street to Rooneem's Bakery and sit at one of their little tables with a cup of coffee. Rooneem's is an Estonian bakery where you can usually find a Mediterranean housewife in a black dress, a child looking at the cakes, and a man talking to himself.

I sit where I can watch the street. I have a feeling X is somewhere in the vicinity. Within a thousand miles, say, within a hundred miles, within this city. He doesn't know my address but he knows I am in Toronto. It would not be so difficult to find me.

At the same time I'm thinking that I have to let go. What you have to decide, really, is whether to be crazy or not, and I haven't the stamina, the pure, seething will, for prolonged craziness.

There is a limit to the amount of misery and disarray you will put up with, for love, just as there is a limit to the amount of mess you can stand around a house. You can't know the limit beforehand, but you will know when you've reached it. I believe this.

When you start really letting go this is what it's like. A lick of pain, furtive, darting up where you don't expect it. Then a lightness. The lightness is something to think about. It isn't just relief. There's a queer kind of pleasure in it, not a self-wounding or malicious pleasure, nothing personal at all. It's an uncalled-for pleasure in seeing how the design wouldn't fit and the structure wouldn't stand, a pleasure in taking into account, all over again, everything that is contradictory and persistent and unaccommodating about life. I think so. I think there's something in us wanting to be reassured about all that, right alongside – and at war with – whatever there is that wants permanent vistas and a lot of fine talk.

I think about my white dream and how it seemed misplaced. It strikes me that misplacement is the clue, in love, the heart of the problem, but like somebody drunk or high I can't quite get a grasp on what I see.

What I need is a rest. A deliberate sort of rest, with new definitions of luck. Not the sort of luck Dennis was talking about. You're lucky to be sitting in Rooneem's drinking coffee, with people coming and going, eating and drinking, buying cakes, speaking Spanish, Portuguese, Chinese, and other languages that you can try to identify.

13

Kay is back from the country. She too has a new outfit, a dark-green schoolgirl's tunic worn without a blouse or brassiere. She has dark-green knee socks and saddle oxfords.

"Does it look kinky?"

"Yes it does."

"Does it make my arms look dusky? Remember in some old poem a woman had dusky arms?"

Her arms do look soft and brown.

"I meant to get down on Sunday but Roy came over with a friend and we all had a corn roast. It was lovely. You should come out there. You should."

"Some day I will."

"The kids ran around like beautiful demons and we drank up the mead. Roy knows how to make fertility dolls. Roy's friend is Alex Walther, the anthropologist. I felt I should have known about him but I didn't. He didn't mind. He's a nice man. Do you know what he did? After dark when we were sitting around the fire he came over to me and just sighed, and laid his head on my lap. I thought it was such a nice simple thing to do. Like a St. Bernard. I've never had anybody do that before."

SERENA

Luke Jennings

Luke Jennings is an author and the dance critic of the *Observer*. As a journalist, he has written for *Vanity Fair*, *The New Yorker* and *Time*, as well as numerous British titles. He was shortlisted for the 2010 Samuel Johnson and William Hill prizes for his memoir, *Blood Knots*, and was nominated for the Booker Prize for his novel *Atlantic*. With Deborah Bull, he wrote *The Faber Guide to Ballet*, and with his daughter Laura, the Stars stage-school novels. He is also the author of the Villanelle thriller series.

I became the familiar of Serena Vance shortly after the death from radon gas inhalation of my previous mistress, Philippa Lapsley. For all her sluttish ways, I had been fond of Philippa, and had been sorry to wake that Saturday afternoon and find her flesh grown cold beneath me. Such a waste, they'd whispered at her funeral. Such a *waste*.

It was with no great excitement, in consequence, that I waited for Miss Vance to clear customs and join me in the pearl-grey Lexus that the company had sent to meet her at Heathrow Airport. I knew nothing about her beyond the fact that she was forty years old and a native of Chicago, where she had something of a reputation in the field of arbitrage. Her transfer to the London office had apparently been arranged at short notice.

I was dozing against the warm upholstery of the back seat (invisible to the driver, of course, who was not one of ours) when a blast of cold air brought me abruptly to my senses. With it came a travel-bruised vestige of Chanel's "Allure", a day-old memory of expensive hairdressing, and an exhausted yawn. Serena, I noted approvingly, was rather beautiful. Pale, with fine-drawn features, a clearly incised mouth and eyes that – well, let's just say that the eyes were less of a surprise. They were the colour of wet slate in February and they had the depthless stare by which we of the craft know each other. I wanted her immediately.

"So," she said, a smile touching her lips. With great care, she lifted me in the palm of her hand. Her fingers were long and slender, and she held me in her grey gaze with an almost nervous delicacy. I burned for her. Did I please her, I wondered? I was wearing an urban camouflage T-shirt and combat pants that Philippa had bought for me at Hamleys (at eight inches in height I'm pretty much a standard size), and at my side was the rapier that had transfixed my former mistress's martini olive on the occasion of her first visit to the Savoy.

"I've never had a familiar in . . . human form," said Serena, raising her phone

to her mouth so that the driver would not think that she was talking to herself. "What did you have in Chicago?" I asked her, and she wrinkled her nose and blew the hair from her eyes. "A kind of lizard thing," she murmured. "It manifested itself once during a meeting with senior officers of Madison Semiconductors. And another time at a polo game outside of Lexington. Both of which were kind of hard to explain." She yawned, absently covering her mouth with the phone, and I prickled with the anticipation of exploring her. "It's rush hour," I said, indicating the backed-up traffic. "And it's still three in the morning Chicago time. Why don't you get some sleep?"

Later, in the South Audley Street flat, she took a bath. This was my idea – when in London, I told her, do as the Londoners do – and as she lay with her eyes half closed and the steaming, stephanotis-scented water lapping at her chin, she admitted that it was a good one. "Hey, you've got little fold-away wings," she murmured dreamily, as I pulled off my T-shirt and combat pants and dropped quietly into the water from the soap dish. "How cute!"

In reply I swam lazily over to her shoulder and bit her ear beneath the sapphire stud – not hard, but sharply enough to make her gasp and turn her head. Grasping a dark tendril of wet hair, I trod water for a moment before easing myself into the temperate bay of her collarbone. From here I considered her body. Her skin was so pale that only her neat cinnamon-brown nipples and the vaguer triangle of her pubic hair prevented her from vanishing altogether in the milky opacity of the water. An affecting sight, I thought.

As if in reaction, Serena adjusted herself, raising the freckled slopes of her breasts from the water. Face first, I slid down the warm spillway between them like an otter, my groin bumping pleasingly on the gentle ridges of her sternum. In the water I swam around her right breast and reached for her nipple, which I was just able to span with the fingers of both hands. Pulling myself against her, I applied my long rasping cat's-tongue to the soft brown boss of flesh until it grew to a quivering tautness, and then, shaking the water briskly from my wings, flew to her other side.

At which point the phone rang. The ensuing conversation, as I recall, concerned the laying of a fibre-optic cable across the Gulf of Tonkin. Serena, ever the professional, gave the matter her full attention – "No rest for the wicked!" was one of her favourite expressions, I would discover – and I climbed in a state of sulky tumescence to her shoulder. For the rest of the day and the night that followed, I deferred my pleasure.

When the company chauffeur came for her the next morning, Serena was wearing something grey and tailored and carrying a thin black briefcase, and I was wearing an Action Man helicopter pilot jumpsuit, my rapier, as ever, swinging at my side. I rode into the city on my mistress's shoulder, nibbling affectionately – and not without a certain anticipation, for her neat little Illinois quim was still *terra incognita* – at her ear lobe. In the twenty-four short hours of our acquaintance I had grown remarkably fond of Serena Vance, with her smoky eyes and voice and her slender, pampered body. Aroused by the smell of her peony-root shampoo I stuck my proud member out of the jumpsuit and waved my rapier at the Fenchurch Street traffic. The chauffeur, a long-time initiate, winked at me in the mirror.

Serena, I discovered, was not the only newcomer to the company, although she was the most senior. A young Anglo-Chinese man named Ganymede Ho had been recruited to the broking team, and had been assigned a female familiar whose pleasure it was to run knickerless along the ranks of terminals with her Barbie mini-kilt lifted to her waist, spraying the coffee cups and soft drink cans of non-initiates with piss. Between these bouts of micturition, the wilful little sprite would lie on her master's keyboard with her legs spread and order the chairman's weasel to lick her.

This was a spectacular exercise – jewelled collar or no jewelled collar, the beast had long teeth and a short temper – and an enthusiastic crowd invariably gathered to watch. To begin with, at least, Serena was a little shocked by these larks; in the United States familiars were expected to maintain a rather more discreet profile in work situations. She soon learned to see and not see, however; a reputation for staring open-mouthed at her colleagues' workstations would not greatly have improved her professional standing.

So, as in all things, she played it cool. And so, for once, did I. Unzipping my jumpsuit I stretched out on her mouse-mat and bathed in the refracted sunshine that angled through the building's plate-glass wall. When a ruttish little pixie attached to one of the other arbitrageurs fluttered over in a Sindy nurse outfit and placed my hand between her legs, I courteously withdrew it. When there was a move afoot to gang rape a pigeon that had strayed into one of the boardrooms I demurred, preferring to be an adoring spectator of my mistress's assault on the epitaxial wafer market. I stayed close to Serena for all of that day, and I sensed that my attentions were appreciated. In the car on the way home, I guessed from her manner that our relationship was shortly to be consummated. "You're a sinister, profligate little imp," she whispered to me, "but you're my sinister profligate little imp."

Back in the flat she fixed herself a drink and put on a CD. It was an old recording of Hawaiian music, all swoops and slide guitars. In the bedroom she drew the curtains and undressed, hanging the grey suit in the wardrobe and laying her underwear out on a chair. Then with her drink still in her hand she lay down on the bed, drew her knees up to her sides, and, as I patiently beat my wings above, laid a long finger down the gathered parting of her flesh. The end of the finger disappeared, and then, shining, was drawn back, and I watched a manicured nail circle the opal gleam of her clitoris. Around it, the humid crest of her pubic hair slowly reasserted itself after a day's constriction under silk. The steel guitars rose and fell. She smelt equatorial, a jungle after rain. Finally her fingers withdrew, leaving a brief trail across her navel, and I heard her place her glass on the side table. "Down you go," she whispered, and I dropped between her thighs, shook out my wings, and began to gorge.

THE DISAPPEARING ISLAND

Henri Breton

Henri Breton is a painter and writer of Anglo-French parentage, has written several short stories and articles for the *Erotic Review*. In his youth, for reasons never fully explained, he took passage on a tramp steamer from Liverpool to Valparaiso, where he remained for some years, earning a living from journalism until his return to Europe. His main love is the Mediterranean and the countries that surround it. He currently divides his time between London and Barcelona.

"I *want to introduce you to my friend Nicky," said the Sea Captain. We shook hands with the tall, fair-haired man who had joined our table. He had a broad open face, full of good humour and intelligence with that attractive Dalmatian mix of Slav and North Italian.*

"Oh . . . qu'il est beau!" *murmured one of the girls, a little too loudly, for the Sea Captain turned to her and said, "Actually, I think we're distantly related. Anyway, we come from the same part of the world. But, unlike me, he comes from one of Dalmatia's thousand islands. I grew up on the mainland and always envied his romantic existence, quite surrounded by the friendly sea and practically living in a boat. But it has to be said, it is a very small island." And he looked at Nicky and they laughed.*

Later, as the evening progressed, we listened to Nicky's story.

One afternoon, I went with some other boys of my age to a favourite place on the island where we could escape from the grownups and just generally laze around and shoot the breeze. It was a superb coign of vantage at the top of a little gorge that led to my father's quarry. Unless the quarry was being worked, it was always deserted, so we were amazed to hear the sound of voices immediately below us. When we looked down we saw a man and a woman whose faces were unfamiliar, which meant that they were mainlanders. Even more unusually, the strangers were both naked, and they were lying on top of each other on a garish beach towel that cushioned them from the heat of the smooth rock enough to be able to do what they were doing without discomfort. We watched silent, engrossed, enrapt, as teenagers usually are when they see something strange and fascinating – and so obviously taboo.

They were "making love". Well that is how Ivo, the wisest of our little group,

described it to us. So that was how babies got made, we thought. Somehow, to a bunch of boys, peeping through a little thicket of pungent wild thyme and rosemary, and seeing a white bottom pumping rhythmically between a pair of splayed thighs ten metres below them, the whole thing appeared to be far from the sublime action we had always dreamed it to be. Comic or acrobatic, perhaps. It was difficult not to snigger. But the man suddenly jumped up between the woman's legs and we saw, for the first time, the adult genitals in action: the gaping maw of the woman's cunt that sat so livid in her black, unruly bush, and the man's jerking (seemingly enormous) cock, spraying her brown belly and her contrastingly pallid, pink-tipped tits with white come. Now – that was *something*. We were instantly more impressed. Here was some information about the human body that our peers certainly didn't possess: it was an important piece of knowledge, the sort that could be traded.

The name of the island where I grew up and where my father's quarry lay has lost any meaning in my language, but I'm told that in Greek it could be understood as "Isle of Stone". For it was the Greeks who, centuries ago, first realized its potential as a quarry-island, situated on a timeless shipping route and therefore conveniently located for loading the creamy white limestone, so easily sheared from the rock face.

Over the centuries, the demand for quality building stone dwindled: trade was lost to the modernized quarries on the mainland; techniques on the island improved, but too late: hydraulic drills with compressors replaced the old, hand-cranked bore-drills which used to pierce the rock face with a neat, carefully spaced row of deep holes, drilled to an exact depth, first horizontally, then vertically, ready for the rusty iron wedge and the swing of a heavy hammer (the island was too small for blasting): this, when deftly wielded, could separate a half-ton block of oolitic limestone from its mother's mass in one blow. The quarrymen had a blunter phraseology for this action, however. They would call the process of drilling "screwing the rock" or "making a cunt" and the process of splitting or wedging, "delivering the child", in an arcane dialect full of crude quarryman's metaphors.

I grew up on this micro-island: however as a child it seemed anything but small to me; after all, to a child, a place is only as big as its imagination. Also, its structure was extremely intricate, since each family had its own quarry, worked, over the generations, into a labyrinthine, gigantic geometry of huge blocks, platforms, water-filled hollows and caves populated by bats. There was no road (for where would it lead to?) and the path that ran around its elliptical circumference could be paced in under half an hour. Most of the houses were grouped around the island's main pier (there were other little jetties that belonged to the quarries, sometimes shared, sometimes not). And most of the houses boasted delightful gardens, that were decorative and practical, a sensible mixture of flowers, fruit-trees and vegetable patches. It was quite normal to see chickens scratching in the dirt of this tiny esplanade.

Behind the houses loomed the narrow quarries, cut into the side of the island's bulk, which in turn rose uncertainly into a hill covered, along with the usual dense Mediterranean scrub, by tall cypress trees and scented, shade-giving pines. It was soon after the incident with the strangers – day trippers,

probably – that I became acutely, no, *painfully* aware of the limitations of my little universe.

Of course I knew of the mainland's existence for there it was, a mile or two across the sea, but it was the islanders' tradition not to concern themselves much with what went on over there: one old man of eighty professed never to have left our shores.

That same summer a pretty, dark-haired girl, a year or so older than me, had arrived on the island to stay with her widowed aunt. Because I was more naturally gregarious than my peers, I immediately set out to befriend this exotic newcomer, but my puppyish enthusiasm was not reciprocated. When I had shown her all our secret places of play and adventure, the minute geography and the even smaller ecology of the island, she remained unimpressed.

With mounting indignation at her indifference, I asked her if she would like to see a truly magnificent edifice, having left the best until last – our own family quarry. The girl, Magdalena, replied scornfully, "Why on earth do you think I would want to look at another pile of rubble, you little hick? Thank God I don't have to stay on this stupid rock with you island bumpkins much longer. It only takes a few minutes to walk around it, and what's more, the people here are so stupid, *every day they make it even smaller . . .*" and she laughed mockingly at me.

Of course, she was perfectly right. The cumulative effect of centuries of working the quarries must have been to make our island smaller, though it was somehow an unpalatable truth and one I had not been properly conscious of until that moment. But she came with me nevertheless, making it clear she had nothing better to do. There was nobody working the stone that day, and we climbed to the hidden ledge where my friends and I had spied on the visitors the year before. Magdalena, sixteen years old, going on twenty-five, idly traced a geometric pattern in the stone dust with the big toe of her right foot. The hiatus in our conversation hung heavily between us in the hot afternoon air, interrupted only by a persistent cicada. For the first time I noticed her long, coltish legs, the graceful arch of her back, the bright bead of sweat that coursed down her neck and the gentle swell inside her starched and pleated cotton blouse.

"I can show *you* something, if you like," she said, the tone of her voice suddenly lower and less harsh, "but you mustn't tell anyone."

I nodded my agreement.

Magdalena slowly undid the mother of pearl buttons of the white blouse. I stared in awed silence. When she had finished I could see the space between her breasts, damp with perspiration from our climb.

"You can feel them if you like." First with one hand, then, more boldly, with both, I felt them. Springy cushions of flesh with hard little nipples. The sensation was interesting, but not particularly arousing. I plucked up courage and asked, "Can I feel between your legs?" At first she pretended to be shocked, but really, she was amused by my presumption; she hitched up her skirt and yanked her knickers down to her knees. "There," she said, in a matter-of-fact tone of voice, "you can have a quick feel if you like." When I saw the dark, furry vee there, it seemed nothing like the genitals of the woman we had watched from above. I reached out and felt her. She gave a shriek of mock outrage and pretended to slap

my hand away. But I was persistent. My fingers traced the outline of her nether lips. Glancing down I saw that they were a delicate coral-pink and swollen, slippery with a wetness that leaked from within. They opened up to my fingers like the shell of a mussel: inside I felt a warm swamp. At the top, where the lips seemed to join, there was a hard little nub of flesh. Magdalena moaned when I stroked it and leaned her head back, eyes half-closed.

Now – I felt excited. But too excited, as things turned out. I asked her if we could fuck. She gave a snort of derision and asked me if I had done it before. I told her no, but that I knew how it was done. She laughed some more, still mockingly, and her laughter and the uncertainty made me nervous, sapped my confidence.

Magdalena immediately sensed this, and laughing, put her hand over the crotch of my shorts and squeezed. "You've got a stiffie all right, but how long would you last?" And without warning she fished inside and brought my cock out. A couple more squeezes and I shot all over her hand. "Ughh! You boys are so *disgusting*," she cried. But I don't think she really meant it.

Four years later, a merchant seaman and still as virginal as the oil my grandmother pressed from the olives I helped her to pick, I found myself in the company of my shipmates in one of the Port of Piraeus' infamous streets of brothels. We cruised up and down in time-honoured sailors' tradition, looking for suitable berths to dock our schooners. Eventually we came to a house where it was said there was a girl from our native land; this appealed to us as something of a novelty, since prostitution was not exactly common back home.

As the youngest of our party, and under suspicion of being a virgin (something which, of course, I hotly denied), I was accorded the dubious honour of being given first place in the queue. The old Athenian *madame* ushered me into a hot room with faded wallpaper where a shrouded lamp cast a pink glow on the bed and its occupant.

Although she looked different, with hair set in a blonde perm and too much makeup, I recognized Magdalena instantly. If she remembered me, she did not say so, but we made some desultory conversation in our own tongue, I gave her the money and we got down to business. She stripped off the diaphanous peignoir and her bra as if she did it a hundred times a day. Perhaps she did. I could see that her breasts had become much fuller and this had the desired effect of making me hard. She rolled the rubber on to me with a practised skill that matched her professional patter: "My what a big boy you are, I've never seen one so huge, why, you're going to fill me completely . . ." and so on. I was more naked than her now, for she had retained her suspender belt and nylons.

As she guided me into her with the assurance of a professional, I thought back to the strangely contemptuous seduction she had treated me to four years before, and for some reason felt a pang of sadness tinged with resentment. As emotion cooled my virginal ardour, it had the effect of prolonging my performance to the point that Magdalena became at first restless, then looked pointedly at her little wristwatch and finally said, "Are you going to finish soon? I haven't got all day, you know!" My resentment grew and I started to fuck her with great lunges,

violently, as if to punish her for the betrayal I felt, the humiliation she had made me feel. But she reacted by raking my back with her fingernails and drumming her heels on my arse just like a jockey spurs on his mount, her features distorted by a grimace of lust. "Yes, give it to me you swine, fuck me hard . . . do me . . . fuck me . . . fuck the shit out of me!" And as she shouted this she started to climax, there was no doubt about it, for next she started to scream with pleasure. I stopped, not realizing that she was enjoying herself and thinking that I had gone too far. But she looked up at me urgently and muttered urgently, "Keep going you bastard . . . *don't . . . stop . . . now*!" So I kept going until I took my pleasure too, by which time the itch between her legs was more or less satisfied. After which Magdalena curled up to me like a sleepy kitten and closed her eyes.

This peaceful scene was only marred by the raddled old procuress waddling in, jowls flapping like dewlaps, to see what was amiss, for she had never heard one of her girls make this sort of noise before, and she was convinced that I was murdering her. My companions were hard on her heels. They too had never come across a tart that climaxed in such an unladylike way; indeed, they had only encountered ones who, on the whole, faked their climaxes most unconvincingly. Later they teased me mercilessly about my "technique" and how I had got the Athenian whore to scream so loud.

Ten more years passed and I returned to my birthplace with no other thought than to court, marry and settle down to have children with an island girl. Usually it would not have done for an islander to find his wife here – mostly the women sought mainland husbands to escape the endogamous group of the island's population. But in any case, this turned out to be no more than a romantic presumption: most of the girls my age or younger were already spoken for. What's more there was little work to be had now, and consequently the lure of the mainland proved hard to resist, with a resulting change in the island's demography. Quite simply, there were too few girls of a nubile disposition.

My widowed father put it rather more bluntly:

"The pick of the crop has been plucked already – you'll not find a girl here to marry now," he pointed out with a certain amount of grim satisfaction; he had never come to terms with my seafaring career, expecting me instead to join him in cutting the family's stone.

After a few weeks I had almost come to agree with the old boy. But then I heard that Magdalena was on the island and, when I saw her again, I fell immediately under her spell, for she had become an entrancingly beautiful woman. Now in her twenty-ninth year, she had a sumptuous figure which she held proudly; wonderful legs; a luxuriant tangle of jet-black curling hair fell around her face, its colour complementing her big black eyes.

Of course she was of little interest to any of the island's single males except as a relatively unusual phenomenon – an attractive, unmarried woman far beyond a marriageable age . . . an object more of pity than lust. I was intrigued to know if she remembered our meeting in Athens' steamy port or, indeed, now that I was more properly placed in context, whether she would remember our first meeting. Apparently she did not.

When I encountered her during the island's *passagiata*, the evening walk that so many Mediterranean communities take part in, she was arm in arm with her first cousin, to whom she bore absolutely no resemblance. She looked straight through me each time that we passed each other: not a glimmer of recognition. She was wearing black, so I presumed that the aunt had died, and that perhaps she had come to sell the house. I made some discreet enquiries and found this to be more or less the case.

It was early in May and the island's craggy contours were softened by the fresh greens of spring growth. I waited until the next evening and asked the cousin to introduce us. Then I asked Magdalena if I might not show her the island, for I had heard that she was a visitor. She declined politely but formally, pleading that her period of mourning was not yet over and that it would be improper to be seen in the company of a single strange man until it was.

I enquired when that might be.

She smiled and said "Tomorrow." We made a time to meet, in the afternoon of the next day.

We walked, our conversation stilted and formal, to the top of the hill and took the path to my father's quarry. Here we found the same ledge where we had "played" ten years before, and we made a fine picnic of fresh figs, soft white goat's cheese wrapped in vine leaves, half a crusty white loaf and a flagon of local red wine.

"The wine is from my village," she told me, after we had drunk most of it. "On a day when the air has been cleared by rain, you can see it from here."

"I didn't realize you came from so close by," I said.

Our talk soon turned to our respective careers and, having told her about mine, I asked her what she did for a living. I have to admit, my motives were not entirely pure. With a completely straight face she told me that she had been working for a seaman's mission. I was half-relieved, half-disappointed by this white lie – in a sense, I told myself, that was just what she *had* been doing.

"But, as you already know, before that I worked as a whore in Athens."

Her face gave nothing away. She had turned the tables on me with such ease and so skilfully that it felt like a blow to the stomach. I floundered for an explanation.

"I wasn't sure that it was you," I lied. "I mean . . . it all happened a long time ago," I mumbled lamely.

"So, would you like to show me your father's quarry again?" Again, her face was deadpan, her eyes were downcast and her mouth evenly set. I led the way. The place was abandoned now, my father having retired some years before; since his son had decided to sail the ocean blue there had been no one who cared to take it over. But in its deserted state the quarry had become hauntingly beautiful. Spring flowers grew in chaotic profusion and the great cuts in the stone had healed with time so that now it was hard to see where it had last been worked. We climbed up to the same ledge we had visited twenty years before.

The last step up was difficult so I gave Magdalena my hand. When she stood by my side she held on to it and looked up at me. "I'm sorry," she said, her face softening, "perhaps it was rather a mean trick to play. In fact, I owe you another apology for the way I treated you the *first* time we met."

"You remember that as well?"

"Of course."

We kissed. Clumsily at first, but with mounting passion. Her mouth tasted of wine and cloves. She pulled away so abruptly that I thought something was wrong. She just smiled, however, and stepped back and started to undo the buttons of her shirt. The gap between her breasts was smaller now, and they felt heavy when I cupped them, one in each hand, the nipples hardening with her need.

She reached under her skirt and pulled down her white cotton briefs. I felt between her legs and was surprised by the wave of animal heat that met my hand. She was already very wet. She undid the clasp of her skirt and it fell to the ground to join her briefs. I knelt and pressed my face to her warm stomach, licked her deep navel, let my tongue continue down the soft slope of her lower belly, through the soaking curls of her luxuriant hair, like soft black moss, until I reached the quick of her, the bubbling, juicy cauldron of her desire. Her fingers pressed into the back of my head and I was aware that she had placed her feet more widely apart and tilted her pelvis upwards. She opened up to my mouth like a hungry, clasping sea anemone, and it seemed that soft tendrils clung to my lips while I tasted the rich salty flavours of her cunt. In what seemed like a few seconds, her thighs gripped the side of my head, quivering, shaking, while above I heard her breathing change to short, staccato gasps of exhalation.

Gradually she relaxed and when I stood up she kissed my lips again, now shiny with her own juices. Then it was her turn to kneel. She looked up at me, her dark eyebrows raised in expectation. I slipped off my trousers and the rest of my clothes. My cock stood out from my body and her fingers closed around it; carefully she brought it towards her mouth. Looking down I saw, as if in slow motion, her pink tongue emerging to meet my glans and the sweat beading on her downy upper lip. Her other hand busied itself with my balls, tickling behind the tightly wrinkled flesh of the scrotum, a long finger burrowing between my buttocks and seeking out yet another centre of male bliss. Her mouth enveloped the head of my cock and she sucked it, swirled her tongue around it and speared the sensitive hole at the end, her cheeks ballooning and hollowing all the while and her head bobbing rapidly with the effort. I couldn't help thinking, that these were all the actions of a street prostitute, and my mind shuttled between the images of Magdalena as serene Madonna of the *passagiata*'s gentle progress, in her black mourning dress, and the head bobbing up and down below me with such whorish animation. Of course it was an unfair juxtaposition to have made, but it made the excitement all the more intense, and I could feel myself approaching a point of no return.

"I'm going to come soon," I grunted, more in warning than anything else.

Her mouth was too busy for an answer, and she merely rolled her eyes sarcastically as if to say "I would never have guessed!" then gave my bottom a slap of encouragement with her free hand.

When I came it took us both by surprise. Neither of us were expecting the force of my ejaculation ("It was like a fireman's hose," she said later), nor its abundance: she swallowed several times then gave up, letting it cascade over her lower lip and chin in a milky dribble.

Later, she removed her clothes too, and rode me until she cried out again, the

sound of her cries making a little echo, so she became self-conscious and gently bit my shoulder instead.

We lay there, naked, talking, until the air became too cool for comfort. As I made to pick up my clothes I glanced up and saw three small heads silhouetted at the top of the gorge.

By the time Magdalena lifted her head to see what I was looking at they had vanished. As we set off on our downward climb I thought to myself, "Mine may be a disappearing island, but at least it has its traditions."

Nicky fell silent and we all wanted to know what had happened next. Had the beautiful Magdalena returned to her previous profession? Or had Nicky married her and even now she was eagerly awaiting his return with a child on her hip? But the Sea Captain sensed that these questions may have been unwelcome so he just said, "Yes, traditions . . . which reminds me . . ." and he started on another story of his own.

SAN SEBASTIAN

Justine Dubois

Justine Dubois is a Parisian, who has lived most of her life in London. She trained as a painter, which explains some of the visual intensity in her writing. She reads widely, and has travelled adventurously. For all her career she has been involved in the Arts, and is now writing full-length fiction. Her favourite place in London is Kensington Gardens; her two favourite places in all the world: Venice, and Jailsamer in Rajasthan.

It is half past five in the morning. The sky is a haze of half grey. Under a canopy of wrought iron the fish market is setting up. The street shutters are painted blue and orange. He is tall and she only a little less so. His dark hair is slicked back from his forehead, above eyes that are cool and grey. His wide mouth, whose smile spells sensuality, is down-turned in disappointment. She dances at his heels. They pass another couple quarrelling. There's something familiar in the shape of the other man's head, distracting him momentarily.

"It seems as though the whole world is quarrelling today," he sighs. "Not just us."

"Can't you understand that I am too tired to climb some damned mountain at five in the morning," she says shrilly, "just in the hope of seeing an exceptional sunrise?" He looks at her with a frown, shocked, as always, by the philistine in her. But she doesn't notice.

"You always were impossible, and selfish," she continues. "Yesterday, we walked all round Madrid in the midday heat, which was your idea. We stood up all night on the train without a seat, and now you want to go for a walk, rather than find our hotel?" The look in her eyes is close to hatred.

"But it is almost dawn and still cool enough to climb," he pleads gently. "The view of the town and the bay will be breathtaking. God knows, we only have one night here. And you can rest as much as you want later on. By this time tomorrow morning we will be back on the train. And it could be years before we return."

He scans her face for some sign of relenting good humour.

"Couldn't you just make the effort?" But she is closed off. The fishermen and traders watch them knowingly, warily. The fish pass through their flat, bronzed hands in flashes of colour, the turquoise of a fin, the rose-pink underside of an octopus. Bouffant heads of carnations form mini hedgerows, dividing the stalls and their produce.

This is a different aesthetic, he thinks to himself, this is Lorca country. The land where hatred and beauty and love form an eternal triangle. "Perhaps it is

fitting for us to quarrel against such a backdrop of emotion and colour," he says.

"How pretentious," she says.

He glances down at his wife's tight features. She is almost unrecognizable. He abandons the argument. "I'll go on my own," he says, trying to conceal his disappointment; he feels that touristic pleasures ought to be shared.

"Which would you prefer," he asks, resorting to chivalry, "to go and find the hotel now on your own? It is too early to check in. Our room won't be vacant until midday, but we could leave the luggage there. Or shall we find a café where you can wait for me, have some breakfast, a *tortilla jamon*?"

She looks up at his handsome head, all its charm dissipated in strain. His eyes are pale, too pale, no feeling animates them. His formality and politeness are a bad sign.

"How long will you be?" she says. He glances away. He can just make out the distant silhouette of the statue of Christ on Monte Urgull, one arm outstretched in benediction. "Difficult to say exactly."

The early-morning heat is still burning off the moisture from the night before. There is a haze in the air. Distances are deceptive. "One hour, two at the most," he hazards.

"You always were a bore," she says. He looks at her coolly, assessing her in terms of distances too.

"Maybe," he replies uncertainly. He is hurt and attempts to explain. "This is something I have always dreamed of doing."

She shrugs. "Very well. Let's find a café. I'll wait for you there and then go to the hotel if I get fed up."

"Won't you change your mind and come with me?" he says, his mood softening.

"No chance. I don't know how you even dare ask after the night we've spent." He tries to smile. Perhaps she is right? Maybe his demands are too many? His stamina is greater than hers. He frowns, but guilt does not sit easily with him.

They choose a café on a street corner midway between the fish market and the near end of the bay. Its chairs are made of glossy wicker, interwoven with strands of bright red and green. The tables are fat, menthol-green circles of glass. She sits down, fussily trying to arrange her luggage around her. The waiter appears, his body like a toreador's, his features immune to charm.

"Are you going to stay and have a coffee with me first?" she says hopefully.

"No, I want to catch the dawn light over the bay." He glances impatiently at his watch and looks towards the statue, just visible now in the distance above the mist. "No time to lose."

"Very well." She orders herself coffee and croissants, a *tortilla jamon* and a small glass of Spanish brandy. He raises his eyebrows.

"You had better go," she says. He turns on his heels. It occurs to him to plant a kiss on her face, but her expression forbids it.

As he turns to leave, he again half registers the back view of the man sitting alone at another table. Was it he and his girlfriend who had also been quarrelling in the fish market? Perhaps they were on the same train? He glances back once more at his wife and then moves on swiftly. He feels guilty, like

a recalcitrant schoolboy who has insisted on his own way. But, as he turns away from the café, his mood begins to improve. He begins to breathe freely again. Two more turnings and he is on the Passeo Nuevo, the wide promenade that almost encircles Monte Urgull and opens on to the Atlantic and La Concha, a superb long curve of bay lined by elegant Edwardian hotels and gardens. His destination is the sculpture of Christ, which stands high above one end.

He walks at an even pace. The sea is still grey with the remnants of the night. The path ahead of him begins to climb, imperceptibly at first. Then, suddenly, he is above the bay, higher up than he anticipated. The walk is part woodland, part shrubbery. He climbs further. The path zigzags from shelf to shelf of terraces. The land has the luxuriant quality of green, uncultivated gardens. Halfway up, he pauses to catch his breath and look back at the view. Now that he is alone, he begins to feel exhilarated.

He feels intoxicatingly free, as though only this minute and this view and this exquisite feeling count. He senses all the possibilities of freedom, of hope; also the senselessness of shackled love. He begins to feel at one with nature.

He stops briefly to light a Gitane, its heady perfume mixing with the bougainvillea and the salt from the Atlantic. As he smokes the cigarette he takes a battered book from his pocket and reads a scrap of poetry by Lorca. By now he has lost all sense of time. His wife and her discomfort have disappeared.

Within the dark eyes of the Nun
Two horsemen gallop . . .

He shuts the book and starts to climb the final stage. Suddenly, towering above his head, is the statue of Christ, welcoming him.

The girl is sitting at the base of the sculpture, as if waiting for him. Her smooth dark hair moves as a single, well-cut shape about the delicate features of her face. She is dressed simply in white skirt and blouse. She looks out greedily over the bay, anxious not to miss the first bright slivers of sunshine. He guesses she is American. She turns her head towards him and smiles.

"I have been watching you climb, saw you stop to read. I thought you might get here too late."

He half apologizes. "I expected to be alone." He laughs thoughtfully. "So, I expect, did you." He sits down next to her.

"I have seen you before," she says. He scans her features. She is beautiful, delicate, with a body as agile as a cat's. A distant glow in the sky; it is getting lighter. "I am ashamed to say that I don't remember."

"You are reading Lorca," she says, surprise in her blue eyes.

Under the blaze of twenty suns
How steep a level plain inclines.

She takes the book from his hand. The first piercing rays of sunshine, pink and gold, appear over the bay. They both fall still, spellbound. As he turns towards her, her features are suffused with the pink light of the sun. They glance at one

another, with a cold hard light of recognition and then they look away. They refocus on conversation.

The book falls from her lap and they both scrabble to retrieve it. In the dust at their feet their hands meet; a quicksilver electricity has run between them. They look at one another in surprise.

"I was quarrelling too," she says. They sit back, seeking some equilibrium. They both feel sharpened by their respective quarrels, both wracked with emotion. The sun is warm on their faces. Around them the light begins to dapple the trees.

The sunshine plays a game of chess
Over her lattice with the trees.

It travels across the cold stone of the statue. They look outwards, tension in their arms, and turn towards one another at the same moment. Afterwards, he cannot remember thinking of kissing her. Yet her lips beneath his are soft and sweet. Her body folds, yielding and urgent, within the circle of his. As his arms engulf her, he feels the narrow, bird-like cage of her diaphragm, feels her rapid heartbeat. Her skin has the dry, burnt musky perfume of sea and sun. They exchange one last glance of recognition, before closing their eyes against the piercing sun.

His hands slip over her, laying her bare on the stone, teasing and spreading her body. She picks shyly at the buttons of his shirt, at the buckle of his trousers. It is her last positive act before he invades her. As he enters her, her legs curl around him. His muffled kisses sweep her breasts, her neck, her mouth. He tastes her skin. She judders in his arms; sweet abandon. He still does not ask her name. Beneath his caresses, she softens.

He pulls her upright in his arms to sit on his lap. Her legs tighten around his waist. The figure of Christ looks down on them in blessing. They move in unison, excitement building. Almost, almost . . . And then he pulls back, and props her in front of the statue, her naked back on the cool stone. She is now a rag doll. His whole body overwhelms her; a threshold of pain, and then twin cries. He falls in love with her. He feels his old life fall from him, like a useless garment. He rocks her in his arms, stroking her hair, kissing her lips and neck, teaching her true ownership. She is pliant, exhausted and joyous. She smiles up at him, a strange familiarity with the unknown.

Hand in hand they walk back to the bay and go, fully dressed, straight into the sea to swim together. By now the sun is hot. As they emerge, their light cotton clothes dry on them. They walk back towards the café. They have both decided to be brave, to explain.

His wife is no longer sitting alone. The man at her table rises to greet him. "Hello, my friend, I thought I recognized you earlier. It must be years since we last met, since I left for America." He turns to the dark-haired girl at his friend's side. "Oh good, I see you have already met my fiancée. How was the view, darling?"

His wife also smiles up at him, no longer ill-tempered. "Was it wonderful . . . ?" she begins enthusiastically, but the question dies in her throat.

TORN LACE

Justine Dubois

Justine Dubois is a Parisian, who has lived most of her life in London. She trained as a painter, which explains some of the visual intensity in her writing. She reads widely, and has travelled adventurously. For all her career she has been involved in the Arts, and is now writing full-length fiction. Her favourite place in London is Kensington Gardens; her two favourite places in all the world: Venice, and Jailsamer in Rajasthan.

There is something gentle about him. He is like a giant sleeping panda. They are both good at sleep, he better at it than she. She leans over him, tucking him in, as though he were a baby. He snuffles contentedly, caught half way between the softness of the duvet and consciousness. He emits sweet smells of lavender, mixed with his own shadowy musk.

She pulls open the curtains and there, framed pictorially in the distance, is the mainland, its coastline of torn lace dazzled by the heave and height of waves formation-dancing towards her. The green land runs low in the picture frame, like ill-pegged tarpaulin sheets, haphazardly dotted with bright white Monopoly-piece houses, local excuses for architectural design and shameful apologies for the crofters' cottages on which they are based. Nothing that is man-made in this landscape is any match for the drama of sea and sky.

Their visitors left yesterday. They are now alone on the island. She wonders if he is afraid. He is not physically brave. His placidity can easily turn to anxiety. From beneath their windows, soft bleatings fade on the buffeting winds; a row of goats congregate in disciplined, follow-my-leader line, their sweet muzzle faces looking peacefully out to sea, as if they silently anticipate something. The sky is streaked with red, "Shepherd's warning"; the calm before the storm.

She turns to find him watching her, his eyes shiny with dark pleasure, against the planes of his handsome, sombre face. They have long dispensed with speech, except in moments when they set out to converse with one another in graceful minuets of shared opinion. For the rest, they rely more precisely on demeanour and bearing, on shared glances. His features are fundamentally impassive. Nevertheless, he has a repertoire of twenty or so inflected faces and she has learned to decipher them all, to read them and say nothing. She knows that he also studies her, keeping his thoughts to himself.

The moment when he first detected her adultery had passed her by. Yet, he had never complained. Was it at the time, three years earlier? She knows him too well. He would simply have accepted her infidelity as a gift of freedom, as a waiving of responsibility that would allow him a platform from which to do

whatever he chose, so long as the status quo prevailed unchallenged. He does not want to lose her, loves her still in his own silent way, loves her more than before perhaps, respectful of her bid for independence. The only outer sign of his perception, the way that she knows he knows, is his new habit of washing himself, soap and warm water, immediately after they make love. And even this habit would remain his secret, if it were not for the way, each time, he instinctively misplaces the soap, left like a fish out of its dish, stranded and guilty on the expanse of bleached ceramic.

Setting had always been an important clue to deciphering him. She remembers the early days, when her love for him was raw and tinged with desperation. She would go out before breakfast to get the Sunday papers, a brief span of minutes, but by the time she returned the phone would be reversed in its cradle (the cord spiralling from the top and not the bottom of its oval shape). At the end of the month when the phone bill arrived, it would be clouded by details of long-distance calls to numbers she neither recognized, nor dared ring. In those days recognition had made her unhappy. Now, her watchfulness is only designed to protect the fine surfaces between them. She knows that these surfaces, strong and elastic as they are, nevertheless camouflage potential chaos.

In her mind, she conjures her lover, temporarily left behind in London. How different he is from the sleeping panda; a man more becoming, more graceful. Yet, she loves them both. Nothing in one overlaps the other. They represent sweet difference, neither better nor worse.

She has ceased to ask questions. She knows that if she is patient the brown eyes and twenty faces will tell her everything. At the moment of her infidelity, her love for him had still been undiluted. Her decision to be unfaithful had been both inspired and calculated. Yet, she had never regretted it.

He sits up in bed, suddenly alert, his attention caught by a distant sail. "Someone is making for the island." She glances behind her. "Are you sure?" He nods. "But we are not expecting anyone." He shrugs. "Day trippers, maybe." In spite of his shrug, she registers his anxiety. The panda in him disappears to be replaced by a bear, a brown grizzly bear, baleful and potentially angry. He gets dressed, not bothering to shower.

In spite of the windswept beauty of the island, he dresses formally in jacket, shirt and tie and grey flannel trousers. He can scarcely conceive of casualness. He vacillates always between formality and abandon; nothing in between. One of his many faces tells her that he is troubled, cross. Five minutes earlier his brown eyes had been benignly appraising. Now they are hard and introspective, his face fierce with the emotion of conflict. She recognizes it as the face that heralds anger at his own miscalculation, and for which she will certainly be blamed. It is as though he has perceived a danger that she has not yet had the wit to anticipate.

The boat draws nearer, no longer skimming the tall waves, the distant sound of its throttle dying against the wind. The man who manoeuvres it, a local fisherman, throws a rope and then lends a sturdy hand to a figure who steps out daintily, clad in camel-coloured layers. He helps her on to the landing stage.

The brown bear, without glancing back, shuts the door spitefully behind him. Gingerly, he negotiates the downwards slippery path to the jetty to meet the intruder. Through their bedroom window she watches his progress as the wind

raises the flaps of his jacket playfully like a skirt. She sees their visitor throw her arms around his neck and kiss him on the mouth, watches as he glances back guiltily towards herself and the window before submitting to the embrace. Swiftly, she removes herself to one side, shielding him from having seen her observe him from behind the curtain. His arms are now around the woman's waist. He looks happy, his face full of smiles. Arms linked, they retrace his steps along the turf-clotted path, half slipping, half stumbling in their progress.

They bypass the little bedroom annex where she waits and go next door to the main dwelling, where the kitchen and sitting room are. Ten minutes elapse in silence. Still, he does not come to explain. She studies herself in the mirror. She looks pale, her delicate features drawn as if with white ink on pale parchment. Her hair is a frizz of disarray. But it is her eyes which surprise her most. They are soft, melting with anguish, hooded in blemishes of shadow. She averts her gaze, showers and gets dressed, does her makeup slowly, carefully, sweeping the parchment of her skin with skilful washes of colour. Unlike him, she is dressed in country clothes: jeans, boots and a ruggedly knit jumper that extends its clever, grey cable design almost to her knees. She creates a chignon of her windswept hair, which has responded to the spray from the wind and sea by twisting into ringlets at the nape of her neck.

She thinks of her lover, of his graceful moments of love and love-making, of the sustenance of energy and good reason he delivers her. How she wishes he were here now. She senses a battle. These are the moments of intense loneliness between herself and the panda man, moments when emotional cruelty is delivered casually and the leviathan chaos threatens to engulf all sensibility between them.

Ready now, she sits down to wait. The door opens behind her. No explanation. "Can you come and make us some breakfast?"; a demand made cursorily. Obediently, she follows him across the brief courtyard leading to the main house. The sky is no longer streaked with pink, but iron grey. The fisherman who delivered their visitor is now departed, almost lost to view on the horizon.

The kitchen is still warm from its log fire from the night before. As they step together into its warm hug of pine furniture, red floor tiles and exposed beams, the room is empty, except for the discarded camel coat. She looks at him questioningly. "Our guest is in the bathroom. She is an old friend of mine. I have known her for twenty years. We met up the other day in New York." No further explanation. "She prefers coffee to tea." His face is still one of conflict, as if exasperated with her for his own miscalculation of human nature that must surely soon reveal itself. Yet he still postpones the moment, saying nothing, playing with his cuff links, fashioned as miniature clock faces, each set to a different time zone.

In this moment she hates him, as he also detests her. It is the moment of discovery, when living on the edge is no longer fun, when all their subtle truths are threatened by the baldness of exposure and ridicule.

A blonde figure, dressed in expensive cashmere trousers and a cream silk blouse, overlaid with numerous gold chains of various weights and links, emerges immaculate from the bathroom. She has clearly redone both her hair and makeup. "Hiii." Her voice betrays a lilt of Australian, over which has been lisped an attempt at the straighter vowels proper to English. The result is a sort

of sing-song. Her handshake is fish-dab limp, vaguely repellent, no communication at all. "Will you have coffee?" her hostess enquires graciously.

"Sure, whatever." The blonde woman turns to the man and sits close by him at the table. She takes his hand in hers. "It's so great to see you," sung high note. "Didn't we have fun last week in New York?" He grunts and half smiles in reply, looking both pleased and wary.

She kisses him on the cheek and stretches her hand to his neck, proprietorially picking pieces of lint from his weather-beaten jacket. Caressingly, she feels his cheeks with the back of her hand. "You need a shave, darling." She glances back at her hostess. "How long have you worked for Peter?"

As the blonde woman turns her face towards her, she has the opportunity to assess it. For one moment, neither speaking, nor moving, but perfectly still, the woman's face is exquisitely lovely, with pale eyes glancing from a delicately made-up face, the blonde helmet of hair smoothly coiffed into an ideally shaped frame for her face. She has all the immaculate polish of a German beauty. And then something extraordinary occurs. Incapable of remaining still, the woman turns back to the man and begins to speak and, in that moment, the division between the image that she has fashioned of herself in the mirror and that of her true personality occurs like a fissure. The serenity and beauty of her mirror stillness is destroyed by the vulgar immediacy of her movements and speech.

Still busy making the coffee, her hostess turns involuntarily towards the man, hoping he will answer the woman's question for her. "How long have I worked for you, Peter?" She glances at him quizzically. He says nothing. "I am his wife," she replies gently. But the woman appears not to hear. "After breakfast, you must show me round the island, Peter, just the two of us. There is so much to discuss." She begins to talk of mutual friends, pals from the past, whom her hostess has never met. Her husband's response, other than a quick smile, is lost in devouring a bowl of cornflakes. As all three eat breakfast, the blonde woman continues to stroke her host's hand.

Her conversation becomes more intimate. She is the mistress of double entendre.

Every innocent remark strikes her as potential for sexual innuendo, which she repeats and emphasizes like a mantra, laughing as she goes. Peter inadvertently chooses the word "action" to describe the mechanism of their new boat and the woman hoots with laughter and repeats the word breathlessly, spluttering that she is sure that it is not the only kind of "action" he had in mind.

She pours her husband a second coffee, considering her remarks coolly. She is not fooled. She knows that no woman in the habit of making love would ever pounce on such a pun, that these are the conversational patterns of a woman starved of sex and love. She remembers noticing once before that the more garrulous women are, the more obvious their celibacy, as though for them the food of emotion must be drained from chatter. She begins to relax. She looks her husband in the eye. His eyes now meet hers in naughty merriment. She thinks of the woman, whose death had inspired her own infidelity, remembers her realization as she had watched her slow transition from life to death that nothing is ever worth assuming. It was then that she had found the strength to accept her handsome lover's gifts of love. Her husband, much as she loved him, had not been

worthy of the exclusiveness of her love. She had seen it then and sees it again now, quite clearly.

She gets to her feet, suddenly resolved. The chaos is upon them and it is up to her to control it. "I think I'll take the boat and go to the mainland," she announces. Her husband glances out of the window. "It is too dangerous. A storm is coming." "The storm is already here," she replies. He looks up at her disconcertedly. From her vantage height she sees that the heavily ringed, manicured hand of their guest now rests below the table on his upper thigh, her knees nudging his. He does not seem to object. She picks up the keys of their boat, a rubberized, high-powered dingy, capable of skimming the highest of waves.

The woman does not even glance up at her departure. It is only her husband who looks anxious, trying to detain her. But she is determined. She knows that his acts of infidelity that night, whether actual or merely flirtatious, will be less fun without herself as silent witness. When she gets to the mainland, she will phone to explain that the storm prevents her return, arrange for someone else to return their boat. And then she will fly back to London to spend the night in the arms of her lover.

She reflects, calculatingly. She knows that the blonde Australian will consider that she has triumphed. She also knows the reverse to be true. She sighs, almost feeling sorry for her. Perhaps, the freedom that she and her husband had created in their marriage was a liability of misunderstanding for others. How could the blonde woman guess that she and her panda husband would again exist happily together in their corrupt consciousness, maybe for many years to come?

As she closes the door behind her, she catches one last glance from her husband. The conflict has disappeared. His face beams upon her with love and joy as he relaxes, yet again, into the fluid mud of marital understanding. She smiles to herself. How very kind of him to continually present her with sufficient reason to love him, whilst never ever feeling guilty about betraying him. It is a gift far greater . . . than anyone might imagine.

GLUTTONY

Rebecca Chance

Rebecca Chance is the name under which Lauren Henderson now writes *Sunday Times* bestselling glamorous thrillers. Born in London, she read English literature at Cambridge, then worked as a journalist for newspapers and music magazines before moving to Tuscany and then Manhattan to write mysteries, chick lit and the non-fiction book *Jane Austen's Guide To Dating*. She has been described in the press as both the Dorothy Parker and the Betty Boop of the British crime novel. She writes for many UK-based publications and national newspapers and has also contributed short stories to several anthologies. Together with Stella Duffy, she edited the anthology *Tart Noir*, a collection of crime stories by leading female mystery writers. Her books have been translated into over twenty languages. She can be found on social media as @msrebeccachance on both Twitter and Instagram, and as Rebecca Chance Author on Facebook.

He's a box of chocolates: his clothes are just wrappings I rip off impatiently and throw on the floor.

There's a tale, from *Morte d'Arthur*, I think, about a knight who wins a contest of strength and courage and is rewarded with the hand of a fair lady.

The only catch is that the fair lady is under a spell, doomed to turn every day into an ugly, graceless hag. The knight is given a choice. He can have her beautiful by day and be envied by all, but a hag when he is alone with her: or he can have the beauty for his eyes only and be mocked by others for being married to an awful old bag.

I almost feel like that with him. No-one knows but I how beautiful he is under his awful clothes. Every time I unwrap him, he's the best present I ever received.

His skin is like milk, his arms thick twists of rope under velvet, his arse tight and firm, buttocks round and full as cherries. He moves like a wrestler, light on his feet, his shoulders rolling forward, his hips narrow and loose. I want to braid his hair into a rope and climb up it as if he were a tower I needed to conquer. He's always hard when I want him. Always.

His cock fills me so tightly my vibrator's a disappointment by contrast. I could lie and sculpt his pectorals with the palm of my hand for hours. I would, if he didn't complain that it tickles. Sometimes I turn him over and massage him from head to toe, digging my fingers as best I can into the tough weave of muscles along his back. I stand over him and dip one heel into the back of his thigh, pressing down into it with my whole weight, because I'm not nearly strong enough to

make any impact on it with my fingers alone. I take his feet into my hands and work each toe gently, knead the soles with my knuckles, sink my thumbs into the softness below the ball, tenderising him a little. And then I make him turn onto his back again and work my way up the soft skin of his inner thighs, trailing my nails up them till his impatient cock jerks up still further into the air.

I kneel over him and rub myself against him, teasing him while I massage his face, smooth out his forehead, pinch lightly along his eyebrows, roll his earlobes between the pads of my fingers, pretending that I'm calming him down while I can feel beneath me how erect he is, how much he wants me.

He's so hard I don't even need to reach down and guide him in. He does that all by himself. And then I'm full, completely full. His arms around me, his cock rocking away inside me, pulling out so I can feel how much I want him, driving back in to plug me up again, fill me to the brim. Even when I'm desperate for him to come, even when I feel I can't take any more, I know that a few minutes afterwards I will want him all over again. He's better than a box of chocolates; I can glut myself on him and never feel sick or guilty. He's my sugar rush. His sperm tastes as delicate as sweet almond paste and his sweat rolls over me like salt water. I lick it out of the hollows of his neck as he fucks me. Bite into the caps of muscle on his shoulders. I want to drown in him.

Only when we're making love do his eyes really look into mine; the rest of the time he's wary, cautious, almost afraid of me. He has never learnt to trust a lover and he won't let me teach him. I will never really have him.

COMING SWIMMINGLY

Roger Moineau

Roger Moineau fiercely protects his or her true identity: this is the pseudonym for an author who occasionally wrote for Erotic Review Books; he (or she) wrote *The Illustrated Book of Dominatrices* (2003), and is no stranger to the world of male sexual humiliation – though whether as 'she' who does the humiliating or, indeed, as the 'he' humiliated, remains a closely guarded secret.

"Duval, I don't believe you've listened to a word I've been saying for the last two hours!"

Sara, at the wheel, looked over quickly in his direction. With her driving Goldie, Duval enjoyed the novel sensation of being the passenger in his own vehicle as they made the long journey southwards. This had been their first real holiday, even though a brief one. Now he replayed in his mind the high points: wandering the immediate vicinity of the loch, visiting a ruined castle and, overwhelmingly, the time spent making love in the chalet.

A considerable part of the time, on reflection. They had never got around to climbing a particular peak from which there would undoubtedly have been a stunning view. They had been exactly like the honeymoon couple in the joke book. And now he was again ignoring his surroundings as they wound their way through some of the most glorious scenery in the world.

"Well?" Sara insisted. "You look as if you're still in a kind of dream."

"Nightmare's more like it. For one moment there I thought I was stuck in a car with Cherie. That's just the kind of thing she used to bark at me."

"You really say the sweetest things. You looked quite blissful to me, darling, but I'd rather not hear exactly what was occupying your waking dream. I might get a nasty surprise. How about you doing some driving after lunch and then I can sit back and drink in the majestic Highlands?"

"Choose the spot. Just look at that view, darling. Let's stop around here." The fresh haze of the early morning had been swept away by a gentle breeze and the sky was now a cloudless blue. Through a gap in the trees they had a new panorama of the loch. This time the hills were gently sloping and the far shore was near enough to make out some small white farmhouses.

"Here's a passing space. You're not supposed to park but it's a big one. And it's shady. This should do nicely for a picnic spot."

She stopped the car and turned off the engine. "You get the lunch out of the back and do a search. I'm off for a swim."

"Another one? You were in the water before breakfast and I thought you said it was freezing."

"Ah, but now I'm hot again. All that driving, you see," she countered, grabbing a towel that had been drying on the back seat. "And anyway this will be quite different." She headed down to the shore without further explanation.

By the time Duval had found a suitable tree stump and unpacked the sandwiches provided by the hotel, Sara was swimming strongly several metres out. She called to him, but Duval was no swimmer as she knew. He came down to the shoreline in bare feet and went in as far as his ankles. He noticed her towel and blue denim dress lying nearby. She was coming to shore so he picked up the towel which was already hot from lying in the sun.

It was then he noticed her pale green bra-top. He had assumed that she had been wearing a swimsuit under the denim dress, but now it appeared not. She was walking through the knee-deep water dressed only in panties, her arms crossed over bare breasts, like some goddess from Greek mythology.

A smile of entreaty for the towel made Duval tease her by whipping it away as she stretched out for it. Although the road was screened by a belt of beechwood there was a chance that a passing vehicle could for a few vital seconds catch an uninterrupted view of the shore.

"Duval, quit fooling about and give me that towel or I'll throw you in the water."

"Just try it, tough gal! Drop your knickers and I'll swap you them for the towel. Do we have a deal or do we not?"

"You pig!" For a few seconds she strained her ears to hear if there was a car coming, at the same time wringing the water from the ends of her honey mane which was now in rats' tails.

Giving him a performance, Sara turned round and waggled her well-rounded bottom in his direction. Then she eased down the pink briefs which rolled up into a tight string as she tugged them past her knees. Whirling the wet item around her head, she turned round to face him. Then she came out of the water without the slightest attempt at modesty, looking him right in the eye.

Before she reached him she tossed the panties in his face and grabbed the towel. She rubbed herself down vigorously before putting on the halter top and then the backless denim dress which buttoned up the front. She kept eye contact with Duval while dressing. She was shivering slightly. He felt himself going hard.

"Wring those out and put them out to dry in the sun. I'll need to get a fresh pair from my case."

"But not until after you have taken lunch, my lady." Duval gestured towards the tree stump with a groundsheet spread on the grass slope nearby. She sat with her legs tucked under her and helped herself. He passed her a can of fruit juice and she ate and drank voraciously for a few minutes.

Feeling the warmth of the sun Duval stripped off his shirt. He might as well add the final touches to quite a decent tan he had picked up in the last three days. He unzipped his slacks and stepped out of them before helping himself to a smoked salmon sandwich. He heard Sara's soft wolf whistle as he reclined at her knees.

"Lucky you're wearing boxer shorts! So long as nothing gets hard," she commented tartly with her mouth half full.

"Now why should that happen?" He looked up at her.

Sara opened her eyes wide in a show of innocent surprise. Then she loosed the bottom two buttons of the denim dress, pointedly looking at his crotch area.

"Nothing to report," he commented, looking there also.

Her hand moved to the top two buttons. Then she slipped the dress off her shoulders so that it lay around her thighs. From the road it would look as if she were demurely sitting in a halter top and shorts.

She reached languidly for another sandwich. "Still nothing?"

"Not really. Not worth writing home about anyway."

She shifted her position and parted her thighs slightly.

"Prove it."

"What here?"

"Why not? Surely you're not ashamed of displaying those manly assets to the world." She smiled knowingly.

"As far as I know the laws in Scotland relating to indecent exposure are much the same as in England. I don't fancy being hauled up before the magistrate."

"Chicken! It's your turn!" Sara accused, pulling her dress back on, re-buttoning it and standing up. "Have you finished the last sandwich? Typical."

Duval stood up as she tugged at the groundsheet and the towel. He was in two minds about this. He suspected she was bluffing and just wanted him to come on more strongly. Could she really want him to stand naked before her? Or was she pushing him into it to confirm some suspicion she had about his sexuality?

"Well?" She was looking him right in the eye. "Are we shy, Mary Ellen?"

He took a deep breath and eased the shorts down over his semi erect shaft which seemed to take on new life once out in the open. He hesitated with them half way down his thighs and then realised he looked ridiculous.

"All the way. And hand them over."

Duval did so, resisting an instinct to cover himself. "Now what? Are you satisfied?"

"Not really. I'm sure if you try just a little bit harder you would, well, get just a little bit harder."

To his horror he heard the faint sound of a motor. So did Sara. She bobbed down, swept up his shirt and trousers, and skipped away towards the road. "I'll see you back at the car. Don't forget to bring my briefs," she called over her shoulder.

He was caught without a stitch. He started to run after her but she saw him and darted away with a shriek of laughter. He cursed as the sound of the approaching motor became unmistakeable. Her pink panties were all that remained. He squatted down quickly on the grass as the car drew level, making himself as small a target as possible. He almost prayed for it to go on. It seemed to slow but didn't stop.

A blessed silence, but his relief was short lived as he heard the sound of his car starting up. Damn! She still had the keys.

He called out in panic. His erection had completely subsided. There was only one thing for it. He stepped into the panties and pulled the damp garment up as far as it would go. It hardly covered him but he couldn't care. He heard the car pulling away.

Slipping his shoes on he tore through the beechwood, collecting several painful scratches on his legs. He could see the rear end of Goldie several metres up the road and he began chasing after it screaming in indignation. To his relief the brake lights came on and then the reversing lights. Sara swept past him smiling sweetly over her shoulder and backed into the passing place. He cursed again. What further tricks did she have up her sleeve?

She wound down the passenger window a crack.

"Did you bring my pants with you?"

"Of course I did. You can see them!"

"Mm, very fetching. Well, if that's you fully dressed, you'd better get in. Otherwise I could hand you out your clothes?"

"No, I'll get in like this. I don't trust you when you're behind the wheel and I'm out here."

She let him in but killed the engine immediately. He reached over to the back for his shorts but stopped as he felt her hand firmly outlining his crotch. He slumped back into his seat as a preliminary wave of pleasure swept over him.

She leant over him and whispered into his ear. "I think these are just a little too tight, so let's have them off." He could not resist.

Resistance was at an even lower ebb as he was taken in her mouth, at first just over the glans but then she sucked him in deeper. He half closed his eyes as he prepared for a journey towards physical ecstasy. The hot sun, dappled by the branches overhead, poured in through the sunroof.

"Lower the seat back, darling. I want to make love to you."

He did so and was reminded of Myra. Now he didn't feel the same guilt, only a sense of justice that he should be sharing something of her experience. He heard a tearing sound and Sara dangled an unwrapped condom above his nose. But when he reached for it she whipped it away.

"Knees up!"

"Pardon?"

"I'm going to make love to you." She bent down and kissed him deeply, pressing her tongue into his mouth. At the same time she reached down and pulled his legs up into an upright position.

She sat up again and massaged his shaft with her left hand but her right was somewhere else. He felt a tickling and then a slow burning at his anal cleft as she inserted two fingers cloaked in the condom. It felt cold and then burned.

"Now, darling, just relax. I think you will enjoy this. And it will help you to get in touch with your feminine side. Just feel me entering you and try to imagine how a woman feels when she is making love."

"No, Sara!"

He tried to take her hand away, but she firmly raised his arm above his head, pumping him slightly harder with her two active fingers. He groaned and felt his sphincter relaxing as she penetrated a few millimetres deeper. It was a sensation that was so novel he didn't know how to respond. At one level Duval was under

attack but on another he knew he was being taken on a seriously circuitous route to a final and cataclysmic orgasm.

Sara took his other hand and moved it up to his crotch. Putting it over his she encouraged him to masturbate himself vigorously, squeezing his bulging glans and spreading the seeping fluid all the way back down his shaft. Her probing fingers below picked up his rhythm. As she slid further in with more aggressive strokes he felt her thumb nail flick his tightly suspended balls.

"Relax, darling. I want to see you really come. This is exciting for me too." He groaned as the numbness of release inexorably approached.

Another car drew close and then crept past with a friendly toot on the horn. Sara looked up, cursed softly, withdrew her fingers from his anus, leaving the condom in place, and waved briefly in response. Immediately she re-entered him and returned to her vigorous penetration, this time spreading his thighs as wide apart as they would go in the confined space.

He frigged himself with an increasing frenzy as he felt the moment of release was imminent. Her fingers must now be in him as far as they would go, making a slow-burning fire as she twisted them first one way then the other. With her thumb she put a slight pressure on each testicle in turn.

He came with a force that was like nothing he had previously experienced. His hand fell away from his penis as it continued to pump bursts as high as his chest. Both arms were above his head in an unconscious gesture of surrender. She gently massaged the last spasms from his spent shaft. Only then did she withdraw from his anal passage, giving him one final moment of raw sensation. She folded the condom in on itself and dropped it out of the window.

Sara bent over to rub the jism into his chest and belly then bent down to kiss him on the forehead. "Next time," she breathed, "do that inside me and you'll have a better idea what I'm feeling."

THE PERFECT ITALIAN WIFE

Alessandra Rivalta

Alessandra Rivalta is originally from Italy but moved to London when she turned eighteen, attracted by the vibrant, multicultural big city. She has a deep love for good food, and in her spare time she enjoys scoping the city for little and unknown restaurants, delicatessens and peculiar fast foods. Her adventurous spirit and trusted backpack have accompanied her on many trips around the globe, where she prefers to travel alone in order to connect with the local people and culture. She is a good cook and likes to experiment, in her stories as much as in her kitchen.

I'm sitting in the hospital lobby, waiting for them to come out and call me. It's packed: everywhere you look, pregnant women sit by themselves, with their partner, with other children clinging to their knees and crying for attention. Some of their faces are happy, some tired and worn out by one too many sleepless nights, some are reading baby parenting books like they hold more truth than the Bible. The high-pitched squeals do nothing to soothe my nerves: my eyes keep darting to the ultrasound room door. I just wish I could tell them all to shut up and be quiet, but somehow I don't think that would go down too well with the hormone-crazed women sharing the room with me. So I just slouch a little in my plastic chair and go back to staring at the door.

The church is beautifully decorated, white satin ribbons flowing in the summer breeze from the open door, people coming in and filling the places on the benches and chatting vivaciously. I look at the groom next to the altar, handsome in his dark blue tux with a white tie, and such a happy look in his brown eyes he seems to light up the entire church. He catches my glance and nods: we're ready. I take my cue and walk briskly to the back room where the bride is waiting.

"Carolina, everybody's here. Are you ready?"

From where she sits at the mirror, her excited blue eyes meet mine and she smiles. She looks so much like me, we could be twins, but my eyes are green and she's my baby sister, getting married today.

"Sure Toni, just help me with this veil, will you? You've got the flowers, right?" I laugh at her anxious tone and nod. "Great. You're the most amazing maid of honour ever, I swear. You'll be an amazing bride, too."

I make a face.

"I'm not sure I'll live to see that day . . . Massimo is so slow! I swear if I have to drop one more hint, I might as well spell it out for him."

She's laughing hard, beautiful in her white dress, her face now covered by the exquisite lace veil, hands modestly clutching the bouquet.

"Trust me, Toni, he'll pop the question soon. Remember: they want the perfect Italian wife, devoted to the house and the children and, most of all, the husband's needs. Keep being who you are, the lovely housewife who makes his house a home, and he'd be a fool to let you go! Now, hurry, dad's waiting for us."

A hand gently shakes my shoulder.

"Antonia, darling, have you been waiting long?"

Massimo's sister looks worried. She seems so out of place in her Chanel tailleur, somehow managing to convey pity and disapproval, taking in my old jeans and paint-streaked hair.

"No, Giulia, just a few minutes. But they said it might be a while, so if you want to go for a smoke, don't worry, there's time. I'll call you if you're not here when we have to go in."

"Thanks, Toni, you're a star." She smiles, grateful for the opportunity to leave this alien environment, so filled with snotty noses, messy hair and dirty clothes. I don't even turn around to watch her go, choosing to get lost in my own head again, while I still can.

There's a letter on the table, official looking, with an embossed logo and header, on display against a bottle of Montepulciano amongst the carefully set dinnerware. I can hear the front door opening and a voice shouting "Honey, I'm home!"

"Come through, I'm just putting the lasagne in the oven. Hurry and take a shower, dinner's ready in twenty!"

Then hands are circling my waist and I turn to give him a kiss. I swat his arms away. "Go get ready: wouldn't want the food to spoil . . ."

Sitting at the table, I pour him a glass of wine as he reads the letter. I'm looking at him expectantly, waiting for his reaction.

"I don't understand, Antonia. What does this mean?" His brow is furrowed and he doesn't look too pleased. I'm confused.

"They offered me a job in one of the best practices in town. They said they're looking for someone with my background to work with bilingual children and their families. And maybe, in a few years, I could be a partner!" I'm almost squealing, but I'm too happy to care. "It's a great job, a fantastic start for my career!"

"But . . . what about the children?"

My face falls, my stomach ties in a knot and I reach for my wine.

"Max, we talked about this. You know what the doctors said . . ."

"I don't care what they said! We can find a way!" Now he looks enraged. "And you want a family, too. But how are you supposed to do that if you take a job that's going to keep you busy all the time? Don't forget, the doctors also said that stress is a huge factor, and this job has such a big responsibility you'll be stressed all the time! Did you think about that?"

"Max, please . . ." I feel the tears welling up but I refuse to cry. "They said another miscarriage might kill me. We've already lost three, I don't think I can . . . I can't do it again, Max."

"Then we can adopt. It's true that I said I didn't want to before, but now . . . if it's our only option, we'll adopt." He takes my hand, lacing our fingers together, and he kisses my palm.

"Really? You mean it, you wouldn't mind . . . ?"

"Really." He smiles at me, and I'm lost into those eyes. They're my downfall: when he stares at me like this, he can make me do whatever he wants, and I don't mind. "But, we won't get considered for adoption if you take this new job. The hours are too long, the responsibilities too big; they need to know you'll be staying home with the children, and you can't take maternity leave if you've just started in your position. I want a child, and I want it now. We're ready."

"You're right, of course. I'll call them . . ." I kiss him gently on the lips. "I'll turn them down."

Mother is furious, I can hear her screaming through the phone even without the loudspeaker.

"You're letting him manipulate you again, Antonia! How can you throw your life away like this? You've got a masters in education for god's sake!"

"Mamma, please, understand. I'm not throwing my life anywhere, I just choose a family over a career. Why can't you just accept that I want this . . ."

"Because this is not you, Toni! This is Max talking. He's a no good, bigoted caveman. And you're letting him walk all over you! One day you'll realise this, and it will be too late: you'll still be working as a behavioural therapist at the nursery, a glorified babysitter, with a pitiful salary, and you'll regret it."

"Mamma, please, let me explain . . ."

"I've heard enough in these past three years, Toni. You want to be just another housewife? Fine. I thought we taught you better than this, but evidently not. Your father and I are very disappointed in you."

She hangs up the phone and I feel like crying, but then I look at the pictures on the wall, of me and Max in the past three years. So my parents don't understand, but it's okay, because I have Massimo and he loves me and he wants a family with me. And this is all that matters.

The door opens and a nurse in a white uniform shouts my name. I get up, take my bag and coat and walk towards her. She leads me to a smaller room with a curtain separating the few chairs and a computer from the bed. I can hear people talking behind the screen as I drop my things to text Giulia and, for a moment, I feel utterly lost.

"If you want to come through here, please," says the nurse, and I avoid looking at her eyes, because I can already feel the pity and I know if I actually see it written all over her face I might either cry or scream, and I refuse to do either. I choose to follow her in silence, to the bed where Massimo is standing talking to a doctor, his hand on the shoulder of a beautiful woman. Her features are striking, olive skin standing out against the hospital's white

sheets, the gown raised so her flat stomach is bared, a paper towel covering her pelvis leaving her legs naked: a mile long of tanned skin, taut and waxed to perfection, stretching out leisurely against the gurney. I can't hear a word they're saying.

I'm too busy remembering the last instance I saw those exposed legs.

It's late afternoon and I'm running home early. I asked for a half day at work to cook dinner: tonight Giorgia, Max's childhood friend, is coming to stay with us for a few days. I went food shopping for her favourites and I'm going to surprise both her and Max tonight with a perfect dinner.

When I open the door, the first thing I see are Max's work boots and bag next to them. Did he have a day off today and I forgot? Before I can think about it, I hear muffled sounds coming from upstairs, so I drop my bags and walk up. I'm being exceedingly quiet, and I'm doing it without even realising, as if I already know what I'm going to find. No amount of thought or imagination could have prepared me for what's waiting for me in my bedroom. I wish I could move, whether to leave or to walk in, or even just to say something, but I'm rooted to the spot, standing against the doorframe.

Max is leaning against the bed, and he's naked. My eyes roam over his muscled back, the light skin of his buttocks, the tan line that ends mid-tights a reminder of our last holiday; his hands are roaming freely over a pair of bronzed legs spread wide, his head in between them moving back and forth, licking and teasing. And there, lying with her head thrown backwards and moaning loudly, is Giorgia. She's wearing only a laced black bra, her hands buried deep into Max's hair as he steadily guides her to orgasm with his tongue. She's screaming now, pulling at the brown curls as if she wants to rip them off, but he doesn't seem to mind. His hands rise from her legs and unhook the small piece of lace still covering her, his fingers finding her hard nipples and playing with them as she shakes her arms to remove the piece of clothing. The moment she reaches her peak her body begins to shudder with waves of pleasure and Max pushes her further on the bed, covering her, and in one fluid movement he enters her. Giorgia's legs wrap around his lower back as he pounds into her, her hands leaving scratch marks on his shoulders, her voice urging him to go faster, harder, to give it to her rough. It doesn't take long for Max to arch his back and shout her name, before Giorgia captures his mouth into an open, messy, tongue-filled kiss, moving with him as he explodes inside her.

As he falls, exhausted, on top of her body, I'm released from my weird paralysis at last and let out a whimpering sound. They both turn towards the door and find me there: standing, staring, tears running down my cheeks. I turn and run away, ignoring Max's shouts that "it's not what it seems" and "please allow me to explain".

Shaking my head to clear it from the images of that night, I force myself to focus on the present. That was the last I'd seen of Max, ignoring his calls and texts for two months until Giulia's call this morning passing on his message to please come to the hospital to meet him. In the gynaecology department. With Giorgia.

"Sorry, Max, can you repeat? I spaced out for a second . . ."

He throws me an amused look and smiles, and gives his head a shake.

"Same old Toni, always with your head in the clouds . . ."

The laughter in his tone irritates me and I turn to leave, almost bumping into Giulia who just made it into the room.

"What did I miss?"

"Nothing, yet, sis. Could I please talk to Toni alone?"

He grabs my arm and leads me on the other side of the office.

"Please, just listen to me for a second, OK?"

Against my better judgement, I nod. He lets out a relieved sigh.

"Let me start by saying how sorry I am for what I've done. It was the biggest mistake of my life. I really need you to forgive me, because I can't live without you."

"Sure, and that's why you called me here. With her. Who is pregnant, it would seem."

He shakes his head in frustration.

"Please, let me finish. What I've done is idiotic, I know, but . . . well, it may be a blessing in disguise! Yes, it's true. Giorgia is pregnant with my baby. But – and here comes the blessing – she doesn't want to keep it!"

I can hear the elation in his voice, and now I'm utterly confused.

"I'm sorry, I fail to see the positive side of this . . ."

"Don't you understand? She's agreed to continue the pregnancy, and then give us the baby. It would be ours. It's perfect, the solution to all our problems!"

"Let me get this straight . . ." (by now I'm so angry I can barely keep my voice from breaking) ". . . you're telling me you want me to forgive you, get back together, and raise the baby you conceived with someone else while cheating on me?"

He must've sensed the cold fury beneath my tone, because he grabs my hand and kneels on the floor.

"I want to be with you, for the rest of my life, and you can't have children. You know I didn't want to adopt because I wanted a baby who was *mine*. But I would've done it for you! So this way, we both get what we want: I get a baby with my DNA, and you get a husband and a family!"

"I can't believe you!" I'm shouting now, and I don't care who hears anymore. "You thought this was a good idea? You seriously thought I would say yes? Who do you think you are, but most of all, who do you think *I* am, to even propose such a thing?"

"Why can't you see my side of things for once? This might be my only chance to have a baby that's mine! How can you be so selfish to deny me this?"

He's angry, and incredulous, as if he really thought he was handing me the keys to heaven. And all of a sudden, I see clearly: my family's warnings, Giulia's pity every time she looked at me, the friends I lost because they hated him. It hits me, and I start laughing, grabbing my clothes and moving to the door.

"You pathetic piece of shit! *I'm* selfish? I gave up *everything* to be with you: my career, my friends, my family's respect! And for what? For a caveman who still believes in values from the seventeenth century. You want this baby so much, you can raise him by yourself, 'cause I'm not wasting another second on you."

I look at his shocked face and land my last blow. “Also, I took the job, so I wouldn’t have the time to be the *perfect Italian wife* anyway.”

I slam the door in his face and leave.

As I’m running out of the hospital, someone grabs my arm and I turn, ready to punch Max in the face, when I see Giulia’s smile.

“You know, I underestimated you. Want a cigarette?”

Laughing, I take one.

“Want to go get drunk, dance on a table and behave like we want to, for once, instead of how good little Italian girls should?”

“Absolutely.”

A BED FOR THE NIGHT

Harriet Warner

Harriet Warner began her career as a journalist writing for *The Times*, *Independent on Sunday*, *Loaded*, the *Erotic Review* and *GQ*. In 2003, her focus switched to writing for television, writing and creating her own shows with the likes of the BBC and TNT in the US, as well as working on a variety of programmes including *Sinbad*, *Mistress* and *Call The Midwife*. One of her episodes of *Call the Midwife* was nominated for a Mind Media Award in 2014.

The journey across the Carpathian mountains had been long and hard. My body ached to such a degree that I felt the slightest stone beneath the wheels of my carriage; but it mattered not. Whenever the coachman, Strepsil, would slow through weariness I rapped hard with my cane against the roof of the carriage and forced him and his horses on, for I was journeying to my beloved, Jonathan.

Jonathan and I were to be married the following month but I had received no word from him since his arrival in the peculiarly named Transylvania. Jonathan was to sort out some business with a fellow who by all accounts was most odd. The whole matter had become an irritation to me. How could the signing of documents be so protracted? No. An end must be put to this foolishness. I was to retrieve my fiancé and return forthwith to England with him, where we should be wed.

Quite suddenly the carriage drew to a shuddering halt. I open the shutter but the night is black and I can see nothing save the flicker of my coachman's torch. I tap against the glass and slowly he turns to me.

"It's no good m'lady. The horses are dead. They've died of fright. We must leave this evil place and find shelter at an inn. Come." And he leads me through the black forest, lit up in shadowy tones by his oil lamp held aloft.

Presently we see a light glowing in the gorge below us and we begin our descent.

The door of the inn is low and made of an oak thickened by age. Strepsil beats heavily against it with his large fist. The gentleman who comes to the door seems wary of us and insists on bathing our foreheads in blessed water. However, once he has branded Strepsil's arm with a holy cross from the fire, he seems in good spirits and I believe we are quite welcome.

I am seated beside the fire and given a piece of cheese while Strepsil enters into discussion with the tavern owner.

"M'lady. There is a problem with the room."

"Oh."

"He says that only couples that be wedded may sleep in the rooms here."

"Well, surely it is permissible if we each have a separate room, Strepsil?"

"M'lady, there is only one room."

My gloved hands flutter to my throat. The walk from the carriage took many hours and I fear that to return would be madness. "Then tell the innkeeper that we are indeed wed."

We look at one another before Strepsil nods.

We climb the narrow stairs while the innkeeper carries a candle and unlocks the door with a heavy key. Pushing open the door I am quite aghast. Why, the room is barely the size of my carriage and is quite completely taken up by a great feather bed! He sets down the candle and creeps from the room locking the door behind him.

"Strepsil, it seems we must both lay down together in this one bed! Why, there is no other place to lay. There is not even room to sleep on your side on the floor. Oh woe!"

"Fear not, m'lady. We shall be clothed and shall face in opposite directions. We shall never speak of this again."

I nod, relieved.

The bed is soft but I cannot sleep. The sounds of wolves and other creatures of the night keep me from dreams. I shake Strepsil.

"Won't you please put your arm around me? I am afraid."

Strepsil in his linen shirt puts an arm lightly around my shoulder. His body is warm, even in such a cold place, and I rather fancy that I enjoy the sensation of his firm chest beside me.

"Do you know that I seek my fiancé?"

"Yes, m'lady." His voice is low.

"Do you think me foolish?"

"Begging your pardon, m'lady, but it is not you who is foolish."

"Then you think my future husband a fool?"

After a silence: "If he could leave such a woman as you for months on end, then, aye, he is a fool."

And then he turns to me and puts hot dry lips against my cheek. I turn my head away. No. This must not be. But he puts a hard rough finger to my cheek and turns me back to him and this time his mouth is hard against mine. I think of Jonathan, but the thought is brief and it brings to mind his thin damp lips that only ever brushed my hand.

He reaches a hand around my waist and pulls me so that I am sitting on his lap and he kisses me again and this time drags down my dress so that he can feel my breasts with his rough hands; and it feels good to have them handled, they billow from my corset and he cups them and rolls them, and all the time his mouth is bearing down on mine and he's pulling my derriere against his lap and I can feel a hardness that I am quite unused to.

He shifts himself and takes my hand and pulls it down to the flap in his britches. "By the gods, unleash me!" His voice is low and urgent and I struggle with the hard tortoise-shell buttons that seem to be holding a great force behind them. And he is this time pulling up the many-layered skirt of my dress and

squeezing at my dumplings and pushing his thumb against my cunt. And it feels quite wonderful and quite strange. I feel as if I want one of the great rolling pins from the kitchen to come up between my legs and push hard inside me. And I have finally got his buttons loosened and I push my hand inside and find a strange hot damp thing that is meaty like the butcher's fine sausages on Sundays; it needs little help before it is standing high from his britches. But Strepsil is busy still with me and he is tearing down my pantaloons and bringing me towards him and his towering meat. Why, verily, I do believe his meat is quite the thing I require for the curious aching in my cunt.

"Strepsil? Might I sit on that?" I whisper and with a moan he nods and pushes his finger deep inside me. "Take this first, m'lady."

"Oh."

But it is not meat enough and I clamber for his cock and suck the thick fellow into me. Strepsil is quite content to serve me and pulls me hard upon him, thrusting upwards and gripping my waist to keep me hard down upon him. His face is amongst my weighty baps which quite cover him and I fear he will suffocate. Then as his thrusting becomes more furious he begins to slap against my rump with a quite uncoordinated hand. I hope to goodness he is not thinking of stopping and I too begin to slap, to drive him on, for the journey I require is a long and hard one.

REVELATIONS OF THE BRIDAL CHAMBER

Diana Gabaldon

Diana Gabaldon is the author of the international bestselling Outlander novels, which have recently been turned into a television drama and is being hailed as the new *Game of Thrones*. *Outlander* (published in the United Kingdom as *Cross Stitch*) is a sweeping tale of 20th-century nurse, Claire Randall, who accidentally travels back in time to 18th-century Scotland and finds adventure and romance with the dashing James Fraser. Dr Gabaldon holds three degrees in science: Zoology, Marine Biology, and a Ph.D. in Quantitative Behavioural Ecology, (plus an honorary degree as Doctor of Human Letters). She spent a dozen years as a university professor with an expertise in scientific computation before beginning to write fiction. Diana and her husband have three adult children and live mostly in Scottsdale, Arizona.

At the inn, food was readily available in the form of a modest wedding feast, including wine, fresh bread and roast beef.

Dougal took me by the arm as I started for the stairs to freshen myself before eating.

"I want this marriage consummated, wi' no uncertainty whatsoever," Dougal instructed me firmly in an undertone. "There's to be no question of it bein' a legal union and no way open for annulment, or we're all riskin' our necks."

"Seems to me you're doing that anyway," I remarked crossly. "Mine, especially."

Dougal patted me firmly on the rump.

"Dinna ye worry about that; ye just do your part." He looked me over critically, as though judging my capacity to perform my role adequately.

"I kent Jamie's father. If the lad's much like him, ye'll have no trouble at all. Ah, Jamie lad!" He hurried across the room to where Jamie had come in from stabling the ponies. From the look on Jamie's face, he was getting his orders as well.

How in the name of God did this happen? I asked myself some time later. Six weeks ago I had been innocently collecting wild flowers on a Scottish hill, to take home to my husband. I was now shut in the room of a rural inn, awaiting a completely different husband, whom I scarcely knew, with firm orders to consummate a forced marriage, at risk of my life and liberty.

And what about my *old* husband? My stomach knotted with grief and fear. What would Frank be thinking now? What would he be feeling? I had been gone for more than a month; he would have been searching for me, calling out the police as his concern turned to fear, turning the Scottish countryside upside down. Not far enough, though; it would never occur to him to look inside a fairies' hill, even were such a thing possible.

I sat on the bed, stiff and terrified in my borrowed finery. There was a faint noise as the heavy door of the room swung open, then shut.

Jamie leaned against the door, watching me. The air of embarrassment between us deepened. It was Jamie who broke the silence finally.

"You dinna need to be afraid of me," he said softly. "I wasna going to jump on ye.' I laughed in spite of myself.

"Well, I didn't think you would." In fact, I didn't think he would touch me, until and unless I invited him to; the fact remained that I was going to have to invite him to do considerably more than that, and soon.

I eyed him dubiously. I supposed it would be harder if I found him unattractive; in fact, the opposite was true. Still, I had not slept with any man but Frank in over eight years. Not only that, this young man, by his own acknowledgement, was completely inexperienced. I had never deflowered anyone before. Even dismissing my objections to the whole arrangement, and considering matters from a completely practical standpoint, how on earth were we to start? At this rate we would still be here, staring at each other, three or four days hence.

I cleared my throat and patted the bed beside me.

"Ah, would you like to sit down?"

"Aye." He came across the room, moving like a big cat. Instead of sitting beside me, though, he pulled up a stool and sat down facing me. Somewhat tentatively he reached out and took my hands between his own. They were large, blunt-fingered and very warm, the backs lightly furred with reddish hairs. I felt a slight shock at the touch, and thought of an Old Testament passage – "For Jacob's skin was smooth, while his brother Esau was an hairy man." Frank's hands were long and slender, nearly hairless and aristocratic-looking. I had always loved watching them as he lectured.

"Tell me about your husband," said Jamie, as though he had been reading my mind. I almost jerked my hands away in shock.

"What?"

"Look ye, lass. We have three or four days together here. While I dinna pretend to know all there is to know, I've lived a good bit of my life on a farm, and unless people are verra different from other animals, it isna going to take that long to do what we have to do. We have a bit of time to talk, and get over being scairt of each other." This blunt appraisal of our situation relaxed me a little bit.

"Are you scared of me?" He didn't look it. Perhaps he was nervous, though. Even though he was no timid sixteen-year-old lad, this *was* the first time. He looked into my eyes and smiled.

"Aye. More scairt than you, I expect. That's why I'm holdin' your hands; to keep my own from shaking." I didn't believe this, but squeezed his hands tightly in appreciation.

"It's a good idea. It feels a little easier to talk while we're touching. Why did you ask about my husband, though?" I wondered a bit wildly if he wanted me to tell him about my sex life with Frank, so as to know what I expected of him.

"Well, I knew ye must be thinking of him. Ye could hardly not, under the circumstances. I do not want ye ever to feel as though ye canna talk of him to me. Even though I'm your husband now – that feels verra strange to say – it isna right that ye should forget him, or even try to. If ye loved him, he must ha' been a good man."

"Yes, he . . . was." My voice trembled, and Jamie stroked the backs of my hands with his thumbs.

"Then I shall do my best to honour his spirit by serving his wife." He raised my hands and kissed each one formally.

I cleared my throat. "That was a very gallant speech, Jamie."

He grinned suddenly. "Aye. I made it up while Dougal was making toasts downstairs."

I took a deep breath. "I have questions," I said.

He looked down, hiding a smile. "I'd suppose ye do," he agreed. "I imagine you're entitled to a bit of curiosity, under the circumstances. What is it ye want to know?" He looked up suddenly, blue eyes bright with mischief in the lamplight. "Why I'm a virgin yet?"

"Er, I should say that that was more or less your own business," I murmured. It seemed to be getting rather warm suddenly, and I pulled one hand free to grope for my handkerchief. As I did so I felt something hard in the pocket of my gown.

"Oh, I forgot! I still have your ring." I drew it out and gave it back to him. It was a heavy gold circlet, set with a cabochon ruby. Instead of replacing it on his finger, he opened his sporran to put it inside.

"It was my father's wedding ring," he explained. "I dinna wear it customarily, but I . . . well, I wished to do ye honour today by looking as well as I might." He flushed slightly at this admission, and busied himself with refastening the sporran.

"You did do me great honour," I said, smiling in spite of myself. Adding a ruby ring to the blazing splendour of his costume was coals to Newcastle, but I was touched by the anxious thought behind it.

"I'll get one that fits ye, so soon as I may," he promised.

"It's not important," I said, feeling slightly uncomfortable. I meant, after all, to be gone soon.

"Er, I have one main question," I said, calling the meeting to order. "If you don't mind telling me. Why did you agree to marry me?"

"Ah." He let go of my hands and sat back a bit. He paused for a moment before answering, smoothing the woollen cloth over his thighs. I could see the long line of muscle taut under the drape of the heavy fabric.

"Well, I would ha' missed talking to ye, for one thing," he said, smiling.

"No, I mean it," I insisted. "Why?"

He sobered then. "Before I tell ye, Claire, there's one thing I'd ask of you," he said slowly.

"What's that?"

"Honesty."

I must have flinched uncomfortably, for he leaned forward earnestly, hands on his knees.

"I know there are things ye'd not wish to tell me, Claire. Perhaps things that ye *can't* tell me."

You don't know just how right you are, I thought.

"I'll not press you, ever, or insist on knowin' things that are your own concern," he said seriously. He looked down at his hands, now pressed together, palm to palm.

"There are things that I canna tell *you*, at least not yet. And I'll ask nothing of ye that ye canna give me. But what I would ask of ye – when you do tell me something, let it be the truth. And I'll promise the same. We have nothing now between us, save – respect, perhaps. And I think that respect has maybe room for secrets, but not for lies. Do ye agree?" He spread his hands out, palms up, inviting me. I could see the dark line of the blood vow across his wrist. I placed my own hands lightly on his palms.

"Yes, I agree. I'll give you honesty." His fingers closed tightly about mine.

"And I shall give ye the same. Now" – he drew a deep breath – "you asked why I wed ye."

"I *am* just the slightest bit curious," I said.

He smiled, the wide mouth taking up the humour that lurked in his eyes. "Well, I canna say I blame ye. I had several reasons. And in fact, there's one – maybe two – that I canna tell ye yet, though I will in time. The main reason, though, is the same reason you wed me, I imagine; to keep ye safe from the hands of Black Jack Randall."

I shuddered a bit at the memory of the Captain, and Jamie's hands tightened on mine.

"You *are* safe," he said firmly. "You have my name and my family, my clan, and if necessary, the protection of my body as well. The man willna lay hands on ye again, while I live."

"Thank you," I said. Looking at the strong, young, determined face, with its broad cheekbones and solid jaw, I felt for the first time that this preposterous scheme of Dougal's might actually have been a reasonable suggestion.

The protection of my body. The phrase struck with particular impact, looking at him – the resolute set of the wide shoulders and the memory of his graceful ferocity, "showing off" at swordplay in the moonlight. He meant it; and young as he was, he knew what he meant, and bore the scars to prove it. He was no older than many of the pilots and infantrymen I had nursed, and he knew as well as they the price of commitment. It was no romantic pledge he had made me, but the blunt promise to guard my safety at the cost of his own. I hoped only that I could offer him something in return.

"That's *most* gallant of you," I said, with absolute sincerity. "But was it worth, well, worth marriage?"

"It was," he said, nodding. He smiled again, a little grimly this time. "I've good reason to know the man, ye ken. I wouldna see a dog given into his keeping if I could prevent it, let alone a helpless woman."

"How flattering," I remarked wryly, and he laughed. He stood up and went to the table near the window. Someone – perhaps the landlady – had supplied

a bouquet of wild flowers, set in water in a whisky cup. Behind this stood two wine glasses and a bottle.

Jamie poured out two glasses and came back, handing me one as he resumed his seat.

"Not quite so good as Callum's private stock," he said with a smile, "but none so bad, either." He raised his glass briefly. "To Mrs Fraser," he said softly, and I felt a thump of panic again. I quelled it firmly and raised my own glass.

"To honesty," I said, and we both drank.

"Well, that's one reason," I said, lowering my glass. "Are there others you can tell me?"

He studied his wine glass with some care. "Perhaps it's just that I want to bed you." He looked up abruptly. "Did ye think of that?"

If he meant to disconcert me, he was succeeding nicely, but I resolved not to show it.

"Well, do you?" I said boldly.

"If I'm bein' honest, yes, I do." The blue eyes were steady over the rim of the glass.

"You wouldn't necessarily have had to marry me for that," I objected.

He appeared honestly scandalized. "You do not think I would take ye without offering you marriage?"

"Many men would," I said, amused at his innocence.

He sputtered a bit, at a momentary loss. Then regaining his composure, he said with formal dignity, "Perhaps I am pretentious in saying so, but I would like to think that I am not 'many men', and that I dinna necessarily place my behaviour at the lowest common denominator."

Rather touched by this speech I assured him that I had so far found his behaviour both gallant and gentlemanly, and apologized for any doubt I might inadvertently have cast on his motives.

On this precariously diplomatic note we paused while he refilled our empty glasses.

We sipped in silence for a time, both feeling a bit shy after the frankness of that last exchange. So, apparently there *was* something I could offer him. I couldn't, in fairness, say the thought had not entered my mind, even before the absurd situation in which we found ourselves arose. He was a very engaging young man. And there had been that moment, right after my arrival at the castle, when he had held me on his lap, and –

I tilted my wine glass back and drained the contents. I patted the bed beside me again.

"Sit down here with me," I said. "And" – I cast about for some neutral topic of conversation to ease us over the awkwardness of close proximity – "and tell me about your family. Where did you grow up?"

The bed sank noticeably under his weight, and I braced myself not to roll against him. He sat closely enough that the sleeve of his shirt brushed my arm. I let my hand lie open on my thigh, relaxed. He took it naturally as he sat, and we leaned against the wall, neither of us looking down, but as conscious of the link as though we had been welded together.

"Well, now, where shall I start?" He put his rather large feet up on the stool and crossed them at the ankles. With some amusement I recognized the Highlander settling back for a leisurely dissection of that tangle of family and clan relationships which forms the background of almost any event of significance in the Scottish Highlands. Frank and I had spent one evening in the village pub, enthralled by the conversation between two old codgers, in which the responsibility for the recent destruction of an ancient barn was traced back through the intricacies of a local feud dating, so far as I could tell, from about 1790. With the sort of minor shock to which I was becoming accustomed, I realized that that particular feud, whose origins I had thought shrouded in the mists of time, had not yet begun. Suppressing the mental turmoil this realization caused, I forced my attention to what Jamie was saying.

"My father was a Fraser, of course; a younger half-brother to the present Master of Lovat. My mother was a MacKenzie, though. Ye'll know that Dougal and Callum are my uncles?" I nodded. The resemblance was clear enough, despite the difference in colouring. The broad cheekbones and long, straight, knife-edged nose were plainly a MacKenzie inheritance.

"Aye, well, my mother was their sister, and there were two more sisters, besides. My Auntie Janet is dead, like my mother, but my Auntie Jocasta married a cousin of Rupert's, and lives up near the edge of Loch Eilean Mhor. Auntie Janet had six children, four boys and two girls, Auntie Jocasta had three, all girls, Dougal's got the four girls, Callum has little Hamish only, and my parents had me and my sister, who's named for my Auntie Janet, but we called her Jenny always."

"Rupert's a MacKenzie, too?" I asked, already struggling to keep everyone straight.

"Aye. He's –" Jamie paused a moment considering. "He's Dougal's, Callum's and Jocasta's first cousin, which makes him my second cousin. Rupert's father and my grandfather Jacob were brothers, along with –"

"Wait a minute. Don't let's go back any farther than we have to, or I shall be getting hopelessly muddled. We haven't even got to the Frasers yet, and I've already lost track of your cousins."

He rubbed his chin, calculating. "Hmm. Well, on the Fraser side it's a bit more complicated, because my grandfather Simon married three times, so my father had two sets of half-brothers and half-sisters. Let's leave it for now that I've six Fraser uncles and three aunts still living, and we'll leave out all the cousins from that lot."

"Yes, let's." I leaned forward and poured another glass of wine for each of us.

The clan territories of MacKenzie and Fraser, it turned out, adjoined each other for some distance along their inner borders, running side by side from the western seacoast past the lower end of Loch Ness. This shared border, as borders tend to be, was an unmapped and most uncertain line, shifting to and fro in accordance with time, custom and alliance. Along this border, at the southern end of the Fraser clan lands, lay the small estate of Broch Tuarach, the property of Brian Fraser, Jamie's father.

"It's a fairly rich bit of ground, and there's decent fishing and a good patch of forest for hunting. It maybe supports sixty tenants, and the small village – Broch

Mordha, it's called. Then there's the farmhouse, of course – that's modern," he said, with some pride, "and the old broch that we use now for the beasts and the grain.

"Dougal and Callum were not at all pleased to have their sister marrying a Fraser, and they insisted that she not be a tenant on Fraser land, but live on her own land. So, Lallybroch – that's what the folk that live there call it – was deeded to my father, but there was a clause in the deed stating that the land was to pass to my mother, Ellen's, issue only. If she died without children, the land would go back to Lord Lovat after my father's death, whether Father had children by another wife or no. But he didn't remarry, and I am my mother's son. So Lallybroch's mine, for what that's worth."

"I thought you were telling me yesterday that you didn't have any property." I sipped the wine, finding it rather good; it seemed to be getting better, the more I drank of it. I thought perhaps I had better stop soon.

Jamie wagged his head from side to side. "Well, it belongs to me, right enough. The thing is, though, it doesna do me much good at present, as I can't go there." He looked apologetic. "There's the minor matter of the price on my head, ye see."

After his escape from Fort William he had been taken to Dougal's house, Beannachd (means "Blessed", he explained), to recover from his wounds and the consequent fever. From there he had gone to France, where he had spent two years fighting with the French army, around the Spanish border.

"You spent two years in the French army and stayed a virgin?" I blurted out incredulously. I had had a number of Frenchmen in my care, and I doubted very much that the Gallic attitude towards women had changed appreciably in two hundred years.

One corner of Jamie's mouth twitched and he looked down at me sideways.

"If ye had seen the harlots that service the French army, Sassenach, ye'd wonder I've the nerve even to touch a woman, let alone bed one."

I choked, spluttering wine and coughing until he was obliged to pound me on the back. I subsided, breathless and red-faced, and urged him to go on with his story.

He had returned to Scotland a year or so ago, and spent six months alone or with a gang of "broken men" – men without clans – living hand to mouth in the forest, or raiding cattle from the Lowlands.

"And then, someone hit me in the head wi' an axe or something o' the sort," he said, shrugging. "And I've to take Dougal's word for what happened during the next two months, as I wasna taking much notice of things myself."

Dougal had been on a nearby estate at the time of the attack. Summoned by Jamie's friends, he had somehow managed to transport his nephew to France.

"Why France?" I asked. "Surely it was taking a frightful risk to move you so far."

"More of a risk to leave me where I was. There were English patrols all over the district – we'd been fairly active thereabouts, ye see, me and the lads – and I suppose Dougal didna want them to find me lying senseless in some cottar's hut."

"Or in his own house?" I said a little cynically.

"I imagine he'd ha' taken me there, but for two things," Jamie replied. "For

one, he'd an English visitor at the time. For a second, he thought from the look of me I was going to die in any case, so he sent me to the abbey."

The Abbey of Ste Anne de Beaupré, on the French coast, was the domain, it seemed, of the erstwhile Alexander Fraser, now abbot of that sanctuary of learning and worship. One of Jamie's six Fraser uncles.

"He and Dougal do not get on, particularly," Jamie explained, "but Dougal could see there was little to be done for me here, while if there was aught to help me, it might be found there."

And it was. Assisted by the monks' medical knowledge and his own strong constitution, Jamie had survived and gradually mended, under the care of the holy brothers of St Benedict.

"Once I was well again, I came back," he explained. "Dougal and his men met me at the coast, and we were headed for the MacKenzie lands when we, er, met with you."

"Captain Randall said you were stealing cattle," I said.

He smiled, undisturbed by the accusation. "Well, Dougal isna the man to overlook an opportunity of turning a bit of a profit," he observed. "We came on a nice bunch of beasts, grazing in a field, and no one about. So . . ." He shrugged with a fatalistic acceptance of the inevitability of life.

Apparently I had come upon the end of the confrontation between Dougal's men and Randall's dragoons. Spotting the English bearing down on them, Dougal had sent half his men around a thicket, driving the cattle before them, while the rest of the Scots had hidden among the saplings, ready to ambush the English as they came by.

"Worked verra well too," Jamie said in approval. "We popped out at them and rode straight through them, yelling. They took after us, of course, and we led them a canty chase uphill and through burns and over rocks and such; and all the while the rest of Dougal's men were making off wi' the kine. We lost the lobsterbacks, then, and denned up at the cottage where I first saw ye."

"I see," I said. "Why did you come back to Scotland in the first place, though? I should have thought you'd be much safer in France."

He opened his mouth to reply, then reconsidered, sipping wine. Apparently I was getting near the edge of his own area of secrecy.

"Well, that's a long story, Sassenach," he said, avoiding the issue. "I'll tell it ye later, but for now, what about you? Will ye tell me about your own family? If ye feel ye can, of course," he added hastily.

I thought for a moment, but there really seemed little risk in telling him about my parents and Uncle Lamb. There was, after all, some advantage to Uncle Lamb's choice of profession. A scholar of antiquities made as much – or as little – sense in the eighteenth century as in the twentieth.

So I told him, omitting only such minor details as automobiles and aeroplanes, and of course the war. As I talked he listened intently, asking questions now and then, expressing sympathy at my parents' death and interest in Uncle Lamb and his discoveries.

"And then I met Frank," I finished up. I paused, not sure how much more I could say without getting into dangerous territory. Luckily Jamie saved me.

"And ye'd as soon not talk about him right now," he said understandingly.

I nodded, wordless, my vision blurring a little. Jamie let go of the hand he had been holding and putting an arm around me, pulled my head gently down on his shoulder.

"It's all right," he said, softly stroking my hair. "Are ye tired, lass? Shall I leave ye to your sleep?"

I was tempted for a moment to say yes, but I felt that that would be both unfair and cowardly. I cleared my throat and sat up, shaking my head.

"No," I said, taking a deep breath. He smelled faintly of soap and wine. "I'm all right. Tell me – tell me what games you used to play, when you were a boy."

The room was furnished with a thick twelve-hour candle, rings of dark wax marking the hours. We talked through three of the rings, only letting go of each other's hands to pour wine or get up to visit the privy stool behind the curtain in the corner. Returning from one of these trips, Jamie yawned and stretched.

"It is awfully late," I said, getting up too. "Maybe we should go to bed."

"All right," he said, rubbing the back of his neck. "To bed? Or to sleep?" He cocked a quizzical eyebrow and the corner of his mouth twitched.

In truth I had been feeling so comfortable with him that I had almost forgotten why we were there. At his words I suddenly felt a hollow panic. "Well –" I said faintly.

"Either way, you're no intending to sleep in your gown, are ye?" he asked in his usual practical manner.

"Well, no, I suppose not." In fact, during the rush of events I had not even thought about a sleeping garment – which I did not possess, in any case. I had been sleeping in my chemise or nothing, depending on the weather.

Jamie had nothing but the clothes he wore; he was plainly going to sleep in his shirt or naked, a state of affairs which was likely to bring matters rapidly to a head.

"Well, then, come here and I'll help ye wi' the laces and such."

His hands did in fact tremble briefly as he began to undress me. He lost some of his self-consciousness, though, in the struggle with the dozens of tiny buttons that attached the bodice.

"Ha!" he said in triumph as the last one came loose, and we laughed together.

"Now let me do you," I said, deciding that there was no point in further delay. I reached up and unfastened his shirt, sliding my hands inside and across his shoulders. I brought my palms slowly down across his chest, feeling the springy hair and the soft indentations around his nipples. He stood still, hardly breathing, as I knelt down to unbuckle the studded belt around his hips.

If it must be some time, it may as well be now, I thought, and deliberately ran my hands up the length of his thighs, hard and lean under his kilt. Though by this time I knew perfectly well what most Scotsmen wore beneath their kilts – nothing – it was still something of a shock to find only Jamie.

He lifted me to my feet then, and bent his head to kiss me. It went on a long while, and his hands roamed downwards, finding the fastening of my petticoats. They fell to the floor in a billow of starched flounces, leaving me in my chemise.

"Where did you learn to kiss like that?" I said, a little breathless. He grinned and pulled me close again.

"I said I was a virgin, not a monk," he said, kissing me again. "If I find I need guidance, I'll ask."

He pressed me firmly to him and I could feel that he was more than ready to get on with the business at hand. With some surprise I realized that I was ready too. In fact, whether it was the result of the late hour, the wine, his own attractiveness or simple deprivation, I wanted him quite badly.

I pulled his shirt loose at the waist and ran my hands up over his chest, circling his nipples with my thumbs. They grew hard in a second, and he crushed me suddenly against his chest.

"Oof!" I said, struggling for breath. He let go, apologizing.

"No, don't worry; kiss me again." He did, this time slipping the straps of the chemise down over my shoulders. He drew back slightly, cupping my breasts and rubbing my nipples as I had done his. I fumbled with the buckle that held his kilt; his fingers guided mine and the clasp sprang free.

Suddenly he lifted me in his arms and sat down on the bed, holding me on his lap. He spoke a little hoarsely.

"Tell me if I'm too rough, or tell me to stop altogether, if ye wish. Any time until we are joined; I dinna think I can stop after that."

In answer I put my hands behind his neck and pulled him down on top of me. I guided him to the slippery cleft between my legs.

"Holy God," said James Fraser, who never took the name of his Lord in vain.

"Don't stop now," I said.

Lying together afterwards, it seemed natural for him to cradle my head on his chest. We fitted well together, and most of our original constraint was gone, lost in shared excitement and the novelty of exploring each other. "Was it like you thought it would be?" I asked curiously. He chuckled, making a deep rumble under my ear.

"Almost; I had thought – nay, never mind."

"No, tell me. What did you think?"

"I'm no goin' to tell ye; ye'll laugh at me."

"I promise not to laugh. Tell me." He caressed my hair, smoothing the curls back from my ear.

"Oh, all right. I didna realize that ye did it face to face. I thought ye must do it the back way, like; like horses, ye know."

It was a struggle to keep my promise, but I didn't laugh.

"I know that sounds silly," he said, defensively. "It's just . . . well, ye know how you get ideas in your head when you're young, and then somehow they just stick there?"

"You've never seen *people* make love?" I was surprised at this, having seen the cot-houses where the whole family shared a single room. Granted that Jamie's family were not cottars, still it must be the rare Scottish child who had never waked to find his elders coupling nearby.

"Of course I have, but generally under the bedclothes, ye know. I couldna tell anything except the man was on top. *That* much I knew."

"Mm. I noticed."

"Did I squash you?" he asked a little anxiously.

"Not much. Really, though, is that what you thought?" I didn't laugh, but couldn't help grinning broadly. He turned slightly pink around the ears.

"Aye. I saw a man take a woman plain, once, out in the open. But that . . . well, it was a rape, was what it was, and he took her from the back. It made some impression on me, and as I say, it's just the idea stuck."

He continued to hold me, using his horse-gentling techniques again. These gradually changed, though, to a more determined exploration.

"I want to ask ye something," he said, running a hand down the length of my back.

"What's that?"

"Did ye like it?" he said a little shyly.

"Yes, I did," I said quite honestly.

"Oh, I thought ye did, though Murtagh told me that women generally do not care for it, so I should finish as soon as I could."

"What would Murtagh know about it?" I said indignantly. "The slower the better, as far as most women are concerned." Jamie chuckled again.

"Well, you'd know better than Murtagh. I had considerable good advice offered me on the subject last night, from Murtagh and Rupert and Ned. A good bit of it sounded verra unlikely to me, though, so I thought I'd best use my own judgement."

"It hasn't led you wrong yet," I said, curling one of his chest hairs around my finger. "What other sage bits of advice did they give you?" His skin was a ruddy gold in the candlelight; to my amusement it grew still redder in embarrassment.

"I could no repeat most of it. As I said, I think it's likely wrong, anyway. I've seen a good many kinds of animals mate with each other, and most seem to manage it without any advice at all. I would suppose people could do the same."

I was privately entertained by the notion of someone picking up pointers on sexual technique from barnyard and forest, rather than locker rooms and dirty magazines.

"What kinds of animals have you seen mating?"

"Oh, all kinds. Our farm was near the forest, ye see, and I spent a good deal of time there, hunting, or seeking cows as had got out and suchlike. I've seen horses and cows, of course, chickens, doves, dogs, cats, deer, squirrels, rabbits, wild boar, oh, and once even a pair of snakes."

"Snakes!?"

"Aye. Did ye know that snakes have two cocks? – male snakes, I mean."

"No, I didn't. Are you sure about that?"

"Aye, and both of 'em forked, like this." He spread his second and third fingers apart in illustration.

"That sounds terribly uncomfortable for the female snake," I said, giggling.

"Well, she appeared to be enjoying herself," said Jamie. "Near as I could tell; snakes havena got much expression on their faces."

I buried my face in his chest, snorting with mirth. His pleasant musky smell mingled with the harsh scent of linen.

"Take off your shirt," I said, sitting up and pulling at the hem of the garment.

"Why?" he asked, but sat up and obliged. I knelt in front of him, admiring his naked body.

"Because I want to look at you," I said. He was beautifully made, with long graceful bones and flat muscles that flowed smoothly from the curves of chest and shoulder to the slight concavities of belly and thigh. He raised his eyebrows.

"Well then, fair's fair. Take off yours, then." He reached out and helped me squirm out of the wrinkled chemise, pushing it down over my hips. Once it was off, he held me by the waist, studying me with intense interest. I grew almost embarrassed as he looked me over.

"Haven't you ever seen a naked woman before?" I asked.

"Aye, but not one so close." His face broke into a broad grin. "And not one that's mine." He stroked my hips with both hands. "You have good wide hips; ye'd be a good breeder, I expect."

"What!?" I drew away indignantly but he pulled me back and collapsed on the bed with me on top of him. He held me until I stopped struggling, then raised me enough to meet his lips again.

"I know once is enough to make it legal, but . . ." He paused shyly.

"You want to do it again?"

"Would ye mind verra much?"

I didn't laugh this time either, but I felt my ribs creak under the strain.

"No," I said gravely. "I wouldn't mind."

"Are you hungry?" I asked softly, some time later.

"Famished." He bent his head to bite my breast softly, then looked up with a grin. "But I need food too." He rolled to the edge of the bed. "There's cold beef and bread in the kitchen, I expect, and likely wine as well. I'll go and bring us some supper."

"No, don't you get up. I'll fetch it." I jumped off the bed and headed for the door, pulling on shawl and shift against the chill of the corridor.

"Wait, Claire!" Jamie called. "Ye'd better let me –" but I had already opened the door.

My appearance at the door was greeted by a raucous cheer from some fifteen men, lounging around the fireplace in the main room below, drinking, eating and tossing dice. I stood nonplussed on the balcony for a moment, fifteen leering faces flickering out of the firelit shadows at me.

"Hey, lass!" shouted Rupert, one of the loungers. "Ye're still able t' walk! Isn't Jamie doin' his duty by ye, then?"

This sally was greeted with gales of laughter and a number of even cruder remarks regarding Jamie's prowess.

"If ye've worn Jamie out a'ready, I'll be happy t' take his place!" offered a short dark-haired youth.

"Nay, nay, 'e's no good, lass, take me!" shouted another.

"She'll ha' none o' ye, lads!" yelled Murtagh, uproariously drunk. "After Jamie, she'll need somethin' like this to satisfy 'er!" He waved a huge meat bone overhead, causing the room to rock with laughter.

I whirled back into the room, slammed the door and stood with my back to it, glaring at Jamie, who lay naked on the bed, shaking with laughter.

"I tried to warn ye," he said, gasping. "You should see your face!"

"Just what," I hissed, "are all those men doing out there?"

Jamie slid gracefully off our wedding couch and began rummaging on his knees through the pile of discarded clothing on the floor. "Witnesses," he said briefly. "Dougal is no takin' any chances of this marriage bein' annulled." He straightened with his kilt in his hands, grinning at me as he wrapped it around his loins. "I'm afraid your reputation's compromised beyond repair, Sassenach."

He turned shirtless for the door. "Don't go out there!" I said in sudden panic. He turned to smile reassuringly, hand on the latch. "Dinna worry, lass. If they're witnesses, they may as well have somethin' to see. Besides, I'm no intendin' to starve for the next three days for fear of a wee bit o' chaff."

He stepped out of the room to a chorus of bawdy applause, leaving the door slightly ajar. I could hear his progress towards the kitchen, marked by shouted congratulations and ribald questions and advice.

"How was yer first time, Jamie? Did ye bleed?" shouted Rupert's easily recognized gravel-pit voice.

"Nay, but ye will, ye auld bugger, if ye dinna clapper yer face," came Jamie's spiked tones in broad Scots reply. Howls of delight greeted this sally, and the raillery continued, following Jamie down the hall to the kitchen and back up the stairs.

I pulled open the door a crack to admit Jamie, face red as the fire below and hands piled high with food and drink. He sidled in, followed by a final burst of hilarity from below. I choked it off with a decisive slam of the door, and shot the bolt to.

"I brought enough so we'll no need to go out again for a bit," Jamie said, laying out dishes on the table, carefully not looking at me. "Will ye have a bite?"

I reached past him for the bottle of wine. "Not just yet. What I need is a drink."

There was a powerful urgency in him that roused me to response despite his awkwardness. Not wanting to lecture nor yet to highlight my own experience, I let him do what he would, only offering an occasional suggestion, such as that he might carry his weight on his elbows and not on my chest.

As yet too hungry and too clumsy for tenderness, still he made love with a sort of unflagging joy that made me think that male virginity might be a highly underrated commodity. He exhibited a concern for my safety, though, that I found at once endearing and irritating.

At some time in our third encounter, I arched tightly against him and cried out. He drew back at once, startled and apologetic.

"I'm sorry," he said. "I didna mean to hurt ye."

"You didn't." I stretched languorously, feeling dreamily wonderful.

"Are you sure?" he said, inspecting me for damage. Suddenly it dawned on me that a few of the finer points had likely been left out of his hasty education at the hands of Murtagh and Rupert.

"Does it happen every time?" he asked, fascinated, once I had enlightened him. I felt rather like the Wife of Bath, or a Japanese geisha. I had never envisioned myself as an instructress in the arts of love, but I had to admit to myself that the role held certain attractions.

"No, not every time," I said, amused. "Only if the man is a good lover."

"Oh." His ears turned faintly pink. I was slightly alarmed to see the look of frank interest being replaced with one of growing determination.

"Will you tell me what I should do next time?" he asked.

"You don't need to do anything special," I assured him. "Just go slowly and pay attention. Why wait, though? You're still ready."

He was surprised. "You don't need to wait? I canna do it again right away after –"

"Well, women are different."

"Aye, I noticed," he muttered.

He circled my wrist with thumb and index finger. "It's just . . . you're so small; I'm afraid I'm going to hurt you."

"You are not going to hurt me," I said impatiently. "And if you did, I wouldn't mind." Seeing puzzled incomprehension on his face, I decided to show him what I meant.

"What are you doing?" he asked, shocked.

"Just what it looks like. Hold still." After a few seconds, I began to use my teeth, pressing progressively harder until he drew in his breath with a sharp hiss. I stopped.

"Did I hurt you?" I asked.

"Yes. A little." He sounded half strangled.

"Do you want me to stop?"

"No!"

I went on, being deliberately rough, until he suddenly convulsed, with a groan that sounded as though I had torn his heart out by the roots. He lay back, quivering and breathing heavily. He muttered something in Gaelic, eyes closed.

"What did you say?"

"I said," he answered, opening his eyes, "I thought my heart was going to burst."

I grinned, pleased with myself. "Oh, Murtagh and company didn't tell you about that, either?"

"Aye, they did. That was one of the things I didn't believe."

I laughed. "In that case, maybe you'd better not tell me what else they told you. Do you see what I meant, though, about not minding if you're rough?"

"Aye." He drew a deep breath and blew it out softly. "If I did that to you, would it feel the same?"

"Well, you know," I said, slowly, "I don't really know." I had been doing my best to keep thoughts of Frank at bay, feeling that there should really be no more than two people in a marriage bed, regardless of how they got there. Jamie was very different from Frank, both in body and mind, but there are in fact only a limited number of ways in which two bodies can meet, and we had not yet established that territory of intimacy in which the act of love takes on infinite variety. The echoes of the flesh were unavoidable, but there were a few territories still unexplored.

Jamie's brows were tilted in an expression of mocking threat. "Oh, so there's something you don't know? Well, we'll find out then, won't we? As soon as I've the strength for it." He closed his eyes again. "Next week, some time."

I woke in the hours before dawn, shivering and rigid with terror. I could not recall the dream that woke me, but the abrupt plunge into reality was equally

frightening. It had been possible to forget my situation for a time the night before, lost in the pleasures of newfound intimacy. Now I was alone, next to a sleeping stranger with whom my life was inextricably linked, adrift in a place filled with unseen threat.

I must have made some sound of distress, for there was a sudden upheaval of bedclothes as the stranger in my bed vaulted to the floor with the heart-stopping suddenness of a pheasant rising underfoot. He came to rest in a crouch near the door of the chamber, barely visible in the predawn light.

Pausing to listen carefully at the door, he made a rapid inspection of the room, gliding soundlessly from door to window to bed. The angle of his arm told me that he held a weapon of some sort, though I could not see what it was in the darkness. Sitting down next to me, satisfied that all was secure, he slid the knife or whatever it was back into its hiding place above the headboard.

"Are you all right?" he whispered. His fingers brushed my wet cheek.

"Yes. I'm sorry to wake you. I had a nightmare. What on earth –" I started to ask what it was that had made him spring so abruptly to the alert.

A large warm hand ran down my bare arm, interrupting my question. "No wonder; you're frozen." The hand urged me under the pile of quilts and into the warm space recently vacated. "My fault," he murmured. "I've taken all the quilts. I'm afraid I'm no accustomed yet to share a bed." He wrapped the quilts comfortably around us and lay back beside me. A moment later he reached again to touch my face.

"Is it me?" he asked quietly. "Can ye not bear me?"

I gave a short hicupping laugh, not quite a sob. "No, it isn't you." I reached out in the dark, groping for a hand to press reassuringly. My fingers met a tangle of quilts and warm flesh, but at last I found the hand I had been seeking. We lay side by side, looking up at the low beamed ceiling.

"What if I said I couldn't bear you?" I asked suddenly. "What on earth could you do?" The bed creaked as he shrugged.

"Tell Dougal you wanted an annulment on the grounds of nonconsummation, I suppose."

This time I laughed outright. "Nonconsummation! With all those witnesses?"

The room was growing light enough to see the smile on the face turned towards me. "Aye well, witnesses or no, it's only you and me that can say for sure, isn't it? And I'd rather be embarrassed than wed to someone that hated me."

I turned towards him. "I don't hate you."

"I don't hate you, either. And there's many good marriages have started wi' less than that." Gently he turned me away from him and fitted himself to my back so we lay nestled together. His hand cupped my breast, not in invitation or demand but because it seemed to belong there.

"Don't be afraid," he whispered into my hair. "There's the two of us now." I felt warm, soothed and safe for the first time in many days. It was only as I drifted into sleep under the first rays of daylight that I remembered the knife above my head, and wondered again, what threat would make a man sleep armed and watchful in his bridal chamber?

BLIND LOVE

John Gibb

John Gibb first started writing questionable stories for the *Erotic Review* when it was the only monthly magazine in Europe committed to serious sexual fiction. He learnt his trade as a journalist writing about crime for the *London Evening Standard*, but the subjects of his stories range from food to education, to the power of innocent love and the erotic potential of the escape mechanism fitted to the Tornado F3 air defence aircraft.

Spicer strolled through the doorway of the Bristol, down the steps, across the deserted lobby until he stood before the desk. "M'sieur?" asked the girl without looking up. "I have a reservation." "Your name?" "Spicer." "How will you pay?" He handed over a credit card, "I am expecting my wife." "Oui, M'sieur." The girl passed him a key, "*Dernier étage, M'sieur*." Looking down, he saw that someone had already relieved him of his case.

He walked across to the lift, a skeletal, *fin-de-siécle ascenseur* with shiny wooden panels. The liftman, grey haired, formally perched on his wooden seat, stared at the floor. "*Dernier étage*," said Spicer. The lift rose slowly, the man leaning forward to open the doors as it hissed to a halt. Spicer's room was tucked away down silent corridors and he let himself in, glancing at the lights hanging in a constellation above the bed. He saw that his suitcase had preceded him and been placed on a folding platform by the door and he sighed, smiling to himself, sitting on the bed, feeling the softness of the mattress, lying slowly back, closing his eyes. Sleeping.

It was long past midnight when consciousness returned, coming upon him with a shaft of moonlight which sneaked through the curtains and struck soft sparks off the crystals on the chandelier. As his head cleared, he eased his feet onto the carpet, pulled back the curtains and gazed out towards the Madeleine which loomed like a slab of cake above the inky rooftops. He stepped out of his crumpled suit, yawned, rubbed his face, stretched his back. The phone hummed softly, once, twice. He sat on the bed. "This is it," he thought. A quiet voice, "*Votre femme est arrivée, M'sieur.*" He slipped on a dressing gown, looked in the bathroom mirror, wondering idly why she was in trouble.

She came into his arms as he opened the door. Florence was smaller than he remembered. He found her mouth, breathed in the Parisian night air from her face, entwined her tongue with his, felt the curve of her bottom through the thin stuff of her dress; fell backwards with her onto the bed, opened his legs, heard her kick away her shoes, felt her fingers in his hair, her breath on his cheek. For a moment he pulled back while she slipped out of her coat. He looked at her

face, white in the dim moonlight, saw the tucks at the corners of her mouth, the slant of her eye, the widow's peak. He smelt her; a dark feral scent spiced with citronella; watched her as she pulled her dress above her hips and tucked her fingers into her white pants; felt her breasts fall from the dress as she slipped the buttons. He reached down and moved aside her coat, turned her over so that his cock, inflamed now and hard, lay along the crease of her buttocks.

"No," she whispered, struggling beneath him until she lay on her back once more, looking into his eyes as she pulled her legs apart, separating, stretching them, holding a foot with each hand, stretching again, knees braced like a ballerina; offering herself. He felt the coarse hair on her pubic mound hard on his stomach, felt the hot, wet flesh as it slipped beneath his cock, heard her cry out as he entered her, felt her shudder as he lanced the chasm of her belly, his groin suddenly wet from her as he slipped his hands beneath her hips, his finger in her pretty, pink, wrinkled anus until he found that he could feel himself through her flesh and then, in the delirium of her orgasm, he joined her, his body curved above her like a figurehead, his eyes above the horizon, staring sightlessly at the silhouette of the Madeleine in the moonlight.

Breakfast arrived at ten o'clock. A discreet knock, followed by a waitress, yellow and black waistcoat tight at her hips, apron to the floor, the trolley crowned with silver trays arranged on a white embroidered cloth, flowers in a crystal flute. She reversed into the room, edging slowly backwards, leaving the food at the end of the bed and departing without turning round, muttering "*M'sieur*, *Dame*," as she closed the door. Florence, still half asleep, groaned, turned and brought her knee up gently into Spicer's groin. He saw that she was sucking her thumb like a child, watched her slowly wake, realise where she was, smiling, opening her eyes and leaning forward so that her breasts touched his collar bone. "*Hola*," she said, running her tongue across her lips, shaking her hair, rotating her shoulders as early-morning energy swept through her.

They took breakfast slowly, peeling nectarines with great care, taking champagne from the fridge and mixing it with the freshly squeezed orange juice. They covered themselves with crumbs, Florence making a hole in a warm brioche and slipping it onto Spicer's cock, spreading curls of salty butter and marmalade on her pussy and sighing as he licked her clean while she sucked her coffee from a bowl. He watched as she crawled, naked and warm, down the bed, making her way to the bathroom then pulling out the old bidet with its green, metal wheels and long hose into the bedroom where she started to wash with meticulous care. Spicer watched as she anointed her pussy with oil and trimmed herself with a pair of gold scissors, took a mirror from her bag and examined every inch of her groin and her thighs, pulled herself apart with long fingers, rubbing her pretty little clitoris, pink as a wild berry, as if to lightly lubricate herself for him, while all the time he watched, his heart pounding against his ribs.

And when she was ready, she came to him and led him to the bathroom where she cleaned him as thoroughly as she had cleaned herself. They heard the maid return at midday and take away the detritus of their meal, but they were too busy to break away from the intricacies of their toilet. "Now there are things that I

want you to do for me," said Florence when, refreshed and tingling, she led him back to the bed and tucked him beneath the sheets. He saw that she had smudged the inside of her thighs with blue powder to accentuate the soft, pastel colours of her vulva and while he watched, his chin sedate on the silk-trimmed blanket, she took a bowl of fruit from the sideboard, lay her pillows beside him and arranged herself on her stomach so that her bottom was raised, her legs apart, knees bent, feet kicking slowly in the air, the bowl by her side.

"*P'tit choufleur*," she said, "I have suffered a misfortune which means that I must spend some time away." And, as Spicer listened with growing interest, Florence told him that the *gendarmerie* were pursuing her and had even issued a warrant for her arrest on suspicion of assault with "*une arme mortelle*".

"It happened at work," she said, "and I am very worried." Spicer, who had been wallowing in post-coital languor spiked with pre-coital anticipation, returned sharply to non-coital reality, turned his head, cocked an eyebrow and focused on her face.

"Tell me what has happened," he said. He knew about her job. Amongst other things, it involved unsocial hours at the Alcazar in the rue Mazarine. She never discussed what she did and, for his part, he had not felt inclined to complicate their relationship with activities which occurred outside the bedroom.

But now, she leaned over, bit him softly on the tip of his nose, picked a grape and described how a group of Englishmen had come to the club. They had been there before; middle-aged, coarse men who dealt in the processing of pigs and spent their company's money to entertain buyers from supermarkets in Britain. The Alcazar is small and intimate; a bar, one or two *salles privées*, a room for the cabaret with a dance floor and a dozen or so tables. It is a place where wealthy Parisians go to relax in peace with beautiful women.

According to Florence, *les Anglais* had, two nights ago, brought with them a man who was staggering, drunk and out of control. He was tall, thin, red-faced, smoked cheap cigars; asked the girls to spend the night with him, pretended to offer them handfuls of money, seemed convinced that he was a man of the world even though he made a habit of public flatulence, which he found amusing. "You can picture the type of *cochon* this man is?" said Florence. Spicer nodded.

Every morning at one o'clock, Florence and her friend Raphael performed their cabaret. It was the culmination of the night's entertainment at the Alcazar, the prelude to the late hours when the serious business of the night was carried out. It incorporated a Harley Davidson *Electra Glide* doctored by the stage manager to act as a prop, a limited helping of lukewarm lesbianism, a soupçon of pussy and a few seconds of mock flagellation with a Brazilian bullwhip. The performance progressed as normal until the *Anglais*, whose name was Postlethwaite, placed his chair on the edge of the dance floor and started inching forward while the act developed. "By the time I had finished with Raphael, he had moved onto the middle of the floor," said Florence. "I began to work the whip. You have to do it slowly, sending the leather cord forward with your wrist, raising it with your arm flexed before moving your hand down, almost in slow motion, so that the tip cracks like a pistol. It's tricky, but I remember watching it snake forward as usual; at the last moment I pulled it back with my wrist. I saw him recoil in the darkness, it comes back to me in slow motion as I think of it,

the chair falling backwards, the man's hands clutching at his face. Blood between his fingers, a brief silence before he falls to the floor."

Entranced, Spicer asked, "Had he been shot?" "No, no, no," said Florence. "It was the whip. It removed the end of his nose. He was too close, an accident. In the confusion, I ran away. Raphael called to say the flics wanted to see me. I haven't been back since."

They lay in silence, side by side, Spicer unable to speak. In the outside world a church bell was tolling the Angelus and an ambulance was wailing on its way down the Faubourg St Honoré. Florence, unburdened, stretched across, wound an arm round his neck, pulled him towards her, took the lobe of his ear in her mouth, ran her tongue into the hollow of his neck, pulled him until he emerged from beneath the warm sheets and lay, his body warm as a freshly toasted croissant, on her curved, receptive back. Sunlight flooded the room illuminating the girl beneath him, catching the motes of dust in the air. He drew back until he was kneeling between her legs, leant forward into the moist cavern of her behind, inhaled her scent, pulled himself along her until he could hear her breathing, feel the flutter of her heart, knew that she was raising herself for him. "Perhaps you could stay here for a while with me?" he said. "No one would ever find you."

It is part of the service at the Bristol that the chandeliers are inspected and cleaned every day. So it was that at one o'clock, M. Roffey together with his aluminium ladder, apron and a wicker basket containing all the necessary cleaning equipment, arrived outside Spicer's room on *le dernier étage*. When his light-knuckled knock was ignored, he slipped a master key in the door, entered the room and erected his ladder at the foot of the bed. Behind him, as he lifted and polished the little cascades of wire and crystal, Spicer and Florence, oblivious to their surroundings, engulfed in their passion, eyes locked together, limbs entwined, breath exploding from their bodies, made love to each other in the Paris sunlight.

They were still at it as Roffey, content with his work, folded his ladder and slipped silently from the room. "*M'sieur, Dame*," he muttered as he closed the door and ticked off the completed job on his schedule.

"Time for lunch," he thought.

GREEN

John Gibb

John Gibb first started writing questionable stories for the *Erotic Review* when it was the only monthly magazine in Europe committed to serious sexual fiction. He learnt his trade as a journalist writing about crime for the *London Evening Standard*, but the subjects of his stories range from food to education, to the power of innocent love and the erotic potential of the escape mechanism fitted to the Tornado F3 air defence aircraft.

When I left University, I took it upon myself to follow the family tradition and became a Green. My mother had, for many years, been Secretary of the Somerset branch of the Campaign for Rural Conservation (CRC), a Council member of the National Trust, a Trustee of the Royal Society for the Protection of Birds and Chairman of the North Devon Conservative Association. Father had left home when I was at prep school, commenting that his wife had mated with him once twelve years ago and had been trying to kill him ever since.

After I came down, Mummy arranged for me to work at the CRC and now I am responsible for recruitment, which is to say I try to encourage more young people to join. We need to make the government sit up and take notice, but the membership is elderly and unimaginative and my priority is to persuade role models from show business to support us because it is only by associating ourselves with youth and glamour that we will attract young people to the cause.

Last year Pike, the singer and musician, wrote to tell us of his love for the English countryside and how he wants to do what he can for the national heritage. "Come and talk to me," he said, "my heart is overflowing with love for our rural landscape." This was manna from heaven to my Director, Winifred Peterkin-Cope. "Run along, Julian," she said to me. "Let us get him on board. See if you can winkle a concert out of him. Let's go!"

Pike lives in a sumptuous Regency villa overlooking Hampstead Heath. It is set back from the road and the wooden shutters give it the look of a French provincial town house. The front door is painted a glossy sea green and is decorated with an ancient brass knocker in the shape of a Native American head. A Range Rover, a Lotus Elise and a Ford Mustang are parked nose to tail in the drive. My knock is answered by a squat, bloodshot man with a short, lowering forehead, wet lips and thick wiry hair. His cigarette, held low between thumb and forefinger, is angled away from his hip. He tells me that his name is Quince, adding gruffly, as he stands back to let me into the library, that "Tracey will probably talk to you but Pike is recording in Guadeloupe." My heart sinks.

So I wait, sitting upright and uncomfortable on a gothic chair in the oak-panelled, book-lined room in the front of the house. There is a Persian rug and a wooden mantel, the surround decorated with Dutch tiles. Someone is moving around upstairs and I can hear Quince as he snuffles angrily in his office beneath the stairs. It is twenty minutes before Tracey appears, walking into the room in a pale green silk dressing gown.

"Lovely," she remarks, kissing me on the cheek. "Please excuse me for a few minutes, I have a little duty to perform, then we'll have a drink." As she speaks, there is a hammering on the front door and a stringy woman appears at the head of a column of twelve primary school kids in neat uniforms carrying clip boards. A little Adonis with his grey cap in his hands casts a furious glance at Tracey as she ruffles his golden locks and says, "This is Hubert, and we all know Hubert, don't we? Now I have a lovely film which I want you all to see."

"Come on, children," says the stringy woman, "sit on the floor. We're in for a treat."

And then, on the television screen before the silent and curious group, appears Pike in his famous Amnesty concert in Rio. He is giving us his inimitable "Mincing on Venus" and the audience is going wild. And then the scene fades and on the screen appears a bed, and on the bed is Tracey, legs apart and face on fire. And she is giving birth and I am watching, entranced, as the head of a child appears, and then the scene fades and it's back to Rio.

"Now children," says Tracey, "I am sure you will all recognize my husband Pike, but do you know what else is happening on the video? No? Well this is Hubert's first venture into the world; a very special moment."

And so a lesson in childbirth begins and ends, cutting from stage to bed and back until the two themes finally merge and the infant Hubert is delivered and safe in the loving arms of his mother and Pike has reached the climax of his song. I can see that Hubert, mortified, is sitting apart from the class with his head bowed, closely studying the rug and biting his nails.

"Well," I think to myself, "that's show business." After twenty long minutes it is over and the children are in the kitchen drinking goat's milk and eating biscuits.

"The house once belonged to Lord Browning," Tracey tells me as we stare at some Hockney cartoons hanging next to a series of platinum discs on the staircase. "Parts of it are Tudor and we bought it in 1996 from David Puttnam. Come and have a look at the bathroom. Pike designed it himself." And so we stroll around the corridors, looking into bedrooms and staring down from the windows at the Heath, damp and mottled brown below.

As I am trying to pluck up courage to raise the subject of a donation, Tracey hands me her wine glass, saying "Hold that a moment, honey," as she opens a stripped pine door to reveal a fine example of an early Thomas Crapper, decorated in willow pattern motif and with the original wall cistern. "Keep talking," she says, lifting her dressing gown and perching on the mahogany seat. I continue to look at her, trying to appear casual as she pees luxuriously, pulling a sheet of paper from the roll and slipping her hand between her legs. Seemingly unaware of the effect she is having on me, she continues her tour of the house. "You'll like this," she remarks, taking a pole from behind a pair of damask

curtains and reaching up to the ceiling to pull down a trapdoor and a hidden ladder, which slides silently down to rest on the floor. "Won't take a minute," she says, climbing up towards the brightly lit space behind the hatch. I look up at her long brown legs, which part fleetingly as she stretches to step into the roof.

The loft runs the length of the house and is planted from wall to wall with hundreds of tall green plants reaching hungrily to the light and heat of a dozen ceiling lamps. The air is heavy with moisture from a hidden network of perforated hoses.

"Pike likes to grow his own," she says, and passes me a small box in which two joints have been neatly wrapped. "I rolled these myself," she says, "just for you. Let's go down and look at the new bathroom."

"Erm," I say, my pulse fluttering like a moth, but she opens another door and we are in a large carpeted room in the middle of which, raised six inches or so on a broad stage above the floor, two baths have been positioned a foot or so apart with a table in between and taps at opposite ends.

Tracey walks across to the window and turns to look at me. A weak sun sinking in the wet sky outlines her legs through the gown, and a mile or so behind her a Jumbo slips past the top of the Post Office tower on its way down to Heathrow.

"We had the taps stolen to order from Blenheim Palace," she says in a matter-of-fact sort of way. And I walk across the room and stare at the dull silver faucets with their enamel buttons and engraved crests. With a sigh, she turns to reach for a bottle of Eau d'Orange Vert and I notice that she has loosened the sash of her gown and let it drop to the ground. As she pours the thick yellow liquid into the bath, the robe separates across her belly and reveals the gentle curve of her pubic bone and a thicket of wiry, black hair. She looks up, arching an eyebrow and staring solemnly at me through the scented, steam-filled room. Well, I suppose I have been waiting for this moment since I first became aware of what a glimpse of thigh could do to me. I have had no real experience of sex, although I was once reduced to a quivering jelly at Ampleforth by a beautiful boy called Ely. So I slip out of my blazer, drop my flannels, tear at the buttons of my shirt and kick off my brogues until I am naked, my heart hammering and my skin tingling as if it had been exposed to something toxic.

Tracey has turned away and is kneeling on the carpet, leaning across the bath to turn off the water. The silk of her gown is stretched tight across her buttocks and she turns to look at me over her shoulder. "Come round behind me, Julian," she says and shifts herself slightly so that her knees are further apart and her bottom is raised as if an offering, and I do as she asks and she pulls the green silk aside and waits for me. And so I kneel behind her and put an arm around her hips and hold my cock, which has regenerated from a flaccid scrap of gristle into something worthwhile, and slip it slowly up and down her pussy and push myself gently inside her.

But it is not yet to be and, almost immediately and without a word, she twists away to gather an armful of bath towels from a cupboard and lay them on the floor beside the bath. She takes some green candles from a drawer, lights them and places them around the room, then closes the palms of her hands before her face, bows her head, looks at me and says, "The act of ritual lovemaking is a participation in cosmic and divine processes."

And then she comes to me across the soft carpet, drops her gown to the floor, winds her fingers into my hair and clamps her open mouth to mine, pressing her body hard against my chest and grabbing my balls in her hot hand. Some instinct, reinforced by the fierce grip which Tracey has instituted on my scrotum, forces me to ignore the cardiac fluttering in my chest and do as she wants and to lie on the towel and to open my legs and to look miserably at my prick which is now lying like a blood-sated, tropical leech across the top of my thigh. She sits cross-legged on the floor and faces me.

"This is your Lingam," says Tracey, encircling the old chap carefully with her thumb and forefinger and anointing it with oil from a small silver phial. "Lingam is Sanskrit for penis, the wand of light," and she starts to move her encircling fingers up and down my prick with her left hand while fondling my balls with the right.

Well, inexperienced as I am, I know that it is but a moment before my loins turn to jelly and I ejaculate prolifically into the hot, perfumed, steamy air. But Tracey, understanding well what I am feeling, slows the rhythm of her hand and lightly grips me at the top of my penis so that the imminent eruption subsides. And then she starts again.

"Women are able to climax many times in the Tantra," she says, "we call it riding the bliss wave." And so we continue for what feels like hours until my "Lingam" and everything else below my waist is on the verge of volcanic detonation. But, as I reach the moment at which I feel that I can take no more, she turns away from me and leans once more across the bath.

"I am offering you my Yoni," she says, pulling her legs apart to reveal the inside of her glistening, pink, slippery pussy. And she gasps "Shiva" as I enter her and she turns her head and looks into my eyes as I slowly and luxuriously flood inside her and float away into oblivion. When I regain consciousness and look at my watch, it is four o'clock and I am covered in a thick towel and lying on my back on the bathroom floor. The water has turned cold and oily in the bath and the candles have guttered down to lumpy gobbets of blackened wax. Hubert has materialized and is standing over me with a cup of tea, which is clanking in its saucer. "Mummy's had to go out," he says, looking up at the ceiling as if trying to remember his lines. "She says can you come back again tomorrow?"

THE ELEGANT DUCHESS

Dean Francis

Dean Francis was born in Belfast, of Anglo-Irish parentage, and was sent to a seminary by his mother who was keen for him to join the Catholic clergy. Six months later he left in disgrace after seducing the under-matron of a local infirmary. He joined the Royal Engineers, and after a brief but distinguished career, he left the army to work in a well-known advertising agency. He currently resides in rural Sussex.

Even though she knew virtually nothing about aeronautics, when the Duchess saw the size of Fred Day's balloon, she realised that it would only carry the pair of them. It was quite the smallest of the dozen or so being inflated in Hurlingham Park that morning, an elegant, almost quilted, purple envelope, swelling gently upwards from its basket. It seemed dwarfed by the monsters grouped on the running track; some of those were fifty feet high; their baskets had canopies and even motor wheels for landing.

Fred was almost too busy to notice the Duchess as she headed towards his balloon. She had to hop over long rubber pipes which snaked about in every direction. There was a fearful smell in the air, unsurprisingly, since a huge motor-pump, supervised by a very worried workman, was delivering gas to all the balloons, except, as it happened, Fred's, which was almost drum tight and ready to fly.

"Hello, Carrie," he shouted, heaving a stepladder over the basket and handing her in. "We're in luck. I've persuaded Sam to follow us in the Napier." He pointed to where Sam Grant, another of the Duchess's acquaintances, was sitting in his motor car with the engine warming noisily.

It was a gorgeous July morning. Not a trace of breeze, at least down there near Putney Bridge. However, just after Fred had cast off and they were rising over the trees near the river, the Duchess noticed that they were beginning to drift westwards quite briskly. No other balloon followed them; evidently Fred had been first in the queue for gas and Sam Grant had the Napier out of Hurlingham Park and on to the Bridge Approach in a trice. The Duchess watched him wait on the north bank for a full minute before it was clear that Fred's track was across Barnes Common, and then he whisked the big motor over the bridge and set off smartly down the Richmond Road.

"Shall we lose him?" asked the Duchess

"Not with the wind this light," Fred said. "But we have to put her up to at least six hundred feet so that he can keep us in view above the houses."

"How many miles of houses?"

"About twelve."

Fred consulted the barometer then poured a gallon can of water over the side of the basket.

"Shower of rain for Barnes High Street," he said, and smiled.

They were moving steadily across Barnes Common now. Looking down the Duchess could see a small boy, racing along, peering up, trying to keep pace with them, but failing. Evidently they were travelling at the speed of a carriage rather than a motorcar's, but unlike motors, balloons did not need to stay on the roads. Now she could see no sign of Sam Grant's Napier. She presumed it was still behind the houses that fringed the Common and would be trying to follow them on the road that ringed it. She could hear dogs barking. Clearly, balloons were unacceptable in the canine world and needed to be urged on their way. A woman hanging out washing gave them a wave and the Duchess waved back.

They were approaching the steeple of the largest church in Barnes. Since its weathercock seemed to be on a level with their basket, it was fortunate that the balloon was on a path to avoid it.

"We're still too low," said Fred, and emptied a second water can over the side. "It's the heat."

This second shower far below seemed more effective. The Duchess saw the passing weathercock dip slightly as they rose. She realised that the balloon's balance was very delicately poised. No doubt, they were gaining height. Richmond Bridge on the great Kew bend of the Thames was in sight now. That meant the balloon was high enough to clear the famous Hill.

"Sweet lass of Richmond Hill," sang Fred.

"Sweet lass of Richmond Hill," sang she.

"I'd crowns resign to call thee mine," he continued.

"Sweet lass of Richmond Hill," she ended.

The balloon had just reached Kew Gardens and the Duchess could clearly pick out the Water Lily Pond and the Queen's Cottage, when Fred made the move she had half-expected, perhaps even half-encouraged. He leant across the basket and lifted her skirt with a firm, almost polite, hoist, holding it up. The cool air wafted around her buttocks with a sudden, delicious, caress.

"Sweet Jesus," he said. "What a glorious pair."

The Duchess, who had been leaning over the edge of the basket on tiptoe for a better view of the sights beneath, just let out a little "Ohhh!" She did not move her hands from the basket's coaming. Nor did she attempt to snatch her skirt down. In a pleasurable blend of guilt and pride, she understood that to fly with a man of Fred's reputation, to bend over in front of him and thus present him with such a delectable and easily gained fleshly temptation, somehow made any plausible protest impossible. Besides, she knew she possessed one of the most superbly modelled bottoms in the country. Two wondrously smooth and supple alabaster cheeks rose in majesty from pale thighs and now trembled from their sudden revelation.

"Ohhh!" she said again. "You are a very naughty man, Fred Day."

"It's the finest bum in London," said Fred, with a slight husk in his voice.

"Only London?"

"Finest in the land," said Fred.

"That's better." The Duchess rose as high as tiptoe would allow, so her bottom would tighten and dimple in one and the same action. Responsive to her effort, Fred gathered her skirt firmly in his fist, and began to stroke her with purpose.

"I hope you are concentrating on your ballooning," said the Duchess.

"It'll manage," said Fred. "That's Syon House on the far side of the river. We should go right over the top of it."

The Duchess glanced forward and saw that they were about to cross the river for the third time. Again, she looked back for the Napier. At first there was no sight of Sam Grant's automobile but then, yes, there he was, a speeding dot on the Richmond Road.

"I can see him," she said, "he's miles behind."

"He'll be a lot further behind soon," said Fred. "On account that he'll need to cross Hammersmith Bridge to follow us north of the river."

He let go of the Duchess's skirt, grabbed another container of water and poured it over the side. Then, as if merely interrupted by his work, he raised her skirt once more.

"There's something very rum indeed about all this," she thought. "Here I am, bare-bottomed, gazing down on London from a balloon, with nobody below wiser as to what's going on. All very rum, but strangely exciting, and new."

Now Fred had begun to stroke her bottom again with consummate skill. He felt her cheeks delicately, almost reverentially, with a sports-hardened hand. He let it race across dimple and cleft and then, with studied casualness, allowed it to stray into the more secret places. The Duchess wondered what else Fred's hand could offer. Perhaps, in far more intimate circumstances, his hand, wielding birch or cane, or merely spanking her, would yield yet more intriguing sensations. Fred was a sportsman, with a sportsman's love of thrills. "I am a thrill for him," she thought, "just as this is thrilling for me. For what could be more exciting than to fly silently over this murmuring city in this venturesome machine while having one's posterior caressed by such a safe and skilled pilot, and one obviously such a connoisseur of female flesh?"

She told him of her appreciation.

Fred grunted, either from pleasure or self-deprecation. She must have provoked him in some mysterious way, for she sensed him bend. Then instead of fondling, he was kissing, her buttocks.

"He needs encouragement," she thought. Keeping one hand on the hide coaming, she reached behind her and pressed her admirer's head to her bottom, using his face as a massage-roller, kneading it into the cleft, retrieving it, bringing it over the arch of each buttock in turn, her fingers entwined in his hair to get a better grasp.

She began to understand her bottom's significance for Fred. He had entirely sacralised her buttocks. To him they offered an altar for his adoration, a firm, supple chantry where he might perform all the rites that were due to the goddess he so revered.

He freed his head from her grasp and stood up close behind her. Close enough to imprison her skirt high on her thighs, leaving no barrier for his impending penetration. He set his hands alongside hers, gripping the leather coaming of the

basket as she was. The Duchess knew immediately that this was a signal that his penetration of her would follow soon. Next to hers, his hands pressed inwards and, as if this was some sort of signal, she moved her feet apart to widen the cleft of her bottom for him.

He was big, frighteningly big. At first his heroic striving was enough for them both. It seemed that, for Fred at least, the effort would be the reward. He wondered if the task was beyond him, even with all the Duchess's help. Her involuntary resistance spurred him on, causing him to thrust more desperately and delightfully.

For her, his struggle to penetrate her, the pressure of his hands upon hers, the turbulence at her buttocks, all combined to give her great pleasure. Try as she might (and she tried, womanfully, with every artifice of her body), Fred could not gain admittance. When eventually Fred's struggles were in danger of becoming more tragic-comic than heroic, the Duchess took pity on her valiant aeronaut. With commendable practicality, she suggested that he reach into the little picnic hamper and avail himself of the butter therein. This achieved, Fred finally entered the Duchess, who gave another little "Ohhh!" and they continued with a greater sense of purpose, both revelling in the strange circumstances of their aerial coupling.

"I've never been had like this before," said the Duchess. This was not entirely true, because lovers of both sexes and several nationalities had breached the fine bastions that Fred had now overcome. She meant, of course, that the circumstances of Fred's onslaught, the setting of his siege, were unique. Her denial could be justified, she thought. "The chances of any other woman being buggered in a balloon over London are so infinitesimally small as to be non-existent, so I'm entitled to a little poetic licence."

And now the roads and houses were starting to become decidedly thinner as they left Chiswick and started to cross Hounslow Heath. Below she could see scrubland, sandy, patched with gorse and young birch and cut through by the odd stream. There were a few isolated cottages and an inn not far from a dilapidated mill. Here and there were market gardens, neat, cultivated properties with working sheds and small stables. Two ponies panicked at the sight of the approaching balloon and galloped frantically around their paddock.

Once or twice amid Fred's giant thrustings, the Duchess asked herself if he might not enjoy penetrating her in the more conventional manner. The "tradesman's entrance", however, had been his first objective, and he was not, she concluded, a man to be deflected from what he had so dramatically set mind and body to achieve.

Over the pond at Hounslow village Fred said, "You're a tight girl, Carrie."

"Serve you right, you bugger," said the Duchess. "That's my tradesman's entrance. You can't expect politeness at the back door."

"Give me a chance," he said.

"Nobody ever had a better one, buggering a lady of quality in a balloon. What more could you wish for?"

Fred finally reached an explosive climax just as they sailed over Feltham Station. The Duchess had grown impressed by his stout endurance. He'd begun to roger her at Chiswick, a long, long twenty minutes before. Fred came with

great thrusts and hoarse cries. He shouted out his pleasure. "Oh, yes, Carrie, oh yes . . ."

"Did you enjoy that?"

There was a mixture of triumph and relief in her voice. It was more or less a rhetorical question, but she took a woman's pride in the extraordinary allure that her buttocks held for him and the comfort of knowing he was effectively "finished".

She answered for him.

"I felt you did. I'm glad you did."

In truth, she was very fond of Fred.

Moreover, she was really taking quite a shine to ballooning.

FATIMA

Adnan Mahmutović

Adnan Mahmutović became a refugee of war in 1993 and ended up in Sweden. He worked for a decade with people with brain damage, while studying English and philosophy. He has a Ph.D. in English literature and an MFA in creative writing, and is currently a lecturer and writer-in-residence at the Department of English, Stockholm University. His stories deal with contemporary European history, and the issues of identity and home for Bosnian refugees.

It's football time in Munich. Every autumn the same thing. Packs of football fans and hooligans rush by me and disappear in local bars, howling, "*Bayern, Bayern*." I don't know if the team won or lost. They always sound the same to me, keyed up for victory or disappointed after a lost game. I can't locate where the crowd is coming from. The arena's not that close to this part of the city. I feel nuts. Every face in the crowd is like one of my customers, people I've pleasured for ten years now.

The closest hooligan-free bar sucks me in and even though I never drink booze, I feel like getting drunk. I've been to this bar before with a couple of girls. They call it *Drei Drei Drei* (Three, Three, Three). It has three fat but clean bartenders, and you have to order at least three *Seidels* of beer before they crack a smile. Everything costs three times as much as in any other decent place. They say the beer's great, but all I've ever had is Schweppes, bitter soda.

The place is small and vibrating with deep male voices. The owners have provided only a small TV, yet every man gazes at the screen. The only man who isn't broken and bald moves a little to the left to make an opening for me at the bar. He sticks out from the usual crowd. His skin is black, he wears a light grey suit and smells like Aqua de Gio, the fresh Armani fragrance, although the man's sweat gives it an extra twist. His fist-long beard has beautifully hanging curls. His hair is bushy, yet his arms seem shaven. I edge closer. He says to the bartender, "Another one." The double-chinned man puts a glass of bright red fluid in front of me.

"I call it the Red Sea," the black man says and takes a long slow sip, hardly changing the level in the glass. I can tell he is at least forty. There are white hairs in his beard and wrinkles on his forehead and around his mouth. He must have been smiling a lot in his life.

"I guess you like to be called Moses."

"Joyce goes just fine."

"May I call you James?"

"Joyce O'Hara."

"All right then Joyce," I switch to English and his eyes brighten. "A bloody Irish, ha. I thought your German was funny." At that moment I don't feel like turning down a drink, so I take a sip and suddenly feel as if I am in another world. It's cranberry juice. I try to keep my face straight, and ask, "You're having your period or what?"

He smiles. He has a small slot between his big front teeth, like my first lover Aziz. I shudder at the thought of him but shake it off, like a dog shakes off water. I breathe deep to relax. I figure Joyce is lying about his name, but I like the *spiel*. If he wants for a moment to be someone else, that's fine, I'm used to it. I say, "Irish, I like that. Been here a while, mate?"

"Couple of years. I'm with Bayern."

"Say no more. Playing?"

He reacts to the irony by slightly biting his lip, and then he says, "Coaching."

"Even worse. So the football-god brought you here?"

"Not really. It was love. A woman."

"Ha, you must be an awful coach."

"You can say that again. Or not really, I mean Bayern is a big team after all. But then you're right, marriage and football zeal, it's tough, like having two mistresses you can't live without. Anyway, my wife split the other year and the rest is, well you've heard this story before, right?" He turns back to face the bartender who's wiping clean a big, ceramic *Seidel* and sneering at him. He mutters, "I'm boring you" and tips his head forward.

I sit beside him and pull my glass close to my cleavage. I can tell he has caught the move with the corner of his eye and is fighting not to stare. He starts to fidget with a coin. I say, "On the contrary, a pitch-black Irishman sipping at a glass of cranberry juice, in Germany of all places. I can swallow that, but to pose as the Bayern coach, now that's sacrilegious. I live here, dammit. The man who leads the Reds to victory nowadays is called Ottmar Hitzfeld, and he looks like Swiss cheese."

He laughs. It's as if he wanted to test me with the bizarre picture of himself. I ask, "So really, where are you from?"

"Ireland. Honest to God. I live there. I'm originally Nigerian but I've lived half my life with the Irish. My mother married one back in the eighties."

"So you weren't totally bullshitting me?"

"No. But my name's not Joyce, it's Jonah."

"What brings you to Munich, Jonah?"

"I'm here to talk to some journalists and writers about a project we're starting."

"No kidding, you a writer?"

"Goodness, no. I'm just a supporter of this organization called the PEN. Ever heard of it?"

I wave my head.

"It's like an international support group for writers under persecution by their governments. We fight for freedom of speech and press, you know, basically help people out. The president is a Nigerian author and that's how I got into it. It's somewhat personal for me, but I'm really just a small businessman. I sell organic food in the UK."

"So you're the good guy, helping people out even when you don't get filthy rich. Reminds me of my . . . ah never mind."

"What?"

"Nothing. You're very original. You stick out, like in this bar."

He turns around and takes a look at the other guests. There is only one bloke in the steamy atmosphere who might be a Turk, but he has bleached his hair. Jonah says, "I never thought of myself as original. You seem to care for that."

"Not really, but it can come in handy at times. A good story's what everyone wants. A year ago, a German immigration judge declined a Somali woman's stay permit, because her story was full of clichés."

"You're kidding? What did she say?"

"Lots of murder, someone burnt down her house, then rape, you know, the usual bitter clichés of war. The damn judge said he'd heard that story before."

"That's horrible. How do you know all this? Are you a lawyer or something?"

I laugh so much it feels as if my lips are cracking. "Not really. Though I have a special bond to law and law-people." I haven't laughed like this in years. I feel vulnerable, open, but also great. I wouldn't mind laughing more. My God, have I come so far in my life I can say "Once upon a time I laughed?"

"This woman, she's a hooker now, just four blocks from here, in the so-called crimson belt of the city."

"Really, where's that?"

"Ah, you're interested already. It's an imaginary ring that cuts through the city, neither the centre nor suburbia. That's where the big brothels are, stuff like that."

Jonah drops the coin but doesn't bend down to get it. He blushes. "Are you . . . ?"

I wipe the sweat breaking from my eyebrow thinking: *Here we go again, you can't hide, you're a 101 prostitute. It's in your blood now, you're a stereotype now, like computer geeks, cops, mad scientists, or fair ladies.* I say, "I have to make a phone call." The bartender directs me with his hitching thumb. I go there and pretend I'm talking to someone for ten minutes.

Back at the bar I grab my glass, which the Nigerian has moved closer to his, and without giving it much thought, drink it all. I laugh again. "Cranberry juice, I hear that's good for bladder infection."

He laughs and I can see his big molars. I love that. He drinks up his juice and says, "So what's your story? You can start with a name. A false one will do."

I never use a false name. I want there to be a little piece of me in every pretending. I say crisply, "Fatima."

His eyes bulge and both his hands glide down to his knees.

"I'd never guess you're Middle Eastern."

"Don't worry. I won't blow you up."

"I'd take you for a regular German girl."

"Bosnian."

"Ha, I see. You got me there. Bosnia, you say? I imagined you'd be more like, I don't know, the Turks."

I say nothing. He goes on, "I heard Germany's sending you all back."

"I guess I had an original story to give and got to stay."

He looks like a kid staring at sweets behind a thick window.

"Which is?"

"Lost love," I say, trying to laugh at myself but failing. I am glad that at least he can laugh at me. "I'm like my father. He left his whole family in Western Bosnia to move in with Mum in this mountain town. He rebelled against the old tradition that a man should stay at home and bring a wife into it. Good that Mum was rich."

He gives me that say-no-more-I-know-what-you-mean look.

I hiss, "Hey, he wasn't like that. He loved her."

"I'm sure."

"Screw that tone!"

He bends his head down then looks up again with puppy eyes and a sad expression. I bite my thumbnail a little then take hold of the empty glass just to remove the finger from my mouth. I laugh.

"What is it?"

"It's just so funny. I can almost see Mum right now, the way she moved like old Bosnian noble people do, flaunting all the exclusive-edition books they bought for me. They put a lot into my education. I guess I'd be something of a disappointment to them now."

Jonah says nothing for a while then, "I assume your parents are dead. I'm sorry."

I feel off guard. Why am I talking about my parents?

"You loved them a lot, didn't you?"

"Yes, but then, I don't know, really. My father was always working. I never got to know him properly, and Mum, I didn't like the way she was living for the moment, everybody gathered, safe and preened, no matter what. She was no visionary. Well yes, I did love them a lot. I've just put all that behind me."

Jonah snaps his fingers at the sulky bartender and gets another round of juice. I take a sip and shudder. When I first saw Jonah, I thought to take him home with me, but now that he has dug up some old memories of mine, I don't know. I don't really feel like having ordinary sex, none of that cosy making love. I don't feel like extraordinary sex either. I don't feel like anything but walking by the Isar and feeding the swans.

Jonah is silent as a fish. I scan him from top to toe and drink up the bitter beverage. I kiss my fingertips and touch the rim of his glass, saying, "Well, I doubt you can afford anything else. Don't get yourself drowned." I leave the bar, wondering if he's watching me as I exit the building.

I flow up the street with the river of people who are crying, "*Bayern. Bayern.*"

Later in the evening, I sit on the toilet, muttering, "That damn cranberry juice." I think I might have some slight infection after all. Or perhaps I am just nervous. I've had this problem for years now. It's not an easy thing to deal with in my profession. Every day's different. Every task demands the best performance. I try not to lie down and simply let myself be screwed in a passive way. That doesn't make a man come back. Sometimes I eat a lot of chocolate and get constipation. Ah, no one wants to hear such things.

The next morning, to cap it all, I have this unexplained butterflies-in-the-belly feeling and I don't like it. I don't like it at all. Is my body trying to tell me I have a crush on the Nigerian already? Why did I get away from him so quickly,

and with that kind of remark? Because I feared he'd wake up the next morning and toss me some money? Have I started to shun men I like?

Butterflies keep multiplying so I decide to put myself and my destiny to a test. In the evening, I will go to the same *Drei Drei Drei* bar, hoping to find the Nigerian fighter for the maladjusted writers. The odds are against me, no doubt, but then maybe I made a great impression. If he isn't there, then the fates decided that way, but if he is, then I'll thank God and start thinking about how to pursue this familiar but uncanny feeling for a man.

I try on every dress I own, every pair of stockings and shoes. I decide which make-up and eau de toilette go with which garments. In the end I shove everything back into my wardrobe and put on black trousers, a purple jumper that Mary knitted for me as thanks for the rich customer I gave her, and finally, a long winter jacket I got from Red Cross back in Bosnia, which I kept as a memento.

I paint my face quite sloppily and rush out. The air is so cold I can hardly open my eyes. Instead, I fumble my way to the *S-Bahn* stop. It takes almost an hour to get downtown. There's an accident close to the city centre. The streetcar stops at one point, close to the river Isar. I take this as a sign. So, before going to the bar, I walk down to the Isar to wash off my make-up. There is a crust of ice over the surface close to the banks. In the middle, the stream is still free. A frozen swan floats by.

The bar door is like a stone slab. My frozen arm feels like shattering as I both push and pull because the door won't open either way. I pant and then push hard. It opens and my eyes become misty, as Max's glasses do when he enters my warm room on a cold day.

I squint. Jonah's not there, of course. I almost wave my hand at the sky thinking, "*You just don't give me a break, do you?*" I feel an instant remorse for my thoughts, as some sense of spirituality tells me I can't hurry the Boss in what he feels is right for me. I got this from *mekteb*, an extra-curricular religious education I went to on weekends for five years. I liked going there with other girls and boys, before *imam* Atif became more and more ill. My parents didn't force me. They weren't particularly religious. Mum only followed other women to the mosque during Ramadan. Father's religious practice boiled down to occasionally crying out, "My God", "*Inshallah*", and "Goddamn", like the bulk of the new Communists, out of old habit. Only my parents never made good Communists either.

I survey the bar once again to make sure Jonah isn't inside, then go for the door.

"Fatima?" My name rings nicely with that strange accent. I want everything around me to freeze for a moment, so I can take a couple more cold breaths, but no such luck, I have to turn round and face him. Water is dripping from his fingers and he dries them against his baggy trousers. He wears a white jumper, like golfers wear. I read from his rapidly opening and closing lids that he's both surprised to see me and that he's been here for a while, perhaps since I first left him, hoping I'd come back. The body never lies. He pulls his shoulders back and up but they are still heavy with desire. Few of us can control our bodies to the extent that they don't betray our secret feelings, and his whole body says he's been waiting. I cannot tell for how long. Obviously, he hasn't been drinking anything

strong, yet his hands tremble and his lips have become thinner and paler. Then the most important sign, he is ready to jump at my wink.

I walk over to Jonah, determined not to ponder on serendipity, coincidence, or fate. I fear that any answers, true or false, would ruin everything. I just let everything be as it is for the moment. I take his extra-large hand into my extra-small one, lead him out into the traffic buzz, kiss him right there for everyone to see, and then take him home. I lead him in without turning on the lights. That way he won't get the sense of the place.

At first, I fuck the Nigerian fast; just to break the already thawing ice and then I let him fall asleep. I put on a negligee and fall asleep myself. My dreams set me on fire and I wake ready to conquer my lover, this time thoroughly. I suck him dry of all his riches, like a real empress. Only, I have no country to back me up, no imperial power behind me.

His sighs rustle like autumn leaves. His black skin is hairless and his palms gentle. I contract. He twitches and moans. I'm wet inside and out. I don't call his name. I sit on him, as gently as my warm silhouette on the wall opposite the window, lighted by crescent moons. He twitches, one, two, three, times, and his head falls back on the pillow. I wait until he goes limp and then I pull myself up from the slack penis. I leave it wet and drenched in my smell. A trickle of blood runs down my thigh. It is lukewarm and quick, but it stops just above my knee and curdles. I don't feel pain.

My negligee vibrates in the draught when I go out of the bedroom and into the kitchen. I take a notebook and a pencil. It's so dark I can't tell the pages from the cool air. It doesn't matter. I know they are blank. Then, as if the pen forces me, I write down a name, Aziz. The written name forces him to life again, where he belongs in a story of me. I press the tip against the paper. It sinks deep and sticks in this self-made hole. The ink seeps out and wets the paper. I walk into the loo, throw the pen into the toilet, but then take it out immediately and put it in between the blank sheets. The paper sucks it dry. I open the book to a new page and write my name on a dry blotch, where I hope it lies next to his. I go back to the kitchen and put it in the large tea jar I received from a Japanese customer a few years ago.

I go back to Jonah, turn the paper lamp on and pull the blanket off him. With hungry eyes, I divide him into parts, like some strange butcher deciding which bits and pieces are good for which dish. Some bits and pieces tingle the tip of the tongue, some are best when they fill the whole mouth, some when they only touch the back of the tongue or the hard cavity.

I touch his circumcised penis. His testicles are unusually small, for a big bloke like that. An old fear drums in my head. I lift up his balls, check and double-check everything. It's my old anxiety kicking in. Even though so many years have passed since Aziz and I separated, whenever I unbutton someone's trousers, my hands shake and I make it a holy ritual, for fear to discover someone else with the same secret. I slow everything down: slowly touching, slowly feeling, slowly smelling, and slowly listening to the person's breathing. Judge Max said this fascinated him about me, the constant anxiety. Most girls know what they have to do and do it mechanically, to get it over and done with. I still fear what's going to happen. Every single time the fear takes over and it shows, even when I have control in my hands. That excites people.

There's nothing wrong with Jonah. I look at his beardy face. He looks like a bust of Spartan king Leonidas that I saw in the office of Professor Stier a year ago. It was made of dirty white plaster. The professor made a bed of books on the carpeted floor, tied me to the huge bust of Leonidas and took me from behind. I stared at the engraved name, as Professor Stier kept impersonating a lion.

I crawl back next to my lover, take his hand, and slip it between my legs. He wakes up. He won't let me suck him. Instead, he wants to please only me now. He kisses me from top to toe, licking me exhausted. Then, when I'm slowly vibrating like the heavy sound that lingers both inside and outside the brass shell of a tube, when I can no longer open my eyes for fear he'll disappear, he enters me and I climax, one two . . . then relax.

Hoping that thought can stream from my head to his, I think, *"Marry me Jonah. Make me legitimate in the eyes of the people, any people. Take me away from here."* I kind of regret thinking the last part. I love Munich, but I once loved Aziz and still I left him.

A couple of nights later, I wave to my Nigerian Leonidas as he drags his feet up the stairs of a green plane to Ireland. In my other hand, I clutch his business card with a number jotted on the back. The secret number. I gave him a number too.

He calls back the following morning, before even Munich traffic has woken up. I try to make myself talk because I'm absolutely stunned. He actually called back. Like my first date, I have nothing to say for fear he will find me boring, but I can't hold his hand and glance at him either. I sit in silence. The clock's tick-tock is like a bell.

"Fatima."

God, I love the way my name breaks in that Irish accent.

"Jonah."

"I think I'm going to apply for the Bayern coach position."

I laugh. "I can be your secretary then."

"You tease. I can't stop thinking about you."

I want to say the same but keep gulping saliva.

"Can you come to Ireland?"

Damn, now I definitely don't know what to say. Whatever he may have guessed about me it's about to stop being guesswork and turn into good hard facts.

"Fatima, are you still there?"

Oh, I'm still here, but I wish I were on the plane to Dublin. "Right here. You see . . . oh my God. All right." I say, the way I used to deliver my oral exams back in school. "I'm an illegal immigrant Jonah. Unless you can find some tough sailor with an old rusty boat to ship me over there, chances are I'll never see U2 playing at home."

Now he doesn't know how to respond.

"Besides, you know what I am, don't pretend you don't."

"I know, I know, I've been thinking about it ever since I met you, but I don't think I care. I want you beside me."

I feel weak and lie on the floor. "I like you too Jonah, and I don't care what you do for a living either."

He laughs nervously. "Is there any way you could come round?"

"I told you. They say Europe is losing its borders, but that doesn't mean you

don't get checked when you cross these non-existing walls."

He hawks and says, "All right. I'll see what I can do. You don't happen to be an exiled writer or something, so I can ask the PEN to help you out?"

That moment an entire vision of a possible future opens up before me, like the projections on old, rotting screens. The romantic flickering type of vision. My God, could this for one second be an opportunity? A writer, does that include a wannabe journalist? I don't dare ask. Instead, as the reel of my alternate future starts tangling in the projector and melts from the heat of the machine, I say, "No, not a writer. But maybe I should give it a try. Write a memoir or some such thing."

"Maybe, Fatima. Can you? You'd have to prove yourself. These people are rather posh. They only support the best, and preferably political writers."

I say, as if it mattered, "No romance?"

"I don't know. I can ask."

"Stop it now."

"What?"

"Stop messing with my head. Stop blowing Irish fantasies into my head. Can you come here? Can you smuggle me out? Can you come like a damn superhero riding on a whale to fetch me by the Isar bank? I didn't think so. It was really nice meeting you Jonah."

I hang up, then think, my God what have I done? Why can't I be nicer? I love fantasies, but I just hate being in one. I'll end up in a lunatic asylum, if they still keep such places. Now that would be a real-life solution, feign I'm crazy, that I'm mental, and, my God, I am losing my mind.

For months, Jonah does not call. I'm still having glimpses of him. One night, I imagine him in the strange shape of one Siamese twin, the other half being my old love Aziz. Jonah to the right, Aziz to the left. They are attached at the hips and shoulders, with only one arm each. I shake my head to separate them or to remove that horrible image completely. Jonah fades away but not Aziz. The mind forgets things easily, but my whole goddamn body remembers my lovers. It's like that mitosis experiment I did in the sixth grade with peas and lukewarm water. The two are completely different but when they meet, the small thing sucks the huge one into itself and then they grow together into something else.

From THE BRONZE HORSEMAN

Paullina Simons

Paullina Simons was born in Leningrad, USSR, and at the age of ten, her family immigrated to the United States. After graduating from university, and after various jobs, including working as a financial journalist and as a translator, Paullina wrote her first novel, *Tully*. She has since written *Red Leaves, Eleven Hours, The Bronze Horseman, The Bridge to Holy Cross* (also known as *Tatiana and Alexander*), *The Summer Garden, TheGirl in Times Square* and *Road to Paradise*. Many of Paullina's novels have become international bestsellers around the world. *The Bronze Horseman* is set during the Siege of Leningrad: For Tatiana, love arrives in the guise of Alexander, who harbours a deadly and extra-ordinary secret.

Alexander carried her in his arms to his tent, setting her down on his blan ket and closing the tent flaps behind them. It was subdued and dusky inside, with only the barest sunlight filtering in through the open ties. "I would have brought you inside the nice, clean house," he said, smiling, "but we have no quilts, no pillows, and it's all wood and a hard furnace top."

"Mmm," Tatiana muttered. "Tent is good." She could have been on a marble floor of the Peterhof Palace for all she cared.

Alexander was hugging her to him, but all she wanted was to be lying down in front of him. How did he do that? "Shura," she whispered.

"Yes," he whispered back, kissing her neck.

But he wasn't . . . he wasn't doing anything else, as if he were waiting, or thinking, or . . .

Alexander pulled away from her, and she saw by the reserve in his eyes that something was troubling him.

"What's the matter?"

He couldn't look at her. "You said so many upset things to me yesterday . . . not that I don't deserve all of them . . ."

"You don't deserve *all* of them." She smiled. "What?"

He took a deep breath.

"Ask me." She knew what he wanted from her.

His eyes remained lowered.

Shaking her head, Tatiana said, "Lift your head. Look at me." He did. Kneeling in front of him, Tatiana held his face between her hands, kissed his lips, and

said, "Alexander, the answer is yes . . . yes . . . of course I've saved myself for you. I belong to you. What are you even thinking?"

His happy, relieved, excited eyes flowed into her. "Oh, Tania." For a moment he didn't speak. "You have no idea . . . what that means to me – "

"Shh," she whispered. She knew.

He closed his eyes. "You were right," he said emotionally. "I don't deserve what you have to give me."

"If not you, who?" said Tatiana, hugging him. "Where are your hands? I want them."

"My *hands?*" He kissed her ardently. "Lift your arms." He took off her sundress and laid her down on the blanket, kneeling over her, roaming over her face and throat with his hungry lips, roaming over her body with his hungry fingers.

"Now I need you completely naked before me, all right?" he whispered.

"All right."

He took off her white cotton panties, and Tatiana in her weakness watched him in his weakness, staring at her and then uttering, "No, I can't take it . . ."

He put his cheek against her breast. "Your heart is pounding like gun-fire . . ." He licked her nipples. "Don't be scared."

"All right," Tatiana whispered, her hands in his damp hair.

Bending over her, Alexander whispered, "You tell me what you want me to do, and I'll do it. I'll go as slow as you need me to. What do you want?"

Tatiana couldn't reply. She wanted to ask him to bring her instant relief from the fire but could not. She had to trust in Alexander.

His palm pressing into her stomach, Alexander whispered, "Look at you, your wet, erect nipples standing up, pleading with me to suck them."

"Suck them," Tatiana whispered, moaning.

He did. "Yes. Moan, moan as loud as you want. No one can hear you but me, and I came sixteen hundred kilometers to hear you, *so moan*, Tania." His mouth, his tongue, his teeth devoured her breasts as her back and chest and hips arched into him.

Lying down on his side next to her, Alexander eased his hand between her thighs.

"Wait, wait," she said, trying to keep her legs together.

"No, open," Alexander said, his hand pushing her legs apart. With his fingers he traced her thigh upward. "Shh," he whispered, wrapping his free arm around her neck. "Tania, you're trembling." His fingers touched her. Her body stiffened. Alexander's breath stopped. Tatiana's breath stopped. "Do you feel how gently I rub you," he whispered, his lips on her cheek. "You . . . so blonde all over."

Her hands were clenched on her stomach under his forearm. Her eyes were closed.

"Do you feel that, Tatia?"

She moaned.

Alexander stroked her up and down and then in small circles. "You feel unbelievable . . ." he whispered.

Her hands clenched tighter.

He rubbed her a little firmer. "Want me to stop?" He groaned slightly.

"No!"

"Tania, do you feel me against your hip?"

"Hmm. I thought that was your rifle."

His hot breath was in her neck. "Whatever you want to call it is fine with me." He bent over her and sucked her nipples as he rubbed her and rubbed against her –

In circles, in circles –

As she moaned and moaned –

And –

He pulled his fingers away and his mouth away and himself away.

"No, no, no. Don't stop," Tatiana murmured in a panic, opening her eyes. In the palpitating tension of her flesh she had begun to feel combustion, and when he stopped, she started to quiver so uncontrollably that Alexander lay on top of her briefly to calm her, pressing his forehead to her forehead. "Shh. It's all right." He paused for a second and got off her. "Tell me what you want me to do."

Unsteadily, Tatiana said, "I don't know. What else have you got?"

He nodded. "All right, then." He pulled off his shorts and knelt in front of her.

When Tatiana saw him, she sat straight up. "Oh, my *God,* Alexander," she muttered incredulously, backing away.

"It's all right," he said, smiling from ear to ear. "Where are you going?" His hands held on to her legs.

"No," she said, shaking her head, staring at him in astonishment. "No, no. Please."

"Somehow, and in His infinite wisdom," Alexander said, "God has ensured that it all works the way it's supposed to."

"Shura, it can't be possible. It'll never – "

"Trust me," Alexander said, staring at her with lust. "It will."

He lay her down flat, and said, "I cannot wait a second longer. Not another second. I need to be inside you *right now.*"

"Oh, God. No, Shura."

"Yes, Tania, yes. Say that to me. Yes, Shura."

"Oh, God. *Yes,* Shura."

Alexander climbed on top of her, supporting himself on his arms. "Tania," he whispered passionately, "you are naked and underneath me!" As if he could not believe it himself.

"Alexander," she said, still trembling, "you are naked and above me." She felt him rubbing against her.

They kissed. "I can't believe it," he said, his breath shallow. "I didn't think this day would ever come." He paused and then whispered, "Yet I couldn't imagine my life without it. You alive, under me. Tania, touch me. Put your hands on me."

Instantly she reached down and took hold of him.

"Do you feel how hard I am," he whispered, ". . . for you?"

"God, yes," she said in crazed disbelief. Seeing him was a profound shock to her. *Feeling* him was entirely too much. "It's impossible," she muttered, stroking him gently. "You will *kill* me."

"Yes," Alexander said. "Let me. Open your legs."

She did.

"No, wider." Alexander kissed her and whispered, "Open yourself for me, Tania. Go ahead . . . open for *me*."

Tatiana did. She continued to stroke him.

"Now, are you ready?"

"No."

"You are, you *are* ready. Let go of me." He smiled. "Hold on to my neck. Hold on tight."

Slowly Alexander pushed himself inside her, little by little, little by little. Tatiana grasped at his arms, at the blanket, at his back, at the grass above her head. "Wait, wait, please . . ." He waited as best he could. Tatiana felt as she had imagined she would – that she was being torn open. But something else, too.

An intemperate hunger for Alexander.

"All right," he said at last. "I'm inside you." He kissed her and breathed deeply out. "I'm inside *you*, Tatiasha."

Softly she moaned, her hands around his neck. "Are you really inside me?"

"Yes." He pulled up slightly. "Feel."

She felt. "I can't believe you . . . fit."

Smiling, Alexander whispered, "Only just, but yes." He kissed her lips. Took a breath. Left his lips on her. "As if God Himself joined our flesh . . ." He took another breath. ". . . Me and you together, and said, they shall be one."

Tatiana lay very still. Alexander was very still, his lips pressed against her forehead. Was there more? Tatiana's body was aching. There was no relief. Her hands went around to hold him a little closer. She looked up into his flushed face. "Is that it? Is that all there is to it?"

Alexander paused a moment. "Not quite." He inhaled her breath. "I'm just – Tania, we've been so desperately longing for this . . ." he whispered into her mouth, "and the moment will never come again." He gazed into her face. "I don't want to let it go."

"All right," she whispered back. She was throbbing. She tilted her hips up to him.

Another moment.

"Ready?" He pulled slowly and slightly out and pushed himself back in. Tatiana gritted her teeth, but through the gritted teeth a moan escaped.

"Wait, wait," she said.

Slowly he pulled halfway out and pushed himself back in.

"Wait . . ."

Alexander pulled all the way out and pushed himself all the way in, and Tatiana, astounded, nearly screamed, but she was too afraid he would stop if he thought she was in pain. She heard him groan, and less slowly he pulled all the way out and pushed himself all the way in. Moaning, she gripped his arms.

"Oh, Shura." She was unable to breathe.

"I know. Just hold on to me."

Less slowly. Less gently.

Tatiana was feverish from the pain, from the flame.

"Am I hurting you?"

Tatiana paused, dizzy and lost. "No."

"I'm going as slow as I can."

"Oh, Shura." Breath, breath, where is my breath . . .

Short panting pause. "Tania . . . God, I'm done for, aren't I?" Alexander whispered hotly. "Done for, *forever*."

Less, less gently.

Speechlessly Tatiana clung to him, her mouth open in a mute scream.

"You want me to stop?"

"No."

Alexander stopped. "Wait," he said, shaking his head against her cheek. "Hang on tight," he whispered. He was still for another moment.

Through his parted lips he breathed, "Oh, Tania . . ." and suddenly he thrust in and out of her so hard and so fast that Tatiana thought she was going to pass out, crying in tumult and pain and gripping his head buried in her neck.

A breathless moment.

And another.

And another.

The heart was wild, and the throat was parched, and the lips were wet, and breath was slowly coming back, and sound, and sensation, and smell.

And her eyes were open.

Blink.

Alexander pulsed to a gradual stop, took a deep relieved breath, and lay on top of her for a few panting minutes.

Her hands continued to grip him.

A bittersweet tingle remained where he had just been. Tatiana felt regret; she wanted him inside her again; it had felt so excessive and absolute.

Lifting himself off her, Alexander blew on her wet forehead and chest. "Are you all right? I hurt you?" he whispered, tenderly kissing her freckles. "Tania, honey, tell me you're all right."

She couldn't answer him. His lips on her face were too warm.

"I'm fine," Tatiana finally replied, smiling shyly, holding him to her. "Are you all right?"

Alexander lay down by her side. "I'm fantastic," he said, his fingers running down the length of her body from her face to her shins and slowly back up again. "I have never been better." His shining smile was so full of happiness that Tatiana wanted to cry. She pressed her face against his face. They didn't speak.

His hand stopped moving and rested on Tatiana's hip. "You were surprisingly more quiet than I had anticipated," he said.

"Mmm, I was trying not to faint," Tatiana said, making him laugh.

"I thought you might be."

She turned on her side to him. "Shura, was it . . . ?"

Alexander kissed her eyes. "Tania," he whispered, "to be inside you, to come inside you . . . it was magic. You know it was."

"What did you think it was going to be like?" she asked, nudging him.

"This was better than anything my pathetic imagination could conjure up."

"Have you been imagining this?"

"You could say that." He held her to him. "Forget me. Tell me – what did *you*

expect?" He grinned, kissed her, and laughed with delight. "No, I'm going to burst," he said. "Tell me everything." Huskily he added, "Have you been imagining this?"

"No," she said, nudging him again. Certainly not *this*. Her fingers floated down from Alexander's throat to his stomach. All she wanted was permission to touch him again. "Why are you looking at me like that? What do you want to know?"

"What were you expecting?"

Tatiana thought about it. "I really don't know."

"Come on, you must have been expecting something."

"Mmm. Not this."

"What then?"

Tatiana was quite embarrassed and wished Alexander wouldn't look at her with such mouthwatering adoration. "I had a brother, Shura," she said. "I knew what you all looked like. Sort of quiet . . . and down . . . and very . . . hmm . . ." Tatiana searched for a proper word. "Unalarming."

Alexander burst out laughing.

"But I've never seen one . . ."

"That was alarming?"

"Hmm." Why was he laughing like that?

"What else?"

Tatiana paused. "I guess I thought this unalarming thing would . . . I don't know . . . quietly sort of . . ." She coughed once. "Let's just say the movement was also quite a surprise to me."

Alexander grabbed her, kissing her happily. "You're the funniest girl. What am I going to do with you?"

Tatiana lay quietly facing him, the aching inside her thoroughly unsubsided. She was fascinated with his body. Her fingers lightly stroked his stomach. "So what now?" She paused. "Are we . . . done?"

"Do you want to be done?"

"No," she said at once.

"Tatiana," Alexander said, his voice filled with emotion, "I love you."

She closed her eyes. "Thank you," she whispered.

"Don't give me that," he said, lifting her face to him. "I have never heard you say it to me."

That couldn't be true, thought Tatiana. I've felt it every minute of every day since we met. Spilling over – "I love you, Alexander."

"Thank you," he whispered, gazing at her. "Tell me again."

"I love you." She hugged him. "I love you breathlessly, my amazing man." With affection she smiled into his face. "But you know, I have never heard you say it to me either."

"Yes, you did, Tatiana," said Alexander. "You heard me say it to you."

A moment passed.

She didn't speak, or breathe, or blink.

"You know how I know?" he whispered.

"How?" she mouthed inaudibly.

"Because you got up off that sled . . ."

Another mute moment passed.

The second time they made love, it hurt less.

The third time Tatiana experienced a floating, incandescent moment of such pain-infused exquisite pleasure that it caught even her by surprise. She cried out.

Crying out, she moaned, "God, don't stop. Please . . ."

"No?" Alexander said, and stopped.

"What are you doing?" she said, opening her eyes, parting her lips, looking up at him. "I said don't stop."

"I want to hear you moan again," he murmured. "I want to hear you moan for me not to stop."

"*Please . . .*" she whispered, milling her hips against him, her hands around his neck.

"No, Shura, no? Or yes, Shura, yes?"

"Yes, Shura, yes." Tatiana closed her eyes, "I beg you . . . don't stop."

Alexander moved in and out of her deeper and slower. She cried out.

"Like this?"

She couldn't speak.

"Or . . ."

Faster and faster. She cried out.

"Like this?"

She couldn't speak.

"Tania . . . is it so good?"

"It's so good."

"How do you want it?"

"Any which way." Her tense hands clenched around him.

"Moan for me, Tania," Alexander whispered, changing his rhythm and his speed. "Go ahead . . . moan for me."

Alexander didn't have to ask twice.

"Don't stop, Shura . . ." she said helplessly.

"I won't stop, Tania."

He didn't stop, and there it was – finally Tatiana felt her entire body stiffen and explode in a convulsive burn, then a lava melt. It was some time before she was able to stop moaning and quivering against Alexander. "What was that?" she uttered at last, still panting.

"That was my Tania discovering what is so fantastic about making love. That was . . . relief," he whispered, pressing his cheek to her cheek.

Tatiana clasped him to her, turning her face away and murmuring through her happy tears, "Oh, my God, Alexander . . ."

"How long have we been here?"

"I don't know. Minutes?"

"Where's your 'precise' watch?"

"Didn't bring it. Wanted time to stop moving forward," said Alexander, blinking and closing his eyes.

"Tania? You're not sleeping?"

"No. My eyes are closed. I'm very relaxed."

"Tania, will you tell me the truth if I ask for it?"

"Of course." She smiled. Her eyes were still closed.

"Have you ever touched a man before? *Touched* a man."

Tatiana opened her eyes and laughed quietly. "Shura, what are you talking about? Besides my brother when we were younger, I've never even seen a man before."

Tatiana was nestled in his arms, her fingers touching his chin, his neck, his Adam's apple. She pressed her index finger to the vividly pulsing artery near his throat. She moved up a little and kissed the artery and then left her mouth on it, feeling it beat against her lips. Why is he so endearing? she thought. And why does he smell so good?

"What about those hordes of young beasts you told me about, chasing you in Luga? None of them?"

"None of them what?"

"Did you touch any of them?" asked Alexander.

She shook her head. "Shura, why are you so funny? No."

"Maybe through clothes?"

"What?" She didn't take her mouth away from his neck. "Of course not." She paused. "What are you trying to get out of me?"

"What kind of things you got up to before me."

Teasingly, Tatiana said, "*Was* there life before Alexander?"

"You tell *me*."

"All right, what else do you want to know?"

"Who has seen your naked body? Other than your family. Other than when you were seven, doing your naked cartwheels."

Is this what he wanted? The complete truth? She had been so afraid to tell him. Would he want to hear it? "Shura, the first time any man saw me even *partly* naked was you in Luga."

"Is that true?" He moved away a little to see her eyes.

She nodded, returning to rubbing her mouth against his neck. "It's true."

"Has anyone touched you?"

"Touched me?"

"Felt your breasts, felt – " His fingers searched for her.

"Shura, please. Of course not."

Through his artery she felt his heart quicken its beat into her mouth. Tatiana smiled. She would tell it all to him right now, if that's what he wanted from her. "Do you remember the woods in Luga?"

"How can I forget?" he said huskily. "It was the sweetest kiss of my life."

Her lips in his neck, Tatiana whispered, "Alexander . . . it was the first kiss of mine."

He shook his head and then turned on his side, peering into her face in skeptical emotional disbelief, as if what she had been giving him were less than the total truth. Tatiana turned on her side to him. "What?" she asked, smiling. "You're embarrassing me. What now?"

"Don't tell me that – "

"All right, I won't tell you."

"Will you tell me, please?"

"I told you."

His stupefied eyes unblinking, Alexander said shallowly, "When I kissed you in Luga . . ."

"Yes?"

"Tell me."

"Shura . . ." She pressed her body flush against his. "What do you want? You want the truth from me or something else?"

"I don't believe you." He shook his head. "I just don't believe you."

"All right," Tatiana said, lying on her back and putting her hands under her head.

Alexander bent over her. "I think you're just telling me that because you think it's what I want to hear," he said, running his fingers over her breasts and stomach. His hands on her were unremitting. They never stopped moving.

"Is it what you want to hear?"

Alexander didn't reply at first. "I don't know. No. Yes, God help me," he said with difficulty. "But I want the truth more."

Tatiana patted him cheerfully on the back. "You have the truth." And smiled. "In my whole life I have never been touched by anyone but you."

But Alexander wasn't smiling. His bronze eyes melting right in front of her, he asked haltingly, "How can that be?"

"I don't know how it can be," she said. "It just is."

"What did you do, walk straight from your mother's womb into my arms?"

Tatiana laughed. "Very nearly." She gazed into his face. "Alexander, I love you," she said. "Do you understand? I never wanted to kiss anyone before you. I wanted you to kiss me so much in Luga I didn't know what to do. I didn't know how to tell you. I stayed up half the night trying to figure out a way to get you to kiss me. Finally in the woods, I wasn't going to give up. If I can't get my Alexander to kiss me in the woods, I thought, I have no hope of ever being kissed by anyone." Her hands were on him.

His face was over hers. "What are you doing to me?" he whispered intensely. "You need to stop right now. What are you doing to me?"

"What are you doing to *me*?" Her fingertips pressed into his back.

When Alexander made love to her, his lips did not leave hers, and in his impassioned climax, which she barely heard through her shattering own, Tatiana was almost sure he groaned as if he were stopping himself from crying. He whispered into her mouth, "I just don't know how I'm going to survive you, Tatiana."

"Honey," Alexander murmured, his body over her, as she lay underneath him. "Open your eyes. Are you all right?"

Tatiana didn't speak. She was listening to the loving cadence of his voice.

"Tania . . ." he whispered, his shimmering fingers circling her face, her throat, the top of her chest. "You have newborn skin," he said quietly. "Do you know that?"

"Well, no," she murmured.

"You have newborn skin and the sweetest breath, and your hair is silk upon your head." Kneeling over her, Alexander tenderly sucked her nipple. "You are divine through and through."

Listening, comforted, she held his head in her hands. He stopped talking and lifted his face to her. There were tears in his eyes.

"Please forgive me, Tatiana," said Alexander, "for hurting your perfect heart with my cold and indifferent face. My own heart was always overflowing with you, and it was never indifferent. You didn't deserve any of what you've been given, of what you've had to bear. None of it. Not from your sister, not from Leningrad, and certainly not from me. You don't even know what it took me not to look at you one last time before I closed the tarpaulin on that truck. I knew that if I did, it would all be over. I would not have been able to hide my face from you or from Dasha. I wouldn't have been able to keep my promise to you for your sister. It wasn't that I didn't look at you. I *couldn't* look at you. I gave you so much when we were alone. I hoped it would be enough to carry you forward."

"It was, Shura," said Tatiana, with tears in her own eyes. "I'm here. And it will be enough in the future." She pressed his head to her chest. "I'm sorry I ever doubted you. But now my heart is light."

Alexander kissed her between her breasts.

"You have fixed me." And Tatiana smiled.

Murmuring and whispering, Tatiana lay happily under Alexander, having been once again loved and relieved, and relieved . . . "Oh, and I thought I loved you before."

His lips pressed into her temple. "This does add a whole new dimension, doesn't it?" His hands did not leave her body. Nothing of him left her body. He was holding her from underneath, still moving inside her.

Turning her face up to him, a smile coming to her lips, a smile of youth and ecstasy, Tatiana said, "Alexander, you are my first love. Did you know that?"

He squeezed her bottom, pressed himself into her, licked the salt off her face, and nodded. "That I know."

"Oh?"

"Tatia, I knew it even before you yourself knew it." He grinned. "Before you finally found the word to describe to yourself what you were feeling, I knew it from the start. How else could you have been so shy and guileless?"

"Guileless?"

"Yes."

"Was I that obvious?"

"Yes." Alexander smiled. "Your inability to look at me in public, yet your total devotion to my face when we were together – like now," he said, kissing her. "Your embarrassment at the smallest things – I couldn't even keep my hand on you in the tram without you blushing . . . your fingers on me when I was telling you about America . . . your smile, your *smile*, Tania, when you ran to me from Kirov." Alexander shook his head at the memory. "What a prison you have set up for me with your first love."

She put her arms tighter around him and said teasingly, "Oh, so the first love part you believe, but the first kiss part you have a problem with? What kind of girl do you think I am?"

"The nicest girl," he whispered.

*

"Are you ready for more?"

"Tania . . ." Alexander shook his head in smiling disbelief. "What's gotten into you?"

She laughed, her hands caressing his stomach. "Shura . . . am I wanting too much?"

"No. But you are going to kill *me*."

Tatiana craved something, but she just couldn't find a way out of her timidity to ask him. Quietly, thoughtfully, she stroked his stomach and then cleared her throat. "Honey? Can I lie on top of you?"

"Of course." Alexander smiled, opening his arms. "Come and lie on top of me."

She lay down on him and softly, wetly kissed his lips. "Shura . . ." she whispered, "do you like that?"

"Mmm."

Her lips were on his face, on his throat, on the top of his chest. She whispered, "You know what your skin feels like to me? The ice cream that I love. Creamy, smooth. Your whole body is the color of caramel, like my crème brûlée, but you're not cold like ice cream, you're warm." She rubbed her lips back and forth against his chest.

"So – better than ice cream?"

"Yes." She smiled, moving up to his lips. "I love you better than ice cream." After kissing him deeply, she gently, gently sucked his tongue. "Do you like that?" she whispered.

He groaned his assent.

"Shura, darling . . ." she asked very shyly, "is there . . . anywhere else you might like me to do that?"

Pulling away, he gaped at her. Silent and tantalized, Tatiana watched his incredulous face.

"I think," Alexander said slowly, "there is a place where I might like you to do that, yes."

She smiled back, trying to hide her excitement. "You'll just – you'll just have to tell me what to do, all right?"

"All right."

Tatiana kissed Alexander's chest, listened to his heart, moved lower, lay her head on his rippled stomach. Moving lower still, she brushed her blonde hair against him and then rubbed her breasts against him, feeling him already swollen underneath her. She kissed the arrow line of his black hair leading down from his navel and then grazed her lips against him.

Kneeling between Alexander's legs, Tatiana took hold of him with both hands. He was extraordinary. "And now . . ."

"Now put me in your mouth," he said, watching her.

Her breath leaving her body, she whispered, "*Whole*?" and took what she could of him into her mouth.

"Move up and down on me."

"Like this?"

There was a thickening pause. "Yes."

"Or . . ."

"Yes, that's good, too."

Tatiana felt him hard against her fervent lips and rubbing fingers. When Alexander gripped her hair, she, stopping for a moment, looked into his face. "Oh, yes," she whispered, hungrily putting him deeper inside her mouth and moaning.

"You're doing so well, Tatia," he whispered. "Keep going, and don't stop."

She stopped. He opened his eyes. Smiling, Tatiana said, "I want to hear you groan for me not to stop."

Alexander sat up and kissed her wet mouth. "Please don't stop." Then he gently pushed her face down on him, falling back on the blanket.

Right before the end he pulled her head away and said, "Tania, I'm going to come."

"So come," Tatiana whispered. "Come in my mouth."

Afterward, as she lay cradled in his chest, Alexander said, gazing at her in stark amazement, "I've decided that I like it."

"Me, too," she said softly.

FORBIDDEN ARIAS

Edward Field

Edward Field is a freelance journalist who occasionally contributes to the *Erotic Review*. He grew up in Dorking, Surrey, and attended Sussex University where he took a degree in psychology; however, to this day, he continues to find human behaviour something of a mystery. He is married with two daughters.

That morning, I woke early. Next to me Andrea was semi-naked and asleep. I got up and showered, then ate a swift, solitary breakfast. By the time I had finished, my wife had woken up and I brought her a mug of coffee. She thanked me and leant on one elbow while she sipped the hot drink, watching me as I dressed.

"I've made a list of things you need to do today," she said. "It's on the kitchen table."

I looked at her as though I were seeing her for the first time. A breast was squashed into an unflattering shape because of her position, her hair was tangled and untidy and a long, vivid sleep-line creased her cheek. She wore the careless deshabille of long-standing familiarity. But really – who was she? Sometimes I experienced this illusion that I was cohabiting with a beautiful, desirable stranger. I wondered whether stale intimacy, while sapping a deeper affinity, could at the same time increase desire.

"I know. I've already got it."

I patted the breast pocket of my jacket.

"I'll be back to help with lunch."

She nodded and made a small noise of affection as I gave her a goodbye peck on the cheek. The ritual kiss, the communication by written list, the carnal closeness of this stranger in my bed, all added to a disconnection and an alienation that seemed quite unfair. This resentment stayed with me as I set off down the road into town, then gently evaporated as I turned into the town's centre. The holiday season was over. There were fewer people around, the voices I heard were local and the shops no longer profiting from tourist tat.

We had moved here from London a year ago. By my early fifties, I had made enough money to retire. It was my decision to move out of the city. Andrea had acquiesced, uncharacteristically, with less resistance than usual. The choice of this seaside resort, however, was hers. I was beginning to regret the move. The Cornish sea air was invigorating and the walks along the coastline revealed a littoral of extraordinary, wild beauty. Occasionally we would drive to Rick Stein's restaurant and have a good lunch. We could afford it. But I failed to see

the charm of this small town in the way that she obviously could. The people were friendly enough but we were still outsiders, accorded much the same status as the holidaymakers that packed the streets in the summer. The town lacked any sort of architectural cohesion. A group of sedate Victorian guesthouses, complete with turrets, gabled Edwardian hotels and the odd 1930s art deco boarding house sat bunched uncomfortably together above its broad sandy beach like a clutch of disapproving spinsters. In the steep main thoroughfares, the only graceful facades were destroyed by garish signage. I passed a triangle of bright green grass at the base of the two main shopping streets. Beneath some yucca trees sat a fake wellhead with a little shingled roof and a sign that said "Wishing Well – proceeds go to Local Rotary Charities". It was the nearest the town came to having any sort of landmark.

The first name on Andrea's neat handwritten list was that of my doctor. But when I reached the surgery, I found that a locum I'd never met had temporarily replaced my usual, crusty, beetle-browed GP. Dr. Alison Rose was a handsome woman in her late thirties with a low, musical voice. She wore her dark hair short, a navy blue cardigan and sensible flats. I found her attractive. No, I caught myself thinking, you're not just attractive, I find you desirable.

Recently, sexual desire hadn't bothered me much. When occasionally it did, it induced a reluctant admission that the sporadic sex I had with Andrea, my beautiful, disconnected list-maker, would never improve or become more frequent. Then I would think of Betjeman's old-age pronouncement of regret about not having had as much sex as he would have liked.

Doctor and patient made small talk. Like me she was from outside Cornwall and had moved west two years ago. "Yes," I said, "but what do you actually *do* here?" Her initial reply was a brittle smile and a slight shrug. Then she said, "Not a lot." We touched lightly on local places and events. We soon established a commonality of tastes in walks and pubs and I found myself speculating inappropriately about what lay under her sensible clothes and, in the absence of a wedding ring, whether she was seeing anybody.

"I can see from Dr. Morrison's notes that your sprain should be OK by now. It's the right one, isn't it? Let's have a look, shall we?" and she reached out and took my hand.

What followed was utterly bizarre, and yet throughout it I felt nothing unusual, all my physical senses and faculties were functioning perfectly well. I could have got up and left the room at any time.

But I didn't.

As she took my hand I glanced up and looked into Dr. Alison Rose's sad grey eyes and immediately she started to sing. I think she had a rather wonderful voice, the sort, I believe, that might belong to a "rich coloratura soprano", although I'm the first to admit, my knowledge of opera is limited. The first, absurd, thought that entered my head was that this was some sort of new therapy. That evaporated quickly. As I listened, I recognised the aria from *La Bohème*, where Mimi sings to Ronaldo *Mi chiamano Mimi* . . . Except that Dr. Rose was singing in English. To begin with, I could only make out individual words but very quickly my ear became completely attuned to what she sang, and what I heard was utterly compelling. I can only paraphrase it now, but it went something like this:

You look like a civilised person, a decent man.
Not like the lying bastard who strung me along all these years.
Now he's in New York and I'm here in this godforsaken place. The fucker left without even saying goodbye.
Look at your hand, it's so elegant, so finely boned.
If only its fingers could cup my aching breast, could delicately enchant and revive my poor, deprived cunt.

It seemed that I was having a psychotic episode. Try as I might, I simply can't recall if there was any musical accompaniment, but throughout her song she held my gaze and I hers and I remember thinking that a doctor's surgery was as good a place as any to lose one's mind. And then she was talking normally again, asking me if I had had any recurrence of the pain.

"Does it hurt when I do this?" and she gave me that brittle smile, and my fourth metacarpal a sharp little squeeze.

It was ten o'clock. My next appointment was at Mario's, the town's unisex hairdressing salon. I didn't feel particularly comfortable surrounded by women in various stages of wash, tint, cut or dry, and it was the retiree's fate that I was the only man having his hair cut that morning. My regular barber Dan, usually so convincingly gay (in both senses of the word), looked depressed today. No sooner than I was seated with a cape tucked around me, I felt Dan's hand at the back of my neck. "Seems like it's grown a bit since the last time," was all he said.

Our eyes met in the mirror and he smiled at me.

Dan started to sing. This time, other than Dan's strong West Country burr, no liberties had been taken with *South Pacific*'s libretto.

I'm gonna wash that man right outta my hair,
I'm gonna wash that man right outta my hair,
I'm gonna wash that man right outta my hair,
And send him on his way.
I'm gonna wave that man right outta my arms,

And here, to my increasing stupefaction, the female customers joined in:

I'm gonna wave that man right outta my arms,
I'm gonna wave that man right outta my arms,
And send him on his way.
Don't try to patch it up
Tear it up, tear it up!
Wash him out, dry him out,
Push him out, fly him out,
Cancel him and let him go!
(Customers)
Yea, sister!
(Dan)
I'm gonna wash that man right outta my hair,

I'm gonna wash that man right outta my hair,
I'm gonna wash that man right outta my hair,
And send him on his way.

I was too shaken to react in any sane sort of way. I just sat there and took it. What could I have done? Dan singing, the customers backing him up, and anyway, it all ended with the last chorus. Surreptitiously, I looked around. Normality reigned once more.

At the dry cleaners (next on the list) there was only one bored, lumpen, teenaged girl behind the counter. I was careful not to touch her hand or look her in the eye, but as she brought my wife's suit to the counter, it slipped out of her grasp and my reaction was to catch it before it hit the floor. In doing so, my wrist touched her hand and she looked up at me gratefully. Then she sang from Handel's *Rinaldo*: *Lascia ch'io pianga mia cruda sorte.* Her voice was exceptional, beautiful, soaring and swooping like a swift through warm evening air. Except the words. The words were . . . well, different.

I'm so horny, I could shag a pony
My bloke's left me and I hate this job
I would even screw an old geezer like you, only
You'd have to be rich and not a total slob.

Well, it was about suffering, chains and liberty, I suppose, but probably not quite as the average opera fan would like to hear them described.

When I got home, I wanted to tell Andrea. But how? How could I possibly convey the weirdness of my morning? In any case, Andrea looked so preoccupied. As we stood side by side at the slate-topped island hob preparing lunch she reached out and almost tenderly put her hand over mine. It was a comforting gesture and I was rather moved by it. She had sensed my disquiet and . . .

But no. To my horror, the small room filled with the swell of a full orchestra. I recognised the introduction to Beethoven's *Ode to Joy*. Andrea, my dear, tone-deaf Andrea, fixed me with a glittering, triumphant stare, took a deep breath, then her mouth opened and the words came tumbling out in perfect, glorious pitch:

Oh joyful day, our last together
Tomorrow I am out of here
I'm leaving you for Marietta
We'll have all our lives to share
We've been lovers since college
And our sex life is still great
All our friends will soon acknowledge
In her I've found my perfect mate.

The sheer banality of the words was in stark contrast to the sublime, almost transcendental, quality of the music. But then I wondered if Schiller's lofty lyrics,

embracing, as they did, all the ideals of the Enlightenment and Romanticism, had ever sounded all that good, either. To my ear they had always seemed orotund and ridiculous. But so what? Perhaps I was just pissed off. Andrea was leaving me (for a *woman* no less!) but appeared to be quite unaware that I was privy to her innermost thoughts, courtesy of Ludwig. As things returned to normal, Andrea glanced sideways at me with concern and asked if I was feeling all right.

"You look a bit pale, darling."

"Really? Well, now you mention it, I do feel a little odd. I think I'll just go and call and make another appointment with Doctor Rose. Maybe she missed something this morning. Maybe we both did."

From THE SILVER CHAIN

Primula Bond

Primula Bond is an Oxford-educated mother of three boys, and has lived in London and Cairo. She currently lives in Hampshire with her husband and younger sons and works part-time as a legal secretary for criminal defence lawyers, as well as writing freelance 'human interest' features for the national press. In *The Silver Chain*, photographer Serena Folkes is indulging her impulsive side with a night-time shoot. But someone is watching her – mysterious entrepreneur Gustav Levi. Serena doesn't know it yet, but this handsome stranger will change her life forever . . .

It's the tall dark mansion on the corner of the square, somewhere in Mayfair. The one the witches swerved past on Halloween night because they were too scared to bang on the knocker to trick or treat. The one he started to walk towards that night then changed course to walk me to that cocktail bar. The one that is now being battered by gusts of wind as a storm revs up and tips buckets of rain over me as I struggle up the hill.

I should have known that's where Gustav Levi lives.

What I didn't expect when he invited me to his house tonight to celebrate our long and happy association was that no-one would answer the door. I ring the bell and bash at the knocker for a few minutes, getting wetter and wetter, before the door swings open apparently of its own accord. I hesitate. It doesn't creak on its hinges, but it's pretty Hammer Horror nonetheless.

I follow a trail of bright lights set into the edges of the floor, the treads of the stairs curving up into the shadows upstairs, enticing me from the darkened, red-lacquer-painted hallway down another flight of stairs into the basement, and the second thing I didn't expect was that I'd find the man of the house in a vast, quartz kitchen wearing chef's whites and breaking eggs into a huge glass bowl.

"Ah, you found us." He looks up at me with a boyish grin and starts whisking so energetically that he has to follow the bowl across the counter. "And so we come back to the square where it all began."

"Us?"

"My household. My underlings." He waves the whisk vaguely. "Usually you'll find all sorts of people coming and going here. But tonight it's skeleton staff, you might say. I've even let Dickson off tonight."

"Dickson?" I look around.

"My chauffeur and pilot. Doubles up as my chef, too. But a man's got to find a way of relaxing when he comes home from running his empire and sealing deals with startling new talents he's picked up in the street. So I'm cooking tonight."

To cover the sudden chill of awkwardness I walk around the kitchen making a show of examining everything. It really is state of the art, with several ovens of various sizes and at least six gas rings the size of hub caps on the oversized central hob. What did I think Gustav was going to be cooking? Toe of frog and eye of newt?

"So you didn't pick me at all. You live right here in the square. You were just taking a constitutional that night and happened to bump into me."

He shakes his head calmly. I see what's different about him tonight. He's had his hair cut. It's sweaty with his culinary efforts, but it makes him look tidier, more formal, but somehow safer. And it means I can see his eyes clearly, and tonight they are very bright. "Believe what you like, Serena. I picked you, as soon as I saw you."

"You thought I was a boy."

"*Touché.*" He grabs at the escaping bowl and we both start to smile. "But very soon you'll see that we're a perfect match. In fact, I can't wait to get started."

"On the exhibition? Or on me?"

He allows himself a brief chuckle. "Both. Although the exhibition I believe is nearly ready for lift off. It's the other part of the contract which is beginning to feel a little like the blind leading the blind."

"The sex part, do you mean?"

"I love that you're so direct, Serena. Was I really that explicit?"

"You didn't have to be. You started off by touching me, remember? Very intimately. I took that as, I don't know, an introduction to what you have in mind?"

He puts down the egg whisk and rubs at his hair. Now that it's shorter it stands up in black spikes and makes his face look more open. "I confess you caught me on the hop. Once I'd met you and seen the work stored on the camera, I wanted to do something to keep you here. Otherwise I feared that you would simply vanish into thin air. Or someone else would snap you up. So I thought of doing it this way. Making it personal as well as professional. Having said all that, I'm not sure I thought it through." He neatly rips a huge paper bag and releases a cloud of flour. "I think it's a case of suck it and see."

I turn my back on him before he sees me blushing, and walk as calmly as I can to the end of the kitchen. The scraping of my feet sounds intrusive on the underheated floor. Through the big doors I can see, in the long thin moonlit paved garden, small trees and rose bushes in pots being bent and buffeted by the rain and rising wind. I lean my forehead on the glass.

I'm well and truly trapped in his web now. Gustav's designers and printers are working all hours. The pictures have already been selected for enlargement and framing, and the railings leading along the street towards the front door of the Levi Building have been cleared to display the publicity poster we've chosen for my exhibition. It will show the crocodile of mini witches caught by my camera on their way to the party, lit by the streetlamps and halted in their tracks by the little one falling over. In the next day or so that image will be developed, enlarged, elongated and fixed to the railings, the witches waiting in their various impatient attitudes under the melancholy statue for the little one to right herself.

"No going back now, Serena." Gustav rubs the foil from a pat of butter round a couple of ramekins. "We're on the slippery slope."

"I like you barefoot," I remark as he dances from what the chefs would call the *mise en scène* over to the fridge and back again. "And I like those dark jeans. You were wearing ones like those the night we met."

"I'm flattered you remember." He stops buttering and whisking and looks down at himself. Holds the white apron out comically like Little Bo Peep. "You like it rough, Serena?"

I bite my lip. He does too, biting down the shocked smile we share at the naughtiness of his remark. *Yes, I like it rough*, I think to myself. *Or I will when I try it.*

"The suit distances you, that's all. Makes you unreachable. Maybe first impressions are the ones that stay with us?"

He frowns as he ponders the question. Ponders me. "I think I like you every which way, Serena. Though I'm glad the tomboy is beating a retreat."

"I can be all things to all men. But yes. It's kind of fun, and kind of pervy, dressing as my cousin."

He laughs lightly and turns to a tray on the counter. I nearly tell him I also prefer him with his arms showing, because I love his strong hands and what I know they can do, and his strong forearms with the ropes of muscle. But I say nothing.

"Have a drink," he says. "Shaken, or stirred?"

I pick up a glass of vodka martini from a tray on the counter and once again relish the slow burn of it down my throat. I hold the glass up and watch how his movements sparkle and undulate through the clear liquid.

"Dip these nachos into the tzatziki. I'm willing to bet you haven't eaten anything today."

I hitch myself onto a stool and drain the entire glass. Take another one. "You'd be right. The cupboard is bare at Polly's flat. I had a sandwich at the gallery today. So what's this going to be? Pavlova? Mousse? Meringue?"

He moves the bowl along the counter to sieve the flour into the eggs. "Double baked cheese soufflé, if you must know."

I watch the way the muscles in his arms flex as he whisks.

He catches me looking. Stops whisking and holds the bowl over his head to check the whites are done. "And if you're lucky, maybe a taste of my famous Coquilles Saint Jacques."

"And for afters?"

"What my grandmother used to call wait and see pudding." He dances back to the huge American fridge and brings out a bright berry coulis and some clotted cream. "Where's my piping bag?"

I snigger like a schoolgirl. He looks at the limp, wrinkled bag in his hands, looking exactly like an oversized condom, and chuckles with me. His face is flushed from the heat of the kitchen. He's unshaven again. Yes. I like him rough. It makes his face shadowy and manly, makes his eyes bright.

He grabs a hunk of mature cheddar and starts grating.

"What's that cheese ever done to you?" I laugh.

"Just getting it prepped for the second bake. Timing is crucial. Hey, look at you," he says suddenly, reducing the hunk of cheese to a few crumbs. "You're soaked. What was I thinking? I should have got Dickson to collect you from the

flat, but now you need to get dry. If you go up the stairs, as far up as you can go, you'll find a shower room and something to put on. It's the old attic. The previous owners claim it's haunted."

I let out a nervous tinkle of laughter. "I'm too tired for jokes, Gustav. You asked me to be at your beck and call, but you don't have to scare me half to death as well."

"I didn't mean to. Some people find that an added attraction. But I'm hoping you will consider this your home." He waves his grater in the direction of the stairs. "And when you come down I have a little gift for you."

I wander obediently through the big house. There's no-one else here. The skeleton staff consists of this mysterious man cutting and chopping and baking in his kitchen. And me.

The night gets wilder, pressing black and insistent against the windows as I climb the stairs, past closed doors, past low lights and pillar candles, soft music piped presumably from a central system Gustav is controlling from the kitchen. For the first time it occurs to me that all this melancholy magnificence, bought with the spoils of success, doesn't amount to a hill of beans if he has no-one to share it with.

The room at the top really is under the eaves, but the beams have been painted white as has all the old, distressed French-style furniture. White muslin curtains stir slightly against the glass doors leading out onto a little balcony. On a large four-poster, like something Scarlett O'Hara might sleep in, someone has laid out a white silk negligee. Why does everyone think I should dress as a vestal virgin? Don't two years of active, adolescent sex with Jake count?

But I shiver suddenly as the rain slaps against the long thin window.

As I step into the warm spray of water in the little shower room attached, Polly's voice in my ear has changed to: *suck it and see. What's not to like?*

I am so ravenous and the jazz music playing in the background is so mellow that it feels perfectly casual and natural half an hour later to be perching barefoot against the quartz island in the kitchen devouring soufflé, warm bread, and cherry mousse. None of this strikes me as at all odd. That I'm eating supper in a strange house, wearing nothing but a white negligee given to me by a man I only met a few days ago. What else would I be doing?

Now softer music is playing throughout the house and Gustav has gone upstairs ahead of me and lit soft lamps everywhere. He has also taken off his whites and is wearing a soft blue and white striped shirt unbuttoned at the neck.

He waits for me solemnly as I come up from the kitchen to the ground floor and puts his hand in the small of my back to usher me into a little art deco cocktail bar off the hallway. The walls in here are of dark purple velvet. The chairs and stools are the same. It's like walking into the cushion of a giant jewellery box. Even the bottles crammed onto every available glass shelf behind the mirrored bar are filled with liquors gleaming in jewel-bright colours.

"Nightcap?" He holds out a champagne bottle. His face looks almost bearded in the flickering candlelight, and the wolfish air has returned. His black eyes are asking questions again. But despite our signed agreement, despite eating together tonight, even though he touched me, pushed his fingers into me so

intimately to pin me down, to make his point, to stake his claim, I still don't know the answer.

"Just one, thanks. And the food was great. Who knew?" I walk a little shakily across the polished wooden floor, over the creamy rug, aware of the silk negligee clinging to my legs. Still sore from his fondling. Aware of his dark eyes trying to read me again. "But then I ought to get going. It's quite a long way back to Gabriel's Wharf."

"You're going nowhere dressed like that, *signorina*!" He twists the cork out with a pop. I was right. He is staring straight up my legs, directly at the place where he touched me. I perch quickly on the arm of the sofa and cross one thigh over the other. He chuckles. "But I would love to see it. You, running through the driving rain in nothing but a petticoat. Hailing a cab on Piccadilly in the middle of a thunderstorm. Eyes huge. Hair streaming down like a waterfall. You'd look like a Hitchcock damsel in distress."

I look down at my body. My arms and legs are bare, my feet are bare, like his, and the lovely garment shimmers, the spaghetti straps slipping down my arms, delicate silk catching the light from the sconces and candles and picking out the tremor of the fabric as I move and breathe, lingering on my curves. And oh God, the low light lingers now on the stiffening of my nipples. I am wearing nothing underneath after the shower, because I had nothing dry to wear.

I'm learning the different ways he looks at me. The businesslike stare, deadpan but flashing with interest and enthusiasm. The concentrated one of this evening as he shuts out the rest of the world and whips egg whites and cheese into an ambrosial fluff. There's another look, too. This one. The magician's sleight of hand, which changes him from a formal, polite, reasonably easy colleague or friend to a man harbouring deeper, darker intentions.

That's the one I glimpsed in the gallery, when he marked me, hooked me with his fingers. And that's the one who seems to be here now, standing behind the bar. The penetrating gaze that sends shivers of doubt, fear, anticipation, and excitement down my spine.

He hasn't laid a finger on me this evening. Hasn't so much as mentioned the pictures which have been framed today, especially the controversial Venetian ones which are bound to cause a stir when the show opens. He hasn't mentioned what else he requires me to do to fulfil the personal part of our agreement. Maybe he's lulling me into a false security, lulling me into forgetting that this is all a lot more complex than just being colleagues, with his soufflé and his easy chat, and now the champagne. Maybe soon he's going to demand the next instalment. And maybe I'm going to shock him by being totally ready, willing and able.

But for now I play his game, assuming nonchalance. I fold my arms. "How am I supposed to get home, then?"

"If our Dickson was here, he'd take you home, semi-naked or not. He knows not to touch my property, however tempting. But as he's not, and I've had too much drink to drive you myself, you're staying here, Serena." Gustav hands me a flute brimming with palest gold and reaches out to run a finger down my jaw. My eyes flutter at the touch. Surely he can see how I react to him even with the slightest contact? Surely he can see what he's awoken?

"But –"

"No more questions," he insists softly, pressing his finger on my mouth in his familiar gesture. His eyes spark as my tongue flicks out to lick his finger. I know he's feeling the same clench of desire inside him that I am.

I reach up to take his hand, lace our fingers together. They are longer than mine, and stronger, and warmer, but somehow they fit so well. "Gustav," I whisper. "When?"

His eyes blaze back at me as he swallows hard. He lifts our joined hands towards his mouth, brushes them over his warm lips. I try not to squeal with impatience.

Then he gently extricates his fingers.

"First we drink to celebrate! That first glass down in one go. And then another, I think, to quench any nerves."

"I'm not nervous." I keep my voice low. Hope it's seductive.

He clears his throat. "Tomorrow we prepare for your private view, and we still have a lot to do. Tonight, I will try to answer your question, Serena. Starting with this."

I do what he says. Drink the flute of champagne in one go, and it feels as if I could float off the floor. Then he hands me a little blue box tied with a scarlet ribbon.

"Open it."

The box is empty. Or so I think. In fact there is a wisp-thin chain lying in a heart shape on the velvet cushion. It's a silver bracelet, so delicate it looks as if it has been woven by a spider. I take it out, turn it in my fingers. It's like fairy hair.

All the ease, mellowness, barefoot familiarity evaporates. I stand stiffly behind the massive purple sofa. The atmosphere has shifted yet again. Gustav Levi is behaving like a suitor of the most old-fashioned sort, but he's taking it much slower than he did yesterday.

I'm confused, and frankly annoyed. Right now he doesn't look like the same man who pushed me up against a window and put his fingers inside me, made me tremble and come like a bird in his hand. Made me want it again, and again.

Tonight he's a handsome, rich, successful host, enticing me into his house and flattering me. The next step I daresay will be him expecting me, demanding that I climb the stairs with him at the end of the evening and sleep with him. It's in black and white in our agreement. Well, the simple words are there in a little clause of their own at the very bottom of the document, below *50:50* and above our joint signatures.

Sex when demanded.

This is the whole reason my work will be hung tomorrow on the white expanses of Gustav Levi's gallery, splendid and stylish for its admiring audience, cajoled by my champion to open their wallets. It's how I will repay him for making my name known nationwide. Worldwide. It's perfectly simple, but now I'm here, in his house, in a diaphanous negligee, full of his food and drink, close enough for him to scoop me up and carry me off, I'm still not sure how it will work. I'm not sure he is, either.

How hard can it be? Polly would be rolling her eyes by now.

"It's beautiful." I tentatively touch the bracelet. "No-one has ever given me anything so exquisite before."

Gustav takes the chain and winds it twice round my wrist. "You've reached the age of twenty and have never been given jewellery?"

We both study it as he holds my wrist up in the candlelight. The bracelet fits perfectly. It's so light that once it's on I can't feel it on my skin. I notice that my name is engraved in a kind of Gothic script on a tiny plaque. I also notice that once the clasp has locked into place, I can't take the bracelet off.

"Never. No-one at home ever saw the point of jewellery. They saw it as extravagant and vain. I got pens, pencils, books, clothes for birthdays and Christmas, practical things that I needed. But nothing unnecessary or flippant or fun. Not even a watch. Nothing to make me look pretty. When I was fourteen my cousin Polly pierced my ears for me with a sterilised safety pin." A sulky sigh escapes me. "But until then I was never adorned."

"In that case, I am thrilled to be the person breaking that chain of deprivation." He keeps his fingers hooked round my wrist. My skin, and the intricate silver, are heating up under his fingers. "This isn't just a gift, though. Not just an adornment."

He keeps his eyes on me as he takes another chain from under the velvet cushion. This one is slightly thicker. He hooks it onto my bracelet and then unwinds it, like he unwound my hair the other day. With a smile creasing his eyes now, he walks backwards away from me to show me how long this second chain is, and then he clips it onto his watch.

"What are you doing?" I jerk my wrist, and the chain between us goes taut.

"It's more than jewellery, Serena." He frowns and tugs it harder, forcing me to take a jerky step towards him. "Think of it as a symbol. Here's the chain, joining us together. I know it's a symbol of captivity. Slavery, even. But I also like to think it represents an anchoring. You know, like the rope thrown over the side of a ship."

I put my hand over my eyes, suddenly tired. "All these symbols are making me dizzy!"

"Look at me, Serena." He takes my hand away from my eyes. "I want it to represent our binding relationship. What we've agreed. What we're going to do for each other. A silver handshake, if you like."

I lift my hand to examine the intricate work. Somehow the chain makes my wrist and hand look elegant, swanlike.

"Isn't that when people say goodbye?"

"A silver handcuff, then."

Suddenly there's a blinding flash of lightning. The flames in the candlesticks dip to one side and I bunch my fingers round my mouth to stifle my automatic scream. I count the minutes to work out how far away the noise is, but it's already here. There's the thunder, thick, fast and deafening, right above the house.

Gustav is in front of me, holding my arms. "Hey, what's this? My young Amazon frightened of thunder?"

"Always have been. Since I was young. They always left me alone when there was a storm." I realise I'm shaking.

"They?"

"We lived in a horrible house on the cliffs. Right at the very end of the country. It felt like the edge of the world. I was terrified of the storms, and they just

shouted at me. I'm certain that thunder is amplified by all that water. Or that's how it sounded to me, anyway."

He holds me close, just as I was hoping, and puts his mouth in my hair just the way I like it, strokes my bare arms, listening, pushing my hair off my face, until I calm down. The temperature has dropped like a stone with the rain still battering against the windows. There are goosebumps on my skin. My nipples are out like corks. I let him sit me down, shivering, on the sofa.

He fills my champagne glass. "Your family were cruel to you?"

I take a long deep swallow, feel it seep through my veins, weigh the delicious heaviness in my head.

"They weren't my family. Not really." I mutter, aware of the coarsening of my voice. "He found me abandoned as a newborn, tripped over me actually on the church steps, and when no-one came forward to claim me they were allowed to adopt me, but they made a mistake. I was always the alien. They chose the wrong child."

"They hurt you?"

"Sometimes. Nothing major. No broken bones, or Social Services, or A and E visits. Just a kind of cold, calculating neglect, punctuated by the odd kick or punch until I was big enough to fight them off." I take another swig of cold bubbles. Blood singing nicely in my ears now. "And then they just ignored me."

"Until you could leave home?"

I nodded, staring over his shoulder at the black windows. "I suppose I should thank them because it was because of them that I had these dreams, to escape the house, the village, to travel, to make real this fantasy life where I had adventures. So as soon as I could I did travel. Sometimes round England and Scotland, later round Europe. They practically shoved me out of the door, they were so glad to be rid of me. I came home occasionally for my things, to nick money off them. I never said a word. And then I'd disappear again."

He is listening intently. The rain is pattering. The fire crackles in the grate. The bubbles pop and fizz in the glasses. The music has slowed.

"The only good thing they ever did was die. I was like Harry Potter living with the Dursleys."

"The muggles." His smiling eyes glint in the firelight. "And you the little orphaned witch."

"Yeah. But it feels great to be alone in the world, especially when you have some money. You can do whatever you want. And here I am, doing it. I want to relish every minute of it, Gustav."

There's a slight pause as we think about the truth of my words.

"And so you shall, Serena. You look enchanting in that negligee by the way."

I gasp at the unexpected quiet compliment. Tilt my head demurely. "Glad my lord approves."

"Bewitching. Now's the time, Serena. I know you're going to please me, very much."

I lift my shoulder coquettishly. Thank the champagne. "Your wish is my command."

He takes a deep breath, as if daring himself. Runs his tongue over his mouth. "Dance for me, Serena. Forget everything that's gone before. I want to see you

move. I want to see your spirit. I want to admire you here in private. I want to see if a mere garment can change you into my dream woman."

I fold my arms. "Please, Gustav. I'll feel stupid. I didn't mean that kind of command. Why can't I just kiss you?"

He frowns and leans forward. "Pretend it's not just me, if that inhibits you. Pretend your cousin and your friends are here. You're stepping out on stage."

The volume rises in the speakers, a sultry Latin tempo with a wailing saxophone accompanied by a low, hypnotic bass beat. Gustav walks in front of me and there's the chain, looping between us as he leads me across the hallway into the big drawing room, where another fire is burning in the kind of fireplace you could roast a whole cow in. He goes to stand by it, stroking his dark chin like a forbidding Victorian patriarch.

"Will you dance with me?"

He shakes his head and sits back down on the sofa. Stretches his arms along the back. So confident suddenly, so sure I'll do what he wants. And I will. I want to. I want to make his eyes gleam with desire. I want to make the pulse in his neck race like a jack hammer.

I pause in the middle of the huge dark red carpet, breathing fast like a frightened animal as the thunder still grumbles outside. Gustav shifts in the cushions, his thighs slightly parted, so relaxed that the casual shirt untucks from his belt where he hasn't bothered to fasten the lower buttons, and I can see a sliver of stomach and a dark line of hair twining enticingly down into the cool jeans.

Remember what he's doing for you, Serena. There's no going back. This is the start of your new, colourful life. The one that you're going to relish. Remember how he makes you feel. How you wanted to stay with him in that bar. How he's gotten under your skin. How you even rejected the advances of that rich, cute American guy at Polly's party because this man had already taken possession of your mind.

I kick my legs out like a pony and start to pace up and down the floor like a matador, glaring at him. Gustav grins and lifts his glass to me in response.

"You look angry," he remarks quietly, his eyes roving over me hungrily. His hair looks wilder than ever, pushed in damp spikes off his forehead. "Like you're going into battle."

"You made me talk about my family. It always makes me angry."

"Anger's good. But forget them. I'm here now. That's all you need to know."

"But you inhibit me."

I tilt my chin so that the glare becomes seductive rather than sulky, then shake my hair round my face. My crowning glory. Rapunzel. I'm thinking mermaid now, not witch. A siren from another world.

"So like I said. Pretend. Think of all of this as a game. Then you'll realise how sexy that can be."

He reaches above his head to dim the lights totally so it's only candlelight now. He doesn't see me glancing again at his stomach when he stretches, the shirt flapping open as if he's a schoolboy running late. The bare strip of skin that my fingers are itching to touch.

He settles back down, biting his finger now as he focuses on me. I let the music direct me, closing my eyes and rotating my neck until I'm dizzy. But dizzy's good.

It makes me feel lightheaded, energetic, daring. An exhibitionist. Best of all, the centre of attention.

I edge the negligee upwards, revealing my ankles, then my knees, pausing as he continues to stare at me. Those eyes appreciate me. I lift the negligee up my thighs, my feet freer now to step apart and together while I run my hands over my ribcage.

A sudden, firm jerk on my wrist reminds me we are still linked, the nearly invisible thread joining us together. The thunder rumbles more distantly now, and the show-off in me takes shape. Let's see what happens. How long will it be before he comes begging. Preferably on his knees.

My hands wander down my throat, over my shoulders, then they're over my breasts, hovering an inch over them, tracing the soft outlines, the protruding little peaks, outlined under the silk and even the suggestion, the threat of touching triggers a sharp tug in my nipples, then another much lower down. My nipples scrape and catch on the silk. I run the tips of my fingers between them, squeeze my breasts briefly together, then flicker and tease down my stomach and down between my legs, holding my softness there for a moment, licking my lips like a stripper. Hands sliding down my thighs, pushing them open and closed.

As the music grows louder I accelerate my moves, bending and straightening and sliding my legs further and further apart. This is a private dance, just for him, no audience. I'm not sure of the programme, what will happen next, but I'm turning myself on, that's for sure, dancing in my new negligee. My fingers want to creep inside to play, but I slap myself away.

"Don't stop, Serena." He can't hide the animal groan of arousal in his deep voice. "This is strumming all the right strings."

My hair sways in front of my face, down my back, I sweep my hands down my body, cup the dampness growing between my legs. I pull the silk up so high that any further and I'd be totally bare to him.

He is leaning forwards, his hands dangling the champagne glass between his knees as he watches me, his eyes burning with desire but the rest of his expression so concentrated it's as if he's at the ballet. It's flattering, but strange. All I'm doing is prancing around his drawing room, really. Awaiting further instructions. The streak of warmth across his cheek-bones, the working of the muscle in his jaw give away what's really on his mind.

The daring is like a pair of hands pushing, pushing me on. I go over to the sofa, bend over him, let my hair fall in a tent around our faces, tip his watching dark face up close to mine, then I push him back into the cushions and swerve away as I see the gleam lighting up his eyes.

I'm making it up as I go along, but I'm tired of dancing solo. I want him to join in now. I'm dancing as I assume he wanted me to dance, burlesque style but without the tassels and the props. I sway towards him, aware of how all my curves push against the shimmering silk.

I hold my hands out to him, wriggling and gyrating.

"Dance with me, Gustav. Let go. Hang loose."

I twist away from him, dance to the other side of the room, crooking my finger like a Scheherazade. And at last I get my reaction. His mouth snaps open in a

wicked grin and my wrist is suddenly pulled out in front of me so that my arm is straight.

"You're gorgeous, Serena. I could watch you all night. Maybe one night I will do just that. You move like a sea creature. But I want you over here now."

He tugs at the silver chain, smiling wolfishly at his game, at this small but potent display of power.

I resist the pull of it at first. But as he goes on pulling, and it takes the strain; that spindly meshing of silver threads has the strength of a tow rope. So I let him pull me until I come to a halt in front of him again, still swaying slightly to the insistent music.

"I'm enjoying myself, Gustav. Dance with me!"

He shakes his head, holding the chain tightly in his fist, moves it from side to side so that my arm is forced to swing like a pendulum.

"That's what couples do. No, don't turn your lovely mouth down like that. Anything's possible, once we're used to each other, but for now we're still working to an agreement. I'm your patron. You're my protégée. What a patron does is take the protégée under his wing. And what protégées do is what they're told."

I fold my arms and look away from him. Tap my bare foot impatiently.

He sighs deeply. "Please would you kneel down, Serena. You've had the effect on me I knew you would. Look."

I look. There's an unmistakable bulge in his jeans, straining at the dark blue denim. His eyes, glittering in the candlelight, half closed behind those thick lashes, are pulling me towards him as irresistibly as the chain.

"I've been in this parlous state, on and off, since I first set eyes on you. You probably guessed that by now." He spreads his hands in a helpless gesture and we both stare at his crotch again.

"Hands and knees, you say? You want me to scrub the floor now? Surely I can do something else for you? Much more fun. Protégée isn't the same as servant."

He laughs, so naughtily. "Very true. How about slave? That sounds a whole lot sexier, don't you think?"

"Maybe. If you're Caligula."

"Hmm. Very tempting, if it wasn't for the toga." He jerks on the silver chain. "So, what does a slave do when her master calls? She hears the command, and she comes, that's what."

But I don't move. I can't bring myself to go down on hands and knees, lick his shoes, his floor, whatever it is he wants me to do. He jerks again on the silver chain. I'm so busy resisting that I stumble and fall towards him, half falling into his arms, but he catches me, stops me in midair before him.

His strong hands are brakes on my hips. I stare down at his silky black hair which seems to grow as fast as his beard. He's about to push me down onto my knees, his word being my command, but I don't want to do that. I fall against him, press into him, his face is against my stomach, his nose is level with my navel, his mouth so close to where his fingers were yesterday.

His breath is hot on the silk at the top of my legs. I'm soft and weak from the dancing, the music, the kiss of silk on my bare skin. I push myself towards him.

"Stay right there, Serena."

He groans into my stomach. Such a primeval, sexy sound. My man, groaning because he wants me.

Then he pulls me slowly, almost thoughtfully towards him, his hands spread over my bottom to keep hold of me. He looks down with that questioning frown, why is he always so unsure, unwilling to let go? He pinches the fabric up between his fingers, right up, so that it's all wrinkled up around my hips and there's nothing between my naked skin and the cool air. I'm bared before him.

He reminds me of the hung-up, insomniac businessman in *Pretty Woman*. The scene where the escort girl comes downstairs late at night and finds him playing sensual jazz on the hotel piano. She sits on the top of the music stand, her legs on either side of him, rousing him from his apathy in the most obvious way possible, and as he pushes her silk nightdress up over her nakedness her toes start to play the keys out of tune.

I wriggle, press my thighs together. He slides his hand in sideways, and parts them.

The saxophone wails suggestively, up the scale, minor key, sad but sexy.

The way he's looking. Examining this part of me like a precious jewel, a long sought specimen. It's because he's so slow, so quiet, his lips working silently as if he's praying. It's as if this core of me is rare, precious, the Holy Grail, something he's somehow been denied. He felt it yesterday, but today he wants to see it.

It fills me with a hot, wild surge of womanly pride. There's nothing special about the way I'm built. But this guy's slow-burning, horny fascination is making me feel like the most special woman in the world. No-one's looked at me like this or made me feel beautiful like he does. Ever. Not even my face, let alone my body.

Jake looked at me because he fancied me. Loved me in his adolescent way. He looked at my face, my eyes. Very occasionally brushed my hair if I begged him. But he was young and he was in a rush, greedy, hungry for me. Desperate all the time to get his rocks off. But he never took time out to look at me in this reverential way, like I was up on a pedestal.

Let's face it. We were both young and hungry.

I lay my hands gently on Gustav's head, on his face, run my fingers down his neck to say yes. Not that I need to. I'm his servant after all. But he's right. The game is fun, whichever way you play it.

Gustav tips his head back to show me he likes my hands in his hair. I go on stroking him as he parts me gently with one hand. His lips are so close to my very core. He blows on the secret place as if blowing flames onto kindling laid in a cold grate. I wriggle invitingly. His fingers hold me open like a prize, wide open, unfurl me like a flower. One finger smoothes out each petal, making each part damp, then wet, as he touches it, and then his mouth is moving against me and he slides his tongue up me, like a cat, in one movement.

The kindling flares into life before I'm ready. I moan and shake uncontrollably, tugging at his hair. It's not just the one small sliver he's touched and inflamed. The wet slick of his tongue has licked right through me, embers catching fire. Literally to the roots of my hair, the tips of my fingers as the sensation shoots through me.

I gasp out loud, a really dirty, wanton sound, grasp his shoulders, tangle his

hair in my fingers so that I'm sure it must hurt, and yank his face into me harder. He pauses. I loosen my grip on him, perhaps this isn't allowed, but I'm not letting go completely. And then he licks again, his fingers still holding me open, the exposure exquisite yet excruciating, I feel like one of those botanical drawings, every detail sketched by a fine pencil.

And by his warm tongue, licking again, his other hand fanned out over my bottom to keep me in place, keeping me pushed against his mouth and thank God he's taking my weight because my legs are buckling as he licks, and then his tongue flicks on the bud that's poking out rudely, waiting.

It's private, but it's no mystery. Certainly not to him. Shades of other women, other intimate kisses, make my desire all the fiercer. Gustav finds the exact spot and touches it with the tip of his tongue. It's an electric probe on me. I close my eyes to shadowy rivals because I'm starting to come now, grinding against his mouth, his fingers, his tongue, ripping at his black hair, squeezing my thighs round his face, falling heavily down onto him when it's finished, crashing onto the sofa as he slides backwards to catch me. I land on top of him and lie there, never wanting to move, listening to the slow, steady thump of his heart beneath me.

His voice is a rumble in my ear as he strokes my hair. "That wasn't supposed to happen. You're supposed to be at my beck and call, not the other way around."

I bury my face in his shoulder.

"I'll do whatever you want me to do."

"Turns out what I wanted was to pleasure you." He sighs. I can smell myself on his breath, just a faint tang. He's tasted me. "So hot. So eager. Such a sexy woman. Not much tuition required here, at least not in the oral arts."

"You make me sound like a tart."

"Classy tart." He chuckles. "Lady, wildcat, virgin, whore. Whatever I can get."

I bury my head against his chest. "I've never behaved like that before."

He pushes me gently up, makes me sit up so he can look at me. His hair is rumpled. His mouth is still glistening with my juices. I long to kiss it.

He picks up his glass though, and tosses the rest of the champagne down.

"You've only ever treated sex as a pastime to get you through those bored teenage years. With the one guy. Am I right?"

I shrug, in a very teenage fashion. "I told you. I'm very inexperienced."

He frames my jaw with his hand. I'm learning this is one of his favourite gestures. It means I can look deep into his eyes, see the way his brows move with his thoughts, the way his upper lip releases the lower before he speaks.

"Maybe you've blossomed very recently. Maybe you were plain as a pikestaff before. You'll have to let me see some photos. How could no-one else have noticed these slender coltish arms and legs, that tiny waist, those beautiful breasts, that amazing hair, your closed, innocent face. How has nobody ever snatched you up and carried you away before?"

"I've never been interested. And I'm no pushover." I roll onto my side at last, still panting, my body still flinching with delicious surprise. This is easier territory. "You've seen how I normally dress. It's easier hiding under unisex clothes."

"And yet you undressed for that lucky boyfriend of yours."

"Just the one. In the dark. Usually pissed. Always in a hurry." I sit up and

move away from him. That's not strictly true or fair, but none of it matters now. "Where I live, by the sea, people look more at boats and rocks than they do people."

"Well, I'm looking at you now, and I want you to look at me. What you've done to me. What you constantly do." He pushes me down and off the sofa until I'm on my knees on the floor in front of him. His eyes burn urgently. "I don't want to lose the moment. I'm not all poetry and compliments, Serena. I've just licked you to orgasm and it's my turn now."

My breath catches in my throat as he pushes his shirt aside and unzips his jeans. He grabs my hand and pushes it inside his pants, pressing me onto the hardness waiting down there. He tugs on the silver chain and I lift it out cradled in my fingers, revealed to me at last. The second penis I've ever seen. A man's, not a boy's. Bigger, harder, curving up so majestically as it meets the air.

He leans back easily, moving my hand up and down the shaft so that it grows even more. "See what you've done to me. Can you make a happy man very old?"

It's more of an order than a question, yet it also sounds like a plea. There's just him and me here. I could jump up now, simply leg it. Yeah, right. Out into the pouring rain. I could tell him to get stuffed. Yeah, and find my photographs out in the trash tomorrow morning.

"Teach me how, Gustav. I'm a quick learner." I lick my lips to cover my naïvety, then realise how suggestive that must look. The answering gleam in his eye tells me I'm right. "Teach me how to take you to heaven and back, just like you did for me."

It jumps in my hand. He pushes my hand off to show me. I can't tear myself away. Why would I want to run from that? It looks like it would fit me so beautifully.

Gustav tugs the silver chain again, pulling me down again with a thump. I start by putting my hands on his thighs. Feel the tensing of muscles there. I stroke my hands up and down, up towards his groin and away. Is he afraid? And if so, why?

"Still your choice, Serena. That agreement can be ripped up at any time. And if you choose to stay here and do what I ask you, you'll find I'll sometimes be tough on you. That's how I've been used to operate, especially with women. I think you'll respond very well to it. I think you'll like it. I think you want to empty your mind sometimes and let your body be ordered about by someone who knows exactly what they're doing."

"And if I don't?"

"Quite simply if you don't start by passing this one little test for me, the deal's off. Pleasure me now, like I've pleasured you, and I promise you we have some truly amazing times ahead of us."

"OK. So quit the lecture." I press my finger to his lips so hard it makes a dent. He tries not to smile at my cheekiness. But then something steely enters me. A new, cool certainty, that this is fine. More than fine. Being around this guy makes me constantly alert, constantly wondering what's happening next, and he's just shown me what a couple of swipes of his tongue can do to me. How the world can tilt in front of my eyes when he licks me. He thinks he's in charge, and yet he's also a slave to my new, feminine power.

Why would I run away from a master class like this? It's only a few weeks of obedience, after all.

I'm not going to let on that I've never sucked a man before.

I grip his legs harder, slide my hands right up to his groin. Now it's my turn to spread his legs a little. My face is right up against him. The heat from him pulses outwards. He smells so clean.

His glorious ready hardness springs forward in his lap. I lean forward. The soft rounded end bumps blindly against my cheek.

His hands come off my shoulders, slide under my hair. Yes. I have taught him something. If he touches my hair, I'll do anything for him. Look at me. I'm kneeling in front of my master. My master, at least until our agreement ceases and we walk away from each other.

To help me I think about what's happened so far. That curtailed cocktail, how I didn't want to leave him. How I obsessed about him all through Polly's Halloween party and couldn't get it on with a readily available American millionaire. How I nearly ran all the way to the gallery to find him after he called me yesterday morning. How distant and scary he looked in his suit, how good and dirty it felt when he took me with his fingers, us both standing by the window overlooking the river. What he's just done to me with his tongue. Cunnilingus. A fantastic old word I'll never laugh at again.

The rounded end prods at the corner of my mouth as if it has a life of its own. Gustav rests his head on the back of the sofa, half closes his constantly burning eyes, and for once that's a relief. His eyelashes leave spidery shadows on his face as it settles into something approaching peace.

I open my mouth and the most precious part of Gustav Levi slips smoothly into my mouth.

The silver chain is lying limp across the base of his stomach, catching in the triangular shock of black curling hair, like a decoration winding round a Christmas tree.

My heart is pounding. Sweat pricks under my arms. But I want to do this. And it's not so bad, is it? Think about what he did to you, what he'll do again if you're a good girl. My body twitches in lazy memory. There's still moisture slicked inside my thighs. He did that to me. I close my lips as the length of him jumps over my tongue. So long. So hard. His hands close over my ears so now I can only hear the thick pulsing of my own blood. I stretch my jaw wider.

This isn't just for him. This is for me.

He is hard now and huge, pushing into my mouth and shoving to the back of my throat and I realise that this cool, mysterious man is about to lose control of himself at my bidding. I try not to gag, ridiculously remember Polly telling me how it was done, demonstrating on a banana when we were on the beach one day, looking really filthy as she licked this curving yellow peeled fruit and pushed it right down her throat.

Guys love you to swallow, she said, biting the banana so that it almost squealed with pain. How I giggled and spluttered. If you swallow they'll be your slave forever.

When I next see her I'll be able to tell her I've done it at last. Or are we too grown up for all those confidences now? I'll tell her what she didn't tell me, that

it only really works if you're falling for the guy. That's why I couldn't have done it for Toga Tomas. Or Jake.

I push the thick shaft back with my tongue, close my lips round it again, and start to suck it into the wetness of my mouth. As it gives a little buck, and starts to grow even more, so does the balloon of triumph inside me.

I'm getting wet all over again. Gustav's big warm hands are jammed over my ears, but stroking and tugging at my hair at the same time. He's stiffening and swelling as I suck. I don't know if it's my breath or his that is gasping and rasping with excitement now, but pride surges through me.

He thinks I'm his pet. But watch this. He's my pet, too. His obvious, thrusting pleasure is turning me on. I can taste him. His hands tug at my head, up and down, moving my mouth up and down, he's a little more rough now, tangling and yanking at my long hair.

My mouth loosens, lips losing their tight grip. I start to bite instead, nip the taut surface, no idea how hard to bite or how much it might hurt.

He moans, his hands growing weaker, and elation surges through me again. Here am I, Serena Folkes, just up from the country, with my lips wrapped round one of the most powerful men in the arts world. I am the one making *him* whimper.

He thrusts deeper into my mouth. I will myself to exercise control for a little bit longer and start to fondle underneath it, the soft balls shrinking shyly as I encircle the base with my finger and thumb. The chain is tangled up between us. He's filling my mouth. He's pushing at the back of my throat and now he's forcing me down over the velvety surface.

I nip once, nip a little harder, then suck, my lips sliding up and down, and then he is jerking, pushing himself into my face, he's jerking against the roof of my mouth, blocking my throat, his fingers are pulling at my hair, pulling me away, pushing me back, and then he's groaning loudly and painfully, sobbing his control away. His life force is spurting and flowing. It's hot and thick, and alien. What did Polly say to think about when you were doing this?

Imagine you're dying of thirst in the desert. I open my throat and swallow every drop.

I kneel back at last, wipe my mouth quickly, and watch him. His eyes are closed now, so I can't tell what he's thinking. His throat bulges as he regains his breath, swallowing down the shouting excitement. His mouth slowly closes and he lies back, totally spent. I could watch him all night. The lovely man I've reduced to this exhausted heap.

Instinct tells me I can watch him but I can't kiss him. Can't do anything except rest my hands on his legs, watch the pulse in his neck judder to a calmer rhythm.

After a few moments, his eyes still closed, he packs his subsiding erection away into his jeans then lifts his hand and finds my bracelet to unhook it from the silver chain.

"Will you leave me now? You can find your own way to bed tonight."

I stop his hand on my wrist. "Have I done something wrong?"

"No, sweet girl. I just need some time. Please."

I want to sit beside him on the sofa and watch the dying embers of the fire in the enormous grate. But I get up obediently and watch the silver chain fall away

from me and trickle against his leg, and as I leave he waves me away as if he really is a Roman emperor. I turn abruptly and walk into the chilly hall.

How can I sleep after this? How can he dismiss me like this after I know I've pleased him? I stop on the landing outside a set of double doors, churning with anger. I've a good mind to go straight back down and tell him to act like a normal lover. At least to talk about it.

I turn to grab the banisters. I'm ready to straddle and slide down them in my fury, and then I catch sight of it. The Rossetti painting he mentioned earlier. The model, Elizabeth Siddal I'm certain, is in typical pre-Raphaelite pose, doomed woman bathed in early evening light from a window outside which a river slowly flows. Her mournful eyes are turned upwards, cheeks and jaw pointing down, a mane of tawny hair falling over a green velvet medieval gown pulled slightly off one shoulder, candles symbolically blown out around her.

I calm down, looking at that. No matter where I go, I know that every time he passes that priceless picture, he will think of me. My hand comes to rest on the doorknob of his bedroom. Is he a collector? Has he more in here? But the door is locked.

I glance down at the hall, the flickering strip of light from the sitting room. He must be sleeping now. One day he'll take me into this bedroom, carry me over its threshold like a prize.

I run up those shadowy stairs to the little room in the attic, lit only by one lamp.

I feel light as a feather. I climb up onto the high four-poster bed and fall into the mountain of white cushions, running my hand over my lips, where I just tasted him. Down to the place where he tasted me.

Then, as the wind rattles insistently at the glass doors to try to get into my bedroom, I fall straight into a deep slumber as if tumbling off a cliff.

THE TALE OF THE ROSE

Emma Donoghue

Emma Donoghue was born in Dublin, Ireland. She earned a first-class honours BA in English and French from University College Dublin. She moved to England, and in 1997 received her Ph.D. (on the concept of friendship between men and women in eighteenth-century English fiction) from the University of Cambridge. Her 2010 novel, *Room*, was a finalist for the Man Booker Prize and was an international bestseller. Donoghue's 1995 novel, *Hood*, won the Stonewall Book Award, and *Slammerkin* (2000) won the Ferro-Grumley Award for Lesbian Fiction. In *Kissing the Witch*, Donoghue spins new tales from the classic fairy-tales. It is made up of thirteen interconnected stories about power and transformation, where women – young and old – tell their own stories of love and hate, honour, revenge, passion and deception. The stories simmer with an understated but palpable eroticism.

In a whisper I asked,
Who were you
before you took to the skies?
And the bird said,
Will I tell you my own story?
It is a tale of a rose.

In this life I have nothing to do but cavort on the wind, but in my last it was my fate to be a woman.

I was beautiful, or so my father told me. My oval mirror showed me a face with nothing written on it. I had suitors aplenty but wanted none of them: their doggish devotion seemed too easily won. I had an appetite for magic, even then. I wanted something improbable and perfect as a red rose just opening.

Then in a spring storm my father's ships were lost at sea, and my suitors wanted none of me. I looked in my mirror, and saw, not myself, but every place I'd never been.

The servants were there one day and gone the next; they seemed to melt into the countryside. Last year's leaves and papers blew across the courtyard as we packed to go. My father lifted heavy trunks till veins embroidered his forehead. He found me a blanket to wrap my mirror in for the journey. My sisters held up their pale sleek fingers and complained to the wind. How could they be expected to toil with their hands?

I tucked up my skirts and got on with it. It gave me a strange pleasure to see

what my back could bend to, my arms could bear. It was not that I was better than my sisters, only that I could see further.

Our new home was a cottage; my father showed me how to nail my mirror to the flaking wall. There were weeds and grasses but no roses. Down by the river, where I pounded my father's shirts white on the black rocks, I found a kind of peace. My hands grew numb and my dark hair tangled in the sunshine. I was washing my old self away; by midsummer I was almost ready.

My sisters sat just outside the door, in case a prince should ride by. The warm breeze carried the occasional scornful laugh my way.

As summer was leaving with the chilly birds, my father got word that one of his ships had come safe to shore after all. His pale eyes stood out like eggs. What he wanted most, he said, was to bring us each home whatever we wanted. My sisters asked for heavy dresses, lined cloaks, fur-topped boots, anything to keep the wind out. I knew that nothing could keep the wind out, so I asked for a red rose just opening.

The first snow had fallen before my father came home, but he did have a rose for me. My sisters waited in the doorway, arms crossed. I ran to greet him, this bent bush who was my father inching across the white ground. I took the rose into my hand before he could drop it. My father fell down. The petals were scarlet behind their skin of frost.

We piled every blanket we possessed on top of him; still his tremors shook the bed. My sisters wept and cursed, but he couldn't hear them. They cried themselves to sleep beside the fire.

That night in his delirium he raved of a blizzard and a castle, a stolen rose and a hooded beast. Then all of a sudden he was wide awake. He gripped my wrist and said, Daughter, I have sold you.

The story came wild and roundabout, in darts and flurries. I listened, fitting together the jagged pieces of my future. For a red rose and his life and a box of gold, my father had promised the beast the first thing he saw when he reached home. He had thought the first thing might be a cat. He had hoped the first thing might be a bird.

My heart pounded on the anvil of my breastbone. Father, I whispered, what does a promise mean when it is made to a monster?

He shut his trembling eyes. It's no use, he said, his tongue dry in his mouth. The beast will find us, track us down, smell us out no matter where we run. And then water ran down his cheeks as if his eyes were dissolving. Daughter, he said in a voice like old wood breaking, can you ever forgive me?

I could only answer his question with one of my own. Putting my hand over his mouth, I whispered, Which of us would not sell all we had to stay alive?

He turned his face to the wall.

Father, I said, I will be ready to leave in the morning.

Now you may tell me that I should have felt betrayed, but I was shaking with excitement. I should have felt like a possession, but for the first time in my life I seemed to own myself. I went as a hostage, but it seemed as if I was riding into battle.

I left the rose drying against my mirror, in case I ever came home. My sisters, onion eyed, watched us leave at dawn. They couldn't understand why my

father carried no gun to kill the beast. To them a word was not something to be kept.

The castle was in the middle of a forest where the sun never shone. Every villager we stopped to ask the way spat when they heard our destination. There had been no wedding or christening in that castle for a whole generation. The young queen had been exiled, imprisoned, devoured (here the stories diverged) by a hooded beast who could be seen at sunset walking on the battlements. No one had ever seen the monster's face and lived to describe it.

We stopped to rest when the light was thinning. My father scanned the paths through the trees, trying to remember his way. His eyes swiveled like a lamb's do when the wolves are circling. He took a deep breath and began to speak, but I said, Hush.

Night fell before we reached the castle, but the light spilling from the great doors led us through the trees. The beast was waiting at the top of the steps, back to the light, swaddled in darkness. I strained to see the contours of the mask. I imagined a different deformity for every layer of black cloth.

The voice, when it came, was not cruel but hoarse, as if it had not been much used in twenty years. The beast asked me, Do you come consenting?

I did. I was sick to my stomach, but I did.

My father's mouth opened and shut a few times, as if he was releasing words that the cold air swallowed up. I kissed his papery cheek and watched him ride away. His face was lost in the horse's mane.

Though I explored the castle from top to bottom over the first few days, I found no trace of the missing queen. Instead there was a door with my name on it, and the walls of my room were white satin. There were a hundred dresses cut to my shape. The great mirror showed me whatever I wanted to see. I had keys to every room in the castle except the one where the beast slept. The first book I opened said in gold letters: You are the mistress: ask for whatever you wish.

I didn't know what to ask for. I had a room of my own, and time and treasures at my command. I had everything I could want except the key to the story.

Only at dinner was I not alone. The beast liked to watch me eat. I had never noticed myself eating before; each time I swallowed, I blushed.

At dinner on the seventh night, the beast spoke. I knocked over my glass, and red wine ran the length of the table. I don't remember what the words were. The voice came out muffled and scratchy from behind the mask.

After a fortnight, we were talking like the wind and the roof slates, the rushes and the river, the cat and the mouse. The beast was always courteous; I wondered what scorn this courtesy veiled. The beast was always gentle; I wondered what violence hid behind this gentleness.

I was cold. The wind wormed through the shutters. I was lonely. In all this estate there was no one like me. But I had never felt so beautiful.

I sat in my satin-walled room, before the gold mirror. I looked deep into the pool of my face, and tried to imagine what the beast looked like. The more hideous my imaginings, the more my own face seemed to glow. Because I thought the beast must be everything I was not: dark to my light, rough to my smooth, hoarse to my sweet. When I walked on the battlements under the waning moon, the beast was the grotesque shadow I threw behind me.

One night at dinner the beast said, You have never seen my face. Do you still picture me as a monster?

I did. The beast knew it.

By day I sat by the fire in my white-satin room reading tales of wonder. There were so many books on so many shelves, I knew I could live to be old without coming to the end of them. The sound of the pages turning was the sound of magic. The dry liquid feel of paper under fingertips was what magic felt like.

One night at dinner the beast said, You have never felt my touch. Do you still shrink from it?

I did. The beast knew it.

At sunset I liked to wrap up in furs and walk in the rose garden. The days were stretching, the light was lingering a few minutes longer each evening. The rosebushes held up their spiked fingers against the yellow sky, caging me in.

One night at dinner the beast asked, What if I let you go? Would you stay of your own free will?

I would not. The beast knew it.

And when I looked in the great gold mirror that night, I thought I could make out the shape of my father, lying with his feverish face turned to the ceiling. The book did say I was to ask for whatever I wanted.

I set off in the morning. I promised to return on the eighth day, and I meant it when I said it.

Taking leave on the steps, the beast said, I must tell you before you go: I am not a man.

I knew it. Every tale I had ever heard of trolls, ogres, goblins, rose to my lips.

The beast said, You do not understand.

But I was riding away.

The journey was long, but my blood was jangling bells. It was dark when I reached home. My sisters were whispering over the broth. My father turned his face to me and tears carved their way across it. The rose, stiff against the mirror, was still red.

By the third day he could sit up in my arms. By the fifth day he was eating at table and patting my knee. On the seventh day my sisters told me in whispers that it would surely kill him if I went back to the castle. Now I had paid my ransom, they said, what could possess me to return to a monster? My father's eyes followed me round the cottage.

The days trickled by and it was spring. I pounded shirts on black rocks down by the river. I felt young again, as if nothing had happened, as if there had never been a door with my name on it.

But one night I woke to find myself sitting in front of my mirror. In its dark pool I thought I could see the castle garden, a late frost on the trees, a black shape on the grass. I found the old papery rose clenched in my fist, flaking into nothing.

This time I asked no permission of anyone. I kissed my dozing father and whispered in his ear. I couldn't tell if he heard me. I saddled my horse, and was gone before first light.

It was sunset when I reached the castle, and the doors were swinging wide. I

ran through the grounds, searching behind every tree. At last I came to the rose garden, where the first buds were hunched against the night air. There I found the beast, a crumpled bundle eaten by frost.

I pulled and pulled until the padded mask lay uppermost. I breathed my heat on it, and kissed the spot I had warmed. I pulled off the veils one by one. Surely it couldn't matter what I saw now?

I saw hair black as rocks under water. I saw a face white as old linen. I saw lips red as a rose just opening.

I saw that the beast was a woman. And that she was breathing, which seemed to matter more.

This was a strange story, one I would have to learn a new language to read, a language I could not learn except by trying to read the story.

I was a slow learner but a stubborn one. It took me days to learn that there was nothing monstrous about this woman who had lived alone in a castle, setting all her suitors riddles they could make no sense of, refusing to do the things queens are supposed to do, until the day when, knowing no one who could see her true face, she made a mask and from then on showed her face to no one. It took me weeks to understand why the faceless mask and the name of a beast might be chosen over all the great world had to offer. After months of looking, I saw that beauty was infinitely various, and found it behind her white face.

I struggled to guess these riddles and make sense of our story, and before I knew it summer was come again, and the red roses just opening.

And as the years flowed by, some villagers told travelers of a beast and a beauty who lived in the castle and could be seen walking on the battlements, and others told of two beauties, and others, of two beasts.

From THIS MAN

Jodi Ellen Malpas

Jodi Ellen Malpas was born and raised in the Midlands town of Northampton, where she lives with her two boys and a beagle. She is a self-professed daydreamer, a Converse and mojito addict, and has a terrible weak spot for Alpha Males. Writing powerful love stories and creating addictive characters has become her passion – a passion she now shares with her devoted readers. Jodi is a proud *New York Times* bestselling author – all six of her published novels having hit the *New York Times* bestsellers list – as well as a *Sunday Times* and international bestseller. Her work is published in over twenty languages across the world.

He kicks the door shut behind him and places me between the sinks on the marble vanity unit before returning to lock the door. My dress is still bunched around my waist, my legs and knickers completely exposed.

I gaze around the vast room that I'm so familiar with, my eyes falling on the gigantic cream marble bath dominating the centre of the room. I smile, remembering the trauma of having to organise a crane to lift it in through the windows. It was a nightmare, but it does look spectacular. The double, open-ended shower on the back wall is made up of floor-to-ceiling sheeted glass and beige Travertine tiles, and the vanity unit that I've been placed on is cream Italian marble, with two sunken sinks and large waterfall taps. A thick, gold-framed, intricately carved mirror spans the entire width of the unit, and a chaise lounge sits at an angle in the window. It really is luxury embodied.

I hear the lock click into place, snapping me from admiring my work and pulling my eyes to the door, where Jesse is watching me closely. As he saunters toward me, he slowly starts unbuttoning his shirt. Anticipation has my stomach churning and my thighs clenching shut. This man is absolutely stunning.

With his final button unfastened, he stands before me with his shirt draped open, and I can't resist reaching up and running my finger down the centre of his hard, tanned chest. He looks down to follow my trail, placing his hands on either side of my hips, nudging his way between my thighs. As he looks back up to me, his lips tip at the edges and his eyes sparkle, the slight creases at the corners softening the usual intensity in them.

"You can't escape now," he teases.

"I don't want to."

"Good," he mouths, dragging my eyes to his lovely lips.

I trail my finger back up his chest, working my way past his throat until my

finger rests on his bottom lip. He opens his mouth, biting my finger playfully, and I smile, continuing upward and running my hand through his hair.

"I like your dress." He drags his eyes down my front.

I follow his stare to the bunched-up material around my waist. "Thank you."

"It's a bit restrictive." He tugs at a piece of material.

"It is," I agree. The anticipation is killing me. *Rip off the dress!*

"Shall we remove it?" He cocks a brow at me, the corners of his mouth twitching.

I smile. "If you like."

"Or maybe, we leave it on?" He breaks into a full-on smile as he holds his hands up.

I melt all over the vanity unit.

His hands are quickly on me again, sliding around my back. "But then again, I have firsthand knowledge of what's under this lovely dress." He reaches up, grasping the zipper, breathing into my ear as he does. "And it's far superior to the dress," he whispers, pulling it down slowly, teasingly. I'm panting hard and desperate. "I think we'll get rid of it." He lifts me off the counter, placing me on my feet before pulling my dress away from my body and letting it drop to the floor. He kicks it to the side without taking his eyes off me.

I frown at him. "I like that dress." I couldn't give a toss about the dress. He could have ripped it off and cleaned the windows with it, for all I care.

"I'll buy you a new one." He shrugs as he places me back on the counter, resuming his position between my thighs. He presses his body up against me and grabs my bum, pulling me in toward him so we're locked tight together. He grinds his hips while staring at me.

The throb at my core is bordering on painful, and I'm at serious risk of falling apart if he continues with that alone. I want to tell him to hurry up; I'm struggling to control myself here.

Reaching up, he unclasps my bra, pulling the straps down my arms and flinging it behind him. I lean back on my hands, exposing my breasts to him, and looking into my eyes he lifts his hand and places it, palm down, under my throat. "I can feel your heart hammering," he says quietly. He glides his palm down between my breasts until it rests on my stomach, as he looks at me – all smouldering and delicious. "You're too fucking beautiful, lady." He grinds firmly. "I think I'll keep you."

I arch my back, thrusting my chest forward, and he smiles before lowering his mouth and taking my nipple deep, sucking hard. When he brings his hand up to massage my other breast, I moan, letting my head fall back against the mirror. Oh, good God. The man is a genius. His arousal is as hard as lead, pressing between my thighs, causing me to roll my hips to ease the throb on a long, drawn-out moan. I don't know what to do with myself. I want to soak up the pleasure because it's so good, but the need to have him is getting the better of me, the pressure in my groin near exploding point. As if reading my mind, he skates his hand up the inside of my thigh, finding the edge of my knickers, and one finger breaches the barrier, lightly brushing the tip of my clit.

"Shit!" I cry, throwing myself up to grab his shoulders, digging my nails into his strained muscles.

"Language, lady," he scorns, then slams his lips against mine, plunging two fingers into me.

My muscles grab onto him as he works them in and out. I might literally die of pleasure. I feel the fast buildup of an impending orgasm, and I know it's going to blow me apart. Holding on to his shoulders for dear life, I moan into his mouth as he continues his assault on me.

Oh, here it is.

"Come," he commands, applying more pressure to the top of my clit.

I fall apart in an explosion of stars, releasing his mouth and tossing my head back in a complete frenzy. I cry out and he grabs my head, yanking it forward to tackle my mouth, catching the tail end of my cries. I'm in pieces. I'm panting, shaking and boneless as I disintegrate all over him, completely uninhibited and unashamed of what he does to me. I'm delirious with pleasure.

His kiss softens and his thrusts slow, easing me gradually down as he scatters tender kisses all over my damp, warm face. Too good, just too, too good.

I feel him brush a stray tendril of hair from my face and I open my eyes, meeting a dark, satisfied stare. He plants a soft kiss on my lips, and I sigh. I feel like a lifetime of pent-up pressure has been extinguished, just like that. I'm relaxed and sated.

"Better?" he asks, sliding his fingers out of me.

"Hmmm," I hum. I have no energy for speech.

His fingers drag across my bottom lip and he leans into me, watching me closely as he runs his tongue across my mouth, licking the remnants of my orgasm away. His eyes burn straight through me as we gaze at each other in silence and my hands instinctively reach up to cup his face, smoothing down his freshly shaven skin. This man is beautiful, intense and passionate. And he could break my heart.

He smiles lightly, turning his face to kiss my palm before returning his eyes to mine. Oh Lord, I'm in trouble.

We're both cruelly snatched from the intensity of the moment when the door handle of the bathroom is jiggled from the other side. I gasp and Jesse slaps his palm over my mouth, looking at me in amusement. He finds this funny?

"I can't hear anything," a strange voice says, as the door handle rattles. My eyes bulge in horror.

Jesse removes his hand, replacing it with his lips. "Shhhhhh," he mumbles against my mouth.

"Oh God, I feel cheap," I whine, leaving his lips and dropping my head to his shoulder. How am I going to walk out of this place without burning bright red and looking as guilty as sin?

"You're not cheap. Talk crap like that, I'll be forced to kick your delicious backside all over my bathroom."

I snap my head up from his shoulder, looking at him in confusion. "Your bathroom?"

"Yes, my bathroom." He smirks at me. "I wish they would stop letting strangers roam around my home."

"You live here?" I'm puzzled. He can't live here. No one lives here.

"Well, I will as of tomorrow. Tell me, is all this Italian shit worth the out-

rageously expensive price tag they attached to this place?" He looks at me expectantly.

"Italian shit?" I splutter, completely insulted. He laughs, and I think I might slap him. "You shouldn't have bought the place if you don't like the *shit* that's in it," I fire at him, completely outraged.

"I can get rid of the shit," he quips.

My eyebrows shoot up in a you-didn't-just-say-that expression. I've spent months breaking my back sourcing all of this Italian *shit* and this unappreciative swine is just going to *get rid of it*? I've never been so insulted, or pissed off. I try to wriggle my hands from under his, but he tightens his grip. I shoot him a scowl.

"Unravel your knickers, lady. I wouldn't *get rid* of anything in this apartment." He kisses me hard. "And you're in this apartment." He's taking my mouth again, possessively, greedily.

I won't read into that statement too much. My libido has just jumped to attention and I'm happy to comply. I attack him with equal force, thrusting my tongue into his mouth, circling his with mine as he lifts his grip from my hands. They impulsively fly to those taut, rippling shoulders that I love so much.

Wrapping his arm around my middle, he releases my lips and lifts me up from the counter, leaving me hovering above the surface as his other hand finds my knickers and yanks them down my legs. He rests me back down and removes my shoes, letting them tumble to the tiled floor on a loud clatter. I'm impatient, so I join him in his stripping party, reaching up and pushing his shirt down his broad shoulders, revealing his bare chest in all of its glory. He's cut to complete perfection. I want to lick every square inch of him.

As I trace my eyes down, I recoil slightly at a nasty scar that's running across his stomach and rounding onto his left hip. I never noticed it before. The light at The Manor was dim, but that is one hefty scar. It's slightly faded but bloody big. How did he get that? I elect to not enquire. It could be a sensitive issue, and I don't want anything to upset this moment. I could just sit here and gawp at him forever. Even with the scar that looks so sinister, he's still beautiful.

I scrunch his shirt up between my hands and chuck it on top of my dress, and he raises his eyebrows at me.

"I'll buy you a new one," I shrug.

He smirks and leans forward, bracing himself on the counter and capturing my lips – all brooding and careful. Reaching for his trousers, I begin unfastening his belt, whipping it out of his loop holes in one swift pull, instigating a snapping sound to erupt around us.

He pulls back on an arched brow. "Are you going to whip me?"

"No," I answer uncertainly, throwing his belt to the floor and sliding my hand between his tight, narrow hips and the waist-band of his trousers. I wrench him forward so we're nose to nose. "Of course, if you want me to . . ." Did I just say that?

"I'll bear that in mind," he says on a half-smile.

Keeping my eyes firmly on his, I start to undo the button on his trousers, my knuckles brushing over his solid erection, causing him to jerk. He squeezes his eyes shut as I slowly undo his fly, sliding my flat hand into his boxers, grazing

across the mass of dark blond hair. He shudders, looking up to the ceiling, the muscles on his chest rolling and undulating. I can't resist leaning forward and flicking my tongue up the centre of his chest bone.

"Ava, you should know that once I've had you, you're mine."

I'm too drunk on lust to take any notice of that statement. "Hmmm," I mumble against his skin, circling his nipple with my tongue and withdrawing my hand from his boxers. I grasp the waistband and ease them down over his tidy, narrow hips until his cock springs free.

My God, it's huge! The involuntary gasp that escapes my mouth is an indication of my shock, and flicking my eyes to his, I find a small smile tickling the corner of his mouth. It's all the mortifying evidence I need to tell me that he's picked up on my reaction.

He steps back, kicking his shoes and socks off before removing his trousers and boxers. I'm instantly drawn to his powerfully lean thighs, and gathering some of my shattered confidence, I reach forward slowly and gently circle my thumb over his tip, watching him as he watches my hand explore him. When I tentatively wrap my hand around the base, I see him struggle with the contact.

"Shit, Ava," he gasps, resting his hands on my hips. I jerk, and he smiles. "Ticklish?"

"Just there," I gasp. Oh, it drives me mad!

"I'll remember that," he says, taking my lips and working my mouth urgently as I begin slow, even strokes of his hardness, increasing the pace when I feel his mouth getting firmer against mine. His hand disappears between my legs, and with one skim of his thumb over my beating clitoris, I'm suddenly catapulted to Central Jesse Cloud Nine. I gasp into his mouth. He bites my lip.

"You ready?" he asks urgently, and I nod, because speech has completely evaded me.

He rips his hand from the apex of my thighs and knocks me away from his throbbing arousal, and in one measured movement, he moves his hands to my backside, lifts me and impales me onto his waiting length.

I yelp.

"Okay?" he pants. "Are you okay?"

"Two seconds. I need a few seconds." I wrap my legs around him, crying out at the mixture of pleasure and pain. I know he's not even all of the way in. Jesus, but the man is enormous.

I'm swung around and thrust up against the wall, the coldness of the tiles not bothering me in the slightest as I try to adjust myself to Jesse's hugeness. He rests his forehead against mine, my hands slipping over his sweat-drenched back as he holds still for a few moments, giving me time to adapt to the intrusion.

Panting, he slowly withdraws from me, re-entering on a deliberate, steady thrust. This time he's in further, and the fullness is making my head spin.

"Can you take more?" he asks urgently.

More? How much more is there? *I can do this, I can do this.* I repeat the mantra over and over as I adjust to his size, taking some calming breaths, and when I know I've got a handle on it, I kiss him slowly, arching my back and pushing my breasts into his chest.

"Ava, tell me you're ready," he breathes.

"I'm ready." I've never been more ready for anything in my life.

With my prompt, he extracts himself and drives back inside of me more forcefully. I sigh, tilting my hips forward in acceptance as he growls in appreciation and repeats his swift thrusts, again and again.

"You're mine now, Ava," he breathes on a deep, delicious plunge. My head drops forward to rest on his. "All mine."

In one fast move, he pulls back and pounds home.

I scream.

I'm full to capacity and loving every wonderful bit of it. I grip his shoulders as he increases his thrusts, slamming into me, and hitting my womb every time. I cry in pleasure when he finds my lips, plunging his tongue into my mouth in a desperate claim as our damp, sweat-riddled bodies clash and slide together. I'm about to splinter into a million pieces. Holy shit! I've never come during penetrative sex!

"You're going to come?" he gasps against my mouth.

"Yes!" I shout, sinking my teeth into his bottom lip. He moans. It's animalistic, but I'm losing control here.

"Wait for me," he demands, pounding harder.

I scream, desperately clenching my muscles around him to try and hold off, but it's not working. How long will he be? I can't hold on.

After three more hard strikes, he shouts, "Now, Ava!" and I burst at his command, throwing my head back and screaming his name as I feel hot liquid shoot into me.

He grips me hard, pulling me as close as he can get me, holding me there and burying his face in my exposed throat.

"Oh, fucccckkkkk!" he groans against my neck. The long, satisfied moan falling from my own lips is symbolic of how I feel right now.

He slows his thrusts to ease us both down from our incredible highs, and I hold him tight, my inner muscles contracting around him as he lazily circles his hips.

"Look at me," he orders softly, and I pull my head down to look at him, sighing happily as he searches my eyes. He rolls his hips again and plants a kiss on the end of my nose. "Beautiful," he says simply, cupping the back of my head and pushing me toward him so my cheek rests against his shoulder. I could stay like this for ever.

My back peels away from the cold wall behind me and I'm carried to the vanity unit with Jesse still buried deep inside me, pulsating and twitching. He slips out and settles me on the counter, clasping his palms on either side of my face and bending to kiss me, his lips lingering on mine in a total display of affection.

"I didn't hurt you, did I?" he asks, his frown line appearing on his forehead.

I dissolve on the spot. I want to smother him in my arms, so I do. I wrap my whole body around him, arms and legs, and cling on to him like my life depends on it. His face buries in my neck and he strokes my back. It's the most calming sensation I've ever felt. I can't even muster up the energy to feel guilty.

Sarah who?

We remain entwined, a bundle of arms and legs, breathing heavy and holding

each other for an age. I want to stay exactly where I am. We could – it is his bathroom. I can't believe he's bought the penthouse.

After far too short a time, he leans back, running the back of his knuckles down the side of my face. "I didn't use a condom," he says with genuine regret in his eyes. "I'm sorry, I got so carried away. You're on birth control, right?"

"Yes, but the pill doesn't protect me from STDs." I'm such a numb-nut. This man is a God with some serious moves. I dread to think of how many women he's slept with.

He smiles at me. "Ava, I've *always* used a condom." He leans forward, kissing my forehead. "Except with you."

"Why?" I ask, a little puzzled.

He pulls away and has a little chew on his bottom lip. "I don't think straight when I'm near you." He puts his boxers and trousers on, then reaches over me to grab a washcloth from the shelf. I'm about to protest, but then I remember . . . it's his. Everything in here is his, except for me. Well, not according to him, but that was just an impending orgasm talking. The throes of passion can make you say some funny things. He doesn't think straight? That makes two of us.

He runs the tap, passing the cloth under it and returns to stand before me. I feel exposed sitting here completely naked. This isn't equal ground, so I close my legs to conceal myself, suddenly uncomfortable with my state of undress. But he looks at me, a mystified look flitting across his handsome face as he pouts, reaches between my legs and spreads them gently.

"Better," he mutters, lifting my arms from my lap and placing them on his shoulders. He rests the warm, damp cloth on the inside of my thigh and begins sweeping it up and down, cleaning the remnants of him away from me. It's a tender act and extremely intimate. I watch his face in fascination, noticing the slight crease across his forehead as he concentrates with his procedure of cleaning me up.

He gazes up at me, his green eyes soft and twinkling. "I want to toss you in that shower and worship every inch of you, but this will have to do. For now, anyway." He leans in and kisses me, lingering briefly. I don't think I could ever tire of these simple, affectionate kisses. His lips are so soft, his scent divine. "Come on, lady. Let's get you dressed." He lifts me from the counter and helps me into my underwear and dress before zipping me up. My entire body convulses when he rests his lips on the nape of my neck, his warm, soft mouth having the hairs on my neck rising. I don't think he's out of my system – not at all. This is bad news.

I pick his pale blue shirt up from the floor and shake it out before handing it to him.

"There really wasn't any need to screw it up, was there?" He flicks me a grin as he pulls it on, fastening the buttons and tucking it into his navy trousers.

"Your jacket will cov – " I abruptly remember tossing that on the floor in the bedroom. "Oh," I whisper, all wide-eyed.

"Yes. Oh." He arches a brow as he snaps his belt, making me flinch and him grin. "Okay, you ready to face the music, lady?" He holds his hand out to me, and I take it without a thought. The man is a magnet. "I'd say quite loud, wouldn't you?"

I gape at him as he gives me a full-on dazzling smile. Then I shake my head, quickly glancing in the mirror. Oh, I'm flushed. My lips are swollen and pink, my hair is still up but with random strands curling down all over the place, and I'm creased. I need five minutes to sort myself out.

"You're perfect," he reassures me, as if sensing the panic rising in me.

Perfect? Perfect wouldn't be a word I would use. I look thoroughly fucked! He tugs me to the door, unlocks it and strides out, devoid of wariness, while I'm more cautious. I see his jacket still sprawled on the floor, and he scoops it up as we pass.

When we hit the curving staircase, I suddenly register my hand still in his, and I try to ease it from his grasp, but he squeezes it tighter, flashing me a scowl. Shit! He has to let go. My boss and colleagues are down here. I can't go prancing through them holding hands with this strange man. I attempt to free my hand again, but he refuses to let it go.

"Jesse, let go of my hand."

"No," he shoots back, short and firm, and without even looking at me.

I stop abruptly halfway down the stairs and scan the room below. No one is looking at us, thank God, but it won't be long before someone clocks us. Jesse turns, looking up at me from a few steps below.

"Jesse, you can't expect me to parade through here holding your hand. That's not fair. Please, let me go."

He looks at our hands locked together, suspended between our bodies. "I'm not letting you go," he murmurs sullenly. "If I let you go, you might forget how it feels. You might change your mind."

There is absolutely no chance of me forgetting how we feel flesh on flesh, but that's not the part of his statement that's bothering me. "Change my mind about what?" I ask, totally perplexed.

"Me," he says simply.

What about him? My mind hasn't been made up on anything, so there's nothing to change. My mind has just twisted further. I need to focus my attention on persuading him to release my hand before someone spots us, so I'll file that comment, just like I've filed the other strange comments he made upstairs.

Holy shit! I nearly fall down the stairs when I see Sarah breezing across the terrace, reality crashing down around me. Surely when he sees her he'll stop being such an unreasonable fool. She's heading back inside. I don't have time to fuck about, so I narrow my eyes on him and use brute force to yank my hand from his, nearly dislocating my shoulder in the process. He scowls at me, but I don't hang around long enough to soak up his annoyance, taking the stairs fast, down to the vast openness of the penthouse. The woman has made it obvious that she dislikes me, and I can hardly blame her. She saw me as a threat and as it turns out, her fear was warranted.

I hit the bottom of the stairs and see Tom come running through the crowd of people, waving his arms about frantically. "There you are! Where have you been? Patrick has been looking for you everywhere." He clasps my shoulders, checking me up and down, ever the drama queen. Noting my disheveled state, he eyes me suspiciously. I feel the heat rise in my cheeks.

"I was giving Mr Ward a tour," I offer, rather unconvincingly, while waving my hand over my shoulder in the general direction of Jesse. I know he's close behind me; I can still feel him brooding. And I can smell him, too, or that could be his scent all over me. I feel like I've been marked . . . claimed, even.

With his hands still clasped on my shoulders, Tom looks past me and gasps, yanking me closer, so his mouth is at my ear. "Darling, who is that divine being growling at me?" he asks, sniffing me.

I struggle out of his hands and turn to see Jesse drilling holes into Tom. I roll my eyes at his pathetic behaviour. Tom's the gayest gay man in London. He can't possibly be threatened by him.

"Tom, this is Mr Ward. Mr Ward, Tom. He's a *colleague*. He's also gay." I add the last bit sarcastically. Tom won't care – not that it isn't bloody obvious anyway.

I look at Tom, who's grinning widely, then cast my eyes over to Jesse, who's stopped growling but doesn't look any less pissed off. Tom prances forward, grabs Jesse's shoulders and air kisses him. I stifle a laugh, watching as Jesse's eyes bulge and his shoulders tense.

"It really is a pleasure," Tom sings in Jesse's face while stroking down his biceps. "Tell me, do you work out?"

A burst of laughter falls from my mouth and, rather immaturely, I decide to leave Jesse to cope with Tom's outrageous flirting on his own. I catch his eyes as I turn to leave, seeing I'm being thrown daggers, but I couldn't care less. He's being stupidly unreasonable.

I find Patrick in the kitchen, and he waves me over, handing me a glass of champagne when I arrive. "Here she is," Patrick announces to a tall man, draping his arm around my shoulder and hugging me against his big body. "This girl has transformed my company. I'm so proud of you, flower. Where have you been?" he asks, his blue eyes twinkling brightly and his cheeks bright red – a clear sign that he's had too much to drink.

"I've been giving a few tours," I lie, smiling sweetly as I'm squeezed against him.

"I've just been talking about you. Your ears must have been burning," Patrick says. "This is Mr Van Der Haus, one of the developers. I was just saying you'll be more than happy to assist on their new venture."

"My partner has told me lots about you," Van Der Haus says, smiling broadly. He's very classy – all tall and white blond, with a bespoke suit and dress shoes. He's quite handsome . . . for a mid-forties man . . . *Another* older man. "I'll look forward to working with you."

I blush. "I would be delighted, Mr Van Der Haus. What have you got in mind for the next project?" I ask eagerly.

"Please, call me Mikael. The building is nearly complete." He broadens his smile. "We have settled on traditional Scandinavian. Being from Denmark, we're going back to our roots." His mild accent is really sexy.

Traditional Scandinavian? This most definitely panics me. Does this mean I'll be hijacking IKEA? Shouldn't they employ someone Scandinavian for this? "It sounds exciting," I say, turning to place my glass on the worktop, spotting Jesse across the room with Sarah as I do.

Oh God. He's drilling holes into me, and Sarah's right bloody there. I swivel back to face my audience. The panic must be clear on my burning face.

"I think so," Mikael agrees. "Once I've discussed a favourable fee with Patrick," he points his champagne glass at my boss, "we can start building a specification. Then you can get started on some designs."

"I look forward to it." I shift on the spot, feeling Jesse's eyes burning into my back.

"She won't disappoint you, Mikael," Patrick chirps.

He smiles. "I know she won't. You're an exceptionally talented young woman, Ava. Your vision is impeccable. Now, if you'll excuse me." I feel the colour deepening in my face as he shakes Patrick's hand and then mine. "I will be in touch," he says, holding my hand in his a little longer than necessary before releasing it and strolling off.

I'm still tucked tightly under Patrick's arm as Victoria approaches us and leans against the worktop in a huff.

"My feet are killing me," she exclaims.

In unison, Patrick and I look down at her six-inch leopard-print platforms with blood red piping. They're ridiculous.

Patrick looks at me, shaking his head, before releasing his hold and declaring his departure. "Irene will be waiting for me downstairs. I've gotten all the photographs." He waves his camera at me. "I'll see you on Monday morning." He kisses each of us. "You've both worked hard tonight. Well done." He takes his big body out of the kitchen, staggering slightly as he does.

Worked hard? I cringe.

"Oh, I nearly forgot." Victoria drags my eyes away from Patrick's swaying body, back to her. "Kate said she couldn't wait around for you any more. She said that she hopes you've had fun and she'll see you at home."

Hopes I've had fun? Sardonic cow!

"Thanks, Victoria. Listen, I think we're done here." I pick up one more glass of champagne as the waiter passes. I can't drive, so I may as well make the most of it. And damn, I need it. "I'm heading home. Go when you're ready. I'll see you on Monday." I kiss her cheek.

"I'm going to hang around for a bit with Tom. He wants to go to Route Sixty for a dance." She shakes her bum.

"Be prepared for a late one," I warn. Once Tom's on the dance floor you need a bulldozer to get him off.

"No! I've told him, I can't stay late. I've got too much to do tomorrow. And I can hardly walk in these stupid shoes."

"Good luck with that. Say bye to Tom for me."

"I will when I find him." She limps off in her ridiculous heels, leaving me to finish my last glass of champagne.

I glance around the kitchen, but I don't see Jesse or Sarah. I'm relieved. I don't think I could look Sarah in the eye. I need to go and kick my loser arse around the flat for being so weak and easy.

I reach the penthouse elevator and punch in the code. It'll be changed tomorrow for the new owner. I huff a little burst of laughter at the thought. Of course, Jesse Ward is the new owner. It's been one hell of a day, and now that I'm alone,

I can feel the foreseeable guilt begin to tumble over me. Oh, what a foolish, desperate woman I am.

"Leaving so soon?"

My shoulders raise and I wince at the cold, unfriendly voice. Straightening my expression, I turn to face Sarah. "It's been a long and tiring day."

She sips her champagne while eyeing me suspiciously. "You're quite a surprise," she purrs.

I really don't know what to say. "Thank you," I utter, turning back to the elevator when it opens.

"It wasn't a compliment."

"I didn't think it was," I retort without looking at her.

"You know Jesse owns this place, right?"

I want to ask her if she'll be living here, too, but of course, I don't. "He mentioned it," I say casually, stepping into the lift and punching the code in. "It was nice to see you."

The doors close and I fall back against the mirrored wall.

Shit!

WHEN IT GETS HOT IN TEHRAN

Ali May

Ali May is International Editor of the *Erotic Review* and an award-winning writer and a broadcaster. In a previous life he has done strange things, including importing lorries to Iran from Japan, and being enlisted as a marine – not by choice – when he didn't know how to swim. His first collection of short stories, *Geography of Attraction*, was published in 2015, and he is currently writing his first novel.

The first time I had sex was on a bus. It was when streets were narrower in Tehran but summers just as hot. City buses were imported second-hand from Germany and Hungary. Their interiors were refurbished to last a little longer; but the new seats, made of metal frames and foam cushions covered with cheap, faux leather, were not strong enough to tolerate vandalism of everyday. The seats were red or blue or green, but the colour didn't make much difference in giving passengers a pleasant experience. They were so worn you could feel the frames underneath. The covers were either jammed to granite hardness with overstuffing, or so yielding that the existence of the cushion over the frame was a moot point in terms of physical experience.

With the bus fare came a possible bonus, which meant a lot in August 1990, during the post-war period of rations and low supplies. If you bought a bus ticket on a summer's day in Tehran you'd already paid for a mobile sauna session. The bonus was the potential for the sauna to turn into a steam room. If a small number of passengers boarded the bus, dry heat might prevail. But with each additional passenger getting onto the moving spa, the humidity level grew. On a bus filled with passengers you were guaranteed the full steam room experience.

There was another attraction to boarding a full bus. Buses in Iran were traditionally a segregated means of travel. Men occupied the front and women the back. As with many such rules, this subdivision was not carried out on an egalitarian principle, nor did it take account of demographic realities. Almost two-thirds of the space was designated male territory. Bars were put in place to make sure division was practically enforced and morality preserved. It was only natural that women invaded the men's section at busy times. When the bus was really full, it felt as if the spa manager had turned up the heat to maximum and forgotten there were perishable humans inside, requiring both oxygen and residual hydration.

To get to the park where I played football with my friends, I always got on

the bus at the beginning of its route. On this particularly day all the windows of the bus were open, but in only a few minutes I felt sweat drops travelling all the way from my temples to my chin, armpits to navel. I was standing in the open space towards the back of the male area. As the bus filled up, I had to retreat, move all the way to the window and submit to being carried by the crowd this way and that. It happened only a few stops from the park. The bus was still quite full, but there was a bit of breathing space. I was looking out the window when I felt something soft and rounded touching my buttocks. It moved rhythmically, and with it I felt the front of my trousers beginning to stick out. I knew what was happening counted as sinful, but I liked it. I liked it so much I was scared to turn around and risk losing it. I'd heard stories. Navid brought "super" magazines to the park every week and we all hid under an old weeping willow and looked at those forbidden pictures in amazement and desire.

I adjusted the bag containing my football boots to my front, trying to conceal my response. I closed my eyes and thought of the naked girls I'd seen in those pages: German girls, Swedish girls, English girls, Japanese girls. But the girl who was rubbing her bottom against mine with so much intention was an Iranian schoolgirl. I could tell by the little bit of the dusty, cotton and polyester uniform I could see in my peripheral vision that she must be in high school, a couple of years older than me. I was aching to turn and look at her, but scared that people might notice what we were up to if I did. Summoning my most innocent expression, I glanced around as though to get my bearings and managed a forty-five degree turn to the right. Now I could see that she was taller than me and was indeed wearing the navy manto and head covering falling to the chest that girls her age were expected to wear to school. Body draped, her round face was left exposed to absorb all the sun. She didn't look like any of the girls in the magazines, but in my new position she managed to grab hold of my hand and press it. Was it a warning? Was she angry with me? As I considered these options, the crowd suddenly pushed us towards the wall.

Now we were standing side by side, but somehow my opened hand was caught between her soft bum and the hard bus wall. I didn't know what to do. My hand, the whole of my arm, my complete being felt paralysed. I was afraid that if I moved my hand she'd get upset and make a noise. I didn't want to be caught. It would be awful, the thirteen-year-old son of a war martyr touching a strange girl's buttock on the bus, in public, in broad daylight. Could there be anything worse?

She kept moving her body slowly. Her left arm was rubbing against my right shoulder; by the terms of our strange dance, it was her turn to make a new contact angle. A turn of only thirty degrees to the left meant that she was driving me crazy with her breast. Wasn't she wearing anything under her uniform? Thanks to summer her nipple was caressing my arm where my short sleeve ended. There were only two things I wanted in the world at that very moment: I wanted the driver to brake hard, and for it to be suddenly night-time and all of Tehran swallowed in darkness. There have been very few occasions in my life when I have been grateful for the mysterious rhythms and spurts of Tehran traffic, but for once it worked for my pleasure. As the urge to give full attention to that bare nipple became alarmingly compelling, the bus suddenly jolted to a brutal stop,

and yes, she was rubbing my entire front with her front for three seconds. Her conspiratorial smile told me that she knew how I felt.

I could stay no longer. With the sports bag clutched where it was required, I ran awkwardly down the steps of the bus and up the street. I'd already missed my stop and stayed on the bus for eight more, quite a long way. But on that day I ran all the way to the park where there was a pond filled with weed and gold fish and ducks, and I jumped right into it with the bag still glued to me. Two guards thought I was trying to mess with their authority and dragged me out and 'taught me a lesson' by repeatedly pinching my ears. I didn't mind; I had cleansed my body.

FOUR IN HAND

John Gibb

John Gibb first started writing questionable stories for the *Erotic Review* when it was the only monthly magazine in Europe committed to serious sexual fiction. He learnt his trade as a journalist writing about crime for the *London Evening Standard*, but the subjects of his stories range from food to education, to the power of innocent love and the erotic potential of the escape mechanism fitted to the Tornado F3 air defence aircraft.

I

"I won't forget December 23rd 1983 in a hurry. Holiday time in the West End and I was on my way to pick up Fowler and take him for lunch at Bentley's. I arrived at Soho Square early and decided to take advantage of the warmth of the recording studio. A black Daimler parked on the kerb, half on a double yellow line, had blocked the way in and I was forced to squeeze between the car and the front door. It was a sharp, clear day, no warmth in the sun and the vapour from the car's exhaust rising in a plume to join the sooty effluvia which in those days floated like grey gas above the London roof tops. A man in a heavy Crombie lounged against the car studying his watch. 'Plod,' I thought, 'doesn't look happy.' As I climbed the wooden staircase, I could hear raised voices, one of which was Fowler's. An argument seemed to be in progress and by the time I reached the fourth floor, words, louder and more formal than is acceptable in polite conversation, were becoming clear: 'You may think yourself qualified to advise others about pronunciation, but these are my words and it is what I say that goes.' To which Fowler replied in that infuriating way he had, eyebrows half way up his forehead, and almost certainly with his fucking monocle jammed into the side of his face. He was employing his calm and patient voice: 'I have to produce a recording of your book which the public will buy, which is why I have been employed to record you reading it. Perhaps if you spent more time mixing with real people instead of having them served up to you like biscuits, you would be aware that EQUERRY is pronounced "EQUERRY" and not "EQUAIRY".' I reached the top floor where there was a single closed door above which a light glowed red and a sign screwed to the wall beneath it reinforced the warning with SILENCE in neon. Insipid daylight seeped in via a grubby sash window and I could see storm clouds gathering black above the City which meant that snow was on the way. Beside the closed door, perched on a typist's chair, was a girl in a riding coat. She stared at me, a handkerchief entwined between her fingers. I said, 'Who are you? What's going on?' She shrugged. 'It's the Duke,' she replied, 'he's not happy at all.'

For a moment, I failed to understand and said, 'What Duke? When is Fowler going to finish?' And it was some moments before I remembered that he had been working for months to publish a book about driving teams of horses with carriages at speed about the countryside. 'Christ,' I said, 'you mean The Duke?' And her nod coincided with an explosive and uninhibited retort to Fowler's remarks: 'Who are you to tell me how to read English; anyway, who's President of the fucking English Speaking Union? I'll tell you who is, I fucking am and either we do this fucking book my way or we don't do it at all.' An impasse, it seemed to me, which would result in Fowler saying something like, 'OK, if you want to make a fool of yourself, who am I to get in your way?' Which in the event was exactly what he said. It was probably time to go, I felt.

I looked at the girl, now on her feet. She was tall and fresh faced, cheeks pink, hair in a bunch. 'Do you fancy lunch, it looks as if I'm going to be stood up?' And she smiled and nodded and we set off downstairs, and that was how I met Nellie."

II

"I'm Nellie Wallis and I work as a groom at Ronnie Whistler's yard in Larkrise. Sometimes the Duke passes the word that he needs a couple of lads to act as back-steppers for his four in hand and he's chosen me ten times in all. I have to hang on the back of the carriage and move about while he barks away at the front and we canter around the obstacles. He kits us out with black riding pants and boots and he looks after us with a good feed and a bit of jocularity. On this particular day, he's picked me up at the yard and we've gone to Windsor and spent an hour or so on the marathon course and then he's told me to come with him to London because he's going to record his book on Competition Carriage Driving and he might need someone to run a couple of 'errands'. Well, of course, we all know what that means, but it never amounts to anything much and it's nothing I can't handle. Then he's fallen out with a beard in the recording studio and seems to have forgotten about me and then this man appears and offers to take me out for tea. He's a broomstick, slick hair with curls on his neck, seems to have broken his nose at some time; pin-striped suit and silk shirt and tie. Probably a bit of a rascal. On the way out I tell Sergeant Hoskins that it looks like being a long day and I'm going to find something to eat, while my new friend whistles up a cab.

"As we progress slowly down Old Compton Street, he says his name is Porteous. He refers to himself only by his sir-name, shakes hands, shoots his cuffs and smiles. Perfect gent. 'Fancy a spot of fish?' he says as we arrive in a lane somewhere at the bottom of Regent Street and a man in a heavy blue coat steps out and opens the cab door and ushers us into Bentley's Oyster Bar. It's a wide, cream-painted restaurant with a zinc-topped bar and little booths where waiters in white aprons are serving oysters and Champagne. The downstairs room is full of smart-looking, well-dressed gentlemen drinking out of silver tankards and reading the *Sporting Life*. These are big, well-fed, pink-faced boys in Holland suits and pale blue ties. Porteous says this is where old rugby players eat when they're just past their best and bored with training. 'Bubbly?' he asks and passes me a heavy goblet of Champagne. He opens his wallet and removes a wad of

notes which he passes to the doorman and turns to me: 'Handy chap, Coleman, places the occasional investment for me over the road.'"

III

"I'm Keith Coleman and I have a small property in Esher, next to the cricket ground. I earn a fair wage doing the door at Bentley's and I've been greeting at lunchtime during the week since 1966. My Father did it before me and passed on all the ins and outs. In the evening I do alternate nights at the Café de Paris and sometimes help out at The Savoy. It was December 23rd when Mr Porteous came in for luncheon with a tall girl in a heavy riding coat which he slipped from her shoulders and handed to me to deal with. She's a striking filly underneath, long legs in a pair of black riding breeches and boots and a saucy little bum-freezer jacket. I have a feeling that I may have seen her in the ring at Epsom from time to time. I never forget an arse and I can see that Mr Porteous has decided to make a modest investment in the hope that something positive may come of it. He passes me a wager which I take across the road to Ladbroke and when I return, they're sitting down to a couple of dozen 'Extra Fine' and flagons of Black Velvet. Nice."

IV

At Bentley's, Porteous is secure in his metier; he finds himself in the company of men he feels at home with; rugged characters with whom he collides on muddy Saturday afternoons at Richmond and Harlequins and who he plays golf with on Sundays at Royal St. George's. These men are the salt of his earth who on week-day evenings, congregate at the Clermont and Boodles and take their pleasures discreetly; men to whom the sacrament of comradeship comes first and foremost. Today he has acquired the accoutrement of a girl who has appeared out of the blue and, he has to admit, taken his breath away. It seems to him that she is perfectly acceptable; she is after all, known to The Duke and is familiar with the social and sporting intricacies of the turf. He glances covertly at her across the table; takes in her eyes, wide apart, her generous mouth, skin firm as an apricot. She knows how to handle an oyster, lifting the slippery meat to her lips and sliding it across her sharp tongue with relish. He has noticed the muscular swell of her thigh as she slides behind the table onto the soft, leather seat. He wants her and has it in his mind to take her back to his pied à terre in the Albany. "I want to show you my little place round the corner," he says as the waiters clear away, "Edward Heath has an apartment there, so does Buccleuch." Nellie looked at him, "Who?" she says. "Well it's a good place for coffee and a brandy. Perhaps a smoke? Get away from here."

The girl considers him. Well watered as she is, she has a strong head and is in control. She has become bored with the ferrety attentions of priapic National Hunt jockeys and likes the look of this runner and is happy to let events take their course. She smiles across the table and the deal is silently done.

It is at this moment that the head waiter, Stokes, sidles up to the table and says, "Mr Porteous, sir, I have a call for you," handing him a bakelite telephone and bending down to plug the cable into a socket by the table. It is Fowler. "Slight difficulty, old boy," he says. "The Duke's on his way down and he's not

at all pleased. He says you've kidnapped his groom and he needs her for an errand. He has his personal protection officer with him and they'll be with you in five minutes. I should scarper if I were you." Porteous quickly fishes out another wad of crisp notes, slips them across the desk to Stokes, nods at Coleman who is watching from the door, and has Nellie in the back of a cab heading south as the bonnet of the Ducal Daimler noses into the top of Swallow Street.

The Albany will turn anyone's head; cut off from the chaos of the city, it is a refuge for powerful men just to the north of Piccadilly, accessed through a discreet wicket gate where residents and their friends are welcomed and strangers eyed with suspicion. Porteous has inherited his apartment from his father and the faded art deco would have been what Wodehouse had in mind when describing the bachelor Wooster at home. He sits and watches the girl looking down across the gardens, her shape at the window caught in black silhouette against the weak afternoon sun. He stands and slips his arm around her waist and she rests her head on his shoulder. He kisses her as she turns in his arms and clings to him and he feels her hard breasts against his chest. There is always a moment as Porteous starts a relationship with a woman, when his heart becomes saturated with heat, causing a shortness of breath and light-headedness. It is a physiological manifestation of his astonishment that a woman is prepared to react to him in a sexual way.

Nellie, swept along by strange events, is herself light-headed, her breath coming in short bursts, her face flushed, a pulse beating in the sinews of her neck. She sinks to the floor where Porteous, spread like a crucifix on the deep carpet, lies waiting for her. He submits to the girl, who is slowly filleting his clothes, de-boning him of his Hackett pants until everything has been peeled away and his cock lies fresh as a tropical fruit across his stomach and she can slip from her jacket and kneel between his legs and take his arms and pull his hands into her clothes and he is able to tug the riding tunic over her head. And she sits back and he pulls down the boots and slides his hands into the waistband of her breeches and the Christmas sun squats, scarlet, on the rooftops of Mayfair and floods gold through the window and catches the gold of her hair. And when Nellie takes him in her hands for the first time, Porteous immediately ejaculates sumptuously into the valley of her breasts while he gazes, terrified, into her startled face.

Nellie knows instinctively that moments like this can be an end or the beginning and she says, "Hello, you certainly needed that didn't you, now it's my turn," and she takes his hand and places it deftly between her thighs. She sits, facing him, legs apart, her back arched like a bow, her index and central fingers holding the lips of her vagina apart and, while she sorts out his hand so that he can do what she wants him to do, she says, "Some days the fever comes at you without warning." And she takes his fingers and sets them to work in her wet, rustling, fecund sex and as she writhes and moans, she holds his gaze and all the gathering shocks and nervous impulses and waves of breathless fear and passion are passing through her eyes and after a while, she falls forward, her body curled, across him until she lies, breathless, along his chest, and his hand deep in her groin and her mouth on his as she shudders and brings up her knees and he feels the wetness flooding from her.

And as the afternoon turns to dusk and the lights come on across London,

Porteous discovers an unknown world inhabited by a girl whose sole desire is to bring him to life. On the bed where his father had died, she resuscitates him impatiently and guides him inside her for the first time, operating him like a muscular machine until he feels that his body will explode; she makes him examine every intimate inch of her body, guiding his tongue and his fingers into her perfect, wrinkled little anus and demonstrating to him the budlike button of her clitoris and showing him how she likes it to be touched, particularly when "I am out and about during the day and you can find a quiet moment," and for hours they lie entwined, her pussy spread across his eager face while she takes his cock into her throat and makes him wait until finally she sucks his impatient come from his shuddering body.

Dusk has come and gone and once more they are looking down at the gardens, illuminated now from a scattering of brightly lit sitting rooms around the square. Porteous lies on top of her, his cock resting in the valley of her bottom, when he sees the little wicket gate open with a jolt and The Duke stalking into the glow of light from the porter's lodge followed by Sergeant Hoskins, holding his bowler hat in his hands and looking self-conscious. Porteous stands up, "It's him," he says, "and he's brought his bloody policeman with him."

Nellie rolls over, pulling on her pants and is dressed before Porteous can find his socks. "Give me the keys," she says, "I'll deal with this," and she is away leaving him to stand forlornly in his underpants, watching from the bedroom as she appears by the gate standing, arms on her hips and having one of those conversations with a man who is somewhere in line to the throne. In five minutes it is done with and The Duke is passing an envelope and touching his rat catcher as he turns to go.

"Got any eggs?" she says when she returns, "we need building up." And Porteous looks at her and says, "What happened?" "Oh well I gave him a piece of my mind, told him to stop following me around and to behave himself and he said he'd only come to give me the wages he owed me for today."

Porteous takes her in his arms and breathes deeply because from that moment he knows he is enslaved. "Early night?" he says, and so they have supper on the carpet and go straight to bed.

ON THE BEACH

Nina Gibb

Nina Gibb has published feature articles, interviews and illustrations in national and international publications including the venerable literary blog *Bookslut*, and was a longtime columnist for 'attack journal' *The Lifted Brow*. She has also run and hosted projects as a part of Melbourne's Emerging Writers' Festival. Nina lives in Melbourne where she works as a bookseller.

They weren't brothers but people thought they were. They had been asked three times since they had come here. Once Richard had agreed when someone asked and the stranger had nodded. They had only known each other two days. Now they sat on the shore.

Richard looked right into her eyes when they fucked but then as he got closer to coming he'd reach up and take a handful of her hair and pull it then twist his other arm under her, between her body and her arms so she was pinned with her breasts arched out against him. He would tell her he was coming and she would turn her head so his breath was warm in her ear. John was different. Slimmer. He was easier to laugh with. With him sex was rough but then he would find her mouth and kiss her with tenderness.

John got up and said "I'm going in."

Richard turned around to face her – "Coming?"

She shook her head. They took off their clothes down to their underwear. The sun was hot. She watched them, rubbing her foot in the sand.

John moved fast and gangly like a boy. His hair in soft curls beside his eyes. Richard's skin was gold from the sun. They really did look like brothers – John younger. They ran down to the surf, jumping over mounded piles of kelp and beached jellyfish that had started to stink in the heat. John picked one up and threw it at Richard, who pulled another one, clear like aspic, and pushed it into John's hair. Then they both dove under. They swam way out.

She lay back in the sand. She thought about John, about last night when she had run back across the road and kissed him quite hard, while Richard had watched from the far kerb, how after a moment he'd kissed her back and it had been like a song, with verses and a chorus and an ecstatic reprise. When she had put her mouth on his time had expanded inside her and then it expanded again as she walked home. Again when she lay down. One kiss all night. She had gone home with Richard and left John on the corner but Richard had only fallen asleep, so she lived in the expanding song of the kiss until morning.

The next morning John had called to say they should all go to the beach. She had wondered where they would stay and he'd said it was hot and they didn't need to stay anywhere. She woke Richard with a coffee.

"We're going to the beach. John will be here in twenty minutes."

And Richard had pulled her into bed and did that thing he did where he only half kissed her, half touched her, until she was crazy with lust but then he pulled away and leapt out of bed when the knock on the door came – sharp and joyful in the clear dry morning.

They had arrived by mid afternoon. They went straight into the water and then afterward they fell asleep on the sand, letting the salt and the wind and the sun melt away their hangovers. After a while they climbed up into the shade in the rocks at the headland and she kissed Richard and then John and John slid his hand up so his thumb rested against her bathers where they were wet between her legs. Richard buried his face in the crook of her neck, from behind, but nothing more happened. It was cooler there and soon they fell asleep, legs tangled, ants crawling over them. When they woke up they came back down to the beach.

The sun was starting to go down but it was still very hot. She sat up in the sand. The boys had gone a long way out and from this distance you couldn't tell one from the other – they were just two shadows sometimes bobbing up in the swell.

She pulled the blanket up over her head like a tent for shade. A man walked past with his daughter trailing behind him. She had seen them earlier way up the beach – the daughter's small hands filling a bucket with sandy mud while her father tried to help, laughing at the urgency of her little voice as it instructed him in proper bucket filling technique. She watched them until they faded away against the light and then when she looked back the boys had come in again. They came up out of the surf towards her. She could not tell one from the other. They came closer. She still could not tell. The one on the left looked down at the sand as he walked and the one on the right looked at her with what she had just now realised was the same look both of them had when they saw her – a look that lovers had. Maybe not lovers: fuckers. It was a look that said "I will have you again." The other one lifted his head up from where he had been watching his feet scuffing up shells and seaweed as he walked. He had the look.

She said "I could murder a beer" and one of them said something funny and they all laughed. They went up to the pub and got drunk. They were slow with sun and sleep. She wondered aloud "Where will we sleep?" and one of them replied that they should go under the pier. "There are fires down there and people hang out all night. We'll take the blankets out of the car."

While they drank, although she watched very closely, she could not tell one from the other. Sometimes one of them would say something to her that was a very "John" or a very "Richard" thing to say, but she thought that these identifying things were not coming distinctly or in a pattern from one or the other in particular. The one on her left made a joke and then a few minutes later the other one picked up the joke and kept it running though it was unlikely they would make this same joke. Then it would reverse and they would both be "John-like" for a while. Or they would do things that were distinct to one of them; one would scratch the back of her neck very softly like John did and the other would

lean back and look at her while he talked, swinging his knee back and forth so it stroked her thigh – like Richard. And then they would swap.

Eventually they went down to the beach, under the pier, to fuck. They had two blankets, one underneath and one over and they made a fire. It was warm and the breeze from the sea was welcome. She thought to herself, part way through the night when she had fallen almost asleep and been almost awakened by one of them sliding inside her again, by a mouth against her breast or arms pulling her shoulders back and pushing her into the softness of the blanket over the sand, that if there were three, four, many others here they would all be this. She wondered what woman she was for them and thought that tomorrow perhaps she would go out and find another woman and they would swim together out past the kelp, past the jellyfish, so that her and the woman were two shadows bobbing in the sea. So that then she could swim back in and just look at the other one to see what it was to be a woman to these men.

THE MIDWESTERNERS

Ruby McNally

Ruby McNally was born in Boston, USA. She double-majored in psychology and cognitive linguistics before ultimately deciding her talents lay elsewhere. She grew up hiding her diary from her five brothers, who will never know she writes in the erotic vein. She continues to live in Boston and has no cats.

One nice thing about Josh having more money than God these days, even if the rest of it is colossally weird: whenever they hang out now, the food is always amazing.

"Remember in high school when we used to cut seventh and go to Taco Bell all the time?" Natalie asks, knifing a slice of cheese off a block that probably cost about as much as this semester's grad stipend. They're sitting on the back porch of Josh's cabin, sun just starting to sink and Lake Michigan glittering through a cluster of pine trees, a long pathway snaking down to a dock.

"Uh-huh." Amanda grins, taking a sip from her wine glass. She's wearing a long stripy sundress, bare feet propped on the outdoor coffee table; they've hardly been here an hour and she looks as relaxed as if she's lived this way all summer, like she fits in seamlessly wherever she goes. Her curly hair's a dark blonde corona around her face. "What're you, jonesing for a gordita right now?"

Josh comes through the sliding door before Nat can explain, tucking his cell phone into the back pocket of his designer jeans. "Julie and Mac just bailed," he says, reaching down for a couple of crackers and some dip Nat's pretty sure has truffle oil in it. "Julie had early contractions, I guess? So they're gonna stay put."

"The baby okay?" Amanda asks, looking concerned. Julie and Mac rounded out their group when they were teenagers in Lake Forest, the two of them pairing off and staying that way in the near-decade since they graduated. Their first kid is due in the fall. Nat and Amanda went to the shower last month, decorated onesies with fabric paint and ate tiny tomato sandwiches. Then they went out and got drunk.

"Yeah, I think everything's fine." Josh scratches at the back of his neck. His hair's less floppy than it used to be, cropped close like he's finally found a decent barber. Nat used to like to sift her hands through it, when they dated. "Just like, not fine enough to make the drive."

"Well." Amanda sets down her wine glass and stands up, nudging politely at Nat's legs until she holds them up and out of the way. "If no pregnant ladies are coming to this party, I vote we switch to the hard stuff."

Natalie hmms noncommittally. Less than three weeks ago, Amanda would have climbed right over the top of her to get to the ice bucket, no respect for personal space at all. She's always been touchy, even when Nat officially came out their sophomore year of college and Julie stopped playing with her hair for two whole weeks, like the petting might somehow be misconstrued. "Cunt," Amanda later pronounced, drunk as a skunk in Nat's childhood bedroom. "Like you'd ever go for her, she's a freaking five at best." Privately, Nat agreed. If it was going to be anyone from high school it would have been Amanda, that button face and all those yards of ridiculous hair, her talking hands that never sat still. But she was smart enough not to say so, and when they finally passed out, sticky with coolers and schnapps, it was with Amanda curled in close and drooling on Nat's neck. Just like always.

Now, six years later, she's treating Nat the same way Julie did in those first homophobic two weeks.

"Hard stuff like tequila?" Josh asks, setting down his craft beer to help Amanda root through the ice bucket. Natalie's been drinking her way through the sixer of Bud she brought along, not even sure herself what kind of point she's making. "I think I have some of the stuff you're supposed to sip."

"Oh, we're not sipping it," Amanda says, yanking the giant bottle out and holding it aloft victoriously. It's that fancy aged tequila from TV, Nat can see even from here. "I don't care what you guys do back in California, Nat and I are shots girls."

Well, that's pointed – they were doing shots the night everything went to shit. But Natalie just shrugs. "We are that," she agrees.

Josh narrows his eyes at her, the same searching look he's been wearing for the past hour. They dated for three years in high school, her and Josh, and Nat loved him even if she didn't *love* him. He used to know her better than anyone. "You sure you don't want dinner first?" he asks quietly, rubbing his bare neck again. All of a sudden, Nat misses his doofy hair more than anything in the world. "Could grill."

"He's afraid of us," Amanda says cheerfully, reaching for three of the tumblers set on the side table like something staged for a Pottery Barn catalogue. "He's worried about what'll happen if he doesn't carb us up first."

"Afraid of *you*, maybe," Josh corrects, but he takes the glass she offers him and swallows. "Everybody here knows what kind of drunk you are, princess."

He's kidding, same grin on his face as when he used to clown around during study hall, but for a second Amanda's eyes cut to Nat's anyway – like maybe Nat *told* him or something, the night of the shower and Amanda fresh off a breakup with a guy from the design firm, her tan skin and the sharp, limey taste of her tongue. Natalie looks back.

"What?" Josh asks, pretty smile fading as he glances between them. "Okay, *what*?"

"Nothing," Natalie tells him, and knocks back the tequila as fast as she can.

They're smashed by the time it's full dark out, the booze mostly gone and the snacks finished too, frogs or crickets or something making noise out in the trees. Josh lit a citronella candle to keep the mosquitos away and their faces are cast in

shadow, all sharp jaws and high cheekbones. They'd make a nice couple, Natalie thinks. Makes a point of examining her toes.

"I have steaks," Josh is insisting. They've covered Amanda's promotion and his boring-sounding girlfriend in LA and now he's circling back to food again, sounding for all the world like his mother. He's got his ankle wrapped around Nat's, familiar.

"Grass-fed rib-eyes?" she teases, although it comes out a little sharper than she means it. "Prepared in your state of the art outdoor kitchen by one of your many servants?"

Josh doesn't laugh. "Okay, are you mad at me?" he asks, looking sort of disproportionately stung. He turns to Amanda for backup. "Is she mad at me?"

Amanda shrugs loosely, cross-legged on a wicker armchair. She's stopped being careful about her dress and it's pulled taut over her knees, a shadowy gap underneath that Nat's trying real hard not to examine too closely. "Dunno," she says, all slippery consonants. "Natalie seems to be mad at everyone these days. You're too rich, I'm too stupid . . . We should start a club."

"'Manda," Nat says, this sensation below her breastbone like she's been sucker-punched. She knows she hurt Amanda's feelings when she refused to hash everything out the morning after the baby shower, but it's not like – God, what would they even have *discussed*? Amanda's straight. Natalie knows that. She doesn't need her nose rubbed in it with a talk about how they made a huge mistake.

"Okay, what's going on?" asks Josh, sitting up and – bizarrely – curving a protective hand around Natalie's knee. "You guys have a fight or something?"

("Do you have a thing for Amanda?" he asked Nat years and years ago, when she was visiting him in California for his twenty-first birthday. He hadn't made all the money yet, was still living in a shitty apartment where all the taps were on backwards.

"Get bent," she told him, zipping her sleeping bag to her chin. She wouldn't talk to him again until he went out at the crack of dawn and bought her an iced cap and a donut.)

"Yikes," Amanda says now, drawing both knees up to her chin. "You too, huh?" Then she looks straight at Nat, eyelashes gone spiky and wet. "I wasn't experimenting, you know, or whatever the fuck you think. I made out with Sophia Taback in tenth grade, remember? *That* was my experimenting." She stands up, sundress falling around her ankles in a whoosh. "If you weren't into it, you should have stopped me."

"What the hell?" Josh asks when she's gone, cupping both of Natalie's cheeks in his warm, drunk hands. They were good at sex, Josh and Nat, however bizarre it seems now. His fumbling teenage moves got her off just fine. "Jesus, Nat, what happened?"

He's close enough to kiss, the way he's peering into her face. Natalie learned how to kiss from Josh; she wonders if they still have all the same habits. "Christ what do you think?" she says, prying his fingers off her wet cheeks. "We fucked." Then she stumbles inside too, fully intent on crying her eyes out in one of the four spare bedrooms until she throws up or passes out, whichever's first.

"Wait," Josh says. Natalie doesn't stop.

*

The next morning is aggressively sunny, white light spilling hot across the expensive sheets until there's no way for Nat to ignore it any longer. She stands motionless in the shower for forty minutes before she goes downstairs.

"Well, hey." Amanda's in the kitchen eating toast and reading the paper; she's got her bathing suit on under a different dress than yesterday, hair up in a knot on top of her head. Her eyes are puffy, so Nat can tell she feels like garbage, but to the casual observer she could be a model for J.Crew's end of summer style guide. All she needs is a floppy hat.

"Look," Natalie begins, padding over to the coffeemaker. They've spent a hundred mornings hungover together – they've gotten in a hundred drunk fights – so there's no reason for this to feel any different except for the part where it really, really does. She mapped out a game plan in the shower, though, figures the best way to handle this is to confront it head-on. "I was an asshole."

Right away, Amanda shakes her head. "We were all assholes," she says, flicking her hand like she's swatting away a bee at a picnic. "Seriously, don't worry about it. It's fine. Josh is out by the water, he said come down when we're ready and we can lay on the dock."

Well. Natalie nods and busies herself digging milk out of the stainless refrigerator. She should have forced herself out of bed earlier – hungover or not, Josh and Amanda are perpetual early birds both and she cringes at the idea of them talking this out over lattes this morning, let's just forget it and get through the weekend. In a weird way those two have always been on the same bro-y, easygoing wavelength.

("You know Josh still loves you, right?" is a thing Amanda's fond of saying. "You are absolutely Josh's perfect woman except for the part where you like girls." She said it the night of the baby shower, too, right before she pulled Natalie's shirt off, like she was worried they were going to wind up hurting him somehow. Nat kissed her hard and sloppy to shut her up.)

"I meant what I said, though," Amanda tells her now, right before she pulls open the sliding door and heads outside into the sunshine. "It wasn't an experiment."

Whatever that means. Natalie blows out a breath, not letting herself hope. Wanting Amanda was easy enough before they slept together – Nat only ever thought about it between girlfriends, and the thinking always had the same hazy focus she imagines other people use to contemplate winning the lottery, planning fantasy boat purchases and trips to Europe. Natalie planned for the lines of Amanda's shoulder blades the same way. She never expected to get them.

Then she did. And – of course, of course, stupid not to plan for that part – she couldn't keep them.

She gulps the coffee and changes into her bathing suit before joining the others, head still pounding. They're on the dock just like Amanda said, lying out next to each other with matching aviators and one of those liter Evian bottles between them on the warm wood. Josh sees her first.

"Hey," he says, sitting up and removing the sunglasses. "How you doing?"

Natalie hasn't seen Josh without a shirt in years, and for a second she just stares. He looks like a grown-up, not the kid who took her to prom and ate her out in his mom's unfinished basement, a hollow in his skinny breastbone

where you could rest a golf ball. He looks tanned. "I'm okay," she tells him finally. "Head's a bitch, though." She chucks the bottle of sunscreen on his towel then drops down beside it, nudging his foot to say sorry. She and Josh hardly ever apologize outright. "Do my back, okay? Not all of us belong in a freaking Coppertone commercial." It's true, too: they would make a good-looking couple, Josh and Amanda, but they could also be siblings, the same tan skin and eyes and thick curly hair, albeit in completely different shades. They've both got real pretty mouths.

I have a type, Natalie thinks, and nearly laughs.

"Oh my god, at least rub it in," Amanda says out of nowhere. "She's going to burn and whine at us all weekend." Natalie hears her sitting up and all of a sudden there are two pairs of hands on her freckly back, Amanda lifting a bikini strap and smearing the sunscreen underneath. "You have to get everywhere, she's like a porcelain doll."

"I'm right here," says Natalie, who is in fact nothing like a porcelain doll. She has brown hair and brown eyes and brown freckles, all in the same uniform shade. Still: she guesses this means the embargo on casual touching has been lifted. She breathes into it, trying not to shiver under their hands.

They spend the rest of the morning and a good chunk of the afternoon that way, Nat lying on the dock letting the hangover bake out of her while Amanda floats on her back in the water and Josh reads last month's *Wired*. It's quiet. When she opens her eyes she finds Josh gazing back at her, his expression mostly hidden by the sunglasses and his neck gone pink and warm-looking in the sun. They've known each other so many years.

"I'm glad you came," he says, reaching for a newer, chillier water bottle and rolling it back and forth across her naked stomach. Natalie grins at him. "Even if you are a pain in the ass."

Later they go into town for dinner, the kind of divey burger bar that exists specifically for rich people in tourist towns, sticky tables and pitchers of beer. Amanda feeds a fistful of ones into the jukebox. "We should dance," she declares, but Natalie shakes her head so Amanda rolls her eyes and takes Josh by the hand instead, their faces gone candy-colored in the twinkle of the Christmas lights strung up on the walls. Natalie drinks her Corona and watches them, tries to put a word to whatever she feels.

Amanda leads Josh back to her when the last song is finished, the faintest sheen of sweat on her skin. Her hair is long and loose down her narrow back. "Now we should go home," she decides.

So: that's what they do.

"I feel like the cast of *Friends*," Josh says on the dock, toeing off his expensive old-man loafers and dangling his feet in the lake. In high school all he ever wore was baggy jeans and t-shirts, these sneakers that Natalie and Amanda stole during one free period and drew all over. They read *Property of Nat Boutilier* down the tongue in purple Sharpie.

"What like, incestuous?" Nat asks, rolling up her cropped jeans to sit beside him. They've been circling around the subject all night, feeling it out, trying on different sorts of jokes. ("It figures," Amanda said over dinner, sucking the rim of

her neon-bright cocktail. "Nat was always the coolest. Probably Julie and Mac would probably jump at the chance to hit that, too." Her mouth left kiss prints in the grainy sugar, the soft outline of her bottom lip.)

"Don't be boring," Amanda tells them now, hands up and fiddling with the halter tie of her sundress. "Come swim."

She isn't wearing a suit. Nat and Josh watch as the dress pools, her bare back and the dimples at the base of her spine, the slow curve of her waist. Then she dives.

"Oh," Josh says, voice like a man who finally heard the pin drop. "Right. Should I, um. Should I go inside?"

Amanda surfaces, twenty feet out. She does a starfish float, breasts exposed like a dare.

"Do you want to?" Natalie asks Josh, turning to face him. "Go inside?"

Josh just stares. "No," he tells her quietly. "But I can."

Nat looks from him to Amanda and back again, his open collar and his solemn face. She's loved him since they were fifteen years old. "Don't," she says, and pulls her tank top and bra over her head in one fell swoop.

The lake's cold now that it's dark out, goosebumps rising everywhere on her body and her bare nipples drawing up right away. It's shallow enough that Nat can touch down. Amanda got closer as Nat tugged her jeans off, Josh slipping into the water behind her with a quiet splash; Amanda left her panties on, this pale cotton thong that stood out against her summer tan, so Natalie did, too. She can feel her heart thrumming in her chest.

"Don't be mad at me," Amanda says, reaching out and lacing her fingers through Natalie's. Nat's body's gone water-weightless, save a heavy ache in her breasts and between her legs. "Josh, tell her not to be mad at me."

"I'm not mad at you," Nat mutters before Josh can answer, thunking her forehead lightly against Amanda's. She stays there for a second, nudging Amanda's chilly nose with hers. "Of course I'm not mad at you."

Amanda kisses her instead of replying, soft mouth and slippery body and a whimper caught in the back of Natalie's throat. Behind her she can hear Josh breathe in. She reaches blindly back for his hand and yanks until he's flush against her, the wet heat of his rib cage expanding and his cock pressing into her ass. He hooks his chin over her shoulder so he can watch. Amanda pushes one long thigh between Natalie's, reaching up to scratch the hair at the back of Josh's vulnerable neck; they're pressing her tighter against one another with every breath, hands and mouths on her stomach and nipples and jaw.

"Okay." Natalie gasps, and it sounds a lot more like a sob than she means for it to. "We should – um. Is this – are we –?"

"Bed," Amanda says, the same tone of voice she used to steer them to dinner, then to the dance floor, then back home again. Natalie breaks away from her slippery mouth to stare. Amanda only smiles.

"Bed," Nat agrees.

The walk inside is awkward, all of them drenched and half-naked. Ridiculously, Natalie finds herself worrying about the expensive birchwood floors, the thick, piled area rugs. Then Josh takes her hand, and she stops worrying.

They end up in Natalie's room, the white queen bed and the floor-to-ceiling windows. "Here," Amanda murmurs, producing one of yesterday's beach towels and rubbing it across Natalie's skin, leftover sand scraping against her stomach and breasts. Nat reaches up and wrings out Amanda's hair gently, then turns to Josh and helps him shuck his sopping boxers. They have lobsters on them.

"Your underwear still sucks," Natalie tells him, wrapping a fist around his cock. It's the only one she's ever seen up close. Amanda slips up beside her to touch too, thumb rolling over the sticky head.

"What's this about sucking?" she teases, sliding a hand down the back of Natalie's boyshorts. Her palm is clammy-warm and Nat pushes into it thoughtlessly, letting Amanda strip her. Then Amanda does something with her fingernail that makes Josh's knees buckle, and they all go swaying into the side of the bed.

"Let's –" Josh starts, but it seems like he's forgotten all words entirely. Natalie crowds him until he lies back, helpless, then climbs on top. Amanda watches them with both hands planted on her hips, cotton thong gone see-through and clinging with water.

"Come here," Natalie says, at the same time Josh asks, "Are we really gonna do this right now?"

Amanda raises her eyebrows as she gets her knees up on the bed behind Natalie, sucks for a moment at the back of Nat's neck. "Do you *want* to do this?" she asks, running her hands down Nat's body: palms flattened over her stomach, two fingers snaking lower to rub between her legs. In Nat's ear a moment later, off Josh's nod: "Do *you*?"

"'Manda." Of course she does, Jesus, how wet she is as Amanda opens her up a bit, slides those curious fingers over her clit: fuck, Josh is getting a show. She reaches back and snaps the elastic on Amanda's underwear like, *take those off*. "Come on."

"You come on," Amanda says, but she does what Nat tells her, backing off long enough to peel them down her legs. Nat's still got one hand on Josh's cock. She's jacking him almost absentmindedly, this twist of her wrist like muscle memory from years and years ago; his gaze is flicking from her face to her breasts to the V of her thighs and back again, his eyes gone impossibly dark. Amanda presses herself against Nat's ass.

"Okay." That's Josh struggling to sit up a bit, tilting both Nat and Amanda onto their backs on the mattress, Amanda's breasts bouncing with the motion. She giggles, trailing one hand up Josh's thigh. He groans as she lifts to nip at the flat of his stomach, threading his fingers through her curly hair and tugging. Groans louder when she rolls over and settles herself between Nat's legs.

"I want to," Amanda says, kissing a hot, wet trail down Natalie's stomach. Josh settles one big hand on the back of her neck. "You gonna let me? Nat Nat Nat, I wanna try."

"*Amanda*." She didn't, the night of the baby shower; every time Amanda's head drifted that way, Nat yanked her back up, finally flipping them over and grinding herself to a teeth-gritting orgasm against Amanda's thigh. "I don't –"

Josh slides an arm between Natalie's back and the bed, lifting. "Come here," he tells her, supporting her lolling neck the way you would a baby. Natalie used to think about their hypothetical kids sometimes, back in high school – even

now, he'd still be her first choice for a donor. She wonders if he knows. "There," Josh says, settling her into the cradle of his chest like he's a human armchair. Then, to Amanda: "She's gonna let you. Right, Nat?"

Natalie swallows, sifting a hand through Amanda's wet curls. "Right." They all three of them smell like the lake, stale water and shadows. Then Josh starts applying pressure with the hand on Amanda's neck, pushing her head down, and Nat loses her breath.

"Good." Amanda's getting situated, hooking an arm around Nat's thigh and nudging her open with one elegant shoulder. Josh plants a kiss on her jaw. Natalie squeezes her eyes shut and opens them again, wanting to see this, Amanda's lashes lowered in concentration as she works two fingers inside.

Nat gasps. She arches into it before Amanda even licks the first broad stripe along the length of her, careful tongue and the faintest, gentlest nip of her teeth. "S'that right?" she asks, more unsure than Natalie's ever heard her; Nat whines her encouragement and tilts her hips so Amanda will go harder, threading her fingers through Josh's in Amanda's soft soft hair.

"That's hot," Josh tells them quietly. He's poker warm against her, pressed along Nat's spine. "I mean, sorry if I'm not supposed to say that? But *fuck*."

Amanda laughs, a huff of air that's got Natalie squirming. Her fingers crook up deep inside. "It's hot," she agrees matter-of-factly; for someone who's new at this she's taking to it real easy, like she understands instinctively how Nat's body works. One more twist of her wrist, sloppy tongue at Nat's clit and Josh sucking at her favorite secret spot behind her ear – yeah. Nat's pretty much done.

"Please," she says. And: "*'Manda*." And then that's it, a sharp arch against Josh and a blinding white light behind her eyes, this helpless keen she would be embarrassed about at any other time, any other place. With any other people. Amanda backs off too soon, unpracticed, but she leaves her fingers inside so it hardly matters.

"Fuck," Josh repeats against Nat's neck, hands skimming around to roll her nipples. His palms are warm warm warm. Natalie reaches back to tug at his hair mindlessly, hard the way he used to like. Thinks about the mechanics of who should fuck who.

Amanda is crawling back up Nat's body to be eye-level with both of them, kissing as she goes. "Was it good?" she asks, breathless herself. Her chin is slippery when she nudges it against Natalie's belly. "Nat, was I good?"

She sounds so eager. "Yeah, babe." Nat laughs, holding out her arms. "You were great."

Amanda grins, tilting her clever face up to kiss Natalie with a sharp-tasting tongue, then crawls up further so she can get Josh next. Nat's never seen them kiss before and she twists her neck around to watch; from the way Josh's hands tighten she can tell he's tasting her too, the tang of it in Amanda's mouth. All three of them are impossibly close.

Not close enough, though: "Okay," Amanda says a minute later, pulling back and rubbing one hand over Natalie's hipbone. Her pretty cheeks are flushed bright pink. She looks a little uncertain all of a sudden, like she had a plan for up to now and not any further. "What are we – Josh, do you –?"

"I want to watch you guys," Natalie hears herself say, followed immediately

by a hot rush of shock. She's doesn't have the slightest idea where that came from – just seeing them kiss, maybe, or some other secret part of her she never knew existed up until now. She loves them both so terminally much.

Josh's eyes widen. "Are you sure?" he asks, both his hands still around Nat's waist, warm chest against her back. Briefly, Natalie entertains the thought of how else he might have wanted this to end.

Still: "*Please*," she tells them, crawling out of Josh's lap so Amanda can take her place. "I just, I want to see." Now that she's said it, it feels like the only thing that will do. The urgency of need almost strikes her dumb.

Amanda seems to understand. "Okay, honey," she says, goosing Nat's cheek as she inches up Josh's body to straddle him, open legs and the familiar-unfamiliar smell of her. "You wanna?" she asks, addressing Josh. "Nat said you were pretty good in high school."

"Oh, Nat said." Josh looks at them both, uncertain, so Nat scoots over and pulls his hand between Amanda's legs. They press up inside her together, one finger each; Amanda hisses. "Yeah," Josh says then, voice cracking like it's sophomore year all over again. "Okay. Let's."

"Okay." Amanda squirms on their fingers, warm and impatient. Nat leans forward and kisses Josh's jaw. They pull out as gently as they can, Amanda's palms curving around Josh's shoulders as he lines them up. Nobody says anything about a condom. Some people, Nat thinks vaguely, there's no reason to protect yourself from. "Nat," Amanda says quietly, right as she sinks down onto his cock. Nat leans over Josh's shoulder for a kiss.

"That's it," Nat says, pulling back and pressing her lips to the side of Josh's neck, feeling his pulse tick against her mouth like a bomb counting down to detonation. She slicks her tongue over the tendon there, hears him inhale. "Love you so much."

Josh groans, a sharp, anguished sound. "*Natalie*."

"Josh," she says back, so he'll know for absolute certain which one of them she means. "Love you." His hand comes up to fist in her hair, desperate. Amanda's working her hips up and down in a rhythm now, soft wet sounds. "Love you both," Nat adds, voice catching a bit as Amanda arches. She means to sneak it in, but the amount of emotion behind the words is so obvious she closes her eyes in embarrassment. "There," she tells them. "Just like that."

"Fuck." Amanda whimpers, head dropping back as Josh leans forward to bite her neck. "Nat, ohmygod, Nat, touch me." When Natalie hesitates, Amanda grabs her hand. "Love you too. Of course, of course I do. Touch me."

So Natalie slides her fingers down between their bodies. She touches Josh first, making a circle around the base of his cock and feeling up to where it disappears into Amanda, skin slick from both of them. She gets her thumb on Amanda's clit and rubs.

It's over so fast after that, Amanda keening loud and long just like she did the night of the baby shower, that sound Nat wants to hear again and again. Josh closes his eyes and thrusts one last time. The expression on his face is so familiar, shock and almost melancholy, like he knows whatever this is feels too good to last.

"I don't think the cast of *Friends* ever did *that*," Nat says when everyone's done, mostly just for something to say. Her hand is still between Amanda's legs,

everything wet and sloppy. She doesn't want to move it. She's afraid of what will happen if she does.

Amanda hums and moves it for her, swinging off of Josh to sit beside them on the bed. She squeezes Nat's wrist as she goes, warm fingers. "They didn't have our deep, loving bond," she says mildly, one hand reaching up to scritch through Natalie's hair. It feels the same as always, the same way Amanda has touched her for a million years. Her bare breasts press against Nat's arm.

"Can we – can we hang out here?" Josh asks. He looks vulnerable, down on his back and his cock just starting to get soft. "Or one of the other rooms, there's a king in the –"

Natalie flops down next to him, taking Amanda with her. "Oh god, shut up, rich kid. We can fit in the queen."

Josh grins at her then, faint and affectionate, all three of them curled on the bed like puppies or children. Nat can hear the wind on the lake outside.

WHAT HAVE I TO DO WITH YOU?

Anna Maconochie

Anna Maconochie is an award-nominated short story writer, a film-maker, and a DJ living in London. She has been published in the *Erotic Review*, *Prole Books*, *The Wells Street Journal*, *The Dublin Review*, *storgy.com* and *The Bitter Oleander*. She is currently writing more short ficition and a short horror film.

Dermot and I broke up over football. That is what I like to tell people. I can even pinpoint the match that set everything off. Norwich City vs. Man U. The argument took off when Dermot checked the score on his phone in the middle of sex. With me. I always switch my phone off during sex but I'm seven years older than Dermot, who is twenty-nine. I remember unplugging the landline in my first rented flat before closing my bedroom door and facing a boy. I still find phone jacks a bit sexual. Maybe Dermot's dismay about Norwich losing contributed to his dwindling of erection. Maybe not. It's too late to ask now.

"He's a bloke, isn't he? Blokes like football," Jojo says to me. Jojo is my best friend, or at least the closest thing to it. I wasn't a "best friend" person at school. But other girls like having best friends, Jojo for example. Maybe football is like that for Dermot, like stepping into a warm bath. Except there is nothing warm about Jojo today. Saying "blokes like football" isn't the same as saying "blokes have testicles", I argue. What Jojo really means, which she goes on to announce, is that your man will always have "things" that you don't like and vice versa and that you learn to accept them. Especially if the "thing" is as big as the sky, so big that everyone likes it apart from you and a crucial score-kick from a dark handsome man can raise the actual GDP of whatever poor tropical country he hails from. She says I haven't been patient enough with Dermot and his "things"; my knowledge of economics doesn't fool her.

"Even if he spends more time on the 'things' than me?" I interject.

"Better than him copping off with some other girl," says Jojo. But is it? I am now a bit stirred by football, the thing that took my baby. Except I'll never know football. I'll never sit in a huge stadium doing a Mexican wave like Billy Crystal and his friend in *When Harry Met Sally* as Billy tells the friend about his wife leaving him and the removal men knowing about it before he does. Football is like a town on my commute where I might run into Dermot; a town where I don't know anyone but keep passing through.

Dermot didn't just watch. He played. Perhaps that justifies his love of football

to me in some way. He used to play up in the countryside of East Anglia where his parents still live. I didn't meet them as we didn't go out for long. I never will, most likely. I mean, of course it's not an immutable law that I won't meet them. It's just deeply unlikely and it's strange to know that fact, like all the people I would get on with but won't meet who live in Hong Kong, or all the girls I'm not friends with because I didn't get into their school. He told me his father pushed him with the football – pushed hard. Clearly there *was* something to push – he was good at it during school, possibly the best. My parents never pushed me at anything. They were too busy writing and putting on plays. Now I'm a theatre-frequenting bankruptcy lawyer and I've helped them buy a flat. Dermot's parents are schoolteachers. Chemistry and geography, I think. I sometimes imagine the conversations we'll never have. I imagine his mother, who I've never seen a picture of, so of course she looks like him in my mind to the point where I almost fancy her – the same pale greyish eyes and reddish-blonde wavy hair. The first thing I said when I met Dermot was "I want your hair". He took this as a come on but it just leapt out of me – I must have spent a fortune in my twenties dyeing my hair to look like that. I imagine Mr and Mrs McAllister sitting opposite me in their kitchen, while Dermot, their pin-striped, code-writing son, blushes like a teenager, wondering how he came to be with a well-off London girl. Even though he's earning nicely too. Mrs McAllister is probably wondering if I dare discuss babies with him and might go so far as to feel sorry for me. Mr McAllister is wondering what sort of nick my body is in, possibly for the same reason, possibly not. These days, in the fantasies that persist even though Dermot is four months gone, they are talking about football and I go quiet (no point mentioning *When Harry Met Sally* to this pair – they've barely seen a movie in decades – this Dermot told me in the real world) and it's "you're awful quiet, Cressie", really hoping I'm OK, do I want tea, knowing I can't be OK because Dermot is leaving me and they already know I'm not the one who will come each year for Christmas and cheer at the edge of the field for their grandson in his first game. Soccer mom. They probably don't know that term either. I don't enjoy the daydream at this point, so I gear the plot towards Dermot taking me away from the dinner table up to his old bedroom where the trophies and the old stud shoes lie strewn and on the walls are pictures of him and The Team, whoever they are, mud spraying off a slide-kick like a paused TV commercial. His face in the photos is twisted with determination. I ask him about them, joke about seeing the exact facial expression in bed, but he doesn't want to talk, he wants to be seventeen again, hiding with a girl in his room, making so few sounds his parents know exactly what's going on. It's ecstasy.

I end it with a dash for the train, claiming I can't stay the night. He drives me to the station and we text during the journey – he misses me already. I switch trains at London Bridge so I pass Millwall Stadium going home to South-East London and think each time how much it resembles a giant paddling pool when you gallop past it. I think this in real life too but now Millwall is fused with the world of Dermot, a world I don't know and he doesn't know either because I've given him that world in my mind. I always imagine the put down I'll deliver if I see him again and how he'd have to provoke me to say it, which I'm sure he won't, he's a nice guy really, but it's always the same. What have I to do with you?

PEARS AND SILK

Veronica Cancio De Grandy

Veronica Cancio De Grandy 'adults' sometimes; sometimes with literature and sometimes with laundry. A singer, composer, editor, writer and managing director, she likes to introduce herself by first name only. She loves to be read to and to listen to other people's stories.

Silk, green, lacy and tiny: I have a pair of panties in my hand, and they are not mine. My curves could never be cramped into something this small. I'm almost insulted; you're not even trying. They feel slinky and tender in my hand. I rub the fabric between my fingers backwards and forwards. It slides together easily until it catches the lace.

How long have they been here? I guess I've been too caught up in my own world to notice. But really, how could you be so careless? The drawer was open. It's usually where you keep your aftershave and things of that nature; the things that I never need to look at. I must have walked into the bathroom two or three times before I saw it, then the green caught my eye. I thought maybe you had bought some new product I didn't know you were using; it would have been hard to guess since we don't get close enough to smell each other anymore.

I've been wearing a new perfume lately – you'd like it – it smells of Jasmine and Myrrh. You've always been led by your nose. I remember when you would dig your face in my neck for hours at a time. Whenever I would walk in the room, you would cup my waist in your right arm and pull back my hair with your left hand, you always wanted to smell me before we spoke, I never asked why, but I would always melt when you did.

And now we're here: two people who were once in love, who share meals once in a while, a passion for reading and a love of good music. Once a week, when we both get home at a reasonable hour, we might crack open a bottle of wine, put on a new record, toast to great beats and then, without noticing, we eventually end up on different sides of the living room, you on the computer and me on the chair, reading or correcting work that has carried over from the day. We haven't even been doing that lately.

The delicate item in my hand is getting warm from being rubbed between my fingers. I want to know how it feels to wear them. I want to feel what she feels when she's wearing them. I slip off my own panties, low-cut, cotton, lacy things that move with me when I walk and keep me cool in the summer. Silk makes you sweat, it makes you wet, it makes your smell more accessible to curious noses.

The lace is cutting off my circulation some, but I don't care; they fit where they need to. I pull my camisole down to the underwear line and look at myself in the

mirror. The colour goes with my skin. Is she dark haired like me? Maybe blonde, very pale, with such a skin tone that emerald would suit her.

I turn the light off in the bathroom and close the door. You're away and won't be coming home for a couple of hours. Are you with her? I don't know, and frankly it's not like we've been controlling each other in that sense. I've had my moments, but I've always been very careful with you. You've never known, you've never suspected, you could never imagine.

That night we were at dinner to celebrate my new book, my lover du jour worked at the restaurant, I told you I had to take a call and he took me in stall number three. When I came back, you asked why I was flushed, and I told you I had been discussing a negative review with my editor. You almost looked sad for me that night.

I turn off the light and strut out of the bathroom. I walk around the house doing mundane tasks. I answer some of my emails. I call the plumber; you're never going to fix that leaky faucet. I make flight reservations for a week in Paris. I think I might be in the mood to walk around Montmartre. I input your credit card instead of mine. This one's on you and you're not coming with me. I smile.

When I start to feel hungry, I walk to the kitchen and pick up a pear from the fruit bowl. Bosc, they're my favourite. I lean over the counter to eat it, wouldn't want to get any juice on these pretty little things. The panties protest my position and rise up a bit on my cheeks and tighten between my thighs. The feeling is unexpected and my body jolts, I bite down on the pear, the juice overruns my mouth and trickles down my chin. Two drops land on me: one on my camisole and one on the silk. Now you're going to know that I found them.

I really don't care. I put the pear down on the counter and lick my fingers 'til they are free of pear juice. When was the last time she wore these? Do they still have her smell? I walk to our bedroom and lie down on our bed. The skin on my hips is delighted with relief when I slip off the silk constriction and run it down my legs. Hooking them with my finger, I let them fall onto my face.

As I take in the scent, I can discern pear, me and a slightly stale presence that is not my own. She sprays perfume everywhere I see. I chuckle; you never stood a chance with this one. Did this happen once or more? She must have made an impact if you kept her panties. Did you have them in your pocket when you came home? Was I here?

The smell is overwhelming my senses. When I close my eyes I imagine a young, fun girl, sitting across the table from you and beginning to feel herself getting wet despite herself. My hands are circling the tips of my nipples over my camisole, both at the same time. The panties are covering my mouth, nose and eyes. I can't see, but I am watching this last moment between you two take place.

You take a stroll around the city. You talk about things that you like. You are telling her about your dreams in life and she is slowly falling for you. What she is producing as a result is this warm, sweet liquid that is pouring out of her. No matter how much perfume she's wearing you're bound to take notice if you get any closer. She becomes self-conscious. I dig my fingers into my breasts and grab handfuls of them.

You stop. She is animatedly talking about her love of art-house films. You have led her to a patch of grass. Gently, you place your hands on her shoulders

and she falls to her knees. You descend on top of her and lock your lips to hers. She closes her eyes in an effort to control herself: you surprised her. I am running my hands down my stomach.

She can hear people walking by; their footsteps make her nervous. Will any of them be people she knows? Will any of them be me? She curls her knee in and cradles your hip. You can now see the wet stain on her panties, they have soaked through and her scent fills the air. You can smell it. I am smelling it.

My hands have reached my lower lips. I part them. I can't see but I don't need to, I know myself well enough. Your hands lift up her dress. She tries to protest but soon surrenders, defenceless to your caresses. You reach in under her panties, with your index and middle fingers you feel down her smooth and hairless surface and you part her pretty, pink opening.

I scissor my fingers around my clit and squeeze them together. All the blood rushes to the tip and it begins to throb. You have your thumb on her clitoris and you have put your fingers inside her. She digs her face into your shoulder to stop herself from moaning. She can still hear people in the distance. She can't help letting out a soft moan – she is getting close. I am getting close. I can feel myself dripping down. I use the juice to slide easier around my opening. Circles – I like my fingers to work in little circles.

The grass is cool underneath her skin. She no longer cares who hears her. She contracts. I contract. I bite down on the panties, I can taste her, I can taste me, I can taste pear. The waves start. First the warmth spirals out from my fingers, to my skin and from my skin to my muscles. I'm tingling all over. She is trembling, her legs want to tighten and close, but your hands won't let her. She can't hold it in anymore.

I'm about to explode. We scream. Our hips rise up into the air taking our chests along with them. Our nipples stand erect and our mouths open to let out the only tool of release we have. You cover her mouth with your hand to muffle the sound. The silk panties make their way deeper into my mouth. Our screams are muffled. I spasm, she spasms, then we spasm again. Our hips come down.

She puts her head on your shoulder and looks at your intently. A little while later, you leave, she takes off her panties and gives them to you. I take them off my face, panting, exhausted from the violent spasms. I drift off into sleep for a few minutes.

When I wake up, I still have the panties in my hand; I lift them up to my face and inhale us together one more time. I get out of bed, walk into the bathroom and put them back. I slip on my own panties and close the drawer. The camisole is damp with sweat; it'll dry. I'm going to the kitchen to finish my pear. I think I'll spend the afternoon working on my latest book, and maybe I'll even chill a bottle of wine for when you get home.

THE WITNESS

Laurence Klavan

Laurence Klavan is the Edgar Award-winning author of *The Cutting Room* and *The Shooting Script*, as well as the short story collection, *The Family Unit and Other Fantasies*. He has twice had stories included in Mammoth's *Best New Erotica* collections. He wrote the libretto to *Bed and Sofa*, produced in New York and London.

"Happy anniversary!"

Gore felt a small plate, which probably carried cake, brush up against his fingers. He couldn't believe it had been ten years; wasn't it amazing how what you did every day added up in increments to your entire life? Like a crude comedian, he thought, asked to host a prestigious awards show, the tiny events didn't deserve to be associated with something so profound. But maybe it was egalitarian and good: every instant played its part in extending and ultimately ending life, the way that all the people in Gore's apartment played their parts in maintaining their arrangement. (And wasn't it weird that such an unconventional living situation should be commemorated in such a traditional way, with a celebration, admittedly private and small? Didn't it take the erotic appeal away from how they lived? Weren't the others disturbed by the noisemakers, the cards, the clapping, and the candles? Apparently not, for they themselves had thrown the party and bought the cake, from which Gore was now starting to fumble a piece loose with his fork.)

In a second, the utensil had found his mouth and he had swallowed, as he had swallowed the whole idea of living like this in the first place. At the start, he'd been a bit reluctant to digest it; now he just thought the whole thing delicious. He began to make his way for more cake, his hand scrambling across the table and banging into – whose hand was it, Annabelle's? Or Shem's? He couldn't tell; they both used lotion and kept their nails short.

Early in his life, he would never have been open to such a thing, but everything had changed after he became impotent and his wife died – not that one thing had caused the other, though maybe one had, for they had actually happened in reverse order (her death, then his impotence), so maybe the second had been a traumatized reaction to the first, or so a shrink had told him; maybe it was true. Why not? It made sense.

At the time, he had considered himself of no more use to women, not as a lover, anyway (and, yes, he knew that there were other acts to perform than "the deed", but call him old-fashioned, this had usually been the denouement of his amorous encounters; without it, he feared it would be like reading a whodunit

with the last page missing: all that information and evidence accrued with no revelation, something that would lead only to frustration, a sense of time frittered away).

In truth, he was embarrassed and just couldn't admit it to anyone. And, yes, he had tried pills but they endowed him with a weird object below his waist that felt both attached to, and detached from, himself, as if he were waving an appliance around, an electric carving knife for turkey, and one that was malfunctioning, sputtering sparks, and incapable of being controlled.

It was peculiar that he minded this, for Gore had always been detached as a person; he knew it and so had his wife, Liesel (sensibly, she felt there was always something to put up with in a relationship; other men were cruel or piggish, for example, and that was worse, and she was no prize, either, etc., more reasons he had loved her). His job for many years had even involved distance and observation: he had managed a movie revival theater downtown, at the time the last of its kind and itself about to be closed, sending Gore into an early (and unwanted) retirement. Without the job, he found he missed less the movies than the experience of being in an audience watching them: slipping into the house, standing in the back, melding into one big eye with the other people, not directly engaging them (asking afterwards how they had liked the picture, how they could be better "served", which he had had to do on occasion) but melting into one mass public perception of a thing. It had made him feel warm as few other things had done in his life, less alone, even loved and loving.

That was why not long after – the what, triple whammy? The three strikes? – his wife's death, his firing, and his becoming impotent, that he had decided to pursue a new line of work.

"Available to witness weddings... Discreet and dependable..." He couldn't remember exactly how he had phrased the ad, but he had placed it online and paid to keep it there. Gore had charged a small amount, enough to show he was sincere but not so much to scare anybody off. Within days, he had received interest from more than one couple and, within a few months, was earning enough to seriously supplement his other income from investments, a small inheritance, etc.

He would meet the couples in the hall outside the city clerk's office, usually before it opened in the morning. He would announce that he was fine with being paid afterwards, but some would insist on splitting the fee – half now, half later – as if he might bolt before it was over, or the bride or the groom would, which was more likely. The couples were young, old, and middle-aged; straight and gay; attractive, passable, and hideous; dressed to kill (a white wedding dress, a powder blue suit) or down (a running suit and sweatpants for them both). They hired him because they had no friends or could not agree on whom to ask (their first fight?) or wished for their own reasons to keep the event a secret. Many shook his hand and took leave of him directly following the finish; some bought him a sandwich and made a hollow vow to keep in touch; a few gave him gifts (the T-shirt saying "Witness" sold as a joke in the store near the chapel; cufflinks).

Once inside, he would sit with each couple while they got a number and waited to be called on a digital bulletin board, as if in a bakery. After being summoned, they would face a clerk behind a counter: one time it was a woman who spoke so softly they had to lean in to hear her, as if she were ashamed of what she

was saying or trying not to divulge such an intimate interaction or trying to test the couples' commitment by putting them through one more hoop, which was constantly asking her to repeat herself. Another clerk, a man, droned questions in a dead voice, as if furnishing a thing as boring as a fishing license: "Have you ever [gone fishing] before?" "Is the person you [went fishing with before] still alive?" "Do you know the date when you [stopped going fishing] with him?"

Then Gore would stand behind them in a small chapel with paint peeling atmospherically from the walls as they took their brief vows. The chaplain who often administered them spoke in a soft and heavy urban accent, like a compassionate cop making inquiries at a crime scene: "Do you take..." "Do you take..." "Does anyone here have a legal reason why..." And each time, by watching, Gore would feel the couples' nervousness and hope fly at and seep into him like snow; and, when they kissed to seal the ceremony, he would absorb the pleasure and relief each experienced (and, despite what someone cynical might have thought, in all the ceremonies he witnessed – and he must have seen three hundred in the five years he did them – no one being married ever evinced hostility or mockery or doubt, no matter how much of these emotions he or she had expressed before entering; and some had from agitation or another spur been jocular or cocky or coarse in the waiting room). It allowed Gore to join in love without attempting an action he could no longer perform, or moving a muscle or sacrificing something, like dignity.

Then, one morning, he witnessed the wedding of Annabel and Shem. She was a tall (over six foot) black woman, British by birth, in her 30s, who used to model and now did the books for her fiancé, who was American, smaller, softer, white, older than she by ten years, and leader, through inheritance, of a shipping business about which he was too bored to explain very much.

Nothing stood out about the ceremony except the obvious high quality of the bride's and groom's clothes, which were admittedly still simple: a business suit; a shirt, skirt and choker of pearls. Yet during the event, Gore noticed something odd: Annabel looked at him even more intently than he did her. And, afterwards, she asked – apparently with her new husband's approval – what Gore was doing that night. When he said, "nothing," she extended an invitation for him to come to their home.

And it was a home, a complete townhouse in an exclusive neighborhood, on a dead-end street that screeched to a stop right before it fell into the river. Gore had never seen a place so opulent; Shem had inherited it after his father's death (his mother had moved to another of their properties, in a suburb a highway, two bridges, and a world away from town).

"Let's eat," she said. "Getting married made me hungry. We don't cook, though. Take-out all right?"

The take-out was from the city's best Japanese restaurant, raw fish that dissolved like delicious tears upon Gore's tongue. He licked his fingers afterwards, he couldn't help it. When she was sure he was finally finished, Annabel asked if he wanted to see the upstairs and, as if hypnotized by sedatives in the sushi, Gore agreed.

The staircase was so ornate that Gore thought Annabel should have been carrying a candelabra to light their way, as if in an old horror movie. When they

reached the top landing, she began to discuss discreetly her love life with Shem.

She said there had always been something missing from it, something she could not quite put her finger on, excuse the suggestive imagery, and now – after watching Gore watch them be wed – she knew what it was.

That night, she put Gore on a chair at the front of their bedroom, near a closed door and turned-off light switch. He had once seen a movie in which a milquetoast husband was tied hand and foot to a chair and made to watch his slutty wife have sex with a repellently appealing escaped convict – a scene he had watched over and over again – but this situation differed in that he was not being forced, but asked nicely, and would not be bound but free to cross his legs and arms and drink from a water bottle thoughtfully provided on the dresser to his left. And while the idea would be the same – for him to watch Annabel and Shem make love – the intention was not to punish him but to give Annabel pleasure, if he didn't mind, which he didn't, for he soon found he got his own pleasure from it, which was different from hers and greater than any other he had experienced in his life.

The first time, they started slowly, or Shem did, anyway, not incompetently or indifferently, but with a certain lack of zing that made Gore understand what Annabel had meant by missing something. But this was quickly changed by Gore watching, for when he caught Annabel's gaze, their four eyes shining in whatever light came through the blinds from the streetlamps or the moon, which was particularly big and brilliant tonight, like a klieg light at the premiere of this idea, she became aroused in a way that made Shem better, made him pick up his game, as it were, like a logy tennis champ inspired to aggressive play by his suddenly adept opponent. The action became more frenzied, Shem drilling into her, Annabel gripping and slapping and spanking him to do so, while Gore and Annabel bore into each other, too, with their eyes, both holding the stare as tightly as she held Shem at the end, forcing her husband to finish by finishing so wildly herself, crying out, "Shem!" and then "Gore!" "Shem!' and then "Gore!" as if making sure to thank them both, from politeness, the way in his youth Gore's mother had insisted on his attending every party to which he was invited, whether he liked the inviting child or not, so as not to hurt any little one's feelings, since there would be so much pain for everyone later on. (And Annabel made sure only to use positions in which she and Gore could see each other: she wouldn't go on top or turn her back to him, not because it was rude – though it may have been partly that – because then only he would see and not she, and what good was that, for her, not him? She didn't know yet that he would enjoy it, he was only learning this himself and slowly). And neither had any temptation to laugh while looking, as you do in staring contests as a kid; there was nothing funny about it; there might have been to other people but not to them, not during it, anyway; afterwards, they all kind of laughed about, well, how intense it had been, not how idiotic.

And it had been intense for Gore – secretly and in a strange way, he found it incredibly exciting, even though physically he felt nothing, the arousal all in his head and not communicated anywhere else, as if a crucial and internal phone cord had been yanked from his wall and he had been talking to no one the entire time ("Hello? Hello? Is anybody there? Jesus Christ! Goodbye!"). The excite-

ment of seeing them had been great, not because he was privy to something private of which Annabel may have been ashamed and so eager to reveal (because it excited her to be punished or condemned? Due to poor parenting, she equated punishment with approval, connection, love? Or did her excitement stem from being exonerated, forgiven, her "immoral" activities made to seem innocent by being so flagrantly public? But then wouldn't she want to do it in the road, to coin the old song lyric, before as many people as possible? Gore didn't know, he was no shrink, and he never asked Annabel, either; she had even less interest in introspection than he). No, he so enjoyed watching them because it meant blending into a big ball of swaying and heaving energy, as he had in the movie theater, obviously, but this was even better, as if he had stepped into the screen and onto the set, mingling with the movie stars. And, being stars, they couldn't be touched, only gazed upon, which was great.

They finished late, and Gore was offered a canopied and super-soft guest-room bed, which he accepted. At breakfast the next morning (where they had all kinds of cereal and toast and egg white omelettes), Annabel told him openly that doing this would save their marriage, as having a child would for other couples. Would he please move in with them? (Annabel had cleared this with Shem, apparently, for he merely read the paper at the table the entire time.) Would he be in their bedroom whenever they wanted to love each other? They would support him, he could quit his witness job downtown; Gore's job had done its job by introducing him to them.

Gore was taken aback, unused to being approached so directly about such a personal thing. Yet he agreed to consider it. The breakfast turned silent while he continued to eat and Annabel stared at him, as she had last night, awaiting a reply. Soon the quality – say it, the deliciousness – of the food did more than preoccupy, it seduced: as soon as he had finished the last irresistible lick of jam and butter and slightly burnt bread and it had slid down and coated his coarse throat, he had agreed, staring into Annabel's limpid and yearning eyes as he had eight hours earlier. Why not, he thought? He was lonely and lovelorn and there was warmth in this place with these two.

Annabel bent forward and kissed him gratefully on the cheek, and maybe a little on the mouth, too; it was awkward leaning forward over other people's plates. Shem looked up for a second and smiled, okay with it, before turning a page of the paper to the crossword.

And so they lived together, Gore as more and less a roommate, all his expenses paid, encouraged to come and go as he pleased, asked to merely be around in the occasion of Annabel and Shem becoming intimate (and it was never truly scheduled but he noticed there came to be a pattern to the times and places: usually at nights, once or twice a week, in the early years, anyway, Gore alerted by a text to his phone if he was in his room, reading, which he usually was, not being a party animal or night owl at this age, sometimes already asleep or in front of a film he had wanted to see, and so slightly inconvenienced, and walking down the hall in his undershirt and shorts or pyjamas or even nude beneath a robe, supplied by his friends free of charge), to take his place on the chair beside the dozing light switch by the closed door.

There was the occasional impulsive episode to break things up, as well, when

the three would be sitting idly on the sofa, slightly drunk, and Annabel would feel the urge and sloppily straddle Shem; or having had Shem join her in the shower, Annabel would become inspired by the water and soap and heat, and Gore would find himself sitting on the closed toilet, Annabel having opened the shower door, indifferent to the spray causing puddles on the floor and making Gore sopping wet (wearing a bathing suit he had found in his dresser drawer), Shem diligently behind Annabel, Annabel especially aroused, slapping the stall wall as if trying to shut up a noisy neighbor, Annabel and Gore only catching glimpses of each other's eyes through the hovering steam as Sherlock Holmes had found the hound on the foggy moor, right? (And was that the movie Gore had been watching before she called? He couldn't remember.)

Gore never knew if they ever did it without him, though Annabel once assured him (when both were in the bag) that they would postpone or cancel the event if he were not around, the way a Broadway show posts a notice and gives exchanges the night a star has stayed home sick. "If a tree falls in the forest, etc.," she had said, though she didn't say "falls" amusingly and crudely attributing a sex act to a stationary, seed-producing, and regenerating plant.

When Shem would go out of town on business or to the country to see his elderly, alcoholic mother, Annabel would sometimes ask Gore to watch her pleasure herself, and the experience would be especially intense for them both, for he sensed at these times that he saw her and knew her in ways that Shem did not, though she never hid the truth from Shem when he returned, usually just casually mentioning it and getting a distracted smile in return, as if he were simply happy she had kept busy while he was gone. (Gore, however, would sometimes remember the strong smell of her perfume and body parts for days, ruing when he could no longer summon them by inhaling his own skin and clothes. At last, on a weekend when Shem was away, he for the first time took the initiative and asked Annabel to do it for him and she agreed, as surprised and pleased as a singer onstage who gets a request for a favorite song no one ever wants to hear. And even though her "performance" seemed slightly intentional and over-the-top, he had never felt closer to her than after it was over and she had made him suck and lick her fingers, as if giving him her autograph or serving him her own delicacy or, no, like a mother breast-feeding her baby boy, a gesture Gore savored, for it would never be repeated, having as much unnerved as it had excited them. Anyway, it had all been a long time ago.)

"Happy anniversary!"

Annabel offered another piece of the cake, which was delicious (Annabel and Shem still didn't cook but provided the best of store-bought and delivered). Gore fluttered his fingers, meaning, I couldn't, maybe a few years ago I could or would have but no longer, it's kind of sad or simply bittersweet (Annabel probably only saw, "No, thanks, I'm stuffed," in his one wave). But it was bittersweet: Gore had been old enough when they began and now was even older: this was the waning of the coda, in other words, not just the end, the very end. Annabel and Shem were older, too, and so made love less often, half as much it seemed sometimes. And it was different for them all now, for Gore could no longer.

In truth, he could still see something – his macular degeneration hadn't gone

that far, he wasn't completely blind – but he mostly picked up globs and throbs of colored matter, like the animation of beating hearts in old educational cartoons. Consequently, he kept his eyes closed most of the time now, not wishing to compare what little he perceived with what he used to take in; it was too painful and pointless, for it was not going to get better, he would only grow weaker and worse.

What he heard mattered most to him now: the sounds of gasps and moans, rubs and slaps, threats and promises, cries and whispers (like the old Bergman movie, only in English not Swedish, so the dubbed edition he had once to his horror booked by mistake at his theater and had to pull midway through the first show before giving refunds), the whole song and dance or even symphony of love; as clichéd as that sounded, that's what it had become to him, a score with themes, arias and recitatives, always unique but always, too, a reinterpretation of something invented eons ago, culminating – in their house, anyway – with a woman shouting "Shem!" and then "Gore!", though Gore wondered if Annabel said it now the way a performer repeats a corny catchphrase out of obligation or compassion, just to please her fans, the same way, he wondered, they let him sit in their room now or let him stay in their house at all, for old times' sake, as they wouldn't have been able to put a dying dog down.

He was being too harsh, at least about himself, for tonight would take him somewhere new. Gore's sight had always been essential to him, especially since his wife's death; but maybe it had really been an impediment, a shield, a screen in itself. Tonight, after the party, in their bedroom, using only his imagination, he saw not just Annabel and Shem but himself and Liesel, and himself and every other woman he had been with and every other couple (or trio! Or more!) who had ever loved each other. In the dark, for the first time in years and the last time of his life, he felt a physical reaction, an arousal rising in and on him, the way they say souls of the living rise at the instant that they die. As Annabel and Shem finished – or pretended to, for him, another anniversary gift? – he melded with all humanity, as he had always wished to do but from a distance; and, no longer detached, he joined all the people who had ever seen others or been seen by the rapt and staring eyes in the frowning face of the earth.

Burning Desire

From FANNY HILL

John Cleland

John Cleland was born into an old Scottish family and educated at Westminster School in London. Travelling extensively abroad, he returned to London, knowing financial hardship upon his father's death. He eked out a precarious existence as a freelance literary journalist, occasionally slipping into serious debt. Indeed, when he put the finishing touches to *Memoirs of a Woman of Pleasure* (1748/9), now more popularly known as *Fanny Hill*, it was apparently from the inside of a debtor's gaol. His book became a bestseller, and despite being hauled up before the Privy Council for indecency, he was eventually awarded a generous life-long annuity by the government of the day.

There are not, on earth at least, eternal griefs; mine were, if not at an end, at least suspended: my heart, which had been so long overloaded with anguish and vexation, began to dilate and open to the least gleam of diversion or amusement. I wept a little, and my tears relieved me; I sighed, and my sighs seemed to lighten me of a load that oppressed me; my countenance grew, if not cheerful, at least more composed and free.

Mr. H . . . , who had watched, perhaps brought on this change, knew too well not to seize it; he thrust the table imperceptibly from between us, and bringing his chair to face me, he soon began, after preparing me by all the endearments of assurances and protestations, to lay hold of my hands, to kiss me, and once more to make free with my bosom, which, being at full liberty from the disorder of a loose dishabille, now panted and throbbed, less with indignation than with fear and bashfulness at being used so familiarly by still a stranger. But he soon gave me greater occasion to exclaim, by stooping down and slipping his hand above my garters: thence he strove to regain the pass, which he had before found so open, and unguarded: but now he could not unlock the twist of my thighs; I gently complained, and begged him to let me alone; told him I was now well. However, as he saw there was more form and ceremony in my resistance than good earnest, he made his conditions for desisting from pursuing his point that I should be put instantly to bed, whilst he gave certain orders to the landlady, and that he would return in an hour, when he hoped to find me more reconciled to his passion for me than I seemed at present. I neither assented nor denied, but my air and manner of receiving this proposal gave him to see that I did not think myself enough my own mistress to refuse it.

Accordingly he went out and left me, when, a minute or two after, before I could recover myself into any composure for thinking, the maid came in with her

mistress's service, and a small silver porringer of what she called a bridal posset, and desired me to eat it as I went to bed, which consequently I did, and felt immediately a heat, a fire run like a hue-and-cry through every part of my body; I burnt, I glowed, and wanted even little of wishing for any man.

The maid, as soon as I was lain down, took the candle away, and wishing me a good night, went out of the room and shut the door after her.

She had hardly time to get down-stairs before Mr. H . . . opened my room-door softly, and came in, now undressed in his night-gown and cap, with two lighted wax candles, and bolting the door, gave me, though I expected him, some sort of alarm. He came a tip-toe to the bed-side, and said with a gentle whisper: "Pray, my dear, do not be startled . . . I will be very tender and kind to you." He then hurried off his clothes, and leaped into bed, having given me openings enough, whilst he was stripping, to observe his brawny structure, strong-made limbs, and rough shaggy breast.

The bed shook again when it received this new load. He lay on the outside, where he kept the candles burning, no doubt for the satisfaction of every sense; for as soon as he had kissed me, he rolled down the bed-clothes, and seemed transported with the view of all my person at full length, which he covered with a profusion of kisses, sparing no part of me. Then, being on his knees between my legs, he drew up his shirt and bared all his hairy thighs, and stiff staring truncheon, red-topped and rooted into a thicket of curls, which covered his belly to the navel and gave it the air of a flesh brush; and soon I felt it joining close to mine, when he had drove the nail up to the head, and left no partition but the intermediate hair on both sides.

I had it now, I felt it now, and, beginning to drive, he soon gave nature such a powerful summons down to her favourite quarters, that she could no longer refuse repairing thither; all my animal spirits then rushed mechanically to that centre of attraction, and presently, inly warmed, and stirred as I was beyond bearing, I lost all restraint, and yielding to the force of the emotion, gave down, as mere woman, those effusions of pleasure, which, in the strictness of still faithful love, I could have wished to have held up.

Yet oh! What an immense difference did I feel between this impression of a pleasure merely animal, and struck out of the collision of the sexes by a passive bodily effect, from that sweet fury, that rage of active delight which crowns the enjoyments of a mutual love-passion, where two hearts, tenderly and truly united, club to exalt the joy, and give it a spirit and soul that bids defiance to that end which mere momentary desires generally terminate in, when they die of a surfeit of satisfaction!

Mr. H . . . , whom no distinctions of that sort seemed to disturb, scarce gave himself or me breathing time from the last encounter, but, as if he had task ed himself to prove that the appearances of his vigour were not signs hung out in vain, in a few minutes he was in a condition for renewing the onset; to which, preluding with a storm of kisses, he drove the same course as before, with unabated fervour; and thus, in repeated engagements, kept me constantly in exercise till dawn of morning; in all which time he made me fully sensible of the virtues of his firm texture of limbs, his square shoulders, broad chest, compact hard muscles, in short a system of manliness that might pass for no bad image of

our ancient sturdy barons, when they wielded the battle-axe: whose race is now so thoroughly refined and frittered away into the more delicate and modern-built frame of our pap-nerved softlings, who are as pale, as pretty, and almost as masculine as their sisters.

Mr. H . . . , content, however, with having the day break upon his triumphs, delivered me up to the refreshment of a rest we both wanted, and we soon dropped into a profound sleep.

Though he was some time awake before me, yet did he not offer to disturb a repose he had given me so much occasion for; but on my first stirring, which was not till past ten o'clock, I was obliged to endure one more trial of his manhood.

About eleven, in came Mrs. Jones, with two basins of the richest soup, which her experience in these matters had moved her to prepare. I pass over the fulsome compliments, the cant of the decent procuress, with which she saluted us both; but though my blood rose at the sight of her, I suppressed my emotions, and gave all my concern to reflections on what would be the consequence of this new engagement.

But Mr. H . . . , who penetrated my uneasiness, did not long suffer me to languish under it. He acquainted me that, having taken a solid sincere affection to me, he would begin by giving me one leading mark of it by removing me out of a house which must, for many reasons, be irksome and disagreeable to me, into convenient lodgings, where he would take all imaginable care of me; and desiring me not to have any explanations with my landlady, or be impatient till he returned, he dressed and went out, having left me a purse with two and twenty guineas in it, being all he had about him, as he expressed it, to keep my pocket till further supplies.

As soon as he was gone, I felt the usual consequence of the first launch into vice (for my love-attachment to Charles never appeared to me in that light). I was instantly borne away down the stream, without making back to the shore. My dreadful necessities, my gratitude, and above all, to say the plain truth, the dissipation and diversion I began to find, in this new acquaintance, from the black corroding thoughts my heart had been a prey to ever since the absence of my dear Charles, concurred to stun all contrary reflections. If I now thought of my first, my only charmer, it was still with the tenderness and regret of the fondest love, embittered with the consciousness that I was no longer worthy of him. I could have begged my bread with him all over the world, but wretch that I was, I had neither the virtue nor courage requisite not to outlive my separation from him!

Yet, had not my heart been thus pre-engaged, Mr. H . . . might probably have been the sole master of it; but the place was full, and the force of conjunctures alone had made him the possessor of my person; the charms of which had, by the bye, been his sole object and passion, and were, of course, no foundation for a love either very delicate or very durable.

He did not return till six in the evening to take me away to my new lodgings; and my moveables being soon packed, and conveyed into a hackney-coach, it cost me but little regret to take my leave of a landlady whom I thought I had so much reason not to be overpleased with; and as for her part, she made no other difference to my staying or going, but what that of the profit created.

We soon got to the house appointed for me, which was that of a plain tradesman who, on the score of interest, was entirely at Mr. H . . .'s devotion, and who let him the first floor, very genteelly furnished, for two guineas a week, of which I was instated mistress, with a maid to attend me.

He stayed with me that evening, and we had a supper from a neighbouring tavern, after which, and a gay glass or two, the maid put me to bed. Mr. H . . . soon followed, and notwithstanding the fatigues of the preceding night, I found no quarter nor remission from him: he piqued himself, as he told me, on doing the honours of my new apartment.

The morning being pretty well advanced, we got to breakfast; and the ice now broke, my heart, no longer engrossed by love, began to take ease, and to please itself with such trifles as Mr. H . . .'s liberal liking led him to make his court to the usual vanity of our sex. Silks, laces, ear-rings, pearl-necklace, gold watch, in short, all the trinkets and articles of dress were lavishly heaped upon me; the sense of which, if it did not create returns of love, forced a kind of grateful fondness something like love; a distinction it would be spoiling the pleasure of nine tenths of the keepers in the town to make, and is, I suppose, the very good reason why so few of them ever do make it.

I was now established the kept mistress in form, well lodged, with a very sufficient allowance, and lighted up with all the lustre of dress.

Mr. H . . . continued kind and tender to me; yet, with all this, I was far from happy; for, besides my regret for my dear youth, which, though often suspended or diverted, still returned upon me in certain melancholic moments with redoubled violences, I wanted more society, more dissipation.

As to Mr. H . . . , he was so much my superior in every sense, that I felt it too much to the disadvantage of the gratitude I owed him. Thus he gained my esteem, though he could not raise my taste; I was qualified for no sort of conversation with him except one sort, and that is a satisfaction which leaves tiresome intervals, if not filled up by love, or other amusements.

Mr. H . . . , so experienced, so learned in the ways of women, numbers of whom had passed through his hands, doubtless soon perceived this uneasiness, and without approving or liking me the better for it, had the complaisance to indulge me. He made suppers at my lodgings, where he brought several companions of his pleasures, with their mistresses; and by this means I got into a circle of acquaintance that soon stripped me of all the remains of bashfulness and modesty which might be yet left of my country education, and were, to a just taste, perhaps the greatest of my charms.

We visited one another in form, and mimicked, as near as we could, all the miseries, the follies, and impertinences of the women of quality, in the round of which they trifle away their time, without its ever entering into their little heads that on earth there cannot subsist any thing more silly, more flat, more insipid and worthless, than, generally considered, their system of life is: they ought to treat the men as their tyrants, indeed! were they to condemn them to it.

But though, amongst the kept mistresses (and I was now acquainted with a good many, besides some useful matrons, who live by their connexions with them), I hardly knew one that did not perfectly detest her keeper, and, of course, made little or no scruple of any infidelity she could safely accomplish, I had still

no notion of wronging mine; for, besides that no mark of jealousy on his side induced in me the desire or gave me the provocation to play him a trick of that sort, and that his constant generosity, politeness, and tender attentions to please me forced a regard to him, that without affecting my heart, insured him my fidelity, no object had yet presented that could overcome the habitual liking I had contracted for him; and I was on the eve of obtaining, from the movements of his own voluntary generosity, a modest provision for life, when an accident happened which broke all the measures he had resolved upon in my favour.

I had now lived near seven months with Mr. H . . . , when one day returning to my lodgings from a visit in the neighbourhood, where I used to stay longer, I found the street door open, and the maid of the house standing at it, talking with some of her acquaintances, so that I came in without knocking; and, as I passed by, she told me Mr. H . . . was above. I stepped up-stairs into my own bed-chamber, with no other thought than of pulling off my hat, etc., and then to wait upon him in the dining room, into which my bed-chamber had a door, as is common enough. Whilst I was untying my hat-strings, I fancied I heard my maid Hannah's voice and a sort of tussle, which raising my curiosity, I stole softly to the door, where a knot in the wood had been slipped out and afforded a very commanding peep-hole to the scene then in agitation, the actors of which had been too earnestly employed to hear my opening my own door, from the landing-place of the stairs, into my bed-chamber.

The first sight that struck me was Mr. H . . . pulling and hauling this coarse country strammel towards a couch that stood in a corner of the dining room; to which the girl made only a sort of awkward boidening resistance, crying out so loud, that I, who listened at the door, could scarce hear her: "Pray sir, don't . . . , let me alone . . . I am not for your turn . . . You cannot, sure, demean yourself with such a poor body as I . . . Lord! Sir, my mistress may come home . . . I must not indeed . . . I will cry out . . ." All of which did not hinder her from insensibly suffering herself to be brought to the foot of the couch, upon which a push of no mighty violence served to give her a very easy fall, and my gentleman having got up his hands to the strong-hold of her Virtue, she, no doubt, thought it was time to give up the argument, and that all further defence would be in vain: and he, throwing her petticoats over her face, which was now as red as scarlet, discovered a pair of stout, plump, substantial thighs, and tolerably white; he mounted them round his hips, and coming out with his drawn weapon, stuck it in the cloven spot, where he seemed to find a less difficult entrance than perhaps he had flattered himself with (for, by the way, this blouse had left her place in the country, for a bastard), and, indeed, all his motions shew'd he was lodged pretty much at large. After he had done, his Deare gets up, drops her petticoats down, and smooths her apron and handkerchief. Mr. H . . . looked a little silly, and taking out some money, gave it her, with an air indifferent enough, bidding her be a good girl, and say nothing.

Had I loved this man, it was not in nature for me to have had patience to see the whole scene through: I should have broke in and played the jealous princess with a vengeance. But that was not the case, my pride alone was hurt, my heart not, and I could easier win upon myself to see how far he would go, till I had no uncertainty upon my conscience.

The least delicate of all affairs of this sort being now over, I retired softly into my closet, where I began to consider what I should do. My first scheme, naturally, was to rush in and upbraid them; this, indeed, flattered my present emotions and vexations, as it would have given immediate vent to them; but, on second thoughts, not being so clear as to the consequences to be apprehended from such a step, I began to doubt whether it was not better to dissemble my discovery till a safer season, when Mr. H . . . should have perfected the settlement he had made overtures to me of, and which I was not to think such a violent explanation, as I was indeed not equal to the management of, could possibly forward, and might destroy. On the other hand, the provocation seemed too gross, too flagrant, not to give me some thoughts of revenge; the very start of which idea restored me to perfect composure; and delighted as I was with the confused plan of it in my head, I was easily mistress enough of myself to support the part of ignorance I had prescribed to myself; and as all this circle of reflections was instantly over, I stole a tip-toe to the passage door, and opening it with a noise, passed for having that moment come home; and after a short pause, as if to pull off my things, I opened the door into the dining room, where I found the dowdy blowing the fire, and my faithful shepherd walking about the room and whistling, as cool and unconcerned as if nothing had happened. I think, however, he had not much to brag of having out-dissembled me: for I kept up, nobly, the character of our sex for art, and went up to him with the same air of frankness as I had ever received him. He stayed but a little while, made some excuse for not being able to stay the evening with me, and went out.

As for the wench, she was now spoiled, at least for my servant; and scarce eight and forty hours were gone round, before her insolence, on what had passed between Mr. H . . . and her, gave me so fair an occasion to turn her away, at a minute's warning, that not to have done it would have been the wonder: so that he could neither disapprove it nor find in it the least reason to suspect my original motive. What became of her afterwards, I know not; but generous as Mr. H . . . was, he undoubtedly made her amends: though, I dare answer, that he kept up no farther commerce with her of that sort; as his stooping to such a coarse morsel was only a sudden sally of lust, on seeing a wholesome-looking, buxom country-wench, and no more strange than hunger, or even a whimsical appetite's making a fling meal of neck-beef, for change of diet.

Had I considered this escapade of Mr. H . . . in no more than that light and contented myself with turning away the wench, I had thought and acted right; but, flushed as I was with imaginary wrongs, I should have held Mr. H . . . to have been cheaply off, if I had not pushed my revenge farther, and repaid him, as exactly as I could for the soul of me, in the same coin.

Nor was this worthy act of justice long delayed: I had it too much at heart. Mr. H . . . had, about a fortnight before, taken into his service a tenant's son, just come out of the country, a very handsome young lad scarce turned of nineteen, fresh as a rose, well shaped and clever limbed: in short, a very good excuse for any woman's liking, even though revenge had been out of the question; any woman, I say, who was disprejudiced, and had wit and spirit enough to prefer a point of pleasure to a point of pride.

Mr. H . . . had clapped a livery upon him; and his chief employ was, after

being shewn my lodgings, to bring and carry letters or messages between his master and me; and as the situation of all kept ladies is not the fittest to inspire respect, even to the meanest of mankind, and, perhaps, less of it from the most ignorant, I could not help observing that this lad, who was, I suppose, acquainted with my relation to his master by his fellow-servants, used to eye me in that bashful confused way, more expressive, more moving and readier catched at by our sex, than any other declarations whatever: my figure had, it seems, struck him, and modest and innocent as he was, he did not himself know that the pleasure he took in looking at me was love, or desire; but his eyes, naturally wanton, and now enflamed with passion, spoke a great deal more than he durst have imagined they did. Hitherto, indeed, I had only taken notice of the comeliness of the youth, but without the least design: my pride alone would have guarded me from a thought that way, had not Mr. H . . .'s condescension with my maid, where there was not half the temptation in point of person, set me a dangerous example; but now I began to look on this stripling as every way a delicious instrument of my designed retaliation upon Mr. H . . . of an obligation for which I should have made a conscience to die in his debt.

In order then to pave the way for the accomplishment of my scheme, for two or three times that the young fellow came to me with messages, I managed so, as without affectation to have him admitted to my bed-side, or brought to me at my toilet, where I was dressing; and by carelessly shewing or letting him see, as if without meaning or design, sometimes my bosom rather more bare than it should be; sometimes my hair, of which I had a very fine head, in the natural flow of it while combing; sometimes a neat leg, that had unfortunately slipped its garter, which I made no scruple of tying before him, easily gave him the impressions favourable to my purpose, which I could perceive to sparkle in his eyes, and glow in his cheeks: then certain slight squeezes by the hand, as I took letters from him, did his business completely.

When I saw him thus moved, and fired for my purpose, I inflamed him yet more, by asking him several leading questions, such as had he a mistress? . . . was she prettier than me? . . . could he love such a one as I was? . . . and the like; to all which the blushing simpleton answered to my wish, in a strain of perfect nature, perfect undebauch'd innocence, but with all the awkwardness and simplicity of country breeding.

When I thought I had sufficiently ripened him for the laudable point I had in view, one day that I expected him at a particular hour, I took care to have the coast clear for the reception I designed him; and, as I laid it, he came to the dining-room door, tapped at it, and, on my bidding him come in, he did so, and shut the door after him. I desired him, then, to bolt it on the inside, pretending it would not otherwise keep shut.

I was then lying at length upon that very couch, the scene of Mr. H . . .'s polite joys, in an undress which was with all the art of negligence flowing loose, and in a most tempting disorder: no stay, no hoop . . . no encumbrance whatever. On the other hand, he stood at a little distance, that gave me a full view of a fine featured, shapely, healthy country lad, breathing the sweets of fresh blooming youth; his hair, which was of a perfect shining black, played to his face in natural side-curls, and was set out with a smart tuck-up behind; new buckskin breeches,

that, clipping close, shew'd the shape of a plump, well made thigh; white stockings, garter-laced livery, shoulder knot, altogether composed a figure in which the beauties of pure flesh and blood appeared under no disgrace from the lowness of a dress, to which a certain spruce neatness seems peculiarly fitted.

I bid him come towards me and give me his letter, at the same time throwing down, carelessly, a book I had in my hands. He coloured, and came within reach of delivering me the letter, which he held out, awkwardly enough, for me to take, with his eyes riveted on my bosom, which was, through the designed disorder of my handkerchief, sufficiently bare, and rather shaded than hid.

I, smiling in his face, took the letter, and immediately catching gently hold of his shirt sleeve, drew him towards me, blushing, and almost trembling; for surely his extreme bashfulness, and utter inexperience, called for, at least, all the advances to encourage him: his body was now conveniently inclined towards me, and just softly chucking his smooth beardless chin, I asked him if he was afraid of a lady? . . . , and, with that took, and carrying his hand to my breasts, I pressed it tenderly to them. They were now finely furnished, and raised in flesh, so that, panting with desire, they rose and fell, in quick heaves, under his touch: at this, the boy's eyes began to lighten with all the fires of inflamed nature, and his cheeks flushed with a deep scarlet: tongue-tied with joy, rapture, and bashfulness, he could not speak, but then his looks, his emotion, sufficiently satisfied me that my train had taken, and that I had no disappointment to fear.

My lips, which I threw in his way, so as that he could not escape kissing them, fixed, fired, and emboldened him: and now, glancing my eyes towards that part of his dress which covered the essential object of enjoyment, I plainly discovered the swell and commotion there; and as I was now too far advanced to stop in so fair a way, and was indeed no longer able to contain myself, or wait the slower progress of his maiden bashfulness (for such it seemed, and really was), I stole my hand upon his thighs, down one of which I could both see and feel a stiff hard body, confined by his breeches, that my fingers could discover no end to. Curious then, and eager to unfold so alarming a mystery, playing, as it were, with his buttons, which were bursting ripe from the active force within, those of his waistband and fore-flap flew open at a touch, when out IT started; and now, disengaged from the shirt, I saw, with wonder and surprise, what? not the play-thing of a boy, not the weapon of a man, but a maypole of so enormous a standard, that had proportions been observed, it must have belonged to a young giant. Its prodigious size made me shrink again; yet I could not, without pleasure, behold, and even ventured to feel, such a length, such a breadth of animated ivory! perfectly well turned and fashioned, the proud stiffness of which distended its skin, whose smooth polish and velvet softness might vie with that of the most delicate of our sex, and whose exquisite whiteness was not a little set off by a sprout of black curling hair round the root, through the jetty sprigs of which the fair skin shew'd as in a fine evening you may have remarked the clear light ether through the branchwork of distant trees over-topping the summit of a hill: then the broad and blueish-casted incarnate of the head, and blue serpentines of its veins, altogether composed the most striking assemblage of figure and colours in nature. In short, it stood an object of terror and delight.

But what was yet more surprising, the owner of this natural curiosity, through

the want of occasions in the strictness of his home-breeding, and the little time he had been in town not having afforded him one, was hitherto an absolute stranger, in practice at least, to the use of all that manhood he was so nobly stocked with; and it now fell to my lot to stand his first trial of it, if I could resolve to run the risks of its disproportion to that tender part of me, which such an oversized machine was very fit to lay in ruins.

But it was now of the latest to deliberate; for, by this time, the young fellow, overheated with the present objects, and too high mettled to be longer curbed in by that modesty and awe which had hitherto restrained him, ventured, under the stronger impulse and instructive promptership of nature alone, to slip his hands, trembling with eager impetuous desires, under my petticoats; and seeing, I suppose, nothing extremely severe in my looks to stop or dash him, he feels out, and seizes, gently, the centre-spot of his ardours. Oh then! the fiery touch of his fingers determines me, and my fears melting away before the glowing intolerable heat, my thighs disclose of themselves, and yield all liberty to his hand: and now, a favourable movement giving my petticoats a toss, the avenue lay too fair, too open to be missed. He is now upon me: I had placed myself with a jet under him, as commodious and open as possible to his attempts, which were untoward enough, for his machine, meeting with no inlet, bore and battered stiffly against me in random pushes, now above, now below, now beside his point; till, burning with impatience from its irritating touches, I guided gently, with my hand, this furious engine to where my young novice was now to be taught his first lesson of pleasure. Thus he nicked, at length, the warm and insufficient orifice; but he was made to find no breach impracticable, and mine, though so often entered, was still far from wide enough to take him easily in. By my direction, however, the head of his unwieldy machine was so critically pointed that, feeling him foreright against the tender opening, a favourable motion from me met his timely thrust, by which the lips of it, strenuously dilated, gave way to his thus assisted impetuosity, so that we might both feel that he had gained a lodgement. Pursuing then his point, he soon, by violent, and, to me, most painful piercing thrusts, wedges himself at length so far in, as to be now tolerably secure of his entrance: here he stuck, and I now felt such a mixture of pleasure and pain, as there is no giving a definition of. I dreaded alike his splitting me farther up, or his withdrawing; I could not bear either to keep or part with him. The sense of pain however prevailing, from his prodigious size and stiffness, acting upon me in those continued rapid thrusts, with which he furiously pursued his penetration, made me cry out gently: "Oh! my dear, you hurt me!" This was enough to check the tender respectful boy even in his midcareer; and he immediately drew out the sweet cause of my complaint, whilst his eyes eloquently expressed, at once, his grief for hurting me, and his reluctance at dislodging from quarters of which the warmth and closeness had given him a gust of pleasure that he was now desire-mad to satisfy, and yet too much a novice not to be afraid of my withholding his relief, on account of the pain he had put me to.

But I was, myself, far from being pleased with his having too much regarded my tender exclaims; for now, more and more fired with the object before me, as it still stood with the fiercest erection, unbonneted, and displaying its broad vermilion head, I first gave the youth a re-encouraging kiss, which he repaid me

with a fervour that seemed at once to thank me, and bribe my farther compliance; and soon replaced myself in a posture to receive, at all risks, the renewed invasion, which he did not delay an instant: for, being presently remounted, I once more felt the smooth hard gristle forcing an entrance, which he achieved rather easier than before. Pained, however, as I was, with his efforts of gaining a complete admission, which he was so regardful as to manage by gentle degrees, I took care not to complain. In the meantime, the soft strait passage gradually loosens, yields, and, stretched to its utmost bearing, by the stiff, thick, indriven engine, sensible, at once, to the ravishing pleasure of the feel and the pain of the distension, let him in about half way, when all the most nervous activity he now exerted, to further his penetration, gained him not an inch of his purpose: for, whilst he hesitated there, the crisis of pleasure overtook him, and the close compressure of the warm surrounding fold drew from him the ecstatic gush, even before mine was ready to meet it, kept up by the pain I had endured in the course of the engagement, from the insufferable size of his weapon, though it was not as yet in above half its length.

I expected then, but without wishing it, that he would draw, but was pleasantly disappointed: for he was not to be let off so. The well breathed youth, hot-mettled, and flush with genial juices, was now fairly in for making me know my driver. As soon, then, as he had made a short pause, waking, as it were, out of the trance of pleasure (in which every sense seemed lost for a while, whilst, with his eyes shut, and short quick breathing, he had yielded down his maiden tribute), he still kept his post, yet unsated with enjoyment, and solacing in these so new delights; till his stiffness, which had scarce perceptibly remitted, being thoroughly recovered to him, who had not once unsheathed, he proceeded afresh to cleave and open to himself an entire entry into me, which was not a little made easy to him by the balsamic injection with which he had just plentifully moistened the whole internals of the passage.

Redoubling, then, the active energy of his thrusts, favoured by the fervid appetite of my motions, the soft oiled wards can no longer stand so effectual a picklock, but yield, and open him an entrance. And now, with conspiring nature, and my industry, strong to aid him, he pierces, penetrates, and at length, winning his way inch by inch, gets entirely in, and finally a mighty thrust sheaths it up to the guard; on the information of which, from the close jointure of our bodies (insomuch that the hair on both sides perfectly interweaved and incircled together), the eyes of the transported youth sparkled with more joyous fires, and all his looks and motions acknowledged excess of pleasure, which I now began to share, for I felt him in my very vitals! I was quite sick with delight! stirred beyond bearing with its furious agitations within me, and gorged and crammed, even to surfeit. Thus I lay gasping, panting under him, till his broken breathings, faltering accents, eyes twinkling with humid fires, lunges more furious, and an increased stiffness, gave me to hail the approaches of the second period: it came . . . and the sweet youth, overpowered with the ecstasy, died away in my arms, melting in a flood that shot in genial warmth into the innermost recesses of my body; every conduit of which, dedicated to that pleasure, was on flow to mix with it. Thus we continued for some instants, lost, breathless, senseless of every thing, and in every part but those favourite

ones of nature, in which all that we enjoyed of life and sensation was now totally concentre'd.

When our mutual trance was a little over, and the young fellow had withdrawn that delicious stretcher, with which he had most plentifully drowned all thoughts of revenge in the sense of actual pleasure, the widened wounded passage refunded a stream of pearly liquids, which flowed down my thighs, mixed with streaks of blood, the marks of the ravage of that monstrous machine of his, which had now triumphed over a kind of second maidenhead. I stole, however, my handkerchief to those parts, and wiped them as dry as I could, whilst he was re-adjusting and buttoning up.

I made him now sit down by me, and as he had gathered courage from such extreme intimacy, he gave me an aftercourse of pleasure, in a natural burst of tender gratitude and joy, at the new scenes of bliss I had opened to him: scenes positively new, as he had never before had the least acquaintance with that mysterious mark, the cloven stamp of female distinction, though nobody better qualified than he to penetrate into its deepest recesses, or do it nobler justice. But when, by certain motions, certain unquietnesses of his hands, that wandered not without design, I found he languished for satisfying a curiosity, natural enough, to view and handle those parts which attract and concentre the warmest force of imagination, charmed as I was to have any occasion of obliging and humouring his young desires, I suffered him to proceed as he pleased, without check or control, to the satisfaction of them.

Easily, then, reading in my eyes the full permission of myself to all his wishes, he scarce pleased himself more than me when, having insinuated his hand under my petticoat and shift, he presently removed those bars to the sight by slyly lifting them upwards, under favour of a thousand kisses, which he thought, perhaps, necessary to divert my attention from what he was about. All my drapery being now rolled up to my waist, I threw myself into such a posture upon the couch, as gave up to him, in full view, the whole region of delight, and all the luxurious landscape round it. The transported youth devoured every thing with his eyes, and tried, with his fingers, to lay more open to his sight the secrets of that dark and delicious deep: he opens the folding lips, the softness of which, yielding entry to any thing of a hard body, close round it, and oppose the sight: and feeling further, meets with, and wonders at, a soft fleshy excrescence, which, limber and relaxed after the late enjoyment, now grew, under the touch and examination of his fiery fingers, more and more stiff and considerable, till the titillating ardours of that so sensible part made me sigh, as if he had hurt me; on which he withdrew his curious probing fingers, asking me pardon, as it were, in a kiss that rather increased the flame there.

Novelty ever makes the strongest impressions, and in pleasures, especially; no wonder, then, that he was swallowed up in raptures of admiration of things so interesting by their nature, and now seen and handled for the first time. On my part, I was richly overpaid for the pleasure I gave him, in that of examining the power of those objects thus abandoned to him, naked and free to his loosest wish, over the artless, natural stripling: his eyes streaming fire, his cheeks glowing with a florid red, his fervid frequent sighs, whilst his hands convulsively squeezed, opened, pressed together again the lips and sides of that deep

flesh wound, or gently twitched the overgrowing moss; and all proclaimed the excess, the riot of joys, in having his wantonness thus humoured. But he did not long abuse my patience, for the objects before him had now put him by all his, and, coming out with that formidable machine of his, he lets the fury loose, and pointing it directly to the pouting-lipid mouth, that bid him sweet defiance in dumb-shew, squeezes in the head, and, driving with refreshed rage, breaks in, and plugs up the whole passage of that soft pleasure-conduit, where he makes all shake again, and put, once more, all within me into such an uproar, as nothing could still but a fresh inundation from the very engine of those flames, as well as from all the springs with which nature floats that reservoir of joy, when risen to its flood-mark.

I was now so bruised, so battered, so spent with this over-match, that I could hardly stir, or raise myself, but lay palpitating, till the ferment of my sense subsiding by degrees, and the hour striking at which I was obliged to dispatch my young man, I tenderly advised him of the necessity there was for parting; which I felt as much displeasure at as he could do, who seemed eagerly disposed to keep the field, and to enter on a fresh action. But the danger was too great, and after some hearty kisses of leave, and recommendations of secrecy and discretion, I forced myself to send him away, not without assurances of seeing him again, to the same purpose, as soon as possible, and thrust a guinea into his hands: not more, lest, being too flush of money, a suspicion or discovery might arise from thence, having every thing to fear from the dangerous indiscretion of that age in which young fellows would be too irresistible, too charming, if we had not that terrible fault to guard against.

Giddy and intoxicated as I was with such satiating draughts of pleasure, I still lay on the couch, supinely stretched out, in a delicious languor diffused over all my limbs, hugging myself for being thus revenged to my heart's content, and that in a manner so precisely alike, and on the identical spot in which I had received the supposed injury. No reflections on the consequences ever once perplexed me, nor did I make myself one single reproach for having, by this step, completely entered myself of a profession more decry'd than disused. I should have held it ingratitude to the pleasure I had received to have repented of it; and since I was now over the bar, I thought, by plunging over head and ears into the stream I was hurried away by, to drown all sense of shame or reflection.

Whilst I was thus making these laudable dispositions, and whispering to myself a kind of tacit vow of incontinency, enters Mr. H . . . . The consciousness of what I had been doing deepened yet the glowing of my cheeks, flushed with the warmth of the late action, which, joined to the piquant air of my dishabille, drew from Mr. H . . . a compliment on my looks, which he was proceeding to back the sincerity of with proofs, and that with so brisk an action as made me tremble for fear of a discovery from the condition of those parts were left in from their late severe handling: the orifice dilated and inflamed, the lips swollen with their uncommon distension, the ringlets pressed down, crushed and uncurled with the over-flowing moisture that had wet every thing round it; in short, the different feel and state of things would hardly have passed upon one of Mr. H . . .'s nicety and experience unaccounted for but by the real cause. But here the woman saved me: I pretended a violent disorder of my head, and a feverish heat, that indisposed me too much to

receive his embraces. He gave in to this, and good-naturedly desisted. Soon after, an old lady coming in made a third, very a-propos for the confusion I was in, and Mr. H . . . , after bidding me take care of myself, and recommending me to my repose, left me much at ease and relieved by his absence.

In the close of the evening, I took care to have prepared for me a warm bath of aromatic and sweet herbs; in which having fully laved and solaced myself, I came out voluptuously refreshed in body and spirit.

From THE LIFE AND AMOURS OF THE BEAUTIFUL, GAY AND DASHING KATE PERCIVAL, THE BELLE OF THE DELAWARE

Kate Percival

Kate Percival is most likely the nom-de-plume of an American writer: on this we can all agree. Whether she (or he) wrote and published the book in 1903 (as is generally supposed) or whether this steamy "memoir" is a later pastiche of Victorian erotica written for the US market, is uncertain.

I am about to do a bold thing. I am about to give to the world the particulars of a life fraught with incident and adventure. I am about to lift the veil from the most voluptuous scenes. I shall disguise nothing, conceal nothing, but shall relate everything that has happened to me just as it occurred. I am what is called a woman of pleasure, and have drained its cup to the very dregs. I have the most extraordinary scenes to depict, but although I shall place everything before the reader in the most explicit language, I shall be careful not to wound his or her sense of decency by the use of coarse words, feeling satisfied there is more charm in a story decently told than in the bold unblushing use of terms which ought never to sully a woman's lips.

I was born in a small village in the state of Pennsylvania, situated on the banks of the Delaware, and about thirty miles from Philadelphia. My father's house was most romantically situated within a few yards of the river. It was supported as it were, at the back by a high hill, which in summer was covered with green trees and bushes. On each side of the dwelling was a wood so dense and thick that a stranger un-acquainted with the paths through it could not enter. In front of the house, the river on sunshiny days gleamed and glistened in the rays of the sun, and the white sails passing and repassing formed quite a picturesque scene. At night, however, especially in the winter time, the scene was different. Then the wind would howl and moan through the leafless trees and the river would beat against the rocks in a most mournful cadence. To this day I can remember the

effect it had on my youthful mind, and whenever I hear the wind whistling at night, it always recalls, to my memory my birth place.

My father was a stern, austere man, usually very silent and reserved. I only remembered seeing him excited once or twice. My mother had died in my infancy – (I was but fifteen months at the time) and my father's sister became his housekeeper. I had but one brother a year older than myself. How well I remember him, a fine noble-hearted boy full of love and affection. We were neglected by our father and aunt, and left to get through our childhood's days as best we could. We would wander together hand in hand by the river side or in the woods, and often cry ourselves to sleep in each other's arms at our father's want of affection for us. We enjoyed none of the gayeties, none of the sports of youth. The chill of our home appeared to follow us wherever we went, and no matter how brightly the sun shone, it could not dissipate the chill around our hearts. I never remember seeing my father even smile. A continual gloom hung over him, and he usually kept himself locked in his room except at meal times.

This life continued until I was ten years of age, when one day my father informed me that the next day I was to go to Philadelphia to a boarding school. At first I was glad to hear it, for any change from the dull monotony of that solitary house must be an agreeable one to me. I ran to the garden to tell my brother; but the moment I mentioned it, Harry threw himself sobbing in my arms.

"Will you leave me, Kate!" he exclaimed. "What will I do when you are gone, I shall be so lonely – so very lonely without you?"

"But Harry, darling," I returned, "I shall be back again in a few months, and then I shall have so much to tell you, and we shall have such nice walks together."

I succeeded in calming him, especially as our father informed him before the day was over that he too was to go to a boarding school in the city of Baltimore. That evening we took our last ramble together before we left home. It was the month of June, and all nature was decked in her gayest apparel. It was a beautiful moonlight night, and the air was fragrant with the odor of June roses, of which there were a large number in the garden. We wandered by the side of the river and watched the moon rays playing on the surface of the water, while a gentle breeze murmured softly through the pine trees. On that evening we settled our future life. It was arranged between us that when Harry grew up to be a man I should go and keep his house. We dwelt a long time on the pleasures of such life. At last it was time for us to return to the house, we embraced each other tenderly and separated.

The next morning I left very early, and in a few hours reached my destination and was enrolled among the pupils of B— Seminary. I shall not dwell long on my school days, although I might devote much of space to them. I was not a popular girl in the school – I was too cold, too reserved, and some of the girls said too proud. I took no pleasure in girlish sports, but my chief amusement was reading. I would retire to a corner of the school room and while the other girls were at play – I would be plunged in the mysteries of Mrs. Radcliff's novels, or some other work of the same character. Frequently the Principal insisted on my shutting up my book and going out to play, but I would creep back when she had left the schoolroom, and resume my favorite occupation. I remained at school seven years, and during that time I never once visited home, for my father made

a special agreement that I was to spend my vacation at school.

It is strange that, considering the prominent part I have played in the Court of Venus, that up to the age of seventeen, not a single thought concerning the relation of the sexes ever entered my head. I had up to that age never experienced the slightest longing or desire and looked on all men with the utmost indifference. And yet I knew that I was called beautiful and was the envy of all my school fellows.

I have not yet given a description of myself to the reader and it is nothing but right that I should do so. At the age of seventeen my charms were well developed, and although they had not attained the ripe fullness which a few years later was the admiration and delight of all my adorers, still I possessed all the insignia of womanhood. In stature I was above the medium height, my hair was a dark auburn and hung in massive bands on a white neck. My eyes were a deep blue and possessed a languishing voluptuous expression; they were fringed with long silky eyelashes and arched with brows so finely penciled that I have often been accused of using art to give them their graceful appearance. My features were classically regular, my skin of dazzling whiteness, my shoulders were gracefully rounded and my bust faultless in its contours. My more secret charms I shall describe at some future time when I shall have to expose them to the reader's gaze.

I have said that up to the age of seventeen I had never experienced the slightest sexual desire. The spark of voluptuousness which has ever since burnt so fiercely in my breast was destined to be lighted up by one of my own sex. Yes, dear Laura, it was you who first taught me the delights and joys of love; it was you who first kindled that flame of desire that has caused me to experience twelve years of delirious bliss; it was to your gentle teaching, sweet friend, that I owe my initiation in all the mysteries of the Court of Venus; it was your soft hand that pointed out to me that path of pleasure – and all the delight shown on the wayside. The incident happened in this manner:

About three months before I left school we were told one morning that a new music and French teacher would take her abode in B— Seminary the next day. We were all extremely anxious to see her, and at the expected hour she made her appearance. Her name was Laura Castleton, and her father lived in St. Mary's County, Maryland. She was a brunette, about twenty years of age, and one of the most beautiful girls I ever saw. She was nearly as tall as myself, but considerably stouter, and her body was molded in a most exquisite manner. Although her eyes were very black and her hair like the raven's plume, her skin was as white as alabaster. Her teeth were as regular as if they had been cut of a solid piece of ivory, and her hands and feet were fairylike in their proportions. I was the eldest girl in the school and Laura immediately made me her companion. She was exceedingly intelligent, well educated, and well read. I was soon attracted to her and we became inseparable. We would pass all our spare time reading to each other or in conversation on literary subjects. I agreed to love her with my whole heart, and was never happy outside of her company.

"Laura," I said to her one day when we were walking on the playground with our arms around each other's waist, "why can't we sleep together?"

"Would you like it, Kate?" she asked, bending her black eyes upon my face

with a peculiar gloom in them which sent the blood rushing to my cheeks – but why and wherefore I did not know.

"Indeed I would, Laura. It would be so nice to lie in your arms all night."

"Well, darling, I will ask Mrs. B—. I have no doubt that she will give her consent."

The lovely girl drew me towards her and gave me a warmer kiss than she had ever before bestowed upon me. The contact of her easy lips to mine sent an indefinable thrill through my body which I had never experienced before. In the evening she informed me that she had spoken to Mrs. B— and that the latter had consented that we should sleep together. I was overjoyed at this news and longed for night to come so that I might recline in my darling's arms.

At last the hour of bedtime arrived and I followed Laura to her chamber. She put the lamp on the dressing table and, kissing me affectionately, bade me undress myself quickly. We began our toilette for the night. I was undressed first, and having put on my nightgown, I sat down on the side of the bed and watched Laura disrobing herself. After she had removed her dress and her petticoats, I could not help being struck with her resplendent charms. Her chemise had fallen off her shoulder, beautifully rounded, and two globes of alabaster reposing on a field of snow. She appeared to be entirely unaware that I was watching her, for she sat down on a chair exactly in front of me, and crossing one leg over the other, she began to remove her garters and stockings. This attitude raised her chemise in front, and allowed me to have a full view of her magnificently formed limbs. I even caught sight of her voluptuous thighs. Laura caught my eye.

"What are you gazing at so earnestly?" she asked.

"I am gazing at your beauties, Laura."

"One would think that you were my lover," returned Laura laughingly.

"So I am, dear – for you know I love you."

"You little witch you, you know well enough what I mean. But if you want to admire beauty, why not look in the glass, for I am not nearly as beautiful as you are, dear Kate."

"What nonsense, Laura," I replied, "but come, let us get into bed."

So saying, I jumped between the sheets and was followed almost immediately by Laura, who first, however, placed the lamp on a chair by the bedside. She clasped me in her arms and pressed me to her breast, while she kissed my lips, cheek and eyes passionately. The warmth of her embraces and her glowing limbs entwined in mine caused a strange sensation to steal through me. My cheeks burned and I returned her kisses with an ardor that equalled her own.

"How delightful it is to be in your arms, dear Laura," I exclaimed.

"Do you really like it?" she replied, pressing me still closer to her. At the same time our nightdresses became disarranged, and I felt her naked thighs pressing against mine.

Laura kissed me again with even greater warmth than before, and while she was thus engaged she slipped one of her soft hands in the opening of my night-chemise, and I felt it descend on one of my breasts. When I felt this, a trembling seized my limbs and I pressed her convulsively to my heart.

"What a voluptuous girl you are, Kate," she said, molding my breasts and titillating my nipples. "You set me on fire."

"I never felt so happy in my life, Laura. I could live and die in your arms."

I now carried my hand to her globes of alabaster and pressed and molded them, imitating her in all her actions. Nay, more, I turned down the bedclothes and, unbuttoning her nightdress in front, I exposed those charming, snowy hillocks to my delighted gaze. The light of the lamp shone directly upon them, and I was never tired of admiring the whiteness, firmness and splendid development of those glowing semiglobes. I buried my face between them and pressed a thousand kisses on the soft velvet surface.

"Why Kate, you are a perfect volcano," said Laura, trembling under my embraces, "and I have been laboring under the delusion that you were an icicle."

"I was an icicle, darling, but now I have been melted by your charms."

"What a happy man your husband will be," said Laura.

"Happy – why?"

"To enfold such a glorious creature as you in his embrace. If you take so much delight with one of your own sex, what will you do when clasped in a man's arms?"

"You are jesting, Laura. Do you suppose for a moment that I will ever allow a man to kiss and embrace me as you do?"

"Certainly, my love – he will do a great deal more than I do."

"More? What can you mean?"

"Is it possible, Kate, that you do not know?"

"I really do not know. Do tell me, there's a dear girl."

"I can scarcely believe it possible that you are seventeen years of age – a perfectly developed woman, and that you know nothing of the mysteries of love. Are you not aware, darling, that you possess a jewel about you that a man would give half his lifetime to ravish?"

"You speak in riddles, Laura. Where is this jewel?"

"Lie perfectly quiet, and I will show you where it is."

My cheeks burned and I was all aglow, for I had pretended to be more ignorant than I really was. Laura fastened her lips on my breast and placed her hand on one of my thighs. She then slowly carried it up the marble column and at last invaded the very sanctuary of love itself. When I felt her fingers roaming in the mossy covering of that hallowed spot, every moment growing more bold and enterprising, I could not help uttering a faint scream – it was the last cry of expiring modesty, and I grew as hardy and lascivious as my beautiful companion. I stretched my thighs open to their widest extent, the better to second the examination Laura was making of my person. The lovely girl appeared to be strangely affected while she was manipulating my secret charms. Her eyes shot fire, her bosom heaved, and she began to wiggle her bottom. For some time she played with the hair which thickly covered my mount of Venus – twisting it around her fingers, she then gently divided the folding lips and endeavored to penetrate the interior of the mystical grotto – but she could not effect an entrance but was obliged to satisfy herself with titillating the inside of the lips. Suddenly flows of pleasure shot through my entire body – for her finger had come in contact with the peeping sentinel that guarded the abode of bliss, an article which until that moment I did not know I possessed. She rubbed it gently, giving me the most exquisite pleasure. If the last remnant of prudery had not taken flight before,

this last act would have routed it completely. With a single jerk I threw off the bedclothes, and thus we both lay naked from the waist down.

"How magnificently you are formed, dear Kate," said Laura, examining all my hidden charms with the aid of the lamp. "What glorious thighs, what a delicious bijou, what a thick forest of hair, and what a splendidly developed clitoris. Now, sweet girl, I will make you taste the most delicious sensation you have ever experienced in your life. Let me do with you as I will."

"Do what you like with me, darling. I resign myself entirely in your hands."

Laura now commenced to gently rub my clitoris with her finger, while she kissed my breasts and lips passionately. I soon began again to experience the delicious sensation I have spoken of before; rivers of pleasure permeated through my system. My breasts bounded up and down – my buttocks were set in motion from the effect of her caressing finger, my thighs were stretched widely apart, and my whole body was under the exquisite influence of her scientific manipulations. At last the acme came, a convulsive shivering seized me, I gave two or three convulsive heaves with my buttocks, and in an agony of delight I poured down my first tribute to the god of love.

For a quarter of an hour I lay in a complete state of annihilation, and was only recalled from it by the kisses of Laura.

"Darling Kate," she exclaimed, "you must give me relief or I shall die – the sight of your enjoyment has lighted up such a fire within me that I shall burn up if you do not quench it."

"I will do my best, dear Laura, to assuage your desires. You have made me experience such unheard-of delight that I should indeed be wanting in gratitude if I were not to attempt to make you some return."

I rose up and, kneeling across her, began to examine at my ease her lovely Mons Veneris.

It was a glorious object, covered over with a mass of black silky hair, through the midst of which I could discern the plump lips folding close together. I placed my finger between them and felt her clitoris swelling beneath it until it actually peeped its little red head from its soft place of concealment. I now advanced one finger and found that it entered her coral sheath with the utmost ease; at the same time it was tightly grasped by the sensitive folds of her vagina. I began to move it in and out, while I kissed her white belly and thighs.

"Stop, darling," said Laura, rising up and going to a drawer, "I will contrive something better to bring on the dissolving period. You are rather a novice as yet in the art of procuring enjoyment."

She took from the drawer a dildo, which she fastened securely around my waist, and making me lie on my back, she leaned over me and guided it into her sensitive quiver. She then commenced to move herself rapidly upon it. It was a delicious sight to me; I could see the instrument entering in and out of her luscious grotto while her features expressed the most entrancing enjoyment and her broad white bottom and breasts shivered with pleasure. Her motions did not continue long, however. In a few minutes she succumbed and the elixir of love poured down her white thighs. The voluptuous sight before me and the rubbing of the dildo on my clitoris caused me to emit again at the same moment that she did, and we both sank exhausted on the bed. I shall not detain the read-

er with all the exquisite enjoyments I experienced for the next three months in my lessons with the beautiful Laura: suffice it to say that we exhausted every method that two young girls of ardent imagination could propose. At last the time approached for us to separate, and with tears and embraces we bade each other adieu.

I returned home and it was several years before I saw the sweet companion of my school days again.

From ULYSSES

James Joyce

James Augustine Aloysius Joyce was an Irish novelist and poet. He contributed to the modernist avant-garde, and is regarded as one of the most influential and important authors of the twentieth century. This final episode from *Ulysses* features a monologue from Molly Bloom, who lies in bed thinking of her husband, her past, her hopes. . .

Yes because he never did a thing like that before as ask to get his breakfast in bed with a couple of eggs since the City Arms hotel when he used to be pretending to be laid up with a sick voice doing his highness to make himself interesting for that old faggot Mrs Riordan that he thought he had a great leg of and she never left us a farthing all for masses for herself and her soul greatest miser ever was actually afraid to lay out 4d for her methylated spirit telling me all her ailments she had too much old chat in her about politics and earthquakes and the end of the world let us have a bit of fun first God help the world if all the women were her sort down on bathingsuits and lownecks of course nobody wanted her to wear them I suppose she was pious because no man would look at her twice I hope Ill never be like her a wonder she didnt want us to cover our faces but she was a welleducated woman certainly and her gabby talk about Mr Riordan here and Mr Riordan there I suppose he was glad to get shut of her and her dog smelling my fur and always edging to get up under my petticoats especially then still I like that in him polite to old women like that and waiters and beggars too hes not proud out of nothing but not always if ever he got anything really serious the matter with him its much better for them to go into a hospital where everything is clean but I suppose Id have to dring it into him for a month yes and then wed have a hospital nurse next thing on the carpet have him staying there till they throw him out or a nun maybe like the smutty photo he has shes as much a nun as Im not yes because theyre so weak and puling when theyre sick they want a woman to get well if his nose bleeds youd think it was O tragic and that dyinglooking one off the south circular when he sprained his foot at the choir party at the sugarloaf Mountain the day I wore that dress Miss Stack bringing him flowers the worst old ones she could find at the bottom of the basket anything at all to get into a mans bedroom with her old maids voice trying to imagine he was dying on account of her to never see thy face again though he looked more like a man with his beard a bit grown in the bed father was the same besides I hate bandaging and dosing when he cut his toe with the razor paring his corns afraid hed get bloodpoisoning but if it was a thing I was sick then wed see what attention only of course the woman hides it not to give

all the trouble they do yes he came somewhere Im sure by his appetite anyway love its not or hed be off his feed thinking of her so either it was one of those night women if it was down there he was really and the hotel story he made up a pack of lies to hide it planning it Hynes kept me who did I meet ah yes I met do you remember Menton and who else who let me see that big babbyface I saw him and he not long married flirting with a young girl at Pooles Myriorama and turned my back on him when he slinked out looking quite conscious what harm but he had the impudence to make up to me one time well done to him mouth almighty and his boiled eyes of all the big stupoes I ever met and thats called a solicitor only for I hate having a long wrangle in bed or else if its not that its some little bitch or other he got in with somewhere or picked up on the sly if they only knew him as well as I do yes because the day before yesterday he was scribbling something a letter when I came into the front room to show him Dignams death in the paper as if something told me and he covered it up with the blotting-paper pretending to be thinking about business so very probably that was it to somebody who thinks she has a softy in him because all men get a bit like that at his age especially getting on to forty he is now so as to wheedle any money she can out of him no fool like an old fool and then the usual kissing my bottom was to hide it not that I care two straws now who he does it with or knew before that way though Id like to find out so long as I dont have the two of them under my nose all the time like that slut that Mary we had in Ontario terrace padding out her false bottom to excite him bad enough to get the smell of those painted women off him once or twice I had a suspicion by getting him to come near me when I found the long hair on his coat without that one when I went into the kitchen pretending he was drinking water 1 woman is not enough for them it was all his fault of course ruining servants then proposing that she could eat at our table on Christmas day if you please O no thank you not in my house stealing my potatoes and the oysters 2/6 per doz going out to see her aunt if you please common robbery so it was but I was sure he had something on with that one it takes me to find out a thing like that he said you have no proof it was her proof O yes her aunt was very fond of oysters but I told her what I thought of her suggesting me to go out to be alone with her I wouldnt lower myself to spy on them the garters I found in her room the Friday she was out that was enough for me a little bit too much her face swelled up on her with temper when I gave her her weeks notice I saw to that better do without them altogether do out the rooms myself quicker only for the damn cooking and throwing out the dirt I gave it to him anyhow either she or me leaves the house I couldnt even touch him if I thought he was with a dirty barefaced liar and sloven like that one denying it up to my face and singing about the place in the W C too because she knew she was too well off yes because he couldnt possibly do without it that long so he must do it somewhere and the last time he came on my bottom when was it the night Boylan gave my hand a great squeeze going along by the Tolka in my hand there steals another I just pressed the back of his like that with my thumb to squeeze back singing the young May moon shes beaming love because he has an idea about him and me hes not such a fool he said Im dining out and going to the Gaiety though Im not going to give him the satisfaction in any case God knows hes a change in a way not to be always and ever wearing the same old hat unless

I paid some nicelooking boy to do it since I cant do it myself a young boy would like me Id confuse him a little alone with him if we were Id let him see my garters the new ones and make him turn red looking at him seduce him I know what boys feel with that down on their cheek doing that frigging drawing out the thing by the hour question and answer would you do this that and the other with the coalman yes with a bishop yes I would because I told him about some dean or bishop was sitting beside me in the jews temples gardens when I was knitting that woollen thing a stranger to Dublin what place was it and so on about the monuments and he tired me out with statues encouraging him making him worse than he is who is in your mind now tell me who are you thinking of who is it tell me his name who tell me who the german Emperor is it yes imagine Im him think of him can you feel him trying to make a whore of me what he never will he ought to give it up now at this age of his life simply ruination for any woman and no satisfaction in it pretending to like it till he comes and then finish it off myself anyway and it makes your lips pale anyhow its done now once and for all with all the talk of the world about it people make its only the first time after that its just the ordinary do it and think no more about it why cant you kiss a man without going and marrying him first you sometimes love to wildly when you feel that way so nice all over you you cant help yourself I wish some man or other would take me sometime when hes there and kiss me in his arms theres nothing like a kiss long and hot down to your soul almost paralyses you then I hate that confession when I used to go to Father Corrigan he touched me father and what harm if he did where and I said on the canal bank like a fool but whereabouts on your person my child on the leg behind high up was it yes rather high up was it where you sit down yes O Lord couldnt he say bottom right out and have done with it what has that got to do with it and did you whatever way he put it I forget no father and I always think of the real father what did he want to know for when I already confessed it to God he had a nice fat hand the palm moist always I wouldnt mind feeling it neither would he Id say by the bullneck in his horsecollar I wonder did he know me in the box I could see his face he couldnt see mine of course hed never turn or let on still his eyes were red when his father died theyre lost for a woman of course must be terrible when a man cries let alone them Id like to be embraced by one in his vestments and the smell of incense off him like the pope besides theres no danger with a priest if youre married hes too careful about himself then give something to H H the pope for a penance I wonder was he satisfied with me one thing I didnt like his slapping me behind going away so familiarly in the hall though I laughed Im not a horse or an ass am I I suppose he was thinking of his fathers I wonder is he awake thinking of me or dreaming am I in it who gave him that flower he said he bought he smelt of some kind of drink not whisky or stout or perhaps the sweety kind of paste they stick their bills up with some liqueur Id like to sip those richlooking green and yellow expensive drinks those stagedoor johnnies drink with the opera hats I tasted once with my finger dipped out of that American that had the squirrel talking stamps with father he had all he could do to keep himself from falling asleep after the last time we took the port and potted meat it had a fine salty taste yes because I felt lovely and tired myself and fell asleep as sound as a top the moment I popped straight into bed till that thunder woke me up God be merciful to us I

thought the heavens were coming down about us to punish us when I blessed myself and said a Hail Mary like those awful thunderbolts in Gibraltar as if the world was coming to an end and then they come and tell you theres no God what could you do if it was running and rushing about nothing only make an act of contrition the candle I lit that evening in Whitefriars street chapel for the month of May see it brought its luck though hed scoff if he heard because he never goes to church mass or meeting he says your soul you have no soul inside only grey matter because he doesnt know what it is to have one yes when I lit the lamp because he must have come 3 or 4 times with that tremendous big red brute of a thing he has I thought the vein or whatever the dickens they call it was going to burst though his nose is not so big after I took off all my things with the blinds down after my hours dressing and perfuming and combing it like iron or some kind of a thick crowbar standing all the time he must have eaten oysters I think a few dozen he was in great singing voice no I never in all my life felt anyone had one the size of that to make you feel full up he must have eaten a whole sheep after whats the idea making us like that with a big hole in the middle of us like a Stallion driving it up into you because thats all they want out of you with that determined vicious look in his eye I had to halfshut my eyes still he hasnt such a tremendous amount of spunk in him when I made him pull out and do it on me considering how big it is so much the better in case any of it wasnt washed out properly the last time I let him finish it in me nice invention they made for women for him to get all the pleasure but if someone gave them a touch of it themselves theyd know what I went through with Milly nobody would believe cutting her teeth too and Mina Purefoys husband give us a swing out of your whiskers filling her up with a child or twins once a year as regular as the clock always with a smell of children off her the one they called budgers or something like a nigger with a shock of hair on it Jesusjack the child is a black the last time I was there a squad of them falling over one another and bawling you couldnt hear your ears supposed to be healthy not satisfied till they have us swollen out like elephants or I dont know what supposing I risked having another not off him though still if he was married Im sure hed have a fine strong child but I dont know Poldy has more spunk in him yes thatd be awfully jolly I suppose it was meeting Josie Powell and the funeral and thinking about me and Boylan set him off well he can think what he likes now if thatll do him any good I know they were spooning a bit when I came on the scene he was dancing and sitting out with her the night of Georgina Simpsons housewarming and then he wanted to ram it down my neck it was on account of not liking to see her a wallflower that was why we had the standup row over politics he began it not me when he said about Our Lord being a carpenter at last he made me cry of course a woman is so sensitive about everything I was fuming with myself after for giving in only for I knew he was gone on me and the first socialist he said He was he annoyed me so much I couldnt put him into a temper still he knows a lot of mixedup things especially about the body and the inside I often wanted to study up that myself what we have inside us in that family physician I could always hear his voice talking when the room was crowded and watch him after that I pretended I had on a coolness on with her over him because he used to be a bit on the jealous side whenever he asked who are you going to and I said over to Floey and he made

me the present of lord Byrons poems and the three pairs of gloves so that finished that I could quite easily get him to make it up any time I know how Id even supposing he got in with her again and was going out to see her somewhere Id know if he refused to eat the onions I know plenty of ways ask him to tuck down the collar of my blouse or touch him with my veil and gloves on going out 1 kiss then would send them all spinning however alright well see then let him go to her she of course would only be too delighted to pretend shes mad in love with him that I wouldnt so much mind Id just go to her and ask her do you love him and look her square in the eyes she couldnt fool me but he might imagine he was and make a declaration to her with his plabbery kind of a manner like he did to me though I had the devils own job to get it out of him though I liked him for that it showed he could hold in and wasnt to be got for the asking he was on the pop of asking me too the night in the kitchen I was rolling the potato cake theres something I want to say to you only for I put him off letting on I was in a temper with my hands and arms full of pasty flour in any case I let out too much the night before talking of dreams so I didnt want to let him know more than was good for him she used to be always embracing me Josie whenever he was there meaning him of course glauming me over and when I said I washed up and down as far as possible asking me and did you wash possible the women are always egging on to that putting it on thick when hes there they know by his sly eye blinking a bit putting on the indifferent when they come out with something the kind he is what spoils him I dont wonder in the least because he was very handsome at that time trying to look like lord Byron I said I liked though he was too beautiful for a man and he was a little before we got engaged afterwards though she didnt like it so much the day I was in fits of laughing with the giggles I couldnt stop about all my hairpins falling out one after another with the mass of hair I had youre always in great humour she said yes because it grigged her because she knew what it meant because I used to tell her a good bit of what went on between us not all but just enough to make her mouth water but that wasnt my fault she didnt darken the door much after we were married I wonder what shes got like now after living with that dotty husband of hers she had her face beginning to look drawn and run down the last time I saw her she must have been just after a row with him because I saw on the moment she was edging to draw down a conversation about husbands and talk about him to run him down what was it she told me O yes that sometimes he used to go to bed with his muddy boots on when the maggot takes him just imagine having to get into bed with a thing like that that might murder you any moment what a man well its not the one way everyone goes mad Poldy anyway whatever he does always wipes his feet on the mat when he comes in wet or shine and always blacks his own boots too and he always takes off his hat when he comes up in the street like that and now hes going about in his slippers to look for £10000 for a postcard Up up O sweetheart May wouldnt a thing like that simply bore you stiff to extinction actually too stupid even to take his boots off now what could you make of a man like that Id rather die 20 times over than marry another of their sex of course hed never find another woman like me to put up with him the way I do know me come sleep with me yes and he knows that too at the bottom of his heart take that Mrs Maybrick that poisoned her husband for what I wonder in love with some other

man yes it was found out on her wasnt she the downright villain to go and do a thing like that of course some men can be dreadfully aggravating drive you mad and always the worst word in the world what do they ask us to marry them for if were so bad as all that comes to yes because they cant get on without us white Arsenic she put in his tea off flypaper wasnt it I wonder why they call it that if I asked him hed say its from the Greek leave us as wise as we were before she must have been madly in love with the other fellow to run the chance of being hanged O she didnt care if that was her nature what could she do besides theyre not brutes enough to go and hang a woman surely are they

theyre all so different Boylan talking about the shape of my foot he noticed at once even before he was introduced when I was in the D B C with Poldy laughing and trying to listen I was waggling my foot we both ordered 2 teas and plain bread and butter I saw him looking with his two old maids of sisters when I stood up and asked the girl where it was what do I care with it dropping out of me and that black closed breeches he made me buy takes you half an hour to let them down wetting all myself always with some brandnew fad every other week such a long one I did I forgot my suede gloves on the seat behind that I never got after some robber of a woman and he wanted me to put it in the *Irish* times lost in the ladies lavatory D B C Dame street finder return to Mrs Marion Bloom and I saw his eyes on my feet going out through the turning door he was looking when I looked back and I went there for tea 2 days after in the hope but he wasnt now how did that excite him because I was crossing them when we were in the other room first he meant the shoes that are too tight to walk in my hand is nice like that if I only had a ring with the stone for my month a nice aquamarine Ill stick him for one and a gold bracelet I dont like my foot so much still I made him spend once with my foot the night after Goodwins botchup of a concert so cold and windy it was well we had that rum in the house to mull and the fire wasnt black out when he asked to take off my stockings lying on the hearthrug in Lombard street west and another time it was my muddy boots hed like me to walk in all the horses dung I could find but of course hes not natural like the rest of the world that I what did he say I could give 9 points in 10 to Katty Lanner and beat her what does that mean I asked him I forget what he said because the stoppress edition just passed and the man with the curly hair in the Lucan dairy thats so polite I think I saw his face before somewhere I noticed him when I was tasting the butter so I took my time Bartell dArcy too that he used to make fun of when he commenced kissing me on the choir stairs after I sang Gounods Ave Maria what are we waiting for O my heart kiss me straight on the brow and part which is my brown part he was pretty hot for all his tinny voice too my low notes he was always raving about if you can believe him I liked the way he used his mouth singing then he said wasnt it terrible to do that there in a place like that I dont see anything so terrible about it Ill tell him about that some day not now and surprise him ay and Ill take him there and show him the very place too we did it so now there you are like it or lump it he thinks nothing can happen without him knowing he hadnt an idea about my mother till we were engaged otherwise hed never have got me so cheap as he did he was 10 times worse himself anyhow begging me to give him a tiny bit cut off my drawers that was the evening coming along Kenilworth square he kissed me in the eye of my glove and I had to take it

off asking me questions is it permitted to enquire the shape of my bedroom so I let him keep it as if I forgot it to think of me when I saw him slip it into his pocket of course hes mad on the subject of drawers thats plain to be seen always skeezing at those brazenfaced things on the bicycles with their skirts blowing up to their navels even when Milly and I were out with him at the open air fete that one in the cream muslin standing right against the sun so he could see every atom she had on when he saw me from behind following in the rain I saw him before he saw me however standing at the corner of the Harolds cross road with a new raincoat on him with the muffler in the Zingari colours to show off his complexion-and the brown hat looking slyboots as usual what was he doing there where hed no business they can go and get whatever they like from anything at all with a skirt on it and were not to ask any questions but they want to know where were you where are you going I could feel him coming along skulking after me his eyes on my neck he had been keeping away from the house he felt it was getting too warm for him so I half turned and stopped then he pestered me to say yes till I took off my glove slowly watching him he said my openwork sleeves were too cold for the rain anything for an excuse to put his hand anear me drawers drawers the whole blessed time till I promised to give him the pair off my doll to carry about in his waistcoat pocket O Maria Santissima he did look a big fool dreeping in the rain splendid set of teeth he had made me hungry to look at them and beseeched of me to lift the orange petticoat I had on with sunray pleats that there was nobody he said hed kneel down in the wet if I didnt so persevering he would too and ruin his new raincoat you never know what freak theyd take alone with you theyre so savage for it if anyone was passing so I lifted them a bit and touched his trousers outside the way I used to Gardner after with my ring hand to keep him from doing worse where it was too public I was dying to find out was he circumcised he was shaking like a jelly all over they want to do everything too quick take all the pleasure out if it and father waiting all the time for his dinner he told me to say I left my purse in the butchers and had to go back for it what a Deceiver then he wrote me that letter with all those words in it how could he have the face to any woman after his company manners making it so awkward after when we met asking me have I offended you with my eyelids down of course he saw I wasnt he had a few brains not like that other fool Henry Doyle he was always breaking or tearing something in the charades I hate an unlucky man and if I knew what it meant of course I had to say no for form sake dont understand you I said and wasnt it natural so it is of course it used to be written up with a picture of a womans on that wall in Gibraltar with that word I couldnt find anywhere only for children seeing it too young then writing a letter every morning sometimes twice a day I liked the way he made love then he knew the way to take a woman when he sent me the 8 big poppies because mine was the 8th then I wrote the night he kissed my heart at Dolphins barn I couldnt describe it simply it makes you feel like nothing on earth but he never knew how to embrace well like Gardner I hope hell come on Monday as he said at the same time four I hate people who come at all hours answer the door you think its the vegetables then its somebody and you all undressed or the door of the filthy sloppy kitchen blows open the day old frostyface Goodwin called about the concert in Lombard street and I just after dinner all flushed and tossed with boil-

ing old stew dont look at me professor I had to say Im a fright yes but he was a real old gent in his way it was impossible to be more respectful nobody to say youre out you have to peep out through the blind like the messengerboy today I thought it was a putoff first him sending the port and the peaches first and I was just beginning to yawn with nerves thinking he was trying to make a fool of me when I knew his tattarrattat at the door he must have been a bit late because it was ¼ after 3 when I saw the 2 Dedalus girls coming from school I never know the time even that watch he gave me never seems to go properly Id want to get it looked after when I threw the penny to that lame sailor for England home and beauty when I was whistling there is a charming girl I love and I hadnt even put on my clean shift or powdered myself or a thing then this day week were to go to Belfast just as well he has to go to Ennis his fathers anniversary the 27th it wouldnt be pleasant if he did suppose our rooms at the hotel were beside each other and any fooling went on in the new bed I couldnt tell him to stop and not bother me with him in the next room or perhaps some protestant clergyman with a cough knocking on the wall then he wouldnt believe next day we didnt do something its all very well a husband but you cant fool a lover after me telling him we never did anything of course he didnt believe me no its better hes going where he is besides something always happens with him the time going to the Mallow Concert at Maryborough ordering boiling soup for the two of us then the bell rang out he walks down the platform with the soup splashing about taking spoonfuls of it hadnt he the nerve and the waiter after him making a holy show of us screeching and confusion for the engine to start but he wouldnt pay till he finished it the two gentlemen in the 3rd class carriage said he was quite right so he was too hes so pigheaded sometimes when he gets a thing into his head a good job he was able to open the carriage door with his knife or theyd have taken us on to Cork I suppose that was done out of revenge on him O I love jaunting in a train or a car with lovely soft cushions I wonder will he take a 1st class for me he might want to do it in the train by tipping the guard well O I suppose therell be the usual idiots of men gaping at us with their eyes as stupid as ever they can possibly be that was an exceptional man that common workman that left us alone in the carriage that day going to Howth Id like to find out something about him 1 or 2 tunnels perhaps then you have to look out of the window all the nicer then coming back suppose I never came back what would they say eloped with him that gets you on on the stage the last concert I sang at where its over a year ago when was it St Teresas hall Clarendon St little chits of missies they have now singing Kathleen Kearney and her like on account of father being in the army and my singing the absentminded beggar and wearing a brooch for Lord Roberts when I had the map of it all and Poldy not Irish enough was it him managed it this time I wouldnt put it past him like he got me on to sing in the Stabat Mater by going around saying he was putting Lead Kindly Light to music I put him up to that till the jesuits found out he was a freemason thumping the piano lead Thou me on copied from some old opera yes and he was going about with some of them Sinner Fein lately or whatever they call themselves talking his usual trash and nonsense he says that little man he showed me without the neck is very intelligent the coming man Griffith is he well he doesnt look it thats all I can say still it must have been him he knew there was a boycott

I hate the mention of their politics after the war that Pretoria and Ladysmith and Bloemfontein where Gardner Lieut Stanley G 8th Bn 2nd East Lancs Rgt of enteric fever he was a lovely fellow in khaki and just the right height over me Im sure he was brave too he said I was lovely the evening we kissed goodbye at the canal lock my Irish beauty he was pale with excitement about going away or wed be seen from the road he couldnt stand properly and I so hot as I never felt they could have made their peace in the beginning or old oom Paul and the rest of the old Krugers go and fight it out between them instead of dragging on for years killing any finelooking men there were with their fever if he was even decently shot it wouldnt have been so bad I love to see a regiment pass in review the first time I saw the Spanish cavalry at La Roque it was lovely after looking across the bay from Algeciras all the lights of the rock like fireflies or those sham battles on the 15 acres the Black Watch with their kilts in time at the march past the 10th hussars the prince of Wales own or the lancers O the lancers theyre grand or the Dublins that won Tugela his father made his money over selling the horses for the cavalry well he could buy me a nice present up in Belfast after what I gave him theyve lovely linen up there or one of those nice kimono things I must buy a mothball like I had before to keep in the drawer with them it would be exciting going around with him shopping buying those things in a new city better leave this ring behind want to keep turning and turning to get it over the knuckle there or they might bell it round the town in their papers or tell the police on me but theyd think were married O let them all go and smother themselves for the fat lot I care he has plenty of money and hes not a marrying man so somebody better get it out of him if I could find out whether he likes me I looked a bit washy of course when I looked close in the handglass powdering a mirror never gives you the expression besides scrooching down on me like that all the time with his big hipbones hes heavy too with his hairy chest for this heat always having to lie down for them better for him put it into me from behind the way Mrs Mastiansky told me her husband made her like the dogs do it and stick out her tongue as far as ever she could and he so quiet and mild with his tingating cither can you ever be up to men the way it takes them lovely stuff in that blue suit he had on and stylish tie and socks with the skyblue silk things on them hes certainly welloff I know by the cut his clothes have and his heavy watch but he was like a perfect devil for a few minutes after he came back with the stoppress tearing up the tickets and swearing blazes because he lost 20 quid he said he lost over that outsider that won and half he put on for me on account of Lenehans tip cursing him to the lowest pits that sponger he was making free with me after the Glencree dinner coming back that long joult over the featherbed mountain after the lord Mayor looking at me with his dirty eyes Val Dillon that big heathen I first noticed him at dessert when I was cracking the nuts with my teeth I wished I could have picked every morsel of that chicken out of my fingers it was so tasty and browned and as tender as anything only for I didnt want to eat everything on my plate those forks and fishslicers were hallmarked silver too I wish I had some I could easily have slipped a couple into my muff when I was playing with them then always hanging out of them for money in a restaurant for the bit you put down your throat we have to be thankful for our mangy cup of tea itself as a great compliment to be noticed the way the world is divided in any case if its

going to go on I want at least two other good chemises for one thing and but I dont know what kind of drawers he likes none at all I think didnt he say yes and half the girls in Gibraltar never wore them either naked as God made them that Andalusian singing her Manola she didnt make much secret of what she hadnt yes and the second pair of silkette stockings is laddered after one days wear I could have brought them back to Lewers this morning and kick up a row and made that one change them only not to upset myself and run the risk of walking into him and ruining the whole thing and one of those kidfitting corsets Id want advertised cheap in the Gentlewoman with elastic gores on the hips he saved the one I have but thats no good what did they say they give a delightful figure line 11/6 obviating that unsightly broad appearance across the lower back to reduce flesh my belly is a bit too big Ill have to knock off the stout at dinner or am I getting too fond of it the last they sent from ORourkes was as flat as a pancake he makes his money easy Larry they call him the old mangy parcel he sent at Xmas a cottage cake and a bottle of hogwash he tried to palm off as claret that he couldnt get anyone to drink God spare his spit for fear hed die of the drouth or I must do a few breathing exercises I wonder is that antifat any good might overdo it thin ones are not so much the fashion now garters that much I have the violet pair I wore today thats all he bought me out of the cheque he got on the first O no there was the face lotion I finished the last of yesterday that made my skin like new I told him over and over again get that made up in the same place and dont forget it God only knows whether he did after all I said to him Ill know by the bottle anyway if not I suppose Ill only have to wash in my piss like beeftea or chickensoup with some of that opoponax and violet I thought it was beginning to look coarse or old a bit the skin underneath is much finer where it peeled off there on my finger after the burn its a pity it isnt all like that and the four paltry handkerchiefs about 6/- in all sure you cant get on in this world without style all going in food and rent when I get it Ill lash it around I tell you in fine style I always want to throw a handful of tea into the pot measuring and mincing if I buy a pair of old brogues itself do you like those new shoes yes how much were they Ive no clothes at all the brown costume and the skirt and jacket and the one at the cleaners 3 whats that for any woman cutting up this old hat and patching up the other the men wont look at you and women try to walk on you because they know youve no man then with all the things getting dearer every day for the 4 years more I have of life up to 35 no Im what am I at all Ill be 33 in September will I what O well look at that Mrs Galbraith shes much older than me I saw her when I was out last week her beautys on the wane she was a lovely woman magnificent head of hair on her down to her waist tossing it back like that like Kitty OShea in Grantham street 1st thing I did every morning to look across see her combing it as if she loved it and was full of it pity I only got to know her the day before we left and that Mrs Langtry the Jersey Lily the prince of Wales was in love with I suppose hes like the first man going the roads only for the name of a king theyre all made the one way only a black mans Id like to try a beauty up to what was she 45 there was some funny story about the jealous old husband what was it all and an oyster knife he went no he made her wear a kind of a tin thing around her and the prince of Wales yes he had the oyster knife cant be true a thing like that like some of those books he brings me the works of

Master Francois Somebody supposed to be a priest about a child born out of her ear because her bumgut fell out a nice word for any priest to write and her a—e as if any fool wouldnt know what that meant I hate that pretending of all things with the old blackguards face on him anybody can see its not true and that Ruby and Fair Tyrants he brought me that twice I remember when I came to page 50 the part about where she hangs him up out of a hook with a cord flagellate sure theres nothing for a woman in that all invention made up about he drinking the champagne out of her slipper after the ball was over like the infant Jesus in the crib at Inchicore in the Blessed Virgins arms sure no woman could have a child that big taken out of her and I thought first it came out of her side because how could she go to the chamber when she wanted to and she a rich lady of course she felt honoured H R H he was in Gibraltar the year I was born I bet he found lilies there too where he planted the tree he planted more than that in his time he might have planted me too if hed come a bit sooner then I wouldnt be here as I am he ought to chuck that Freeman with the paltry few shillings he knocks out of it and go into an office or something where hed get regular pay or a bank where they could put him up on a throne to count the money all the day of course he prefers plottering about the house so you cant stir with him any side whats your programme today I wish hed even smoke a pipe like father to get the smell of a man or pretending to be mooching about for advertisements when he could have been in Mr Cuffes still only for what he did then sending me to try and patch it up I could have got him promoted there to be the manager he gave me a great mirada once or twice first he was as stiff as the mischief really and truly Mrs Bloom only I felt rotten simply with the old rubbishy dress that I lost the leads out of the tails with no cut in it but theyre coming into fashion again I bought it simply to please him I knew it was no good by the finish pity I changed my mind of going to Todd and Burns as I said and not Lees it was just like the shop itself rummage sale a lot of trash I hate those rich shops get on your nerves nothing kills me altogether only he thinks he knows a great lot about a womans dress and cooking mathering everything he can scour off the shelves into it if I went by his advices every blessed hat I put on does that suit me yes take that thats alright the one like a wedding cake standing up miles off my head he said suited me or the dishcover one coming down on my backside on pins and needles about the shop girl in that place in Grafton street I had the misfortune to bring him into and she as insolent as ever she could be with her smirk saying Im afraid were giving you too much trouble whats she there for but I stared it out of her yes he was awfully stiff and no wonder but he changed the second time he looked Poldy pigheaded as usual like the soup but I could see him looking very hard at my chest when he stood up to open the door for me it was nice of him to show me out in any case Im extremely sorry Mrs Bloom believe me without making it too marked the first time after him being insulted and me being supposed to be his wife I just half smiled I know my chest was out that way at the door when he said Im extremely sorry and Im sure you were

yes I think he made them a bit firmer sucking them like that so long be made me thirsty titties he calls them I had to laugh yes this one anyhow stiff the nipple gets for the least thing Ill get him to keep that up and Ill take those eggs beaten up with marsala fatten them out for him what are all those veins and things cu-

rious the way its made 2 the same in case of twins theyre supposed to represent beauty placed up there like those statues in the museum one of them pretending to hide it with her hand are they so beautiful of course compared with what a man looks like with his two bags full and his other thing hanging down out of him or sticking up at you like a hatrack no wonder they hide it with a cabbageleaf that disgusting Cameron highlander behind the meat market or that other wretch with the red head behind the tree where the statue of the fish used to be when I was passing pretending he was pissing standing out for me to see it with his babyclothes up to one side the Queens own they were a nice lot its well the Surreys relieved them theyre always trying to show it to you every time nearly I passed outside the mens greenhouse near the Harcourt street station just to try some fellow or other trying to catch my eye or if it was 1 of the 7 wonders of the world O and the stink of those rotten places the night coming home with Poldy after the Comerfords party oranges and lemonade to make you feel nice and watery I went into 1 of them it was so biting cold I couldnt keep it when was that 93 the canal was frozen yes it was a few months after a pity a couple of the Camerons werent there to see me squatting in the mens place meadero I tried to draw a picture of it before I tore it up like a sausage or something I wonder theyre not afraid going about of getting a kick or a bang or something there the woman is beauty of course thats admitted when he said I could pose for a picture naked to some rich fellow in Holles street when he lost the job in Helys and I was selling the clothes and strumming in the coffee palace would I be like that bath of the nymph with my hair down yes only shes younger or Im a little like that dirty bitch in that Spanish photo he has the nymphs used they go about like that I asked him about her and that word met something with hoses in it and he came out with some jawbreakers about the incarnation he never can explain a thing simply the way a body can understand then he goes and burns the bottom out of the pan all for his Kidney this one not so much theres the mark of his teeth still where he tried to bite the nipple I had to scream out arent they fearful trying to hurt you I had a great breast of milk with Milly enough for two what was the reason of that he said I could have got a pound a week as a wet nurse all swelled out the morning that delicate looking student that stopped in no 28 with the Citrons Penrose nearly caught me washing through the window only for I snapped up the towel to my face that was his studenting hurt me they used to weaning her till he got doctor Brady to give me the Belladonna prescription I had to get him to suck them they were so hard he said it was sweeter and thicker than cows then he wanted to milk me into the tea well hes beyond everything I declare somebody ought to put him in the budget if I only could remember the 1 half of the things and write a book out of it the works of Master Poldy yes and its so much smoother the skin much an hour he was at them Im sure by the clock like some kind of a big infant I had at me they want everything in their mouth all the pleasure those men get out of a woman I can feel his mouth O Lord I must stretch myself I wished he was here or somebody to let myself go with and come again like that I feel all fire inside me or if I could dream it when he made me spend the 2nd time tickling me behind with his finger I was coming for about 5 minutes with my legs round him I had to hug him after O Lord I wanted to shout out all sorts of things fuck or shit or anything at all only not to look ugly or those

lines from the strain who knows the way hed take it you want to feel your way with a man theyre not all like him thank God some of them want you to be so nice about it I noticed the contrast he does it and doesnt talk I gave my eyes that look with my hair a bit loose from the tumbling and my tongue between my lips up to him the savage brute Thursday Friday one Saturday two Sunday three O Lord I cant wait till Monday

frseeeeeeeefronnnng train somewhere whistling the strength those engines have in them like big giants and the water rolling all over and out of them all sides like the end of Loves old sweeeetsonnnng the poor men that have to be out all the night from their wives and families in those roasting engines stifling it was today Im glad I burned the half of those old Freemans and Photo Bits leaving things like that lying about hes getting very careless and threw the rest of them up in the W C Ill get him to cut them tomorrow for me instead of having them there for the next year to get a few pence for them have him asking wheres last Januarys paper and all those old overcoats I bundled out of the hall making the place hotter than it is the rain was lovely and refreshing just after my beauty sleep I thought it was going to get like Gibraltar my goodness the heat there before the levanter came on black as night and the glare of the rock standing up in it like a big giant compared with their 3 Rock mountain they think is so great with the red sentries here and there the poplars and they all whitehot and the smell of the rainwater in those tanks watching the sun all the time weltering down on you faded all that lovely frock fathers friend Mrs Stanhope sent me from the B Marche paris what a shame my dearest Doggerina she wrote on it she was very nice whats this her other name was just a p c to tell you I sent the little present have just had a jolly warm bath and feel a *very* clean dog now enjoyed it wogger she called him wogger wd give anything to be back in Gib and hear you sing Waiting and in old Madrid Concone is the name of those exercises he bought me one of those new some word I couldn't make out shawls amusing things but tear for the least thing still there lovely I think dont you will always think of the lovely teas we had together scrumptious currant scones and raspberry wafers I adore well now dearest Doggerina be sure and write soon kind she left out regards to your father also Captain Grove with love yrs affly Hester x x x x x she didnt look a bit married just like a girl he was years older than her wogger he was awfully fond of me when he held down the wire with his foot for me to step over at the bullfight at La Linea when that matador Gomez was given the bulls ear these clothes we have to wear whoever invented them expecting you to walk up Killiney hill then for example at that picnic all staysed up you cant do a blessed thing in them in a crowd run or jump out of the way thats why I was afraid when that other ferocious old Bull began to charge the banderillos with the sashes and the 2 things in their hats and the brutes of men shouting bravo toro sure the women were as bad in their nice white mantillas ripping all the whole insides out of those poor horses I never heard of such a thing in all my life yes he used to break his heart at me taking off the dog barking in bell lane poor brute and it sick what became of them ever I suppose theyre dead long ago the 2 of them its like all through a mist makes you feel so old I made the scones of course I had everything all to myself then a girl Hester we used to compare our hair mine was thicker than hers she showed me how to settle it at the back when I put

it up and whats this else how to make a knot on a thread with the one hand we were like cousins what age was I then the night of the storm I slept in her bed she had her arms round me then we were fighting in the morning with the pillow what fun he was watching me whenever he got an opportunity at the band on the Alameda esplanade when I was with father and Captain Grove I looked up at the church first and then at the windows then down and our eyes met I felt something go through me like all needles my eyes were dancing I remember after when I looked at myself in the glass hardly recognised myself the change he was attractive to a girl in spite of his being a little bald intelligent looking disappointed and gay at the same time he was like Thomas in the shadow of Ashlydyat I had a splendid skin from the sun and the excitement like a rose I didn't get a wink of sleep it wouldnt have been nice on account of her but I could have stopped it in time she gave me the Moonstone to read that was the first I read of Wilkie Collins East Lynne I read and the shadow of Ashlydyat Mrs Henry Wood Henry Dunbar by that other woman I lent him afterwards with Mulveys photo in it so as he see I wasnt without and Lord Lytton Eugene Aram Molly bawn she gave me by Mrs Hungerford on account of the name I dont like books with a Molly in them like that one he brought me about the one from Flanders a whore always shoplifting anything she could cloth and stuff and yards of it O this blanket is too heavy on me thats better I havent even one decent nightdress this thing gets all rolled up under me besides him and his fooling thats better I used to be weltering then in the heat my shift drenched with the sweat stuck in the cheeks of my bottom on the chair when I stood up they were so fattish and firm when I got up on the sofa cushions to see with my clothes up and the bugs tons of them at night and the mosquito nets I couldnt read a line Lord how long ago it seems centuries of course they never come back and she didnt put her address right on it either she may have noticed her wogger people were always going away and we never I remember that day with the waves and the boats with their high heads rocking and the swell of the ship those Officers uniforms on shore leave made me seasick he didnt say anything he was very serious I had the high buttoned boots on and my skirt was blowing she kissed me six or seven times didnt I cry yes I believe I did or near it my lips were taittering when I said goodbye she had a Gorgeous wrap of some special kind of blue colour on her for the voyage made very peculiarly to one side like and it was extremely pretty it got as dull as the devil after they went I was almost planning to run away mad out of it somewhere were never easy where we are father or aunt or marriage waiting always waiting to guiiiide him toooo me waiting nor speeeed his flying feet their damn guns bursting and booming all over the shop especially the Queens birthday and throwing everything down in all directions if you didnt open the windows when general Ulysses Grant whoever he was or did supposed to be some great fellow landed off the ship and old Sprague the consul that was there from before the flood dressed up poor man and he in mourning for the son then the same old bugles for reveille in the morning and drums rolling and the unfortunate poor devils of soldiers walking about with messtins smelling the place more than the old longbearded jews in their jellibees and levites assembly and sound clear and gunfire for the men to cross the lines and the warden marching with his keys to lock the gates and the bagpipes and only Captain Groves and father talking

about Rorkes drift and Plevna and sir Garnet Wolseley and Gordon at Khartoum lighting their pipes for them everytime they went out drunken old devil with his grog on the windowsill catch him leaving any of it picking his nose trying to think of some other dirty story to tell up in a corner but he never forgot himself when I was there sending me out of the room on some blind excuse paying his compliments the Bushmills whisky talking of course but hed do the same to the next woman that came along I supposed he died of galloping drink ages ago the days like years not a letter from a living soul except the odd few I posted to myself with bits of paper in them so bored sometimes I could fight with my nails listening to that old Arab with the one eye and his heass of an instrument singing his heah heah aheah all my compriments on your hotchapotch of your heass as bad as now with the hands hanging off me looking out of the window if there was a nice fellow even in the opposite house that medical in Holles street the nurse was after when I put on my gloves and hat at the window to show I was going out not a notion what I meant arent they thick never understand what you say even youd want to print it up on a big poster for them not even if you shake hands twice with the left he didnt recognise me either when I half frowned at him outside Westland row chapel where does their great intelligence come in Id like to know grey matter they have it all in their tail if you ask me those country gougers up in the City Arms intelligence they had a damn sight less than the bulls and cows they were selling the meat and the coalmans bell that noisy bugger trying to swindle me with the wrong bill he took out of his hat what a pair of paws and pots and pans and kettles to mend any broken bottles for a poor man today and no visitors or post ever except his cheques or some advertisement like that wonderworker they sent him addressed dear Madam only his letter and the card from Milly this morning see she wrote a letter to him who did I get the last letter from O Mrs Dwenn now whatever possessed her to write from Canada after so many years to know the recipe I had for pisto madrileno Floey Dillon since she wrote to say she was married to a very rich architect if Im to believe all I hear with a villa and eight rooms her father was an awfully nice man he was near seventy always goodhumoured well now Miss Tweedy or Miss Gillespie theres the piannyer that was a solid silver coffee service he had too on the mahogany sideboard then dying so far away I hate people that have always their poor story to tell everybody has their own troubles that poor Nancy Blake died a month ago of acute neumonia well I didnt know her so well as all that she was Floeys friend more than mine poor Nancy its a bother having to answer he always tells me the wrong things and no stops to say like making a speech your sad bereavement symphathy I always make that mistake and newphew with 2 double yous in I hope hell write me a longer letter the next time if its a thing he really likes me O thanks be to the great God I got somebody to give me what I badly wanted to put some heart up into me youve no chances at all in this place like you used long ago I wish somebody would write me a loveletter his wasnt much and I told him he could write what he liked yours ever Hugh Boylan in Old Madrid stuff silly women believe love is sighing I am dying still if he wrote it I suppose thered be some truth in it true or no it fills up your whole day and life always something to think about every moment and see it all around you like a new world I could write the answer in bed to let him imagine me short just a few

words not those long crossed letters Atty Dillon used to write to the fellow that was something in the four courts that jilted her after out of the ladies letterwriter when I told her to say a few simple words he could twist how he liked not acting with precipit precip itancy with equal candour the greatest earthly happiness answer to a gentlemans proposal affirmatively my goodness theres nothing else its all very fine for them but as for being a woman as soon as youre old they might as well throw you out in the bottom of the ashpit.

Mulveys was the first when I was in bed that morning and Mrs Rubio brought it in with the coffee she stood there standing when I asked her to hand me and I pointing at them I couldnt think of the word a hairpin to open it with ah horquilla disobliging old thing and it staring her in the face with her switch of false hair on her and vain about her appearance ugly as she was near 80 or a 100 her face a mass of wrinkles with all her religion domineering because she never could get over the Atlantic fleet coming in half the ships of the world and the Union Jack flying with all her carabineros because 4 drunken English sailors took all the rock from them and because I didnt run into mass often enough in Santa Maria to please her with her shawl up on her except when there was a marriage on with all her miracles of the saints and her black blessed virgin with the silver dress and the sun dancing 3 times on Easter Sunday morning and when the priest was going by with the bell bringing the vatican to the dying blessing herself for his Majestad an admirer he signed it I near jumped out of my skin I wanted to pick him up when I saw him following me along the Calle Real in the shop window then he tipped me just in passing I never thought hed write making an appointment I had it inside my petticoat bodice all day reading it up in every hole and corner while father was up at the drill instructing to find out by the handwriting or the language of stamps singing I remember shall I wear a white rose and I wanted to put on the old stupid clock to near the time he was the first man kissed me under the Moorish wall my sweetheart when a boy it never entered my head what kissing meant till he put his tongue in my mouth his mouth was sweetlike young I put my knee up to him a few times to learn the way what did I tell him I was engaged for fun to the son of a Spanish nobleman named Don Miguel de la Flora and he believed that I was to be married to him in 3 years time theres many a true word spoken in jest there is a flower that bloometh a few things I told him true about myself just for him to be imagining the Spanish girls he didnt like I suppose one of them wouldnt have him I got him excited he crushed all the flowers on my bosom he brought me he couldnt count the pesetas and the perragordas till I taught him Cappoquin he came from he said on the black water but it was too short then the day before he left May yes it was May when the infant king of Spain was born Im always like that in the spring Id like a new fellow every year up on the tiptop under the rockgun near OHaras tower I told him it was struck by lightning and all about the old Barbary apes they sent to Clapham without a tail careering all over the show on each others back Mrs Rubio said she was a regular old rock scorpion robbing the chickens out of Inces farm and throw stones at you if you went anear he was looking at me I had that white blouse on open at the front to encourage him as much as I could without too openly they were just beginning to be plump I said I was tired we lay over the firtree cove a wild place I suppose it must be the highest rock in existence the

galleries and casemates and those frightful rocks and Saint Michaels cave with the icicles or whatever they call them hanging down and ladders all the mud plotching my boots Im sure thats the way down the monkeys go under the sea to Africa when they die the ships out far like chips that was the Malta boat passing yes the sea and the sky you could do what you liked lie there for ever he caressed them outside they love doing that its the roundness there I was leaning over him with my white ricestraw hat to take the newness out of it the left side of my face the best my blouse open for his last day transparent kind of shirt he had I could see his chest pink he wanted to touch mine with his for a moment but I wouldn't let him he was awfully put out first for fear you never know consumption or leave me with a child embarazada that old servant Ines told me that one drop even if it got into you at all after I tried with the Banana but I was afraid it might break and get lost up in me somewhere because they once took something down out of a woman that was up there for years covered with limesalts theyre all mad to get in there where they come out of youd think they could never go far enough up and then theyre done with you in a way till the next time yes because theres a wonderful feeling there so tender all the time how did we finish it off yes O yes I pulled him off into my handkerchief pretending not to be excited but I opened my legs I wouldnt let him touch me inside my petticoat because I had a skirt opening up the side I tormented the life out of him first tickling him I loved rousing that dog in the hotel rrrsssst awokwokawok his eyes shut and a bird flying below us he was shy all the same I liked him like that moaning I made him blush a little when I got over him that way when I unbuttoned him and took his out and drew back the skin it had a kind of eye in it theyre all Buttons men down the middle on the wrong side of them Molly darling he called me what was his name Jack Joe Harry Mulvey was it yes I think a lieutenant he was rather fair he had a laughing kind of a voice so I went around to the whatyoucallit everything was whatyoucallit moustache had he he said hed come back Lord its just like yesterday to me and if I was married hed do it to me and I promised him yes faithfully Id let him block me now flying perhaps hes dead or killed or a Captain or admiral its nearly 20 years if I said firtree cove he would if he came up behind me and put his hands over my eyes to guess who I might recognise him hes young still about 40 perhaps hes married some girl on the black water and is quite changed they all do they havent half the character a woman has she little knows what I did with her beloved husband before he ever dreamt of her in broad daylight too in the sight of the whole world you might say they could have put an article about it in the Chronicle I was a bit wild after when I blew out the old bag the biscuits were in from Benady Bros and exploded it Lord what a bang all the woodcocks and pigeons screaming coming back the same way that we went over middle hill round by the old guardhouse and the jews burialplace pretending to read out the Hebrew on them I wanted to fire his pistol he said he hadnt one he didnt know what to make of me with his peaked cap on that he always wore crooked as often as I settled it straight H M S Calypso swinging my hat that old Bishop that spoke off the altar his long preach about womans higher functions about girls now riding the bicycle and wearing peak caps and the new woman bloomers God send him sense and me more money I suppose theyre called after him I never thought that would be my name Bloom when I used to write it in

print to see how it looked on a visiting card or practising for the butcher and oblige M Bloom youre looking blooming Josie used to say after I married him well its better than Breen or Briggs does brig or those awful names with bottom in them Mrs Ramsbottom or some other kind of a bottom Mulvey I wouldnt go mad about either or suppose I divorced him Mrs Boylan my mother whoever she was might have given me a nicer name the Lord knows after the lovely one she had Lunita Laredo the fun we had running along Willis road to Europa point twisting in and out all round the other side of Jersey they were shaking and dancing about in my blouse like Millys little ones now when she runs up the stairs I loved looking down at them I was jumping up at the pepper trees and the white poplars pulling the leaves off and throwing them at him he went to India he was to write the voyages those men have to make to the ends of the world and back its the least they might get a squeeze or two at a woman while they can going out to be drowned or blown up somewhere I went up Windmill hill to the flats that Sunday morning with captain Rubios that was dead spyglass like the sentry had he said hed have one or two from on board I wore that frock from the B Marche paris and the coral necklace the straits shining I could see over to Morocco almost the bay of Tangier white and the At!as mountain with snow on it and the straits like a river so clear Harry Molly darling I was thinking of him on the sea all the time after at mass when my petticoat began to slip down at the elevation weeks and weeks I kept the handkerchief under my pillow for the smell of him there was no decent perfume to be got in that Gibraltar only that cheap peau dEspagne that faded and left a stink on you more than anything else I wanted to give him a memento he gave me that clumsy Claddagh ring for luck that I gave Gardner going to South Africa where those Boers killed him with their war and fever but they were well beaten all the same as if it brought its bad luck with it like an opal or pearl must have been pure 18 carat gold because it was very heavy but what could you get in a place like that the sandfrog shower from Africa and that derelict ship that came up to the harbour Marie the Marie whatyoucallit no he hadnt a moustache that was Gardner yes I can see his face clean shaven Frseeeeeeeeeeeeeeeeeeeefrong that train again weeping tone once in the dear deaead days beyondre call close my eyes breath my lips forward kiss sad look eyes open piano ere oer the world the mists began I hate that istsbeg comes loves sweet sooooooooooong Ill let that out full when I get in front of the footlights again Kathleen Kearney and her lot of squealers Miss This Miss That Miss Theother lot of sparrowfarts skitting around talking about politics they know as much about as my backside anything in the world to make themselves someway interesting Irish homemade beauties soldiers daughter I am ay and whose are you bootmakers and publicans I beg your pardon coach I thought you were a wheelbarrow theyd die down dead off their feet if ever they got a chance of walking down the Alameda on an officers arm like me on the bandnight my eyes flash my bust that they havent passion God help their poor head I knew more about men and life when I was 15 than theyll all know at 50 they dont know how to sing a song like that Gardner said no man could look at my mouth and teeth smiling like that end not think of it I was afraid he mightnt like my accent first he so English all father left me in spite of his stamps Ive my mothers eyes and figure anyhow he always said theyre so snotty about themselves some of those

cads he wasnt a bit like that he was dead gone on my lips let them get a husband first thats fit to be looked at and a daughter like mine or see if they can excite a swell with money that can pick and choose whoever he wants like Boylan to do it 4 or 5 times locked in each others arms or the voice either I could have been a prima donna only I married him comes looooves old deep down chin back not too much make it double My Ladys Bower is too long for an encore about the moated grange at twilight and vaulted rooms yes Ill sing Winds that blow from the south that he gave after the choirstairs performance Ill change that lace on my black dress to show off my bubs and Ill yes by God Ill get that big fan mended make them burst with envy my hole is itching me always when I think of him I feel I want to I feel some wind in me better go easy not wake him have him at it again slobbering after washing every bit of myself back belly and sides if we had even a bath itself or my own room anyway I wish hed sleep in some bed by himself with his cold feet on me give us room even to let a fart God or do the least thing better yes hold them like that a bit on my side piano quietly sweeeee theres that train far away pianissimo eeeee one more tsong

that was a relief wherever you be let your wind go free who knows if that pork chop I took with my cup of tea after was quite good with the heat I couldnt smell anything off it Im sure that queerlooking man in the porkbutchers is a great rogue I hope that lamp is not smoking fill my nose up with smuts better than having him leaving the gas on all night I couldnt rest easy in my bed in Gibraltar even getting up to see why am I so damned nervous about that though I like it in the winter its more company O Lord it was rotten cold too that winter when I was only about ten was I yes I had the big doll with all the funny clothes dressing her up and undressing that icy wind skeeting across from those mountains the something Nevada sierra nevada standing at the fire with the little bit of a short shift I had up to heat myself I loved dancing about in it then make a race back into bed Im sure that fellow opposite used to be there the whole time watching with the lights out in the summer and I in my skin hopping around I used to love myself then stripped at the washstand dabbing and creaming only when it came to the chamber performance I put out the light too so then there were 2 of us goodbye to my sleep for this night anyhow I hope hes not going to get in with those medicals leading him astray to imagine hes young again coming in at 4 in the morning it must be if not more still he had the manners not to wake me what do they find to gabber about all night squandering money and getting drunker and drunker couldnt they drink water then he starts giving us his orders for eggs and tea Findon haddy and hot buttered toast I suppose well have him sitting up like the king of the country pumping the wrong end of the spoon up and down in his egg wherever he learned that from and I love to hear him falling up the stairs of a morning with the cups rattling on the tray and then play with the cat she rubs up against you for her own sake I wonder has she fleas shes as bad as a woman always licking and lecking but I hate their claws I wonder do they see anything that we cant staring like that when she sits at the top of the stairs so long and listening as I wait always what a robber too that lovely fresh place I bought I think Ill get a bit of fish tomorrow or today is it Friday yes I will with some blancmange with black currant jam like long ago not those 2 lb pots of mixed plum and apple from the London and Newcastle Williams and Woods

goes twice as far only for the bones I hate those eels cod yes Ill get a nice piece of cod Im always getting enough for 3 forgetting anyway Im sick of that everlasting butchers meat from Buckleys loin chops and leg beef and rib steak and scrag of mutton and calfs pluck the very name is enough or a picnic suppose we all gave 5/- each and or let him pay and invite some other woman for him who Mrs Fleming and drive out to the furry glen or the strawberry beds wed have him examining all the horses toenails first like he does with the letters no not with Boylan there yes with some cold veal and ham mixed sandwiches there are little houses down at the bottom of the banks there on purpose but its as hot as blazes he says not a bank holiday anyhow I hate those ruck of Mary Ann coalboxes out for the day Whit Monday is a cursed day too no wonder that bee bit him better the seaside but Id never again in this life get into a boat with him after him at Bray telling the boatmen he knew how to row if anyone asked could he ride the steeplechase for the gold cup hed say yes then it came on to get rough the old thing crookeding about and the weight all down my side telling me to pull the right reins now pull the left and the tide all swamping in floods in through through the bottom and his oar slipping out of the stirrupits a mercy we werent all drowned he can swim of course me no theres no danger whatsoever keep yourself calm in his flannel trousers Id like to have tattered them down off him before all the people and give him what that one calls flagellate till he was black and blue do him all the good in the world only for that longnosed chap I dont know who he is with that other beauty Burke out of the City Arms hotel was there spying around as usual on the slip always where he wasnt wanted if there was a row on you vomit a better face there was no love lost between us thats I consolation I wonder what kind is that book he brought me Sweets of Sin by a gentleman of fashion some other Mr de Kock I suppose the people gave him that nickname going about with his tube from one woman to another I couldnt even change my new white shoes all ruined with the saltwater and the hat I had with that feather all blowy and tossed on me how annoying and provoking because the smell of the sea excited me of course the sardines and the bream in Catalan bay round the back of the rock they were fine all silver in the fishermens baskets old Luigi near a hundred they said came from Genoa and the tall old chap with the earrings I dont like a man you have to climb up to go get at I suppose theyre all dead and rotten long ago besides I dont like being alone in this big barracks of a place at night I suppose Ill have to put up with it I never brought a bit of salt in even when we moved in the confusion musical academy he was going to make on the first floor drawingroom with a brassplate or Blooms private hotel he suggested go and ruin himself altogether the way his father did down in Ennis like all the things he told father he was going to do and me but I saw through him telling me all the lovely places we could go for the honeymoon Venice by moonlight with the gondolas and the lake of Como he had a picture cut out of some paper of and mandolines and lanterns O how nice I said whatever I liked he was going to do immediately if not sooner will you be my man will you carry my can he ought to get a leather medal with a putty rim for all the plans he invents then leaving us here all day you never know what old beggar at the door for a crust with his long story might be a tramp and put his foot in the way to prevent me shutting it like that picture of that hardened criminal he was called in Lloyds

Weekly News 20 years in jail then he comes out and murders an old woman for her money imagine his poor wife or mother or whoever she is such a face youd run miles away from I couldnt rest easy till I bolted all the doors and windows to make sure but its worse again being locked up like in a prison or a madhouse they ought to be all shot or the cat of nine tails a big brute like that that would attack a poor old woman to murder her in her bed Id cut them off him so I would not that hed be much use still better than nothing the night I was sure I heard burglars in the kitchen and he went down in his shirt with a candle and a poker as if he was looking for a mouse as white as a sheet frightened out of his wits making as much noise as he possibly could for the burglars benefit there isnt much to steal indeed the Lord knows still its the feeling especially now with Milly away such an idea for him to send the girl down there to learn to take photographs on account of his grandfather instead of sending her to Skerrys academy where shed have to learn not like me getting all 1s at school only hed do a thing like that all the same on account of me and Boylan thats why he did it Im certain the way he plots and plans everything out I couldnt turn round with her in the place lately unless I bolted the door first gave me the fidgets coming in without knocking first when I put the chair against the door just as I was washing myself there below with the glove get on your nerves then doing the loglady all day put her in a glasscase with two at a time to look at her if he knew she broke off the hand off that little gimcrack statue with her roughness and carelessness before she left that I got that little Italian boy to mend so that you cant see the join for 2 shillings wouldnt even teem the potatoes for you of course shes right not to ruin her hands I noticed he was always talking to her lately at the table explaining things in the paper and she pretending to understand sly of course that comes from his side of the house he cant say I pretend things can he Im too honest as a matter of fact and helping her into her coat but if there was anything wrong with her its me shed tell not him I suppose he thinks Im finished out and laid on the shelf well Im not no nor anything like it well see well see now shes well on for flirting too with Tom Devans two sons imitating me whistling with those romps of Murray girls calling for her can Milly come out please shes in great demand to pick what they can out of her round in Nelson street riding Harry Devans bicycle at night its as well he sent her where she is she was just getting out of bounds wanting to go on the skatingrink and smoking their cigarettes through their nose I smelt it off her dress when I was biting off the thread of the button I sewed on to the bottom of her jacket she couldnt hide much from me I tell you only I oughtnt to have stitched it and it on her it brings a parting and the last plumpudding too split in 2 halves see it comes out no matter what they say her tongue is a bit too long for my taste your blouse is open too low she says to me the pan calling the kettle blackbottom and I had to tell her not to cock her legs up like that on show on the windowsill before all the people passing they all look at her like me when I was her age of course any old rag looks well on you then a great touchmenot too in her own way at the Only Way in the Theatre royal take your foot away out of that I hate people touching me afraid of her life Id crush her skirt with the pleats a lot of that touching must go on in theatres in the crush in the dark theyre always trying to wiggle up to you that fellow in the pit at the pit at the Gaiety for Beerbohm Tree in Trilby the last time Ill ever go

there to be squashed like that for any Trilby or her barebum every two minutes tipping me there and looking away hes a bit daft I think I saw him after trying to get near two stylishdressed ladies outside Switzers window at the same little game I recognised him on the moment the face and everything but he didn't remember me and she didnt even want me to kiss her at the Broadstone going away well I hope shell get someone to dance attendance on her the way I did when she was down with the mumps her glands swollen wheres this and wheres that of course she cant feel anything deep yet I never came properly till I was what 22 or so it went into the wrong place always only the usual girls nonsense and giggling that Conny Connolly writing to her in white ink on black paper sealed with sealingwax though she clapped when the curtain came down because he looked so handsome then we had Martin Harvey for breakfast dinner and supper I thought to myself afterwards it must be real love if a man gives up his life for her that way for nothing I suppose there are few men like that left its hard to believe in it though unless it really happened to me the majority of them with not a particle of love in their natures to find two people like that nowadays full up of each other that would feel the same way as you do theyre usually a bit foolish in the head his father must have been a bit queer to go and poison himself after her still poor old man I suppose he felt shes lost always making love to my things too the few old rags I have wanting to put her hair up at 15 my powder too only ruin her skin on her shes time enough for that all her life after of course shes restless knowing shes pretty with her lips so red a pity they wont stay that way I was too but theres no use going to the fair with the thing answering me like a fishwoman when I asked to go for a half a stone of potatoes the day we met Mrs Joe Gallaher at the trottingmatches and she pretended not to see us in her trap with Friery the solicitor we werent grand enough till I gave her 2 damn fine cracks across the ear for herself take that now for answering me like that and that for your impudence she had me that exasperated of course contradicting I was badtempered too because how was it there was a weed in the tea or I didnt sleep the night before cheese I ate was it and I told her over and over again not to leave knives crossed like that because she has nobody to command her as she said herself well if he doesnt correct her faith I will that was the last time she turned on the teartap I was just like that myself they darent order me about the place its his fault of course having the two of us slaving here instead of getting in a woman long ago am I ever going to have a proper servant again of course then shed see him coming Id have to let her know or shed revenge it arent they a nuisance that old Mrs Fleming you have to be walking round after her putting the things into her hands sneezing and farting into the pots well of course shes old she cant help it a good job I found that rotten old smelly dishcloth that got lost behind the dresser I knew there was something and opened the window to let out the smell bringing in his friends to entertain them like the night he walked home with a dog if you please that might have been mad especially Simon Dedalus son his father such a criticiser with his glasses up with his tall hat on him at the cricket match and a great big hole in his sock one thing laughing at the other and his son that got all those prizes for whatever he won them in the intermediate imagine climbing over the railings if anybody saw him that knew us wonder he didnt tear a big hole in his grand funeral trousers as if the one nature gave wasnt

enough for anybody hawking him down into the dirty old kitchen now is he right in his head I ask[illegible] pity it wa[illegible]n't washing day my old pair of drawers might have been hanging u[illegible] too on th[illegible] line on exhibition for all hed ever care with the ironmould mark th[illegible] stupid o[illegible] bundle burned on them he might think was something else and[illegible]e never e[illegible]n rendered down the fat I told her and now shes going such as she [illegible]s on acc[illegible]nt of her paralysed husband getting worse theres always somethin[illegible]wrong w[illegible] them disease or they have to go under an operation or if its not [illegible]at its dri[illegible] and he beats her Ill have to hunt around again for someone every [illegible]y I get u[illegible]eres some new thing on sweet God sweet God well when Im stretc[illegible]d out de[illegible]n my grave I suppose Ill have some peace I want to get up a minut[illegible] Im let [illegible] O Jesus wait yes that thing has come on me yes now wouldnt that a[illegible]lict you [illegible] course all the poking and rooting and ploughing he had up in me [illegible]w what[illegible]n I to do Friday Saturday Sunday wouldnt that pester the soul out o[illegible] body [illegible]ess he likes it some men do God knows theres always something wr[illegible]g with [illegible] 5 days every 3 or 4 weeks usual monthly auction isnt it simply sicke[illegible]ng tha[illegible]ight it came on me like that the one and only time we were in a box [illegible]at Mi[illegible]ael Gunn gave him to see Mrs Kendal and her husband at the Gaiety s[illegible]ethi[illegible]he did about insurance for him Drimmies I was fit to be tied though I w[illegible]ldnt [illegible]ve in with that gentleman of fashion staring down at me with his glasses[illegible]d hi[illegible] the other side of me talking about Spinoza and his soul thats dead I sup[illegible]se m[illegible]ions of years ago I smiled the best I could all in a swamp leaning forward[illegible]s if [illegible]vas interested having to sit it out then to the last tag I wont forget tha[illegible]wife [illegible]f Scarli in a hurry supposed to be a fast play about adultery that id[illegible] in [illegible]e gallery hissing the woman adulteress he shouted I suppose he went[illegible]d h[illegible] a woman in the next lane running round all the back ways after to ma[illegible]up f[illegible] it I wish he had what I had then hed boo I bet the cat itself is better off [illegible]n u[illegible]have we too much blood up in us or what O patience above its pouring [illegible] of [illegible]e like the sea anyhow he didnt make me pregnant as big as he is I dont [illegible]nt t[illegible]ruin the clean sheets I just put on I suppose the clean linen I wore broug[illegible]t o[illegible]too damn it damn it and they always want to see a stain on the bed to [illegible]w [illegible]ure a virgin for them all thats troubling them theyre such fools too you c[illegible]d b[illegible] widow or divorced 40 times over a daub of red ink would do or blackb[illegible]jui[illegible]no[illegible] purply O Jamesy let me up out of this pooh sweets of sin [illegible]eve[illegible]ugg[illegible]hat business for women what between clothes and cooking [illegible]chi[illegible]en[illegible]mned old bed too jingling like the dickens I suppose they c[illegible]he[illegible]s[illegible]over the other side of the park till I suggested to put the qu[illegible]the[illegible] the pillow under my bottom I wonder is it nicer in the day I [illegible]it is[illegible]k Ill cut all this hair off me there scalding me I might look li[illegible]oun[illegible]dnt he get the great suckin the next time he turned up my [illegible]on [illegible] anything to see his face wheres the chamber gone easy Iv[illegible]ho[illegible]reaking under me after that old commode I wonder w[illegible]ea[illegible] his knee I made him sit on the easychair purpos[illegible]ouse and skirt first in the other room he was so[illegible] never felt me I hope my breath was sweet after [illegible] I remember one time I could scout it out straight [illegible]ost easy O Lord how noisy I hope theyre bubbles on it [illegible] from some fellow Ill have to perfume it in the morning dont

forget I bet he never saw a better pair of thighs than that look how white they are the smoothest place is right there between this bit here how soft like a peach easy God I wouldnt mind being a man and get up on a lovely woman O Lord what a row youre making like the jersey lily easy O how the waters come down at Lahore

who knows is there anything the matter with my insides or have I something growing in me getting that thing like that every week when was it last I Whit Monday yes its only about 3 weeks I ought to go to the doctor only it would be like before I married him when I had that white thing coming from me and Floey made me go to that dry old stick Dr Collins for womens diseases on Pembroke road your vagina he called it I suppose thats how he got all the gilt mirrors and carpets getting round those rich ones off Stephens green running up to him for every little fiddlefaddle her vagina and her cochinchina theyve money of course so theyre all right I wouldnt marry him not if he was the last man in the world besides there something queer about their children always smelling around those filthy bitches all sides asking me if what I did had an offensive odour what did he want me to do but the one thing gold maybe what a question if I smathered it all over his wrinkly old face for him with all my compriment I suppose hed know then and could you pass it easily pass what I thought he was talking about the rock of Gibraltar the way he puts it thats a very nice invention too by the way only I like letting myself down after in the hole as far as I can squeeze and pull the chain then to flush it nice cool pins and needles still theres something in it I suppose I always used to know by Millys when she was a child whether she had worms or not still all the same paying him for that how much is that doctor one guinea please and asking me had I frequent omissions where do those old fellows get all the words they have omissions with his shortsighted eyes on me cocked sideways I wouldnt trust him too far to give me chloroform or God knows what else still I liked him when he sat down to write the thing out frowning so severe his nose intelligent like that you be damned you lying strap O anything no matter who except an idiot he was clever enough to spot that of course that was all thinking of him and his mad crazy letters my Precious one everything connected with your glorious Body everything underlined that comes from it is a thing of beauty and of joy for ever something he got out of some nonsensical book that he had me always at myself 4 or 5 times a day sometimes and I said I hadnt are you sure O yes I said I am quite sure in a way that shut him up I knew what was coming next only natural weakness it was he excited me I dont know how the first night ever we met when I was living in Rehoboth terrace we stood staring at one another for about 10 minutes as if we met somewhere I suppose on account of my being jewess looking after my mother he used to amuse me the things he said with the half sloothering smile on him and all the Doyles said he was going to stand for a member of Parliament O wasnt I the born fool to believe all his blather about home rule and the land league sending me that long strool of a song out of the Huguenots to sing in French to be more classy O beau pays de la Touraine that I never even sang once explaining and rigmaroling about religion and persecution he wont let you enjoy anything naturally then might he as a great favour the very 1st opportunity he got a chance in Brighton square running into my bedroom pretending the ink got on his hands to wash it off with the

Albion milk and sulphur soap I used to use and the gelatine still round it O I laughed myself sick at him that day Id better not make an alnight sitting on this affair they ought to make chambers a natural size so that a woman could sit on it properly he kneels down to do it I suppose there isnt in all creation another man with the habits he has look at the way hes sleeping at the foot of the bed how can he without a hard bolster its well he doesnt kick or he might knock out all my teeth breathing with his hand on his nose like that Indian god he took me to show one wet Sunday in the museum in Kildare street all yellow in a pinafore lying on his side on his hand with his ten toes sticking out that he said was a bigger religion than the jews and Our Lords both put together all over Asia imitating him as hes always imitating everybody I suppose he used to sleep at the foot of the bed too with his big square feet up in his wifes mouth damn this stinking thing anyway wheres this those napkins are ah yes I know I hope the old press doesnt creak ah I knew it would hes sleeping hard had a good time somewhere still she must have given him great value for his money of course he has to pay for it from her O this nuisance of a thing I hope theyll have something better for us in the other world tying ourselves up God help us thats all right for tonight now the lumpy old jingly bed always reminds me of old Cohen I suppose he scratched himself in it often enough and he thinks father bought it from Lord Napier that I used to admire when I was a little girl because I told him easy piano O I like my bed God here we are as bad as ever after 16 years how many houses were we in at all Raymond Terrace and Ontario terrace and Lombard street and Holles street and he goes about whistling every time were on the run again his huguenots or the frogs march pretending to help the men with our 4 sticks of furniture and then the City Arms hotel worse and worse says Warden Daly that charming place on the landing always somebody inside praying then leaving all their stinks after them always know who was in there last every time were just getting on right something happens or he puts his big foot in it Thoms and Helys and Mr Cuffes and Drimmies either hes going to be run into prison over his old lottery tickets that was to be all our salvations or he goes and gives impudence well have him coming home with the sack soon out of the Freeman too like the rest on account of those Sinner Fein or the freemasons then well see if the little man he showed me dribbling along in the wet all by himself round by Coadys lane will give him much consolation that he says is so capable and sincerely Irish he is indeed judging by the sincerity of the trousers I saw on him wait theres Georges church bells wait 3 quarters the hour 1 wait 2 oclock well thats a nice hour of the night for him to be coming home at to anybody climbing down into the area if anybody saw him Ill knock him off that little habit tomorrow first Ill look at his shirt to see or Ill see if he has that French letter still in his pocketbook I suppose he thinks I dont know deceitful men all their 20 pockets arent enough for their lies then why should we tell them even if its the truth they dont believe you then tucked up in bed like those babies in the Aristocrats Masterpiece he brought me another time as if we hadnt enough of that in real life without some old Aristocrat or whatever his name is disgusting you more with those rotten pictures children with two heads and no legs thats the kind of villainy theyre always dreaming about with not another thing in their empty heads they ought to get slow poison the half of them then tea and toast for him buttered on both

sides and newlaid eggs I suppose Im nothing any more when I wouldnt let him lick me in Holles street one night man man tyrant as ever for the one thing he slept on the floor half the night naked the way the jews used when somebody dies belonged to them and wouldnt eat any breakfast or speak a word wanting to be petted so I thought I stood out enough for one time and let him he does it all wrong too thinking only of his own pleasure his tongue is too flat or I dont know what he forgets that wethen I dont Ill make him do it again if he doesnt mind himself and lock him down to sleep in the coalcellar with the blackbeetles I wonder was it her Josie off her head with my castoffs hes such a born liar too no hed never have the courage with a married woman thats why he wants me and Boylan though as for her Denis as she calls him that forlornlooking spectacle you couldn't call him a husband yes its some little bitch hes got in with even when I was with him with Milly at the College races that Hornblower with the childs bonnet on the top on his nob let us into by the back way he was throwing his sheeps eyes at those two doing skirt duty up and down I tried to wink at him first no use of course and thats the way his money goes this is the fruits of Mr Paddy Dignam yes they were all in great style at the grand funeral in the paper Boylan brought in if they saw a real officers funeral thatd be something reversed arms muffled drums the poor horse walking behind in black L Bloom and Tom Kernan that drunken little barrelly man that bit his tongue off falling down the mens W C drunk in some place or other and Martin Cunningham and the two Dedaluses and Fanny MCoys husband white head of cabbage skinny thing with a turn in her eye trying to sing my songs shed want to be born all over again and her old green dress with the lowneck as she cant attract them any other way like dabbling on a rainy day I see it all now plainly and they call that friendship killing and then burying one another and they all with their wives and families at home more especially Jack Power keeping that barmaid he does of course his wife always sick or going to be sick or just getting better of it and hes a goodlooking man still though hes getting a bit grey over the ears theyre a nice lot all of them well theyre not going to get my husband again into their clutches if I can help it making fun of him then behind his back I know well when he goes on with his idiotics because he has sense enough not to squander every penny piece he earns down their gullets and looks after his wife and family goodfornothings poor Paddy Dignam all the same Im sorry in a way for him what are his wife and 5 children going to do unless he was insured comical little teetotum always stuck up in some pub corner and her or her son waiting Bill Bailey wont you please come home her widows weeds wont improve her appearance theyre awfully becoming though if youre goodlooking what men wasn't he yes he was at the Glencree dinner and Ben Dollard base barreltone the night he borrowed the swallowtail to sing out of in Holles street squeezed and squashed into them and grinning all over his big Dolly face like a wellwhipped childs botty didnt he look a balmy ballocks sure enough that must have been a spectacle on the stage imagine paying 5/- in the preserved seats for that to see him trotting off in his trowlers and Simon Dedalus too he was always turning up half screwed singing the second verse first the old love is the new was one of his so sweetly sang the maiden on the hawthorn bough he was always on for flirtyfying too when I sang Maritana with him at Freddy Mayers private opera he had a delicious glorious

voice Phoebe dearest goodbye sweetheart *sweet*heart he always sang it not like Bartell dArcy sweet *tart* goodbye of course he had the gift of the voice so there was no art in it all over you like a warm showerbath O Maritana wildwood flower we sang splendidly though it was a bit too high for my register even transposed and he was married at the time to May Goulding but then hed say or do something to knock the good out of it hes a widower now I wonder what sort is his son he says hes an author and going to be a university professor of Italian and Im to take lessons what is he driving at now showing him my photo its not good of me I ought to have got it taken in drapery that never looks out of fashion still I look young in it I wonder he didnt make him a present of it altogether and me too after all why not I saw him driving down to the Kingsbridge station with his father and mother I was in mourning thats 11 years ago now yes hed be 11 though what was the good in going into mourning for what was neither one thing nor the other the first cry was enough for me I heard the deathwatch too ticking on the wall of course he insisted hed go into mourning for the cat I suppose hes a man now by this time he was an innocent boy then and a darling little fellow in his lord Fauntleroy suit and curly hair like a prince on the stage when I saw him at Mat Dillons he liked me too I remember they all do wait by God yes wait yes hold on he was on the cards this morning when I laid out the deck union with a young stranger neither dark nor fair you met before I thought it meant him but hes no chicken nor a stranger either besides my face was turned the other way what was the 7th card after that the 10 of spaces for a journey by land then there was a letter on its way and scandals too the 3 queens and the 8 of diamonds for a rise in society yes wait it all came out and 2 red 8s for new garments look at that and didnt I dream something too yes there was something about poetry in it I hope he hasnt long greasy hair hanging into his eyes or standing up like a red Indian what do they go about like that for only getting themselves and their poetry laughed at I always liked poetry when I was a girl first I thought he was a poet like Byron and not an ounce of it in his composition I thought he was quite different I wonder is he too young hes about wait 88 I was married 88 Milly is 15 yesterday 89 what age was he then at Dillons 5 or 6 about 88 I suppose hes 20 or more Im not too old for him if hes 23 or 24 I hope hes not that stuck up university student sort no otherwise he wouldnt go sitting down in the old kitchen with him taking Eppss cocoa and taking of course he pretended to understand it all probably he told him he was out of Trinity college hes very young to be a professor I hope hes not a professor like Goodwin was he was a patent professor of John Jameson they all write about some woman in their poetry well I suppose he wont find many like me where softly sighs of love the light guitar where poetry is in the air the blue sea and the moon shining so beautifully coming back on the nightboat from Tarifa the lighthouse at Europa point the guitar that fellow played was so expressive will I ever go back there again all new faces two glancing eyes a lattice hid Ill sing that for him theyre my eyes if hes anything of a poet two eyes as darkly bright as loves own star arent those beautiful words as loves young star itll be a change the Lord knows to have an intelligent person to talk to about yourself not always listening to him and Billy Prescotts ad and Keyess ad and Tom the Devils ad then if anything goes wrong in their business we have to suffer Im sure hes very distinguished Id like

to meet a man like that God not those other ruck besides hes young those fine young men I could see down in Margate strand bathingplace from the side of the rock standing up in the sun naked like a God or something and then plunging into the sea with them why arent all men like that thered be some consolation for a woman like that lovely little statue he bought I could look at him all day long curly head and his shoulders his finger up for you to listen theres real beauty and poetry for you I often felt I wanted to kiss him all over also his lovely young cock there so simply I wouldnt mind taking him in my mouth if nobody was looking as if it was asking you to suck it so clean and white he looks with his boyish face I would too in ½ a minute even if some of it went down what its only like gruel or the dew theres no danger besides hed be so clean compared with those pigs of men I suppose never dream of washing it from 1 years end to the other the most of them only thats what gives the women the moustaches Im sure itll be grand if I can only get in with a handsome young poet at my age Ill throw them the 1st thing in the morning till I see if the wishcard comes out or Ill try pairing the lady herself and see if he comes out Ill read and study all I can find or learn a bit off by heart if I knew who he likes so he wont think me stupid if he thinks all women are the same and I can teach him the other part Ill make him feel all over him till he half faints under me then hell write about me lover and mistress publicly too with our 2 photographs in all the papers when he becomes famous O but then what am I going to do about him though

no thats no way for him has he no manners nor no refinement nor no nothing in his nature slapping us behind like that on my bottom because I didn't call him Hugh the ignoramus that doesnt know poetry from a cabbage thats what you get for not keeping them in their proper place pulling off his shoes and trousers there on the chair before me so barefaced without even asking permission and standing out that vulgar way in the half of a shirt they wear to be admired like a priest or a butcher or those old hypocrites in the time of Julius Caesar of course hes right enough in his way to pass the time as a joke sure you might as well be in bed with what with a lion God Im sure hed have something better to say for himself an old Lion would O well I suppose its because they were so plump and tempting in my short petticoat he couldnt resist they excite myself sometimes its well for men all the amount of pleasure they get off a womans body were so round and white for them always I wished I was one myself for a change just to try with that thing they have swelling upon you so hard and at the same time so soft when you touch it my uncle John has a thing long I heard those cornerboys saying passing the corner of Marrowbone lane my aunt Mary has a thing hairy because it was dark and they knew a girl was passing it didnt make me blush why should it either its only nature and he puts his thing long into my aunt Marys hairy etcetera and turns out to be you put the handle in a sweepingbrush men again all over they can pick and choose what they please a married woman or a fast widow or a girl for their different tastes like those houses round behind Irish street no but were to be always chained up theyre not going to be chaining me up no damn fear once I start I tell you for stupid husbands jealousy why cant we all remain friends over it instead of quarrelling her husband found it out what they did together well naturally and if he did can he undo it hes coronado anyway whatever he does and then he going to the other mad extreme about the

wife in Fair Tyrants of course the man never even casts a 2nd thought on the husband or wife either its the woman he wants and he gets her what else were we given all those desires for Id like to know I cant help it if Im young still can I its a wonder Im not an old shrivelled hag before my time living with him so cold never embracing me except sometimes when hes asleep the wrong end of me not knowing I suppose who he has any man thatd kiss a womans bottom Id throw my hat at him after that hed kiss anything unnatural where we havent 1 atom of any kind of expression in us all of us the same 2 lumps of lard before ever I do that to a man pfooh the dirty brutes the mere thought is enough I kiss the feet of you senorita theres some sense in that didnt he kiss our halldoor yes he did what a madman nobody understands his cracked ideas but me still of course a woman wants to be embraced 20 times a day almost to make her look young no matter by who so long as to be in love or loved by somebody if the fellow you want isnt there sometimes by the Lord God I was thinking would I go around by the quays there some dark evening where nobodyd know me and pick up a sailor off the sea thatd be hot on for it and not care a pin whose I was only to do it off up in a gate somewhere or one of those wildlooking gipsies in Rathfarnham had their camp pitched near the Bloomfield laundry to try and steal our things if they could I only sent mine there a few times for the name model laundry sending me back over and over some old ones old stockings that blackguardlooking fellow with the fine eyes peeling a switch attack me in the dark and ride me up against the wall without a word or a murderer anybody what they do themselves the fine gentlemen in their silk hats that K C lives up somewhere this way coming out of Hardwicke lane the night he gave us the fish supper on account of winning over the boxing match of course it was for me he gave it I knew him by his gaiters and the walk and when I turned round a minute after just to see there was a woman after coming out of it too some filthy prostitute then he goes home to his wife after that only I suppose the half of those sailors are rotten again with disease O move over your big carcass out of that for the love of Mike listen to him the winds that waft my sighs to thee so well he may sleep and sigh the great Suggester Don Poldo de la Flora if he knew how he came out on the cards this morning hed have something to sigh for a dark man in some perplexity between 2 7s too in prison for Lord knows what he does that I dont know and Im to be slooching around down in the kitchen to get his lordship his breakfast while hes rolled up like a mummy will I indeed did you ever see me running Id just like to see myself at it show them attention and they treat you like dirt I dont care what anybody says itd be much better for the world to be governed by the women in it you wouldnt see women going and killing one another and slaughtering when do you ever see women rolling around drunk like they do or gambling every penny they have and losing it on horses yes because a woman whatever she does she knows where to stop sure they wouldn't be in the world at all only for us they dont know what it is to be a woman and a mother how could they where would they all of them be if they hadnt all a mother to look after them what I never had thats why I suppose hes running wild now out at night away from his books and studies and not living at home on account of the usual rowdy house I suppose well its a poor case that those that have a fine son like that theyre not satisfied and I none was he not able to make one it wasnt my fault we came to-

gether when I was watching the two dogs up in her behind in the middle of the naked street that disheartened me altogether I suppose I oughtnt to have buried him in that little woolly jacket I knitted crying as was but give it to some poor child but I knew well Id never have another our 1st death too it was we were never the same since O Im not going to think myself into the glooms about that any more I wonder why he wouldnt stay the night I felt all the time it was somebody strange he brought in instead of roving around the city meeting God knows who nightwalkers and pickpockets his poor mother wouldnt like that if she was alive ruining himself for life perhaps still its a lovely hour so silent I used to love coming home after dances the air of the night they have friends they can talk to weve none either he wants what he wont get or its some woman ready to stick her knife in you I hate that in women no wonder they treat us the way they do we are a dreadful lot of bitches I suppose its all the troubles we have makes us so snappy Im not like that he could easy have slept in there on the sofa in the other room I suppose he was as shy as a boy he being so young hardly 20 of me in the next room hed have heard me on the chamber arrah what harm Dedalus I wonder its like those names in Gibraltar Delapaz Delagracia they had the devils queer names there father Vilaplana of Santa Maria that gave me the rosary Rosales y OReilly in the Calle las Siete Revueltas and Pisimbo and Mrs Opisso in Governor street O what a name Id go and drown myself in the first river if I had a name like her O my and all the bits of streets Paradise ramp and Bedlam ramp and Rodgers ramp and Crutchetts ramp and the devils gap steps well small blame to me if I am a harumscarum I know I am a bit I declare to God I dont feel a day older than then I wonder could I get my tongue round any of the Spanish como esta usted muy bien gracias y usted see I haven't forgotten it all I thought I had only for the grammar a noun is the name of any person place or thing pity I never tried to read that novel cantankerous Mrs Rubio lent me by Valera with the questions in it all upside down the two ways I always knew wed go away in the end I can tell him the Spanish and he tell me the Italian then hell see Im not so ignorant what a pity he didnt stay Im sure the poor fellow was dead tired and wanted a good sleep badly I could have brought him in his breakfast in bed with a bit of toast so long as I didnt do it on the knife for bad luck or if the woman was going her rounds with the watercress and something nice and tasty there are a few olives in the kitchen he might like I never could bear the look of them in Abrines I could do the criada the room looks all right since I changed it the other way you see something was telling me all the time Id have to introduce myself not knowing me from Adam very funny wouldnt it Im his wife or pretend we were in Spain with him half awake without a Gods notion where he is dos huevos estrellados senor Lord the cracked things come into my head sometimes itd be great fun supposing he stayed with us why not theres the room upstairs empty and Millys bed in the back room he could do his writing and studies at the table in there for all the scribbling he does at it and if he wants to read in bed in the morning like me as hes making the breakfast for 1 he can make it for 2 Im sure Im not going to take in lodgers off the street for him if he takes a gesabo of a house like this Id love to have a long talk with an intelligent welleducated person Id have to get a nice pair of red slippers like those Turks with the fez used to sell or yellow and a nice semitransparent morning gown that I badly want or a

peachblossom dressing jacket like the one long ago in Walpoles only 8/6 or 18/6 Ill just give him one more chance Ill get up early in the morning Im sick of Cohens old bed in any case I might go over to the markets to see all the vegetables and cabbages and tomatoes and carrots and all kinds of splendid fruits all coming in lovely and fresh who knows whod be the 1st man Id meet theyre out looking for it in the morning Mamy Dillon used to say they are and the night too that was her massgoing Id love a big juicy pear now to melt in your mouth like when I used to be in the longing way then Ill throw him up his eggs and tea in the moustachecup she gave him to make his mouth bigger I suppose hed like my nice cream too I know what Ill do Ill go about rather gay not too much singing a bit now and then mi fa pieti Masetto then Ill start dressing myself to go out presto non son pill forte Ill put on my best shift and drawers let him have a good eyeful out of that to make his micky stand for him Ill let him know if thats what he wanted that his wife is fucked yes and damn well fucked too up to my neck nearly not by him 5 or 6 times handrunning theres the mark of his spunk on the clean sheet I wouldnt bother to even iron it out that ought to satisfy him if you dont believe me feel my belly unless I made him stand there and put him into me Ive a mind to tell him every scrap and make him do it in front of me serve him right its all his own fault if I am an adulteress as the thing in the gallery said O much about it if thats all the harm ever we did in this vale of tears God knows its not much doesnt everybody only they hide it I suppose thats what a woman is supposed to be there for or He wouldnt have made us the way He did so attractive to men then if he wants to kiss my bottom Ill drag open my drawers and bulge it right out in his face as large as life he can stick his tongue 7 miles up my hole as hes there my brown part then Ill tell him I want £1 or perhaps 30/- Ill tell him I want to buy underclothes then if he gives me that well he wont be too bad I dont want to soak it all out of him like other women do I could often have written out a fine cheque for myself and write his name on it for a couple of pounds a few times he forgot to lock it up besides he wont spend it Ill let him do it off on me behind provided he doesnt smear all my good drawers O I suppose that cant be helped Ill do the indifferent 1 or 2 questions Ill know by the answers when hes like that he cant keep a thing back I know every turn in him Ill tighten my bottom well and let out a few smutty words smellrump or lick my shit or the first mad thing comes into my head then Ill suggest about yes O wait now sonny my turn is coming Ill be quite gay and friendly over it O but I was forgetting this bloody pest of a thing pfooh you wouldn't know which to laugh or cry were such a mixture of plum and apple no Ill have to wear the old things so much the better itll be more pointed hell never know whether he did it nor not there thats good enough for you any old thing at all then Ill wipe him off me just like a business his omission then Ill go out Ill have him eyeing up at the ceiling where is she gone now make him want me thats the only way a quarter after what an unearthly hour I suppose theyre just getting up in China now combing out their pigtails for the day well soon have the nuns ringing the angelus theyve nobody coming in to spoil their sleep except an odd priest or two for his night office the alarmclock next door at cockshout clattering the brains out of itself let me see if I can dose off 1 2 3 4 5 what kind of flowers are those they invented like the stars the wallpaper in Lombard street was much nicer the apron he gave me was like that

something only I only wore it twice better lower this lamp and try again so as I can get up early Ill go to Lambes there beside Findlaters and get them to send us some flowers to put about the place in case he brings him home tomorrow today I mean no no Fridays an unlucky day first I want to do the place up someway the dust grows in it I think while Im asleep then we can have music and cigarettes I can accompany him first I must clean the keys of the piano with milk whatll I wear shall I wear a white rose or those fairy cakes in Liptons I love the smell of a rich big shop at 71/2d a lb or the other ones with the cherries in them and the pinky sugar 11d a couple of lbs of course a nice plant for the middle of the table Id get that cheaper in wait wheres this I saw them not long ago I love flowers Id love to have the whole place swimming in roses God of heaven theres nothing like nature the wild mountains then the sea and the waves rushing then the beautiful country with fields of oats and wheat and all kinds of things and all the fine cattle going about that would do your heart good to see rivers and lakes and flowers all sorts of shapes and smells and colours springing up even out of the ditches primroses and violets nature it is as for them saying theres no God I wouldnt give a snap of my two fingers for all their learning why dont they go and create something I often asked him atheists or whatever they call themselves go and wash the cobbles off themselves first then they go howling for the priest and they dying and why why because theyre afraid of hell on account of their bad conscience ah yes I know them well who was the first person in the universe before there was anybody that made it all who ah that they dont know neither do I so there you are they might as well try to stop the sun from rising tomorrow the sun shines for you he said the day we were lying among the rhododendrons on Howth head in the grey tweed suit and his straw hat the day I got him to propose to me yes first I gave him the bit of seedcake out of my mouth and it was leapyear like now yes 16 years ago my God after that long kiss I near lost my breath yes he said was a flower of the mountain yes so we are flowers all a womans body yes that was one true thing he said in his life and the sun shines for you today yes that was why I liked him because I saw he understood or felt what a woman is and I knew I could always get round him and I gave him all the pleasure I could leading him on till he asked me to say yes and I wouldnt answer first only looked out over the sea and the sky I was thinking of so many things he didnt know of Mulvey and Mr Stanhope and Hester and father and old captain Groves and the sailors playing all birds fly and I say stoop and washing up dishes they called it on the pier and the sentry in front of the governors house with the thing round his white helmet poor devil half roasted and the Spanish girls laughing in their shawls and their tall combs and the auctions in the morning the Greeks and the jews and the Arabs and the devil knows who else from all the ends of Europe and Duke street and the fowl market all clucking outside Larby Sharans and the poor donkeys slipping half asleep and the vague fellows in the cloaks asleep in the shade on the steps and the big wheels of the carts of the bulls and the old castle thousands of years old yes and those handsome Moors all in white and turbans like kings asking you to sit down in their little bit of a shop and Ronda with the old windows of the posadas 2 glancing eyes a lattice hid for her lover to kiss the iron and the wineshops half open at night and the castanets and the night we missed the boat at Algeciras the watchman going about serene

with his lamp and O that awful deepdown torrent O and the sea the sea crimson sometimes like fire and the glorious sunsets and the figtrees in the Alameda gardens yes and all the queer little streets and pink and blue and yellow houses and the rosegardens and the jessamine and geraniums and cactuses and Gibraltar as a girl where I was a Flower of the mountain yes when I put the rose in my hair like the Andalusian girls used or shall I wear a red yes and how he kissed me under the Moorish wall and I thought well as well him as another and then I asked him with my eyes to ask again yes and then he asked me would I yes to say yes my mountain flower and first I put my arms around him yes and drew him down to me so he could feel my breasts all perfume yes and his heart was going like mad and yes I said yes I will Yes.

From QUIET DAYS IN CLICHY

Henry Miller

Henry Miller sought to re-establish the freedom to live without the conventional restraints of civilization. His books are potpourris of sexual description, quasi-philosophical speculation, reflection on literature and society, surrealistic imaginings, and autobiographical incident. After living in Paris in the 1930s, he returned to the United States and settled in Big Sur, California. Miller's first two works, *Tropic of Cancer* (1934) and *Tropic of Capricorn* (1939), were denied publication in the USA until the early 1960s because of alleged obscenity. *The Colossus of Maroussi* (1941), a travel book of modern Greece, is considered by some critics his best work. His other writings include the *Rosy Crucifixion Trilogy – Sexus* (1949), *Plexus* (1953), and *Nexus* (1960). In 1976 Norman Mailer edited a selection of Miller's writings, *Genius and Lust*.

At one corner of the Place Clichy is the Café Wepler, which was for a long period my favourite haunt. I have sat there inside and out at all times of the day in all kinds of weather. I knew it like a book. The faces of the waiters, the managers, the cashiers, the whores, the clientele, even the attendants in the lavatory, are engraved in my memory as if they were illustrations in a book which I read every day. I remember the first day I entered the Café Wepler, in the year 1928, with my wife in tow; I remember the shock I experienced when I saw a whore fall dead drunk across one of the little tables on the terrace and nobody ran to her assistance. I was amazed and horrified by the stoical indifference of the French; I still am, despite all the good qualities in them which I have since come to know. "*It's nothing, it was just a whore . . . she was drunk.*" I can still hear those words. Even today they make me shudder. But it is very French, this attitude, and, if you don't learn to accept it, your stay in France won't be very pleasant.

On the grey days, when it was chilly everywhere except in the big cafés, I looked forward with pleasure to spending an hour or two at the Café Wepler before going to dinner. The rosy glow which suffused the place emanated from the cluster of whores who usually congregated near the entrance. As they gradually distributed themselves among the clientele, the place became not only warm and rosy but fragrant. They fluttered about in the dimming light like perfumed fireflies. Those who had not been fortunate enough to find a customer would saunter slowly out to the street, usually to return in a little while and resume their old places. Others swaggered in, looking fresh and ready for the evening's

work. In the corner where they usually congregated it was like an exchange, the sex market, which has its ups and downs like other exchanges. A rainy day was usually a good day, it seemed to me. There are only two things you can do on a rainy day, as the saying goes, and the whores never wasted time playing cards.

It was in the late afternoon of a rainy day that I espied a newcomer at the Café Wepler. I had been out shopping, and my arms were loaded with books and phonograph records. I must have received an unexpected remittance from America that day because, despite the purchases I had made, I still had a few hundred francs in my pocket. I sat down near the place of exchange, surrounded by a bevy of hungry, itching whores whom I had no difficulty whatever in eluding because my eyes were fastened on this ravishing beauty who was sitting apart in a far corner of the café. I took her to be an attractive young woman who had made a rendezvous with her lover and who had come ahead of time perhaps. The *apéritif* which she had ordered had hardly been touched. At the men who passed her table she gave a full, steady glance, but that indicated nothing – a French-woman doesn't avert her glance as does the English or the American woman. She looked around quietly, appraisingly, but without obvious effort to attract attention. She was discreet and dignified, thoroughly poised and self-contained. She was waiting. I too was waiting. I was curious to see whom she was waiting for. After a half hour, during which time I caught her eye a number of times and held it, I made up my mind that she was waiting for anyone who would make the proper overture. Ordinarily one has only to give a sign with the head or the hand and the girl will leave her table and join you – if she's that kind of girl. I was not absolutely sure even yet. She looked too good to me, too sleek, too well – nurtured, I might say.

When the waiter came round again I pointed her out and asked him if he knew her. When he said no I suggested that he invite her to come over and join me. I watched her face as he delivered the message. It gave me quite a thrill to see her smile and look my way with a nod of recognition. I expected her to get up immediately and come over, but instead she remained seated and smiled again, more discreetly this time, whereupon she turned her head away and appeared to gaze out the window dreamily. I allowed a few moments to intervene and then, seeing that she had no intention of making a move, I rose and walked over to her table. She greeted me cordially enough, quite as if I were a friend indeed, but I noticed that she was a little flustered, almost embarrassed. I wasn't sure whether she wanted me to sit down or not, but I sat down nevertheless and, after ordering drinks, quickly engaged her in conversation. Her voice was even more thrilling than her smile; it was well-pitched, rather low, and throaty. It was the voice of a woman who is glad to be alive, who indulges herself, who is careless and indigent, and who will do anything to preserve the modicum of freedom which she possesses. It was the voice of a giver, of a spender; its appeal went to the diaphragm rather than the heart.

I was surprised, I must confess, when she hastened to explain to me that I had made a *faux pas* in coming over to her table. "I thought you had understood," she said, "that I would join you outside. That's what I was trying to tell you telegraphically." She intimated that she did not want to be known here as a professional. I apologised for the blunder and offered to withdraw, which she accepted

as a delicate gesture to be ignored by a squeeze of the hand and a gracious smile.

"What are all these things?" she said, quickly changing the subject by pretending to be interested in the packages which I had placed on the table.

"Just books and records," I said, implying that they would hardly interest her.

"Are they French authors?" she asked, suddenly injecting a note of genuine enthusiasm, it seemed to me.

"Yes," I replied, "but they are rather dull, I fear. Proust, Céline, Elie Faure . . . You'd prefer Maurice Dekobra, no?"

"Let me see them, please. I want to see what kind of French books an American reads."

I opened the package and handed her the Elie Faure. It was *The Dance over Fire and Water.* She riffled the pages, smiling, making little exclamations as she read here and there. Then she deliberately put the book down, closed it, and put her hand over it as if to keep it closed. "Enough, let us talk about something more interesting." After a moment's silence, she added: *"Ce-lui-là, est-il vraiment français?"*

"Un vrai de vrai," I replied, with a broad grin.

She seemed puzzled. "It's excellent French," she went on, as if to herself, "and yet it's not French either . . . *Comment dirais-je?"*

I was about to say that I understood perfectly when she threw herself back against the cushion, took hold of my hand and, with a roguish smile which was meant to reinforce her candour, said: "Look, I am a thoroughly lazy creature. I haven't the patience to read books. It's too much for my feeble brain."

"There are lots of other things to do in life," I answered, returning her smile. So saying, I placed my hand on her leg and squeezed it warmly. In an instant her hand covered mine, removed it to the soft, fleshy part. Then, almost as quickly, she drew my hand away with an – *"Assez, nous ne sommes pas seuls ici."*

We sipped our drinks and relaxed. I was in no hurry to rush her off. For one thing, I was too enchanted by her speech, which was distinctive and which told me that she was not a Parisian. It was a pure French she spoke, and for a foreigner like myself a joy to listen to. She pronounced every word distinctly, using almost no slang, no colloquialisms. The words came out of her mouth fully formed and with a retarded tempo, as if she had rolled them on her palate before surrendering them to the void wherein the sound and the meaning are so swiftly transformed. Her laziness, which was voluptuous, feathered the words with a soft down; they came floating to my ears like balls of fluff. Her body was heavy, earth-laden, but the sounds which issued from her throat were like the clear notes of a bell.

She was made for it, as the saying goes, but she did not impress me as an out-and-out whore. That she would go with me, and take money for it, I knew – but that doesn't make a woman a whore.

She put a hand on me and, like a trained seal, my pecker rose jubilantly to her delicate caress.

"Contain yourself," she murmured, "it's bad to get excited too quickly."

"Let's get out of here," said I, beckoning the waiter.

"Yes," she said, "let's go somewhere where we can talk at leisure."

The less talking the better, I thought to myself, as I gathered my things and escorted her to the street. A wonderful piece of ass, I reflected, watching her sail

through the revolving door. I already saw her dangling on the end of my cock, a fresh, hefty piece of meat waiting to be cured and trimmed.

As we were crossing the boulevard she remarked how pleased she was to have found someone like me. She knew no one in Paris, she was lonesome. Perhaps I would take her around, show her the city? It would be amusing to be guided about the city, the capital of one's own country, by a stranger. Had I ever been to Amboise or Blois or Tours? Maybe we could take a trip together some day. *"Ca vous plairait?"*

We tripped along, chatting thus, until we came to a hotel which she seemed to know. "It's clean and cozy here," she said. "And if it's a little chilly, we will warm each other in bed." She squeezed my arm affectionately.

The room was as cozy as a nest. I waited a moment for soap and towels, tipped the maid, and locked the door. She had taken off her hat and fur piece, and stood waiting to embrace me at the window. What a warm, plantular piece of flesh! I thought she would burst into seed under my touch. In a few moments we started to undress. I sat down on the edge of the bed to unlace my shoes. She was standing beside me, pulling off her things. When I looked up she had nothing on but her stockings. She stood there, waiting for me to examine her more attentively. I got up and put my arms around her again, running my hands leisurely over the billowy folds of flesh. She pulled out of the embrace and, holding me at arm's length enquired coyly if I were not somewhat deceived.

"Deceived?" I echoed. "How do you mean?"

"Am I not too fat?" she said, dropping her eyes and resting them on her navel.

"Too fat? Why, you're marvellous. You're like a Renoir."

At this she blushed. "A Renoir?" she repeated, almost as if she had never heard the name. "No, you're joking."

"Oh, never mind. Come here, let me stroke that pussy of yours."

"Wait, I will first make my toilette." As she moved towards the *bidet* she said: "You get into bed. Make it nice and toasty, yes?"

I undressed quickly, washed my cock out of politeness, and dove between the sheets. The *bidet* was right beside the bed. When she had finished her ablutions she began to dry herself with the thin, worn towel. I leaned over and grabbed her tousled bush, which was still a little dewy. She pushed me back into bed and, leaning over me, made a quick dive for it with her warm red mouth. I slipped a finger inside her to get the juice working. Then, pulling her on top of me, I sank it in up to the hilt. It was one of those cunts which fit like a glove. Her adroit muscular contractions soon had me gasping. All the while she licked my neck, my armpits, the lobes of my ears. With my two hands I lifted her up and down, rolling her pelvis round and round. Finally, with a groan, she bore down on me full weight; I rolled her over on her back, pulled her legs up over my shoulders, and went at her slam-bang. I thought I'd never stop coming; it came out in steady stream, as if from a garden hose. When I pulled away it seemed to me that I had an even bigger erection then when I plugged in.

"Ca c'est quelque chose," she said, putting her hand around my cock and fingering it appraisingly. "You know how to do it, don't you?"

We got up, washed, and crawled back into bed again. Reclining on an elbow,

I ran my hand up and down her body. Her eyes were glowing as she lay back, thoroughly relaxed, her legs open, her flesh tingling. Nothing was said for several minutes. I lit a cigarette for her, put it in her mouth, and sank deep into the bed, staring contentedly at the ceiling.

"Are we going to see more of each other?" I asked after a time.

"That is up to you," she said, taking a deep puff. She turned over to put her cigarette out and then, drawing close, gazing at me steadily, smiling, but serious, she said in her low, warbling voice: "Listen, I must talk to you seriously. There is a great favour I wish to ask of you . . . I am in trouble, great trouble. Would you help me, if I asked you to?"

"Of course," I said, "but how?"

"I mean money," she said, quietly and simply. "I need a great deal . . . I *must* have it. I won't explain why. Just believe me, will you?"

I leaned over and yanked my pants off the chair. I fished out the bills and all the change that was in my pocket, and handed it to her.

"I'm giving you all I have," I said. "That's the best I can do."

She laid the money on the night table beside her without looking at it and, bending over, she kissed my brow. "You're a brick," she said. She remained bent over me, looking into my eyes with mute, strangled gratitude, then kissed me on the mouth, not passionately, but slowly, lingeringly, as if to convey the affection which she couldn't put into words and which she was too delicate to convey by offering her body.

"I can't say anything now," she said, falling back on the pillow. *"Je suis émue, c'est tout."* Then, after a brief pause, she added: "It's strange how one's own people are never as good to one as a stranger. You Americans are very kind, very gentle. We have much to learn from you."

It was such an old song to me, I almost felt ashamed of myself for having posed once again as the generous American. I explained to her that it was just an accident, my having so much money in my pocket. To this she replied that it was all the more wonderful, my gesture. "A Frenchman would hide it away," she said. "He would never give it to the first girl he met just because she was in need of help. He wouldn't believe her in the first place. *'Je connais la chanson,'* he would say."

I said nothing more. It was true and it wasn't true. It takes all sorts to make a world and, though up to that time I had never met a generous Frenchman, I believed that they existed. If I had told her how ungenerous my own friends had been, my countrymen, she would never have believed me. And if I had added that it was not generosity which had prompted me, but self-pity, myself giving to myself (because nobody could be as generous to me as I myself), she would probably have thought me slightly cracked.

I snuggled up to her and buried my head in her bosom. I slid my head down and licked her navel. Then farther down, kissing the thick clump of hair. She drew my head up slowly and, pulling me on top of her, buried her tongue in my mouth. My cock stiffened instantly; it slid into her just as naturally as an engine going into a switch. I had one of those long, lingering hard-ons which drive a woman mad. I jibbed her about at will, now over, now under her, then sidewise, then drawing it out slowly, tantalisingly, massaging the lips of the vulva with the

bristling tip of my cock. Finally I pulled it out altogether and twirled it around her breasts. She looked at it in astonishment. "Did you come?" she asked. "No," I said. "We're going to try something else now," and I dragged her out of bed and placed her in position for a proper, thorough back-scuttling. She reached up under her crotch and put it in for me, wiggling her ass around invitingly as she did so. Gripping her firmly around the waist, I shot it into her guts. "Oh, oh, that's marvellous, that's *wonderful*," she grunted, rolling her ass with a frenzied swing. I pulled it out again to give it an airing, rubbing it playfully against her buttocks. "No, no," she begged, "don't do that. Stick it in, stick it all the way in . . . I can't wait." Again she reached under and placed it for me, bending her back still more now, and pushing upward as if to trap the chandelier. I could feel it coming again, from the middle of my spine; I bent my knees slightly and pushed it in another notch or two. Then bango! it burst like a sky rocket.

It was well into the dinner hour when we parted down the street in front of a urinal. I hadn't made any definite appointment with her, nor had I enquired what her address might be. It was tacitly understood that the place to find her was at the café. Just as we were taking leave it suddenly occurred to me that I hadn't even asked her what her name was. I called her back and asked her – not for her full name but for her first name. "N-Y-S," she said, spelling it out. "Like the city, Nice." I walked off, saying it over and over again to myself. I had never heard of a girl being called by that name before. It sounded like the name of a precious stone.

When I reached the Place Clichy I realised that I was ravenously hungry. I stood in front of a fish restaurant on the Avenue de Clichy, studying the menu which was posted outside. I felt like having clams, lobsters, oysters, snails, a broiled bluefish, a tomato omelette, some tender asparagus tips, a savoury cheese, a loaf of bread, a bottle of chilled wine, some figs and nuts. I felt in my pocket, as I always do before entering a restaurant, and found a tiny sou. "Shit," I said to myself, "she might at least have spared me a few francs."

THE GREAT SWITCHEROO

Roald Dahl

Roald Dahl was a British novelist, short story writer, poet, screenwriter, and fighter pilot. Born in Wales to Norwegian parents, his books have sold over 200 million copies worldwide. Dahl served in the Royal Air Force during World War II, during which he became a flying ace and intelligence officer, rising to the rank of Acting Wing Commander. He rose to prominence in the 1940s with works for both children and adults, and he became one of the world's best-selling authors. *Switch Bitch* (1974) is a short story collection for adults. Originally published in *Playboy* magazine in 1965, each story deals with sex and deception.

There were about forty people at Jerry and Samantha's cocktail-party that evening. It was the usual crowd, the usual discomfort, the usual appalling noise. People had to stand very close to one another and shout to make themselves heard. Many were grinning, showing capped white teeth. Most of them had a cigarette in the left hand, a drink in the right.

I moved away from my wife Mary and her group. I headed for the small bar in the far corner, and when I got there, I sat down on a bar-stool and faced the room. I did this so that I could look at the women. I settled back with my shoulders against the bar-rail, sipping my Scotch and examining the women one by one over the rim of my glass.

I was studying not their figures but their faces, and what interested me there was not so much the face itself but the big red mouth in the middle of it all. And even then, it wasn't the whole mouth but only the lower lip. The lower lip, I had recently decided, was the great revealer. It gave away more than the eyes. The eyes hid their secrets. The lower lip hid very little. Take, for example, the lower lip of Jacinth Winkleman, who was standing nearest to me. Notice the wrinkles on that lip, how some were parallel and some radiated outward. No two people had the same pattern of lip-wrinkles, and come to think of it, you could catch a criminal that way if you had his lip-print on file and he had taken a drink at the scene of the crime. The lower lip is what you suck and nibble when you're ruffled, and Martha Sullivan was doing that right now as she watched from a distance her fatuous husband slobbering over Judy Martinson. You lick it when lecherous. I could see Ginny Lomax licking hers with the tip of her tongue as she stood beside Ted Dorling and gazed up into his face. It was a deliberate lick, the tongue coming out slowly and making a slow wet wipe along the entire length of the lower lip. I saw Ted Dorling looking at Ginny's tongue, which was what she wanted him to do.

It really does seem to be a fact, I told myself, as my eyes wandered from lower lip to lower lip across the room, that all the less attractive traits of the human animal, arrogance, rapacity, gluttony, lasciviousness, and the rest of them, are clearly signalled in that little carapace of scarlet skin. But you have to know the code. The protuberant or bulging lower lip is supposed to signify sensuality. But this is only half true in men and wholly untrue in women. In women, it is the thin line you should look for, the narrow blade with the sharply delineated bottom edge. And in the nymphomaniac there is a tiny just visible crest of skin at the top centre of the lower lip.

Samantha, my hostess, had that.

Where was she now, Samantha?

Ah, there she was, taking an empty glass out of a guest's hand. Now she was heading my way to refill it.

"Hello, Vic," she said. "You all alone?"

She's a nympho-bird all right, I told myself. But a very rare example of the species, because she is entirely and utterly monogamous. She is a married monogamous nympho-bird who stays for ever in her own nest.

She is also the fruitiest female I have ever set eyes upon in my whole life.

"Let me help you," I said, standing up and taking the glass from her hand. "What's wanted in here?"

"Vodka on the rocks," she said. "Thanks, Vic." She laid a lovely long white arm upon the top of the bar and she leaned forward so that her bosom rested on the bar-rail, squashing upward. "Oops," I said, pouring vodka outside the glass.

Samantha looked at me with huge brown eyes, but said nothing.

"I'll wipe it up," I said.

She took the refilled glass from me and walked away. I watched her go. She was wearing black pants. They were so tight around the buttocks that the smallest mole or pimple would have shown through the cloth. But Samantha Rainbow had not a blemish on her bottom. I caught myself licking my own lower lip. That's right, I thought. I want her. I lust after that woman. But it's too risky to try. It would be suicide to make a pass at a girl like that. First of all, she lives next door, which is too close. Secondly, as I have already said, she is monogamous. Thirdly, she is thick as a thief with Mary, my own wife. They exchange dark female secrets. Fourthly, her husband Jerry is my very old and good friend, and not even I, Victor Hammond, though I am churning with lust, would dream of trying to seduce the wife of a man who is my very old and trusty friend.

Unless . . .

It was at this point, as I sat on the bar-stool letching over Samantha Rainbow, that an interesting idea began to filter quietly into the centre of my brain. I remained still, allowing the idea to expand. I watched Samantha across the room, and began fitting her into the framework of the idea. Oh, Samantha, my gorgeous and juicy little jewel, I shall have you yet.

But could anybody seriously hope to get away with a crazy lark like that?

No, not in a million nights.

One couldn't even *try* it unless Jerry agreed. So why think about it?

Samantha was standing about six yards away, talking to Gilbert Mackesy. The

fingers of her right hand were curled around a tall glass. The fingers were long and almost certainly dexterous.

Assuming, just for the fun of it, that Jerry did agree, then even so, there would still be gigantic snags along the way. There was, for example, the little matter of physical characteristics. I had seen Jerry many times at the club having a shower after tennis, but right now I couldn't for the life of me recall the necessary details. It wasn't the sort of thing one noticed very much. Usually, one didn't even look.

Anyway, it would be madness to put the suggestion to Jerry point-blank. I didn't know him *that* well. He might be horrified. He might even turn nasty. There could be an ugly scene. I must test him out, therefore, in some subtle fashion.

"You know something," I said to Jerry about an hour later when we were sitting together on the sofa having a last drink. The guests were drifting away and Samantha was by the door saying goodbye to them. My own wife Mary was out on the terrace talking to Bob Swain. I could see through the open french windows. "You know something funny?" I said to Jerry as we sat together on the sofa.

"What's funny?" Jerry asked me.

"A fellow I had lunch with today told me a fantastic story. Quite unbelievable."

"What story?" Jerry said. The whisky had begun to make him sleepy.

"This man, the one I had lunch with, had a terrific letch after the wife of his friend who lived nearby. And his friend had an equally big letch after the wife of the man I had lunch with. Do you see what I mean?"

"You mean two fellers who lived close to each other both fancied each other's wives."

"Precisely," I said.

"Then there was no problem," Jerry said.

"There was a very big problem," I said. "The wives were both very faithful and honourable women."

"Samantha's the same," Jerry said. "She wouldn't look at another man."

"Nor would Mary," I said. "She's a fine girl."

Jerry emptied his glass and set it down carefully on the sofa-table. "So what happened in your story?" he said. "It sounds dirty."

"What happened," I said, "was that these two randy sods cooked up a plan which made it possible for each of them to ravish the other's wife without the wives ever knowing it. If you can believe such a thing."

"With chloroform?" Jerry said.

"Not at all. They were fully conscious."

"Impossible," Jerry said. "Someone's been pulling your leg."

"I don't think so," I said. "From the way this man told it to me, with all the little details and everything, I don't think he was making it up. In fact, I'm sure he wasn't. And listen, they didn't do it just once, either. They've been doing it every two or three weeks for months!"

"And the wives don't know?"

"They haven't a clue."

"I've got to hear this," Jerry said. "Let's get another drink first."

We crossed to the bar and refilled our glasses, then returned to the sofa.

"You must remember," I said, "that there had to be a tremendous lot of preparation and rehearsal beforehand. And many intimate details had to be exchanged to give the plan a chance of working. But the essential part of the scheme was simple:

"They fixed a night, call it Saturday. On that night the husbands and wives were to go up to bed as usual, at say eleven or eleven thirty.

"From then on, normal routine would be preserved. A little reading, perhaps, a little talking, then out with the lights.

"After lights out, the husbands would at once roll over and pretend to go to sleep. This was to discourage their wives from getting fresh, which at this stage must on no account be permitted. So the wives went to sleep. But the husbands stayed awake. So far so good.

"Then at precisely one a.m., by which time the wives would be in a good deep sleep, each husband would slip quietly out of bed, put on a pair of bedroom slippers and creep downstairs in his pyjamas. He would open the front door and go out into the night, taking care not to close the door behind him.

"They lived," I went on, "more or less across the street from one another. It was a quiet suburban neighbourhood and there was seldom anyone about at that hour. So these two furtive pyjama-clad figures would pass each other as they crossed the street, each one heading for another house, another bed, another woman."

Jerry was listening to me carefully. His eyes were a little glazed from drink, but he was listening to every word.

"The next part," I said, "had been prepared very thoroughly by both men. Each knew the inside of his friend's house almost as well as he knew his own. He knew how to find his way in the dark both downstairs and up without knocking over the furniture. He knew his way to the stairs and exactly how many steps there were to the top and which of them creaked and which didn't. He knew on which side of the bed the woman upstairs was sleeping.

"Each took off his slippers and left them in the hall, then up the stairs he crept in his bare feet and pyjamas. This part of it, according to my friend, was rather exciting. He was in a dark silent house that wasn't his own, and on his way to the main bedroom he had to pass no less than three children's bedrooms where the doors were always left slightly open."

"Children!" Jerry cried. "My God, what if one of them had woken up and said, 'Daddy, is that you?'"

"That was all taken care of," I said. "Emergency procedure would then come into effect immediately. Also if the wife, just as he was creeping into her room, woke up and said, 'Darling, what's wrong? Why are you wandering about?'; then again, emergency procedure."

"What emergency procedure?" Jerry said.

"Simple," I answered. "The man would immediately dash downstairs and out the front door and across to his own house and ring the bell. This was a signal for the other character, no matter what he was doing at the time, also to rush downstairs at full speed and open the door and let the other fellow in while he went out. This would get them both back quickly to their proper houses."

"With egg all over their faces," Jerry said.

"Not at all," I said.

"That doorbell would have woken the whole house," Jerry said.

"Of course," I said. "And the husband, returning upstairs in his pyjamas, would merely say, 'I went to see who the hell was ringing the bell at this ungodly hour. Couldn't find anyone. It must have been a drunk.'"

"What about the other guy?" Jerry asked. "How does he explain why he rushed downstairs when his wife or child spoke to him?"

"He would say, 'I heard someone prowling about outside, so I rushed down to get him, but he escaped.' 'Did you actually see him?' his wife would ask anxiously. "Of course I saw him," the husband would answer. 'He ran off down the street. He was too damn fast for me.' Whereupon the husband would be warmly congratulated for his bravery."

"Okay," Jerry said. "That's the easy part. Everything so far is just a matter of good planning and good timing. But what happens when these two horny characters actually climb into bed with each other's wives?"

"They go right to it," I said.

"The wives are sleeping," Jerry said.

"I know," I said. "So they proceed immediately with some very gentle but very skilful love-play, and by the time these dames are fully awake, they're as randy as rattle-snakes."

"No talking, I presume," Jerry said.

"Not a word."

"Okay, so the wives are awake," Jerry said. "And their hands get to work. So just for a start, what about the simple question of body size? What about the difference between the new man and the husband? What about tallness and shortness and fatness and thinness? You're not telling me these men were physically identical?"

"Not identical, obviously," I said. "But they were more or less similar in build and height. That was essential. They were both clean-shaven and had roughly the same amount of hair on their heads. That sort of similarity is commonplace. Look at you and me, for instance. We're roughly the same height and build, aren't we?"

"Are we?" Jerry said.

"How tall are you?" I said.

"Six foot exactly."

"I'm five eleven," I said. "One inch difference. What do you weigh?"

"One hundred and eighty-seven."

"I'm a hundred and eighty-four," I said. "What's three pounds among friends?"

There was a pause. Jerry was looking out through the french windows on to the terrace where my wife, Mary, was standing. Mary was still talking to Bob Swain and the evening sun was shining in her hair. She was a dark pretty girl with a bosom. I watched Jerry. I saw his tongue come out and go sliding along the surface of his lower lip.

"I guess you're right," Jerry said, still looking at Mary. "I guess we are about the same size, you and me." When he turned back and faced me again, there was a little red rose high up on each cheek. "Go on about these two men," he said. "What about some of the other differences?"

"You mean faces?" I said. "No one's going to see faces in the dark."

"I'm not talking about faces," Jerry said.

"What are you talking about, then?"

"I'm talking about their cocks," Jerry said. "That's what it's all about, isn't it? And you're not going to tell me . . ."

"Oh yes, I am," I said. "Just so long as both men were either circumcised or uncircumcised, then there was really no problem."

"Are you seriously suggesting that all men have the same size in cocks?" Jerry said. "Because they don't."

"I know they don't," I said.

"Some are enormous," Jerry said. "And some are titchy."

"There are always exceptions," I told him. "But you'd be surprised at the number of men whose measurements are virtually the same, give or take a centimetre. According to my friend, ninety per cent are normal. Only ten per cent are notably large or small."

"I don't believe that," Jerry said.

"Check on it sometime," I said. "Ask some well-travelled girl."

Jerry took a long slow sip of his whisky, and his eyes over the top of his glass were looking again at Mary on the terrace. "What about the rest of it?" he said.

"No problem," I said.

"No problem, my arse," he said. "Shall I tell you why this is a phony story?"

"Go ahead."

"Everybody knows that a wife and husband who have been married for some years develop a kind of routine. It's inevitable. My God, a new operator would be spotted instantly. You know damn well he would. You can't suddenly wade in with a totally different style and expect the woman not to notice it, and I don't care how randy she was. She'd smell a rat in the first minute!"

"A routine can be duplicated," I said. "Just so long as every detail of that routine is described beforehand."

"A bit personal, that," Jerry said.

"The whole thing's personal," I said. "So each man tells his story. He tells precisely what he usually does. He tells everything. The lot. The works. The whole routine from beginning to end."

"Jesus," Jerry said.

"Each of these men," I said, "had to learn a new part. He had, in effect, to become an actor. He was impersonating another character."

"Not so easy, that," Jerry said.

"No problem at all, according to my friend. The only thing one had to watch out for was not to get carried away and start improvising. One had to follow the stage directions very carefully and stick to them."

Jerry took another pull at his drink. He also took another look at Mary on the terrace. Then he leaned back against the sofa, glass in hand.

"These two characters," he said. "You mean they actually pulled it off?"

"I'm damn sure they did," I said. "They're still doing it. About once every three weeks."

"Fantastic story," Jerry said. "And a damn crazy dangerous thing to do. Just imagine the sort of hell that would break loose if you were caught.

Instant divorce. Two divorces, in fact. One on each side of the street. Not worth it."

"Takes a lot of guts," I said.

"The party's breaking up," Jerry said. "They're all going home with their goddamn wives."

I didn't say any more after that. We sat there for a couple of minutes sipping our drinks while the guests began drifting towards the hall.

"Did he say it was fun, this friend of yours?" Jerry asked suddenly.

"He said it was a gas," I answered. "He said all the normal pleasures got intensified one hundred per cent because of the risk. He swore it was the greatest way of doing it in the world, impersonating the husband and the wife not knowing it."

At that point, Mary came in through the french windows with Bob Swain. She had an empty glass in one hand and a flame-coloured azalea in the other. She had picked the azalea on the terrace.

"I've been watching you," she said, pointing the flower at me like a pistol. "You've hardly stopped talking for the last ten minutes. What's he been telling you, Jerry?"

"A dirty story," Jerry said, grinning.

"He does that when he drinks," Mary said.

"Good story," Jerry said. "But totally impossible. Get him to tell it to you sometime."

"I don't like dirty stories," Mary said. "Come along, Vic. It's time we went."

"Don't go yet," Jerry said, fixing his eyes upon her splendid bosom. "Have another drink."

"No thanks," she said. "The children'll be screaming for their supper. I've had a lovely time."

"Aren't you going to kiss me good night?" Jerry said, getting up from the sofa. He went for her mouth, but she turned her head quickly and he caught only the edge of her cheek.

"Go away, Jerry," she said. "You're drunk."

"Not drunk," Jerry said. "Just lecherous."

"Don't you get lecherous with me, my boy," Mary said sharply. "I hate that sort of talk." She marched away across the room, carrying her bosom before her like a battering-ram.

"So long, Jerry," I said. "Fine party."

Mary, full of dark looks, was waiting for me in the hall. Samantha was there, too, saying goodbye to the last guests – Samantha with her dexterous fingers and her smooth skin and her smooth, dangerous thighs. "Cheer up, Vic," she said to me, her white teeth showing. She looked like the creation, the beginning of the world, the first morning. "Good night, Vic darling," she said, stirring her fingers in my vitals.

I followed Mary out of the house. "You feeling all right?" she asked.

"Yes," I said. "Why not?"

"The amount you drink is enough to make anyone feel ill," she said.

There was a scrubby old hedge dividing our place from Jerry's and there was a gap in it we always used. Mary and I walked through the gap in silence. We

went into the house and she cooked up a big pile of scrambled eggs and bacon, and we ate it with the children.

After the meal, I wandered outside. The summer evening was clear and cool and because I had nothing else to do I decided to mow the grass in the front garden. I got the mower out of the shed and started it up. Then I began the old routine of marching back and forth behind it. I like mowing grass. It is a soothing operation, and on our front lawn I could always look at Samantha's house going one way and think about her going the other.

I had been at it for about ten minutes when Jerry came strolling through the gap in the hedge. He was smoking a pipe and had his hands in his pockets and he stood on the edge of the grass, watching me. I pulled up in front of him, but left the motor ticking over.

"Hi, sport," he said. "How's everything?"

"I'm in the doghouse," I said. "So are you."

"Your little wife," he said, "is just too goddamn prim and prissy to be true."

"Oh, I know that."

"She rebuked me in my own house," Jerry said.

"Not very much."

"It was enough," he said, smiling slightly.

"Enough for what?"

"Enough to make me want to get a little bit of my own back on her. So what would you think if I suggested you and I have a go at that thing your friend told you about at lunch?"

When he said this, I felt such a surge of excitement my stomach nearly jumped out of my mouth. I gripped the handles of the mower and started revving the engine.

"Have I said the wrong thing?" Jerry asked.

I didn't answer.

"Listen," he said. "If you think it's a lousy idea, let's just forget I ever mentioned it. You're not mad at me, are you?"

"I'm not mad at you, Jerry," I said. "It's just that it never entered my head that *we* should do it."

"It entered mine," he said. "The set-up is perfect. We wouldn't even have to cross the street." His face had gone suddenly bright and his eyes were shining like two stars. "So what do you say, Vic?"

"I'm thinking," I said.

"Maybe you don't fancy Samantha."

"I don't honestly know," I said.

"She's lots of fun," Jerry said. "I guarantee that."

At this point, I saw Mary come out on to the front porch. "There's Mary," I said. "She's looking for the children. We'll talk some more tomorrow."

"Then it's a deal?"

"It could be, Jerry. But only on condition we don't rush it. I want to be dead sure everything is right before we start. Damn it all, this is a whole brand-new can of beans!"

"No, it's not!" he said. "Your friend said it was a gas. He said it was easy."

"Ah, yes," I said. "My friend. Of course. But each case is different." I opened

the throttle on the mower and went whirring away across the lawn. When I got to the far side and turned around, Jerry was already through the gap in the hedge and walking up to his front door.

The next couple of weeks was a period of high conspiracy for Jerry and me. We held secret meetings in bars and restaurants to discuss strategy, and sometimes he dropped into my office after work and we had a planning session behind the closed door. Whenever a doubtful point arose, Jerry would always say, "How did your friend do it?" And I would play for time and say, "I'll call him up and ask him about that one."

After many conferences and much talk, we agreed upon the following main points:

1. That D Day should be a Saturday.
2. That on D Day evening we should take our wives out to a good dinner, the four of us together.
3. That Jerry and I should leave our houses and cross over through the gap in the hedge at precisely one a.m. Sunday morning.
4. That instead of lying in bed in the dark until one a.m. came along, we should both, as soon as our wives were asleep, go quietly downstairs to the kitchen and drink coffee.
5. That we should use the front doorbell idea if an emergency arose.
6. That the return cross-over time was fixed for two a.m.
7. That while in the wrong bed, questions (if any) from the woman must be answered by an "Uh-uh" sounded with the lips closed tight.
8. That I myself must immediately give up cigarettes and take to a pipe so that I would "smell" the same as Jerry.
9. That we should at once start using the same brand of hair oil and after-shave lotion.
10. That as both of us normally wore our wrist-watches in bed, and they were much the same shape, it was decided not to exchange. Neither of us wore rings.
11. That each man must have something unusual about him that the woman would identify positively with her own husband. We therefore invented what became known as "The Sticking Plaster Ploy". It worked like this: on D Day evening, when the couples arrived back in their own homes immediately after the dinner, each husband would make a point of going to the kitchen to cut himself a piece of cheese. At the same time, he would carefully stick a large piece of plaster over the tip of the forefinger of his right hand. Having done this, he would hold up the finger and say to his wife, "I cut myself. It's nothing, but it was bleeding a bit." Thus, later on, when the men have switched beds, each woman will be made very much aware of the plaster-covered finger (the man would see to that), and will associate it directly with her own husband. An important psychological ploy, this, calculated to dissipate any tiny suspicion that might enter the mind of either female.

So much for the basic plans. Next came what we referred to in our notes as "Familiarization with the Layout". Jerry schooled me first. He gave me three

hours' training in his own house one Sunday afternoon when his wife and children were out. I had never been into their bedroom before. On the dressing table were Samantha's perfumes, her brushes, and all her other little things. A pair of her stockings was draped over the back of a chair. Her nightdress, white and blue, was hanging behind the door leading to the bathroom.

"Okay," Jerry said. "It'll be pitch dark when you come in. Samantha sleeps on this side, so you must tiptoe around the end of the bed and slide in on the other side, over there. I'm going to blindfold you and let you practise."

At first, with the blindfold on, I wandered all over the room like a drunk. But after about an hour's work, I was able to negotiate the course pretty well. But before Jerry would finally pass me out, I had to go blindfold all the way from the front door through the hall, up the stairs, past the children's rooms, into Samantha's room and finish up in exactly the right place. And I had to do it silently, like a thief. All this took three hours of hard work, but I got it in the end.

The following Sunday morning when Mary had taken our children to church, I was able to give Jerry the same sort of work-out in my house. He learned the ropes faster than me, and within an hour he had passed the blindfold test without placing a foot wrong.

It was during this session that we decided to disconnect each woman's bedside lamp as we entered the bedroom. So Jerry practised finding the plug and pulling it out with his blindfold on, and the following week-end, I was able to do the same in Jerry's house.

Now came by far the most important part of our training. We called it "Spilling the Beans", and it was here that both of us had to describe in every detail the procedure we adopted when making love to our own wives. We agreed not to worry ourselves with any exotic variations that either of us might or might not occasionally practise. We were concerned only with teaching one another the most commonly used routine, the one least likely to arouse suspicion.

The session took place in my office at six o'clock on a Wednesday evening, after the staff had gone home. At first, we were both slightly embarrassed, and neither of us wanted to begin. So I got out the bottle of whisky, and after a couple of stiff drinks, we loosened up and the teach-in started. While Jerry talked I took notes, and vice versa. At the end of it all, it turned out that the only real difference between Jerry's routine and my own was one of tempo. But what a difference it was! He took things (if what he said was to be believed) in such a leisurely fashion and he prolonged the moments to such an extravagant degree that I wondered privately to myself whether his partner did not sometimes go to sleep in the middle of it all. My job, however, was not to criticize but to copy, and I said nothing.

Jerry was not so discreet. At the end of my personal description, he had the temerity to say, "Is that really what you do?"

"What do you mean?" I asked.

"I mean is it all over and done with as quickly as that?"

"Look," I said. "We aren't here to give each other lessons. We're here to learn the facts."

"I know that," he said. "But I'm going to feel a bit of an ass if I copy your

style exactly. My God, you go through it like an express train whizzing through a country station!"

I stared at him, mouth open.

"Don't look so surprised," he said. "The way you told it to me, anyone would think . . ."

"Think what?" I said.

"Oh, forget it," he said.

"Thank you," I said. I was furious. There are two things in this world at which I happen to know I excel. One is driving an automobile and the other is you-know-what. So to have him sit there and tell me I didn't know how to behave with my own wife was a monstrous piece of effrontery. It was he who didn't know, not me. Poor Samantha. What she must have had to put up with over the years.

"I'm sorry I spoke," Jerry said. He poured more whisky into our glasses. "Here's to the great switcheroo!" he said. "When do we go?"

"Today is Wednesday," I said. "How about this coming Saturday?"

"Christ," Jerry said.

"We ought to do it while everything's still fresh in our minds," I said. "There's an awful lot to remember."

Jerry walked to the window and looked down at the traffic in the street below. "Okay," he said, turning around. "Next Saturday it shall be!" Then we drove home in our separate cars.

"Jerry and I thought we'd take you and Samantha out to dinner Saturday night," I said to Mary. We were in the kitchen and she was cooking hamburgers for the children.

She turned around and faced me, frying-pan in one hand, spoon in the other. Her blue eyes looked straight into mine. "My Lord, Vic," she said. "How nice. But what are we celebrating?"

I looked straight back at her and said, "I thought it would be a change to see some new faces. We're always meeting the same old bunch of people in the same old houses."

She took a step forward and kissed me on the cheek. "What a good man you are," she said. "I love you."

"Don't forget to phone the baby-sitter."

"No, I'll do it tonight," she said.

Thursday and Friday passed very quickly, and suddenly it was Saturday. It was D Day. I woke up feeling madly excited. After breakfast, I couldn't sit still, so I decided to go out and wash the car. I was in the middle of this when Jerry came strolling through the gap in the hedge, pipe in mouth.

"Hi, sport," he said. "This is the day."

"I know that," I said. I also had a pipe in my mouth. I was forcing myself to smoke it, but I had trouble keeping it alight, and the smoke burned my tongue.

"How're you feeling?" Jerry asked.

"Terrific," I said. "How about you?"

"I'm nervous," he said.

"Don't be nervous, Jerry."

"This is one hell of a thing we're trying to do," he said. "I hope we pull it off."

I went on polishing the windshield. I had never known Jerry to be nervous of anything before. It worried me a bit.

"I'm damn glad we're not the first people ever to try it," he said. "If no one had ever done it before, I don't think I'd risk it."

"I agree," I said.

"What stops me being too nervous," he said, "is the fact that your friend found it so fantastically easy."

"My friend said it was a cinch," I said. "But for Chris-sake, Jerry, don't be nervous when the time comes. That would be disastrous."

"Don't worry," he said. "But Jesus, it's exciting, isn't it?"

"It's exciting all right," I said.

"Listen," he said. "We'd better go easy on the booze tonight."

"Good idea," I said. "See you at eight thirty."

At half past eight, Samantha, Jerry, Mary, and I drove in Jerry's car to Billy's Steak House. The restaurant, despite its name, was high-class and expensive, and the girls had put on long dresses for the occasion. Samantha was wearing something green that didn't start until it was halfway down her front, and I had never seen her looking lovelier. There were candles on our table. Samantha was seated opposite me and whenever she leaned forward with her face close to the flame, I could see that tiny crest of skin at the top centre of her lower lip. "Now," she said as she accepted a menu from the waiter, "I wonder what I'm going to have tonight."

Ho-ho-ho, I thought, that's a good question.

Everything went fine in the restaurant and the girls enjoyed themselves. When we arrived back at Jerry's house, it was eleven forty-five, and Samantha said, "Come in and have a nightcap."

"Thanks," I said, "but it's a bit late. And the baby-sitter has to be driven home." So Mary and I walked across to our house, and *now*, I told myself as I entered the front door, *from now on* the countdown begins. I must keep a clear head and forget nothing.

While Mary was paying the baby-sitter, I went to the fridge and found a piece of Canadian cheddar. I took a knife from the drawer and a strip of plaster from the cupboard. I stuck the plaster around the tip of the forefinger of my right hand and waited for Mary to turn around.

"I cut myself," I said holding up the finger for her to see. "It's nothing, but it was bleeding a bit."

"I'd have thought you'd had enough to eat for the evening," was all she said. But the plaster registered on her mind and my first little job had been done.

I drove the baby-sitter home and by the time I got back up to the bedroom it was round about midnight and Mary was already half asleep with her light out. I switched out the light on my side of the bed and went into the bathroom to undress. I pottered about in there for ten minutes or so and when I came out, Mary, as I had hoped, was well and truly sleeping. There seemed no point in getting into bed beside her. So I simply pulled back the covers a bit on my side to make it easier for Jerry, then with my slippers on, I went downstairs to the kitchen and switched on the electric kettle. It was now twelve seventeen. Forty-three minutes to go.

At twelve thirty-five, I went upstairs to check on Mary and the kids. Everyone was sound asleep.

At twelve fifty-five, five minutes before zero hour, I went up again for a final check. I went right up close to Mary's bed and whispered her name. There was no answer. Good. *That's it! Let's go!*

I put a brown raincoat over my pyjamas. I switched off the kitchen light so that the whole house was in darkness. I put the front door lock on the latch. And then, feeling an enormous sense of exhilaration, I stepped silently out into the night.

There were no lamps on our street to lighten the darkness. There was no moon or even a star to be seen. It was a black black night, but the air was warm and there was a little breeze blowing from somewhere.

I headed for the gap in the hedge. When I got very close, I was able to make out the hedge itself and find the gap. I stopped there, waiting. Then I heard Jerry's footsteps coming toward me.

"Hi, sport," he whispered. "Everything okay?"

"All ready for you," I whispered back.

He moved on. I heard his slippered feet padding softly over the grass as he went toward my house. I went toward his.

I opened Jerry's front door. It was even darker inside than out. I closed the door carefully. I took off my rain-coat and hung it on the door knob. I removed my slippers and placed them against the wall by the door. I literally could not see my hands before my face. Everything had to be done by touch.

My goodness, I was glad Jerry had made me practise blindfold for so long. It wasn't my feet that guided me now but my fingers. The fingers of one hand or another were never for a moment out of contact with something, a wall, the banister, a piece of furniture, a window-curtain. And I knew or thought I knew exactly where I was all the time. But it was an awesome eerie feeling trespassing on tiptoe through someone else's house in the middle of the night. As I fingered my way up the stairs, I found myself thinking of the burglars who had broken into our front room last winter and stolen the television set. When the police came next morning, I pointed out to them an enormous turd lying in the snow outside the garage. "They nearly always do that," one of the cops told me. "They can't help it. They're scared.'

I reached the top of the stairs. I crossed the landing with my right fingertips touching the wall all the time. I started down the corridor, but paused when my hand found the door of the first children's room. The door was slightly open. I listened. I could hear young Robert Rainbow, aged eight, breathing evenly inside. I moved on. I found the door to the second children's bedroom. This one belonged to Billy, aged six and Amanda, three. I stood listening. All was well.

The main bedroom was at the end of the corridor, about four yards on. I reached the door. Jerry had left it open, as planned. I went in. I stood absolutely still just inside the door, listening for any sign that Samantha might be awake. All was quiet. I felt my way around the wall until I reached Samantha's side of the bed. Immediately, I knelt on the floor and found the plug connecting her bedside lamp. I drew it from its socket and laid it on the carpet. Good. Much safer now. I stood up. I couldn't see Samantha, and at first I couldn't hear anything either. I bent low over the bed. Ah yes, I could hear her breathing. Suddenly I caught a

whiff of the heavy musky perfume she had been using that evening, and I felt the blood rushing to my groin. Quickly I tiptoed around the big bed, keeping two fingers in gentle contact with the edge of the bed the whole way.

All I had to do now was get in. I did so, but as I put my weight upon the mattress, the creaking of the springs underneath sounded as though someone was firing a rifle in the room. I lay motionless, holding my breath. I could hear my heart thumping away like an engine in my throat. Samantha was facing away from me. She didn't move. I pulled the covers up over my chest and turned toward her. A female glow came out of her to me. Here we go, then! *Now!*

I slid a hand over and touched her body. Her nightdress was warm and silky. I rested the hand gently on her hips. Still she didn't move. I waited a minute or so, then I allowed the hand that lay upon the hip to steal onward and go exploring. Slowly, deliberately, and very accurately, my fingers began the process of setting her on fire.

She stirred. She turned on to her back. Then she murmured sleepily, "Oh, dear . . . Oh, my goodness me . . . Good heavens, darling!"

I, of course, said nothing. I just kept on with the job.

A couple of minutes went by.

She was lying quite still.

Another minute passed. Then another. She didn't move a muscle.

I began to wonder how much longer it would be before she caught alight.

I persevered.

But why the silence? Why this absolute and total immobility, this frozen posture?

Suddenly it came to me. I had forgotten completely about Jerry! I was so hotted up, I had forgotten all about his own personal routine! I was doing it my way, not his! His way was far more complex than mine. It was ridiculously elaborate. It was quite unnecessary. But it was what she was used to. And now she was noticing the difference and trying to figure out what on earth was going on.

But it was too late to change direction now. I must keep going.

I kept going. The woman beside me was like a coiled spring lying there. I could feel the tension under her skin. I began to sweat.

Suddenly, she uttered a queer little groan.

More ghastly thoughts rushed through my mind. Could she be ill? Was she having a heart attack? Ought I to get the hell out quick?

She groaned again, louder this time. Then all at once, she cried out, "Yes-yes-yes-yes-yes!" and like a bomb whose slow fuse had finally reached the dynamite, she exploded into life. She grabbed me in her arms and went for me with such incredible ferocity, I felt I was being set upon by a tiger.

Or should I say tigress?

I never dreamed a woman could do the things Samantha did to me then. She was a whirlwind, a dazzling frenzied whirlwind that tore me up by the roots and spun me around and carried me high into the heavens, to places I did not know existed.

I myself did not contribute. How could I? I was helpless. I was the palm-tree spinning in the heavens, the lamb in the claws of the tiger. It was as much as I could do to keep breathing.

Thrilling it was, all the same, to surrender to the hands of a violent woman, and for the next ten, twenty, thirty minutes – how would I know? – the storm raged on. But I have no intention here of regaling the reader with bizarre details. I do not approve of washing juicy linen in public. I am sorry, but there it is. I only hope that my reticence will not create too strong a sense of anticlimax. Certainly, there was nothing anti about my own climax, and in the final searing paroxysm I gave a shout which should have awakened the entire neighbourhood. Then I collapsed. I crumpled up like a drained wineskin.

Samantha, as though she had done no more than drink a glass of water, simply turned away from me and went right back to sleep.

Phew!

I lay still, recuperating slowly.

I had been right, you see, about that little thing on her lower lip, had I not?

Come to think of it, I had been right about more or less everything that had to do with this incredible escapade. What a triumph! I felt wonderfully relaxed and well-spent.

I wondered what time it was. My watch was not a luminous one. I'd better go. I crept out of bed. I felt my way, a trifle less cautiously this time, around the bed, out of the bedroom, along the corridor, down the stairs and into the hall of the house. I found my raincoat and slippers. I put them on. I had a lighter in the pocket of my raincoat. I used it and read the time. It was eight minutes before two. Later than I thought, I opened the front door and stepped out into the black night.

My thoughts now began to concentrate upon Jerry. Was he all right? Had he gotten away with it? I moved through the darkness toward the gap in the hedge.

"Hi, sport," a voice whispered beside me.

"Jerry!"

"Everything okay?" Jerry asked.

"Fantastic," I said. "Amazing. What about you?"

"Same with me," he said. I caught the flash of his white teeth grinning at me in the dark. "We made it, Vic!" he whispered, touching my arm. "You were right! It worked! It was sensational!"

"See you tomorrow," I whispered. "Go home."

We moved apart. I went through the hedge and entered my house. Three minutes later, I was safely back in my own bed, and my own wife was sleeping soundly alongside me.

The next morning was Sunday. I was up at eight thirty and went downstairs in pyjamas and dressing-gown, as I always do on a Sunday, to make breakfast for the family. I had left Mary sleeping. The two boys, Victor, aged nine, and Wally, seven, were already down.

"Hi, daddy," Wally said.

"I've got a great new breakfast," I announced.

"What?" both boys said together. They had been into town and fetched the Sunday paper and were now reading the comics.

"We make some buttered toast and we spread orange marmalade on it," I said. "Then we put strips of crisp bacon on top of the marmalade."

"*Bacon!*" Victor said. "With *orange marmalade*!"

"I know. But you wait till you try it. It's wonderful."

I dished out the grapefruit juice and drank two glasses of it myself. I set another on the table for Mary when she came down. I switched on the electric kettle, put the bread in the toaster, and started to fry the bacon. At this point, Mary came into the kitchen. She had a flimsy peach-coloured chiffon thing over her nightdress.

"Good morning," I said, watching her over my shoulder as I manipulated the frying-pan.

She did not answer. She went to her chair at the kitchen table and sat down. She started to sip her juice. She looked neither at me nor at the boys. I went on frying the bacon.

"Hi, mummy," Wally said.

She didn't answer this either.

The smell of the bacon fat was beginning to turn my stomach.

"I'd like some coffee," Mary said, not looking around. Her voice was very odd.

"Coming right up," I said. I pushed the frying-pan away from the heat and quickly made a cup of black instant coffee. I placed it before her.

"Boys," she said, addressing the children, "would you please do your reading in the other room till breakfast is ready."

"Us?" Victor said. "Why?"

"Because I say so."

"Are we doing something wrong?" Wally asked.

"No, honey, you're not. I just want to be left alone for a moment with daddy."

I felt myself shrink inside my skin. I wanted to run. I wanted to rush out the front door and go running down the street and hide.

"Get yourself a coffee, Vic," she said, "and sit down." Her voice was quite flat. There was no anger in it. There was just nothing. And she still wouldn't look at me. The boys went out, taking the comic section with them.

"Shut the door," Mary said to them.

I put a spoonful of powdered coffee into my cup and poured boiling water over it. I added milk and sugar. The silence was shattering. I crossed over and sat down in my chair opposite her. It might just as well have been an electric chair, the way I was feeling.

"Listen, Vic," she said, looking into her coffee cup. "I want to get this said before I lose my nerve and then I won't be able to say it."

"For heaven's sake, what's all the drama about?" I asked. "Has something happened?"

"Yes, Vic, it has."

"What?"

Her face was pale and still and distant, unconscious of the kitchen around her.

"Come on, then, out with it," I said bravely.

"You're not going to like this very much," she said, and her big blue haunted-looking eyes rested a moment on my face, then travelled away.

"What am I not going to like very much?" I said. The sheer terror of it all was beginning to stir my bowels. I felt the same way as those burglars the cops had told me about.

"You know I hate talking about love-making and all that sort of thing," she

said. "I've never once talked to you about it all the time we've been married."

"That's true," I said.

She took a sip of her coffee, but she wasn't tasting it. "The point is this," she said. "I've never liked it. If you really want to know, I've hated it."

"Hated what?" I asked.

"Sex," she said. "Doing it."

"Good Lord!" I said.

"It's never given me even the slightest little bit of pleasure."

This was shattering enough in itself, but the real cruncher was still to come, I felt sure of that.

"I'm sorry if that surprises you," she added.

I couldn't think of anything to say, so I kept quiet.

Her eyes rose again from the coffee cup and looked into mine, watchful, as if calculating something, then fell again. "I wasn't ever going to tell you," she said. "And I never would have if it hadn't been for last night."

I said very slowly, "What about last night?"

"Last night," she said, "I suddenly found out what the whole crazy thing is all about."

"You did?"

She looked full at me now, and her face was as open as a flower. "Yes," she said. "I surely did."

I didn't move.

"Oh darling!" she cried, jumping up and rushing over and giving me an enormous kiss. "Thank you so much for last night! You were marvellous! And I was marvellous! We were both marvellous! Don't look so embarrassed, my darling! You ought to be proud of yourself! You were fantastic! I love you! I do! I do!"

I just sat there.

She leaned close to me and put an arm around my shoulders. "And now," she said softly, "now that you have . . . I don't quite know how to say this . . . now that you have sort of discovered what it is I *need*, everything is going to be so marvellous from now on!"

I still sat there. She went slowly back to her chair. A big tear was running down one of her cheeks. I couldn't think why.

"I was right to tell you, wasn't I?" she said, smiling through her tears.

"Yes," I said. "Oh, yes." I stood up and went over to the cooker so that I wouldn't be facing her. Through the kitchen window, I caught sight of Jerry crossing his garden with the Sunday paper under his arm. There was a lilt in his walk, a little prance of triumph in each pace he took, and when he reached the steps of his front porch, he ran up them two at a time.

From THE CLAIMING OF SLEEPING BEAUTY

Anne Rice writing as A. N. Roquelaure

Anne Rice was born and raised in New Orleans, Louisiana. She holds a Master of Arts Degree in English and Creative Writing from San Francisco State University, as well as a Bachelor's Degree in Political Science. She is the author of over thirty novels. Her first, *Interview with the Vampire*, was published in 1976 and has gone on to become one of the bestselling novels of all time. She continued her saga of the Vampire Lestat in a series of books, collectively known as *The Vampire Chronicles*, which have both great mainstream and cult followings.

The Prince had all his young life known the story of Sleeping Beauty, cursed to sleep for a hundred years, with her parents, the King and Queen, and all of the Court, after pricking her finger on a spindle.

But he did not believe it until he was inside the castle.

Even the bodies of those other Princes caught in the thorns of the rose vines that covered the walls had not made him believe it. They had come believing it, true enough, but he must see for himself inside the castle.

Careless with grief for the death of his father, and too powerful under his mother's rule for his own good, he cut these awesome vines at their roots, and immediately prevented them from ensnaring him. It was not his desire to die so much as to conquer.

And picking his way through the bones of those who had failed to solve the mystery, he stepped alone into the great banquet hall.

The sun was high in the sky and those vines had fallen away, so the light fell in dusty shafts from the lofty windows.

And all along the banquet table, the Prince saw the men and women of the old Court, sleeping under layers of dust, their ruddy and slack faces spun over with spider webs.

He gasped to see the servants dozing against the walls, their clothing rotted to tatters.

But it was true, this old tale. And, fearless as before, he went in search of the Sleeping Beauty who must be at the core of it.

In the topmost bedchamber of the house he found her. He had stepped over sleeping chambermaids and valets, and, breathing the dust and damp of the place, he finally stood in the door of her sanctuary.

Her flaxen hair lay long and straight over the deep green velvet of her bed, and

And the Prince went to the door to speak to her.

"Go to your master, the King. Tell him the Prince has come who was foretold to remove the curse on this household. Tell him I shall be closeted now with his daughter."

He shut the door, bolting it, and turned to look at Beauty.

Beauty was covering her breasts with her hands, and her long straight golden hair, heavy and full of a great silky density, flared down to the bed around her.

She bowed her head so that the hair covered her.

But she looked at the Prince and her eyes struck him as devoid of fear or cunning. She was like those tender animals of the wood just before he slew them in the hunt: eyes wide, expressionless.

Her bosom heaved with anxious breath. And now he laughed, drawing near, and lifting her hair back from her right shoulder. She looked up at him steadily, her cheeks suffused with a raw blush, and again he kissed her.

He opened her mouth with his lips, and taking her hands in his left hand he laid them down on her naked lap so that he might lift her breasts now and better examine them.

"Innocent beauty," he whispered.

He knew what she was seeing as she looked at him. He was only three years older than she had been. Eighteen, newly a man, but afraid of nothing and no one. He was tall, black haired; he had a lean build which made him agile. He liked to think of himself as a sword – light, straight, and very deft, and utterly dangerous.

And he had left behind him many who would concur with this.

He had not so much pride in himself now as immense satisfaction. He had gotten to the core of the accursed castle.

There were knocks at the door, cries.

He didn't bother to answer them. He laid Beauty down again.

"I'm your Prince," he said, "and that is how you will address me, and that is why you will obey me."

He parted her legs again. He saw the blood of her innocence on the cloth and this made him laugh softly to himself as again he gently entered her.

She gave a soft series of moans that were like kisses to his ear.

"Answer me properly," he whispered.

"My Prince," she said.

"Ah," he sighed, "that is lovely."

When he opened the door, the room was almost dark. He told the servants he would have his supper now, and he would receive the King immediately.

Beauty he ordered to dine with him, and to remain with him, and he told her firmly that she was to wear no clothing.

"It's my wish to have you naked and always ready for me," he said.

He might have told her she was incomparably lovely, with only her golden hair to clothe her, and the blushes on her cheeks to cover her, and her hands trying so vainly to shield her sex and her breasts, but he didn't say this aloud.

Rather he took her little wrists and held them behind her back as the table was brought in, and then he ordered her to sit opposite.

The table was not so wide that he couldn't reach her easily, touch her, caress her breasts if he liked. And reaching out he lifted her chin so that he could inspect

her by the light of the servants' candles.

The table was laid with roast pork and fowl, fruit in big glistening silver bowls, and immediately the King stood in the door, dressed in his heavy ceremonial robes, a gold crown atop his head as he bowed to the Prince and waited for the command to enter.

"Your Kingdom has been neglected for a hundred years," said the Prince as he lifted his wine goblet. "Your vassals have many of them fled to other lords; good land lies fallow. But you have your wealth, your Court, your soldiers. So much lies ahead of you."

"I am in your debt, Prince," the King answered. "But will you tell me your name, the name of your family?"

"My mother, Queen Eleanor, lives on the other side of the forest," said the Prince. "In your time, it was my great-grandfather's kingdom; he was King Heinrick, your powerful ally."

The Prince saw the King's immediate surprise and then his look of confusion. The Prince understood it perfectly. And when a blush came to the King's face, the Prince said:

"And in those times you served your time in my great-grandfather's castle, did you not, and perhaps your queen also?"

The King pressed his lips together in resignation and slowly nodded. "You are the son of a powerful monarch," he whispered. And the Prince could see that the King would not raise his eyes to see his naked daughter, Beauty.

"I will take Beauty to serve," said the Prince. "She is mine now." He took out his long silver knife and, cutting the hot, succulent pork, he laid several pieces on his own plate. The servants all about him vied with one another to place other dishes near him.

Beauty sat with her hands over her breasts again; her cheeks were moist with tears, and she was trembling slightly.

"As you wish," said the King. "I am in your debt."

"You have your life and your Kingdom now," said the Prince. "And I have your daughter. I will spend the night here. And tomorrow set out to make her my Princess across the mountains."

He had placed some fruit on his plate, and other hot morsels of cooked food, and now he snapped his fingers gently and in a whisper told Beauty to come around the table to him.

He could see her shame before the servants.

But he brushed her hand away from her sex.

"Never cover yourself like that again," he said. He spoke these words almost tenderly, as he lifted her hair back from her face.

"Yes, my Prince," she whispered. She had a lovely little voice. "But it's so difficult."

"Of course it is," he smiled. "But for me you'll do it."

And now he took her and placed her on his lap, cradling her in his left arm. "Kiss me," he said, and feeling her warm mouth on his again, he felt his desire rising too soon for his taste, but he decided he could savor this slight torment.

"You may go," he said to the King. "Tell your servants to have my horse ready in the morning. I won't need a horse for Beauty. My soldiers you've found, no doubt, at your gates," and the Prince laughed. "They were afraid to come in with me. Tell them to be ready at dawn, and then you can say goodbye to your daughter, Beauty."

The King glanced up very quickly to accept the Prince's commands and with unfailing courtesy he backed out of the doorway.

The Prince turned his full attention to Beauty.

Lifting a napkin he wiped at her tears. She kept her hands obediently on her thighs, exposing her sex, and he observed that she did not try to hide her stiff little pink nipples with her arms and he approved of this.

"Now don't be frightened," he said to her softly, feeding a little on her trembling mouth again, and then slapping her breasts so they shivered lightly. "I could be old and ugly."

"Ah, but then I could feel sorry for you," she said in a sweet, tremulous voice.

He laughed. "I'm going to punish you for that," he said to her tenderly. "But now and then just a little very ladylike impertinence is amusing."

She blushed darkly, biting her lip.

"Are you hungry, beautiful one?" he asked.

He could see she was afraid to answer.

"When I ask you will say, 'Only if it pleases you, my Prince,' and I shall know the answer is yes. Or, 'Not unless it should please you, my Prince,' and I shall know the answer is no. Do you understand me?"

"Yes, my Prince," she answered. "I'm hungry only if it pleases you."

"Very good, very good," he said to her with genuine feeling. He lifted a small cluster of glistening purple grapes and fed them to her one by one, taking the seeds out of her mouth and casting them aside.

And he watched with obvious pleasure as she drank deeply from the wine cup he held to her lips. Then he wiped her mouth and kissed her.

Her eyes were glistening. But she had stopped crying. He felt the smooth flesh of her back, and her breasts again.

"Superb," he whispered. "And were you terribly spoilt before and given everything that you wished?"

She was confused, blushing again, and then full of shame she nodded.

"Yes, my Prince, I think perhaps . . ."

"Don't be afraid to answer me with many words," he coaxed, "as long as they are respectful. And never speak unless I speak to you first, and in all these things, be careful to note what pleases me. You were very spoilt, given everything, but were you willful?"

"No, my Prince, I don't think I was that," she said. "I tried to be a joy to my parents."

"And you'll be a joy to me, my dear," he said lovingly.

Still holding her firmly in his left arm, he turned to his supper.

He ate heartily, pork, roast fowl, some fruit, and several cups of wine. Then he told the servants to take it all away and leave them.

New sheets and coverlets had been laid on the bed; there were fresh down pillows, and roses in a vase nearby, and several candelabra.

"Now," he said as he rose and set her before him. "We must get to bed as we have a long journey before us tomorrow. And I have still to punish you for your earlier impertinence."

Immediately the tears stood in her eyes; she looked up at him imploring. She

almost reached to cover her breasts and her sex, and then remembering herself she made her hands into two little helpless fists at her sides.

"I won't punish you very much," he said gently, lifting her chin. "It was just a little offense, and your first after all. But Beauty, to confess the truth, I shall love punishing you."

She was biting her lip, and he could see she wanted to speak, and the effort to control her tongue and her hands was almost too much for her.

"All right, lovely one, what do you want to say?" he asked.

"Please, my Prince," she begged. "I'm so afraid of you."

"You'll find me more reasonable than you expect," he said.

He removed his long cloak, tossing it over a chair, and bolted the door. Then he snuffed all but a few candles.

He would sleep in his clothes as he did most nights, in the forest, or in the country inns, or in the houses of those humble peasants at which he sometimes stopped, and that was no great inconvenience to him.

And as he drew near her now, he thought he must be merciful and make her punishment quick. And seating himself on the side of the bed, he reached out for her, and pulling her wrists into his left hand he brought her naked body down over his lap so that her legs dangled over the floor helplessly.

"Very, very lovely," he said, his right hand moving languidly over her rounded buttocks, forcing them ever so slightly apart.

Beauty was crying aloud, but muffling her cries into the bed, her hands held out in front of her by his long left arm.

And now with his right hand he spanked her buttocks hard and heard her cries grow louder. It wasn't really much of a slap.

But it left a red mark on her. And he spanked her hard again, and he felt her writhing against him, the heat and moisture of her sex against his leg, and again he spanked her.

"I think you are sobbing more from the humiliation than the pain," he scolded her in a soft voice.

She was struggling not to make her cries too loud.

He flattened out his right hand, and feeling the heat of her reddened buttocks drew it up and delivered another series of hard, loud slaps, smiling as he watched her struggle.

He could have spanked her much harder, for his own pleasure, and without really hurting her. But he thought the better of it. He had so many nights ahead of him for these delights.

He lifted her up now so that she was standing in front of him.

"Toss your hair back," he commanded. Her tear-stained face was unspeakably beautiful, her lips trembling, her blue eyes gleaming with the dampness of the tears. She obeyed immediately.

"I don't think you were so very spoilt," he said. "I find you very obedient and eager to please, and this makes me very happy."

He could see her relief.

"Clasp your hands behind your neck," he said, "under your hair. That's it. Very good." He lifted her chin again. "And you have a lovely modest habit of looking down. But now I want you to look directly at me."

She obeyed shyly, miserably. It seemed she felt her nakedness and her helplessness more fully now as she looked at him. Her lashes were matted and dark, and her blue eyes larger than he had thought.

"Do you find me handsome?" he asked her. "Ah, but before you answer, I should like to know the truth from you, not what you think I should like to hear, or what would be best for you to say, you understand me?"

"Yes, my Prince," she whispered. She seemed calmer.

He reached out, massaged her right breast lightly, and then stroked her downy underarms, feeling the little curve of the muscle there beneath the tiny wisp of golden hair, and then he stroked that full, moist hair between her legs so that she sighed and trembled.

"Now," he said, "answer my question, and describe what you see. Describe me as if you had only just met me and were confiding in your chambermaid."

Again she bit her lip, which he dearly loved, and then, her voice a little diminished by uncertainty, she said:

"You are very handsome, my Prince, no one could deny that. And for one . . . for one . . ."

"Go on," he said. He drew her just a little closer so that her sex was against his knee, and putting his right arm about her, he cradled her breast in his left hand and let his lips touch her cheek.

"And for one so young to be so commanding," she said, "it's not what one might expect."

"And tell me how does that show itself in me, other than my actions?"

"Your manner, my Prince," she said, her voice gaining a little strength. "The look of your eyes, such dark eyes . . . your face. There are none of the doubts of youth in it."

He smiled and kissed her ear. He wondered why the wet little cleft between her legs was so very hot. His fingers could not keep from touching it. Twice already he'd had her today, and he would have her again, but he was thinking he should go about it more slowly.

"Would you like it if I were older?" he whispered.

"I had thought," she said, "that it would be easier. To be commanded by one so very young," she said, "is to feel one's helplessness."

It seemed the tears had welled up and were spilling out of her eyes, so he pushed her gently back so he might see them.

"My darling, I have awakened you from a century's sleep, and restored your father's Kingdom. You're mine. And you won't find me such a hard master. Only a very thorough master. When you think night and day and every moment only of pleasing me, things will be very easy for you."

And as she struggled not to look away, he could see again the relief in her face, and that she was in complete awe of him.

"Now," he said, pushing his left fingers between her legs, and drawing her close again so that she let out a little gasp before she could stop herself, "I want more of you than I've had before. Do you know what I mean, my Sleeping Beauty?"

She shook her head; for this moment she was in terror.

He lifted her up onto the bed and laid her down.

The candles threw a warm, almost rosy light over her. Her hair fell down on

either side of the bed, and she seemed on the verge of crying out, her hands struggling to keep still at her sides.

"My darling, you have a dignity about you that shields you from me, much like your lovely golden hair shrouds you and shields you. Now I want you to surrender to me. You'll see, and you'll be very surprised that you wept when I first suggested it."

The Prince bent over her. He parted her legs. He could see the battle she fought not to cover herself or turn away from him. He stroked her thighs. Then with his finger and thumb, he reached into the silky damp hair itself and felt those tender little lips and forced them very wide open.

Beauty gave a terrible shudder. With his left hand he covered her mouth, and behind his hand she cried softly. It seemed easier for her with him covering her mouth and that was all right for now, he thought. She shall be taught everything in time.

And with his right fingers, he found that tiny nodule of flesh between her tender nether lips and he worked it back and forth until she raised her hips, arching her back, in spite of herself. Her little face under his hand was the picture of distress. He smiled to himself.

But even as he smiled, he felt the hot fluid between her legs for the first time, the real fluid which had not come before with her innocent blood. "That's it, that's it, my darling," he said. "And you mustn't resist your Lord and master, hmmmm?"

Now he opened his clothing and took out his hard, eager sex, and mounting her he let it rest against her thigh as he continued to stroke her and work her.

She was twisting from one side to the other, her hands gathering up the soft sheets at her sides into knots, and it seemed her whole body grew pink, and the nipples of her breasts looked as hard as if they were tiny stones. He could not resist them.

He bit at them with his teeth, playfully, not hurting her. He licked them with his tongue, and then he licked her sex, too, and as she struggled, and blushed and moaned beneath him, he mounted her, slowly.

Again she arched her back. Her breasts were suffused with red. And as he drove his organ into her, he felt her shudder violently with unwilling pleasure.

An awful cry was muffled by the hand over her mouth; she was shuddering so violently it seemed she all but lifted him on top of her.

And then she lay still, moist, pink, with her eyes closed, breathing deeply as the tears flowed silently.

"That was lovely, my darling," he said. "Open your eyes."

She did it timidly.

But then she lay looking up at him.

"This has been so hard for you," he whispered. "You could not even imagine these things happening to you. And you are red with shame, and shaking with fear, and you believe perhaps it's one of the dreams you dreamed in your hundred years. But it's real, Beauty," he said. "And it is only the beginning! You think I've made you my Princess. But I've only started. The day will come when you can see nothing but me as if I were the sun and the moon, when I mean all to you, food, drink, the air you breathe. Then you will truly be mine, and these first lessons . . . and pleasures . . ." he smiled, "will seem like nothing."

He bent over her. She lay so very still, gazing up at him.

"Now kiss me," he commanded. "And I mean, really . . . kiss me."

From THREE RIVERS

Roberta Latow

Roberta Latow was born in Westchester, New York, but escaped her suburban background for Manhattan, where she was at the heart of the dynamic pop art scene in the 1960s. She was a noted art expert and gallery owner and has been credited with giving Andy Warhol the original idea to paint Campbell's soup cans. In the early 1970s she went to Europe and moved around different exotic parts of the Mediterranean, which form the background for many of her novels. She lived in Greece for many years, earning her living as an art dealer and interior decorator. Later she moved to London in the early eighties and wrote *Three Rivers* (1981), the first of her twenty-one erotic novels. It caused a storm and became an international bestseller.

They sailed up river for about forty-five minutes, and then the felucca moved into a new, makeshift mooring. Close by, two cars were parked: one was the plum-colored Rolls and the other a black Mercedes 600. The chauffeurs stood next to the cars, waiting for the guests to disembark so that they could drive them back to Cairo.

Once the felucca came to a stop next to the dock, the guests all said good-bye very quickly. Within minutes, the felucca set sail for Upper Egypt.

Alexis, in all the excitement, had forgotten to cut the wedding cake. He laughed at the idea that he was nervous enough that all should go well that he forgot something. "Never mind, darling," he said. "The wedding cake is for us. We will cut it together tonight."

They walked to the center of the felucca where, on a raised section of the deck, there were soft silk Oriental carpets and heavy cushions. There were small ivory-inlaid tables and a magnificent old brass brazier with a conical top.

Alexis went first up the steps and then pulled Isabel up to him. He touched her nipple through her dress as they fell upon the cushions.

Gamal arrived with an ice bucket and a bottle of chilled champagne. A hookah was already lit. The smell of the Indonesian grass reached Isabel even before she drew on the pipe.

They rested with arms around each other on the cushions. From the raised deck they had a wonderful view of the river.

They smoked and kissed, and Alexis told her how much he loved her and how happy he was to have her as his wife. He fondled her breast and pulled on her nipples through the silk Fortuny dress. He slipped his hand under her dress and was surprised and pleased when he found her so tight he could not get in.

He pushed one finger high into her and felt her divine tightness. He was able to move his finger in and out easily because she was so wet.

"Oh, my dear, tonight you will be loved like you have never been before. The old woman has done well by us for our wedding night. We will have a delicious time opening you back to your normal size. How did it feel when I was touching you?"

"Alexis," Isabel asked. "What has she done to me? Every part of me is ten times more sensitive to your touch. When you were simply playing with my labia, I had to bite the inside of my cheek not to scream from passion."

Alexis teased her, saying that all the city of Memphis would be thinking about the beautiful bride in her sparkling jewels tonight. That the men would be thinking of ways that they would take her, the women would have endless discussions among themselves about her cunt and then about the size of his cock.

"About my cunt? Alexis, you are exaggerating. Why ever would they think about my cunt?"

"Oh, my dear, among Egyptian women of the village class the curiosity would be high. They would be very interested in your cunt and what it looked like and what had been done to it. You know, all of the women you have seen have been circumcised. Their clitorises have been removed."

"Alexis, I know that it is done occasionally, but surely not to all women?"

"No, not all women, but ninety percent of them. And in the villages you can be sure it is one hundred percent. Here in Egypt we have three forms of circumcision for women. The mildest is known as sunna, the tip is removed and the labia minora. The next stage involves taking a bigger piece of the clitoris. But the most dramatic of all is what they call the Pharaonic method – total removal of the clitoris and the labia minora. The vagina is then stitched up. Some of the Sudanese tribes do this with thorns, leaving only a small opening for menstruation and urination. On the wedding night the bridegroom rips the thorns out and then fucks his lady, if she can take it.

"Don't look so appalled, darling, most of the women in Egypt have suffered the milder method of sunna and it is done when they are between the ages of six and ten. Now you understand why they will all be wondering what your cunt is like."

Alexis bent over and kissed her tenderly, and said, "Actually, I would love them to see it because it is so divine – the color, the size. Your clitoris, so sensitive and lovely, and how you are always wet. Yes, if I were to show you to them, to go down on you and they were to see the pleasure that you get, that would do more to reform the practice of circumcision in Egypt than all the campaigns at work!"

He laughed at her and pinched her nipple and said, "Let them wonder and have a good time thinking about us. Tonight is, after all, our night, and I hope the whole world is as happy as we are."

She unzipped his fly, bent her head down and took Alexis in her mouth and sucked on him for a few seconds, tenderly. When she stopped, he said, "More, more," and she laughed and said, "No, darling, no more. I do not want to get lipstick on your banana-colored trousers."

With much difficulty, she managed to put his tumescent cock back into his

trousers and zip him up. She snuggled up next to him, and he said, "I will get you tonight and make you pay for teasing me like that."

They lay there quietly in each other's arms listening to the sounds of the river, the distant sounds of birds and cicadas coming from the bank, the occasional order being given from below somewhere on the felucca.

Suddenly Alexis sat bolt upright and struck his forehead. "A wedding picture! We do not have a wedding picture. Shall we have one of us lying here among the cushions in all our wedding clothes?"

"Oh, that is a good idea."

He clapped his hands and called for Gamal to bring a camera. He pulled her up and arranged some cushions the way he thought they would look best. He used Gamal as a stand-in while he set up the camera. When he had everything just as he wanted it, then Gamal and he switched places and Gamal punched the button.

"There we are, darling, our first picture together." Alexis smiled. He slapped Isabel on the ass. "Now let's go down below and get out of our wedding clothes."

There was one huge room below the main deck, and it was quite amazing. It stretched from the center of the felucca to the stern. It was a bedroom-cum-sitting-room with a huge bed that could have slept four. The bed was covered with a mustard-yellow kilim. It was very old, worn almost thin in places, and the pattern was a big and bold geometric, very beautiful and very rare. The cushions thrown on it were oversize and covered with other kilims in shades of yellow and white, with a strong accent of terracotta color.

The walls of the room were of white linen, and the carpet on the floor was a huge, red, antique Bokhara. One of the walls was a cupboard made of antique mushrabiya in its naturally dark wood color. There was also a white marble desk, quite large, with a walnut-and-cane chair for it, and a pair of easy chairs, covered in the same white linen as the walls. Above the bed hung the Modigliani nude, given to Alexis by his mother.

Isabel told Alexis that she thought the room was superb. He smiled and began to undress her, saying that there was something else about the room: it was air-conditioned and sound-proofed. "So, my darling, you will be able to scream to your heart's content when I beat you, and no one will ever hear. Come! I think I will make love to you."

Alexis had removed the Saladin necklaces and dropped them on the bed and now he undid the bumblebee and dropped that on the bed, too. He took the diamonds from her ears and lifted the Fortuny dress over her head. He looked at his wife and folded her in his arms, tight against him, telling her how lovely he found her.

It was true, Isabel knew. The girls had elongated her nipples a quarter to a half inch. She could see from the way that Alexis looked at them that he liked that very much. He took one in his mouth and sucked on it, telling her how much he liked her nipples that way, and that she must work to keep them like that. Would she do that for him?

Yes, she would do that for him. Isabel smiled. She stood on the bed as he requested. He opened the lips of her vagina and put his tongue on her clitoris, moving it round and round. He sat on the bed and she lowered herself above his face. With his tongue he went into her, then he pulled her down on his lap.

"Tonight, darling, I will take you like an Arab man takes his virgin," he murmured. "We will wait for now, but tonight, after I have broken you in, then I will do wonderful things to you. You will have a little pain, I think, because you are so tight, but you can pretend you are a virgin. We will make love all night and before you sleep, you will know that you are not. I will never let you sleep until you feel like a spent, satiated whore. Will you like that?"

Isabel was completely spellbound. When they kissed, she knew that Alexis was, as well.

They both changed their clothes. He put on a simple white cotton galabia, and Isabel put on her tobacco raw-silk one, and the great silver and amber necklace that he had given her. In her ears she put the Phoenician gold loops. Alexis rang for Gamal, who was instructed to gather up the jewels on the bed and put them in the safe. He sent Isabel with Gamal so she could learn to open it and be able to take what she wanted from it, when she pleased. After, Gamal remained behind and put their things away while they went to explore.

The felucca was a large one, very traditional in style, and about seventy years old. It was brilliantly fitted out. It did not look like a luxury boat, but rather like a simple, large, working craft of the Nile. The crew of four wore no uniform of any kind, but simple cotton galabias and white turbans. As extra hands, Alexis had brought Gamal and Doreya to serve them. The crew's quarters were in the lower level, up in the bow of the felucca and completely away from Alexis and Isabel.

The deck was sectioned off into a dining area and the raised section. The dining area was out in the open, and since it hardly ever rained, there was little problem about that. When it did rain, there was a canopy that could be pulled across on cables. Today there was an extra addition on the deck, the flowered *huppah*.

When they looked at the *huppah* and its flowers, they both decided to have a large double bed made up under it for their first night as man and wife. Alexis called Gamal and told him. Just as the servant was leaving, he was called back and given more instructions. Gamal disappeared down in the bow of the boat.

A few minutes later, up out of nowhere rushed Winston and Rita. They had been hidden away in Gamal's cabin. They barked and howled and jumped and leaped all over the couple. Isabel was overjoyed.

"Now, darling, with all that noise, you are sure to think you are at home," Alexis kidded.

She kissed him and said he was wonderful. He replied by saying that he knew that, and if he needed any proof, keeping those two dogs was it. "By God, they are spoiled, Isabel. Will you spoil me as much?"

She said, "Yes, but only in bed."

They lay among the cushions and talked. The sun went down and suddenly it was dark. Gamal and Doreya had lit the candles in the old pierced-copper and glass lanterns so that the felucca was lit up in soft yellow candlelight.

Alexis suggested to Isabel that she go downstairs and put on her chocolate-brown lace nightdress and peignoir. "They are going to set all the food out in a buffet for us, and we will serve ourselves. They are going to drop anchor a bit further up near a village where they know the boat will be safe. The crew, all

the crew, including Doreya and Gamal, will take the dinghy and row ashore to celebrate our wedding. They will not come back until the early morning so that we can have our wedding night alone on the felucca."

"Just the two of us is perfect!" Isabel exclaimed. "I would love that."

"And the dogs, of course?" Alexis teased.

"Yes, and the dogs, of course," she agreed, laughing, and went below to change.

The bathroom aboard the felucca was large and included a bathtub for two, a dressing room and a pair of washbasins. The fittings were white, while the entire bathroom was in beige travertine marble. All the towels were mustard-yellow and there were kilims on the marble floor.

After she had bathed and put on fresh makeup, she slipped into the magnificent nightdress he had bought her for this night.

Isabel looked at herself in it and realized what great erotic feelings and fantasies Alexis must have about her. The nightgown was elegant but evoked a feeling of base sexuality. Her nipples and the dark flesh around them protruded through the openings in the lace, and the slits up the side exposed her thighs, hips and legs. It was, without question, a nightdress to tantalize the sexual appetites of a man. When she put the peignoir over it and pinned the diamond dragonfly at the closing under her breasts, she realized that she did not feel like Isabel at all, but like some sexual object designed, prepared and ready for her man to use.

She was deeply excited. This would be a night of pure sexuality. Tonight she would use Alexis as the sexual animal that he was, and together they would reach new heights, as husband and wife.

She sighed and went to the safe for her diamond earrings. She would wear them this evening.

When Alexis came for her, she was looking out of the oversized portholes to the banks of the river. She could see fires twinkling in the distance.

He looked at her and said, "I cannot believe we have done it, and you are my wife."

He could not help but take each of her nipples in his hands and roll them around with his fingers. Then they went up on deck together.

The felucca looked an absolute dream. It was totally silent on board except for the sounds of the Nile lapping up against the boat, and Rita and Winston, who were on the raised deck lying among the cushions, snoring away.

The deck was lit by lanterns, and under the *huppah* of flowers a large bed had been made and covered in silk embroideries. It looked like the most magnificent four-poster bed in the world with its canopy of glorious flowers above.

Towards the stern of the boat a sumptuous table had been laid. There were quail in a casserole of rice, several different salads and fruits, along with cheeses and baked ham. And for dessert – the wedding cake.

When they cut their wedding cake, both their hands were on the knife. They repeated their vows exactly as they had under the *huppah*, only hours before. She knew then that he loved her in a way that she had never been loved. It was all that she had ever wanted.

They kissed each other, their mouths tasting of the sweet and rich wedding cake. They went up and lay among the cushions on the raised deck. They found set on one of the small ivory-inlaid tables a jug of hot, sweet coffee, and a pair

of small cups on a tray. Alexis poured for them, and they sipped and smiled at each other lovingly.

He leaned back, took a box from one of the tables and prepared a few lines of coke. They sniffed them and floated off together as the boat rocked them gently. Occasionally they could hear laughter above the cicadas' symphony, somewhere in the distance. They lay on their backs looking up at a ceiling of stars, like diamonds thrown helter-skelter on black velvet.

They were silent now for a very long time. He pulled her up to her feet, undid the dragonfly and took off the peignoir. He undid his kaftan and dropped it where they were standing. He picked up a large box from among the cushions and put one arm around her waist; they started down the stairs. He moved his hand from her waist to the cheek of her ass and walked her that way to the bed under the *huppah*.

He put the large box and the small box of coke down among the cushions and looked at her, taking her in his arms. His cock was huge and erect. With one hand around it, he lifted it and offered it to her; with the other he held his scrotum.

She dropped to her knees, ready to make love to him, but he caught her as she was going down and he lifted her. She could feel his erection pushing against her, he held her so tight to him.

"No, do nothing now," he told her. "I want to take you, make love to you, be tender and cruel to you and keep doing it for a long time. You must not touch me yet. Later, much later, I will give myself to you. It will be different for you tonight. You will be very tight. I will play on you, work on you, open you wide again."

He took the little box of coke and put his fingers in it and rubbed it on her nipples and then put a bit on the tip of her tongue. It made her feel instantly sexier as he went down and sucked the coke off her nipples. All the time his hands were moving over her hindquarters, separating them and pushing them together. Finally he lifted her nightdress over her head and then caught her breasts as they fell into the palms of his hands.

He put his finger inside her, and she was wet. He pushed up as high as he could and found her very tight. Reaching over to the large box, he took out a small jar of cream, and rubbed it high up into her vagina.

Isabel was longing to have him. She knew her smallness excited him so that he grew to even larger proportions. She could feel the throbbing of his blood pumping in his penis.

Alexis moved himself slowly along the outside of her genitals and then between the wet and slippery lips. Finally he dipped the very tip of it into the small opening of her vagina. She was amazed at how small the opening was. She wanted him so much, but now she was afraid that he would never get it into her. He was tender with her about it and treated her as if she were a virgin bride. He slowly managed to get the head of his cock inside her.

With his arms under her armpits, he drew her up towards him, her legs high up now on his shoulders. He kissed her, and when he saw her passion rising, he let her down gently on the cushions. Then, pulling her legs even higher on his shoulders, he felt her wet orgasm running over the knob of his cock. Suddenly he rammed as hard as he could up through her, and she screamed from the pain.

Although Isabel had screamed, at that very same moment she was flooded

with an enormous orgasm. That first scream was not the only one that came from the felucca that night. It was as if she had been a virgin. Whatever the old woman had done, she had done well for the both of them. Alexis had her many times. They slept in between and were never satiated.

The sun came up and the lanterns were still burning when Alexis lay looking at the sleeping Isabel. He wanted to see the sun rise on the Nile with his wife, and so he woke her by gently spreading her legs and licking her like a pussycat.

She woke from his tongue and lazily sat up. She kissed him good morning while he slipped her nightgown over her head. He lifted her breasts and adjusted them in her gown by drawing the nipples into the holes cut through the lace. Then he cupped her breasts in his hands and smiled at her. He found her peignoir where they had dropped it the night before, and he helped her on with it.

She took his kaftan and dressed him, tying the strings on the side. Then they went together to the bow of the felucca and, stepping up on the small raised platform, sat on some cushions and watched the sun rise.

They heard the sounds of early morning – birds, and the rustling of small animals on the banks of the river. Far up the Nile, in the magnificent sunrise, they saw a felucca in full sail. The sun was up about half an hour when they heard voices and turned to see the dinghy coming towards the *Mamounia* with the crew, Gamal and Doreya.

Alexis said, "Come, let's pick up our things from under the canopy and go to bed below."

She picked up the cocaine box, and in the larger box he put the jars of ointments and the other accessories they had used. He noticed a few bloodstains on the cushions, and for all his Western education, the Arab in him came out and he felt a kind of pride. He quickly turned Isabel away from seeing them, but it was too late.

Isabel looked at him and said, "We have to be the most depraved, debauched couple in the world," and had the good grace to blush.

"Yes, aren't we lucky!" Alexis roared.

They laughed and then hurried down to the cabin before everyone arrived on board.

Isabel was awake, that is, her mind was awake, but her body was asleep, and her eyes were still closed. She was feeling very lazy and sensual. She felt herself moving up and down and round and round with her pelvis, hardly moving the rest of her body. She opened her eyes and realized that she was moving with Alexis's cock. She closed her eyes again and reached out her arms to pull him against her. They kissed, and he said, "Good morning, my lady wife."

Isabel opened her eyes again and smiled up at him. They rolled together on their sides and faced each other as he kept pumping in and out. He had her coming now in stronger orgasms, could wait no longer himself. He let go and flooded her. Isabel squeezed hard on him, and he felt himself held there by her. They kissed while they were together like that and then lay there and dozed.

Much later Alexis woke and unfolded himself from Isabel and went into the bathroom. He ran the bath and filled it with a wonderful scent and soap bubbles while he shaved. Later he went back to kiss Isabel awake, then dragged her out of bed and into the double bathtub with him. She had only just enough time to

wrap a towel around her hair and brush her teeth while Alexis ordered breakfast for them.

When they finally went up on deck and were greeted by some of the crew and Gamal, they realized they had slept the day away. It was five in the afternoon. They sat in their simple white galabias on the beautiful felucca that was in full sail, making great speed up the Nile. Isabel adored the movement of the boat, and loved watching the crew at work. They were all smiles and happy to be traveling up the river.

From THE SWIMMING-POOL LIBRARY

Alan Hollinghurst

Alan Hollinghurst is the author of five internationally-acclaimed novels, *The Swimming-Pool Library, The Folding Star, The Spell, The Line of Beauty* and, most recently, *The Stranger's Child.* Winner of the 2004 Man Booker Prize, the E. M. Forster Award and the James Tait Black Memorial Prize, he was chosen as one of the twenty Best of Young British Novelists in 1993. Set in 1983, *The Swimming-Pool Library* describes the bohemian lifestyle of the promiscuous Will Beckwith, a young man of aristocratic descent, who spends his days gorging on culture and young men, and frequently picking up boys at the Corinthian club.

The Brutus Cinema occupied the basement of one of those Soho houses which, above ground-floor level, maintain their beautiful Caroline fenestration, and seemed a kind of emblem of gay life (the *piano nobile* elegant above the squalid, jolly *sous-sol*) in the far-off spring of 1983. One entered from the street by pushing back the dirty red curtain in the doorway beside an unlettered shop window, painted over white but with a stencil of Michelangelo's David stuck in the middle. This tussle with the curtain – one never knew whether to shoulder it aside to the right or the left, and often tangled with another punter coming out – seemed a symbolic act, done in the sight of passers-by, and always gave me a little jab of pride. Inside was a small front room, the walls bearing porn-mags on racks, and the glossy boxes of videos for sale; and there were advertisements for clubs and cures. In a locked case by the counter leather underwear was displayed, with cock-rings, face masks, chains and the whole gamut of dildoes from pubertal pink fingers to mighty black jobs, two feet long and as thick as a fist.

As I entered, the spotty Glaswegian attendant was getting stuck into a helping of fish and chips, and the room stank of grease and vinegar. I idled for a minute and flicked through some mags. These were really dog-eared browsers, thumbed through time and again by those rent-boys who had the blessing of the management and waited there for pick-ups; curiously incredible stations of sexual intercourse, whose moving versions, or something similar, could be seen downstairs. I looked at the theatrical expressions of ecstasy without interest. The attendant had a small television behind the counter which was a monitor for the films being shown in the cinema; but as there was no one else in the shop he had broken the endless circuit of video sex and was watching a real TV programme

instead. He sat there stuffing chips and oozing, batter-covered sections of flaky white cod into his mouth, his short-sighted attention rapt by the screen, as if he had been a teenaged boy getting his first sight of a porn film. I sidled along and looked over his shoulder; it was a nature programme, and contained some virtuoso footage shot inside a termite colony. First we saw the long, questing snout of the ant-eater outside, and then its brutal, razor-sharp claws cutting their way in. Back inside, perched by a fibre-optic miracle at a junction of tunnels which looked like the triforium of some Gaudí church, we saw the freakishly extensile tongue of the ant-eater come flicking towards us, cleaning the fleeing termites off the wall.

It was one of the most astonishing pieces of film I had ever seen, and I felt a thrill at the violent intrusion as well as dismay at the smashing of something so strange and intricate; I was disappointed when the attendant, realising I was there and perhaps in need of encouragement, tapped a button and transformed the picture into the relative banality of American college boys sticking their cocks up each other's assholes.

"Cinema sir?" he said. "We've got some really hot-core hard films . . ." His heart wasn't in it so I paid him my fiver and left him to the wonderful world of nature.

I went down the stairs, lit by one gloomy red-painted bulb. The cinema itself was a small cellar room, the squalor of which was only fully apparent at the desolating moment in the early hours when the show ended for the night and the lights were suddenly switched on, revealing the bare, damp-stained walls, the rubbish on the floor, and the remaining audience, either asleep or doing things best covered by darkness. It had perhaps ten tiers of seats, salvaged from the refurbishment of some bona fide picture house: some lacked arms, which helped patrons get to know each other, and one lacked a seat, and was the repeated cause of embarrassment to diffident people, blinded by the dark, who chose it as the first empty place to hand and sat down heavily on the floor instead.

I had not been there for months and was struck again by its character: pushing open the door I felt it weigh on sight, smell and hearing. The smell was smoke and sweat, a stale, male odour tartishly overlaid with a cheap lemon-scented air-freshener like a taxi and dusted from time to time with a trace of Trouble for Men. The sound was the laid-back aphrodisiac pop music which, as the films had no sound-track, played continuously and repetitively to enhance the mood and cover the quieter noises made by the customers. The look of the place changed in the first minute or so, as I waited just inside the door for my eyes to accustom themselves to the near dark. The only light came from the small screen, and from a dim yellow "Fire Exit" sign. I had once taken this exit, which led to a fetid back staircase with a locked door at the top. Smoke thickened the air and hung in the projector's beam.

It was important to sit near the back, where it was darker and more went on, but also essential to avoid the attentions of truly gruesome people. Slightly encumbered with my bag I moved into a row empty except for a heavy businessman at the far end. It was not a very good house, so I settled down to watch and wait. Occasionally cigarettes were lit and the men shifted in their seats and looked around; the mood faltered between tension and lethargy.

The college boys were followed by a brief, gloomy fragment of film involving older, moustachioed types, one of them virtually bald. This broke off suddenly, and without preamble another film, very cheery and outdoors, was under way. As always with these films, though I relished the gross abundance of their later episodes, it was the introductory scenes, buoyant with expectation, the men on the street or the beach, killing time, pumping iron, still awaiting the transformation our fantasy would demand of them, that I found the most touching.

Now, for instance, we were in a farmyard. A golden-haired boy in old blue jeans and a white vest was leaning in the sun against a barn door, one foot raised behind him. A close-up admired him frowning against the sun, a straw jerking between his lips. Slowly we travelled down, lingering where his hand brushed across his nipples which showed hard through his vest, lingering again at his loose but promising crotch. On the other side of the yard, a second boy, also blond, was shifting bags of fertiliser. We watched his shirtless muscular torso straining as he lifted the bags on to his shoulder, traced the sweat running down his neck and back, got a load of his chunky denim-clad ass as he bent over. The eyes of the two boys met; one close-up and then another suggested curiosity and lust. In what seemed to be very slightly slow motion the shirtless boy ambled across to the other. They stood close together, both extremely beautiful, perhaps eighteen or nineteen years of age. Their lips moved, they spoke and smiled, but as the film had no sound-track, and we heard only the cinema's throbbing, washing music, they communicated in a dreamlike silence, or as if watched from out of earshot through binoculars. The picture was irradiated with sunlight and, being fractionally out of focus, blurred the boys' smooth outlines into a blond nimbus. The one in the vest appeared to put a question to the other, they turned aside and were swallowed up into the darkness of the barn.

Where did they get them from, I wondered, these boys more wonderful than almost everything one came across in real life? And I remembered reading somewhere that a Californian talent-spotter had photographic records of three thousand or more of them ranging back over twenty or thirty years and that a youngster, after a session in the studio, mooching through the files, had found pictures of his own father, posed long before.

In the meantime there were other arrivals at the cinema, though it was difficult to make them out; while the sunlit introduction had brightened up the room and cast its aura over the scattered audience in the forward rows, the sex scenes within the barn were enacted in comparative gloom, allowing the viewers a secretive darkness. I tugged my half-hard cock out through my fly and stroked it casually.

One new entrant tottered to the deserted front row, which in this tiny space was only a few feet from the screen. There was a rustle of papers, and I could see him in silhouette remove his coat, fold it neatly and place it on the seat next to that in which he then sat down. The rustling recurred intermittently, and I guessed he must be a man I'd seen at the Brutus the very first time I went there, a spry little chap of sixty-five or so who, like a schoolgirl taken to a romantic U picture, sat entranced by the movies and worked his way through a bag of boiled sweets as the action unfolded. A fiver from his pension, perhaps, and 30p for the humbugs, might be set aside weekly for this little outing. How he must look forward to it! His was a complete and innocent absorption in the fantasy

world on screen. Could he look back to a time when he had behaved like these glowing, thoughtless teenagers, who were now locked together sucking on each other's cocks in the hay? Or was this the image of a new society we had made, where every desire could find its gratification?

The old man was happy with his cough-drops, but I wanted some other oral pleasure (the Winchester slang "suction", meaning sweets, I realised was the comprehensive term). Not, however, from the person who came scouting up to the rear rows now, one of the plump, bespectacled Chinese youths who, with day-return businessmen and quite distinguished Oxbridge dons, made a haunt of places like this, hopping hopefully from row to row, so persistent that they were inevitably, from time to time, successful.

The man on the end of the row had to shift, and I realised I was to be the next recipient of Eastern approaches. The boy sat down next to me, and though I carried on looking at the screen and laid my hand across my cock, I was aware that he was staring at me intently to try and make out my face in the darkness, and I felt his breath on my cheek. Then there was the pressure of his shoulder against mine. I gathered myself emphatically, and leant across into the empty place on the other side. He sprawled rather, with his legs wide apart, one of them straying into my space and pressing against my thigh.

"Leave off, will you," I whispered, thinking that a matter-of-fact request would do the trick. At the same time I crossed my legs, squashing my balls uncomfortably, to emphasise that I was not available. The sack-lifting boy was now sliding his finger up the other one's ass, spitting on his big, blunt cock and preparing for the inevitable penetration. As he pressed its head against the boy's glistening sphincter, which virtually filled the screen in lurid close-up, I felt an arm go along the back of the seat and a moment later a hand descend unfalteringly on my dick. I didn't move but, sensing the power that speech had in this cryptic gathering, I said loudly and firmly: "If you come anywhere near me again I'll break your neck." A couple of people looked round, there was an "Oooh" from the other side of the room, spoken in a uniquely homosexual tone of bored outrage, the tentacles withdrew, and after a few moments, compatible perhaps with some fantastic notion of the preservation of dignity, the advancer retreated, earning a curse from the man at the end of the row, who was forced to get up again, attempting to conceal his erection as he did so.

Exhilarated by my control of the situation, I spread myself again; the boy duly came over the other's face, and very pretty it looked, the blobs and strings of spunk smeared over his eyelids, nose, and thick half-opened lips. Then, abruptly, it was another film. Half a dozen boys entered a locker-room, and at just the same moment the door from the stairs opened and something came in that looked, in the deep shadow, as if it might be nice. It was a sporty-looking boy with, evidently, a bag. He was not sure what to do, so I bent my telepathic powers on him. The poor creature struggled for a moment . . . but it was hopeless. He stumbled up towards the back, groped past the businessman (I heard him say "Sorry") and sat a seat away from me, putting his bag on the seat between us.

I let a little time elapse and distinctly heard him swallow, as if in lust and amazement, as the boys stripped off and, before we knew where we were, one of them was jacking off in the shower. Something made me certain that it was the

first time he had been to a place like this, and I remembered how enchanting it is to see one's first porn-film. "Christ! They're really doing it," I recalled saying to myself, quite impressed by the way the actors seemed genuinely to be having sex for the pleasure of it, and by the blatant innocence of it all.

I then proceeded by a succession of distinct and inexorable moves, shifting into the place between us and at the same time pushing his bag along the floor to where I had been sitting. I sensed some anxiety about this, but he carried on looking at the screen. Next I slid my arm along the back of his seat, and as he remained immobile I made it as clear as I could in the dark that I had my cock out and was playing with it. Then I leant over him more, and ran my hand over his chest. His heart was racing, and I felt all the tension in his fixed posture between excitement and fear, and knew that I could take control of him. He had on a kind of bomber jacket, and under that a shirt. I let my hand linger at his waist, and admired his hard, ridged stomach, slipping my fingers between his shirt buttons, and running my hand up over his smooth skin. He had beautiful, muscular tits, with small, frosted nipples, quite hairless. My left hand gently rubbed the base of his thick neck; he seemed to have almost a crew-cut and the back of his head was softly bristly. I leant close to him and drooled my tongue up his jaw and into his ear.

At this he could no longer remain impassive. He turned towards me with a gulp, and I felt his fingertips shyly slide on to my knee and shortly after touch my cock. "Oh no," I think he said under his breath, as he tried to get his hand around it, and then jerked it tentatively a few times. I continued stroking the back of his neck, thinking it might relax him, but he kept on feeling my dick in a very polite sort of way, so I brought pressure to bear, and pushed his head firmly down into my lap. He had to struggle around to get his stocky form into the new position, encumbered by the padded arm between our seats; but once there he took the crown of my cock into his mouth and with me moving his head puppet-like up and down, sucked it after a fashion.

This was all very good and with my hangover I felt it with electric intensity. But I was aware of his reluctance, and let him stop. He was inexpert, and though he was excited, needed help. We sat back for a while, my hand all the time on his shoulder. I loved the nerve with which I'd done all this, and like most random sex it gave me the feeling I could achieve anything I wanted if I were only determined enough. There was now a fairly complicated set-up on screen, with all six boys doing something interesting, and one of them I realised was Kip Parker, a famous tousle-headed blond teen star. I ran my hand between my new friend's legs and felt his cock kicking against the tightish cotton of his slacks. He helped me take it out, a short, punchy little number, which I went down on and polished off almost at once. God he must have been ready. After a shocked recuperation he felt for his bag and went out without a word.

I'd had a growing suspicion throughout this sordid but charming little episode, which rose to a near certainty as he opened the door and was caught in a slightly brighter light, that the boy was Phil from the Corry. He had smelt of sweat rather than talcum powder and there was a light stubble on his jaw, so I concluded that if it were Phil he was on his way to rather than from the club, as I knew he was fastidiously clean, and that he always shaved in the evening before having his shower. I was tempted to follow him at once, to make sure, but I

realised it would be easy enough to tell from seeing him later; and besides, a very well-hung kid, who'd already been showing an interest in our activities, moved in to occupy the boy's former seat, and brought me off epically during the next film, an unthinkably tawdry picture which all took place in a kitchen.

A MODEL

Anaïs Nin

Angela Anaïs Juana Antolina Rosa Edelmira Nin y Culmell, was an author born to Cuban parents in France, where she was also raised. She spent some time in Spain and Cuba but lived most of her life in the United States where she became an established author. She wrote journals (which span more than sixty years, beginning when she was eleven years old and ending shortly before her death), novels, critical studies, essays, short stories and erotica. A great deal of her work, including *Delta of Venus* (1977) and *Little Birds* (1979), was published posthumously.

My mother had European ideas about young girls. I was sixteen. I had never gone out alone with young men, I had never read anything but literary novels, and by choice I never was like girls my own age. I was what you would call a sheltered person, very much like some Chinese woman, instructed in the art of making the most of the discarded dresses sent to me by a rich cousin, singing and dancing, writing elegantly, reading the finest books, conversing intelligently, arranging my hair beautifully, keeping my hands white and delicate, using only the refined English I had learned since my arrival from France, dealing with everybody in terms of great politeness.

This was what was left of my European education. But I was very much like the Orientals in one other way: long periods of gentleness were followed by bursts of violence, taking the form of temper and rebellion or of quick decision and positive action.

I suddenly decided to go to work, without consulting anybody or asking anybody's approval. I knew my mother would be against my plan.

I had rarely gone to New York alone. Now I walked the streets, answering all kinds of advertisements. My accomplishments were not very practical. I knew languages but not typewriting. I knew Spanish dancing but not the new ballroom dances. Everywhere I went I did not inspire confidence. I looked even younger than my age and over-delicate, over-sensitive. I looked as if I could not bear any burdens put on me, yet this was only an appearance.

After a week I had obtained nothing but a sense of not being useful to anyone. It was then I went to see a family friend who was very fond of me. She had disapproved of my mother's way of protecting me. She was happy to see me, amazed at my decision and willing to help me. It was while talking to her humorously about myself, enumerating my assets, that I happened to say that

a painter had come to see us the week before and had said that I had an exotic face. My friend jumped up.

"I have it," she said. "I know what you can do. It is true that you have an unusual face. Now I know an art club where artists go for their models. I will introduce you there. It is a sort of protection for the girls, instead of having them walk about from studio to studio. The artists are registered at the club, where they are known, and they telephone when they need a model."

When we arrived at the club on Fifty-seventh Street, there was great animation and many people. It turned out that they were preparing for the annual show. Every year all the models were dressed in costumes that best suited them and exhibited to the painters. I was quickly registered for a small fee and was sent upstairs to two elderly ladies who took me into the costume room. One of them chose an eighteenth-century costume. The other fixed my hair above my ears. They taught me how to wax my eyelashes. I saw a new self in the mirrors. The rehearsal was going on. I had to walk downstairs and stroll around the room. It was not difficult. It was like a masquerade ball.

The day of the show everyone was rather nervous. Much of a model's success depended on this event. My hand trembled as I made up my eyelashes. I was given a rose to carry, which made me feel a little ridiculous. I was received with applause. After all the girls had walked slowly around the room, the painters talked with us, took down our names, made engagements. My engagement book was filled like a dance card.

Monday at nine o'clock I was to be at the studio of a well-known painter; at one, at the studio of an illustrator; at four, at the studio of a miniaturist, and so on. There were women painters too. They objected to our using make-up. They said that when they engaged a made-up model and then got her to wash her face before posing, she did not look the same. For that reason posing for women did not attract us very much.

My announcement at home that I was a model came like a thunderbolt. But it was done. I could make twenty-five dollars a week. My mother wept a little, but was pleased deep down.

That night we talked in the dark. Her room connected with mine and the door was open. My mother was worrying about what I knew (or did not know) about sex.

The sum of my knowledge was this: that I had been kissed many times by Stephen, lying on the sand at the beach. He had been lying over me, and I had felt something bulky and hard pressing against me, but that was all, and to my great amazement when I came home I had discovered that I was all wet between the legs. I had not mentioned this to my mother. My private impression was that I was a great sensualist, that this getting wet between the legs at being kissed showed dangerous tendencies for the future. In fact, I felt quite like a whore.

My mother asked me, "Do you know what happens when a man takes a woman?"

"No," I said, "but I would like to know *how* a man takes a woman in the first place."

"Well, you know the small penis you saw when you bathed your brother – that gets big and hard and the man pushes it inside of the woman."

That seemed ugly to me. "It must be difficult to get it in," I said.

"No, because the woman gets wet before that, so it slides in easily."

Now I understood the mystery of wetness.

In that case, I thought to myself, I will never get raped, because to get wet you have to like the man.

A few months before, having been violently kissed in the woods by a big Russian who was bringing me home from a dance, I had come home and announced that I was pregnant.

Now I remembered how one night when several of us were returning from another dance, driving along the speedway, we had heard girls screaming. My escort, John, stopped the car. Two girls ran to us from the bushes, disheveled, dresses torn and eyes haggard. We let them into the car. They were mumbling chaotically about having been taken for a ride on a motorcycle and then attacked. One of them kept saying: "If he broke through, I'll kill myself."

John stopped at an inn and I took the girls to the ladies' room. They immediately went into the toilet together. One was saying: "There is no blood. I guess he didn't break through." The other one was crying.

We took them home. One of the girls thanked me and said, "I hope that never happens to you."

While my mother was talking, I was wondering if she feared this and was preparing me.

I cannot say that when Monday came I was not uneasy. I felt that if the painter was attractive I would be in greater danger than if he was not, for if I liked him I might get wet between the legs.

The first one was about fifty, bald, with a rather European face and a little mustache. He had a beautiful studio.

He placed the screen in front of me so that I could change my dress. I threw my clothes over the screen. As I threw my last piece of underwear over the top of the screen, I saw the painter's face appear at the top, smiling. But it was done so comically and ridiculously, like a scene in a play, that I said nothing, got dressed and took the pose.

Every half-hour I would get a rest. I could smoke a cigarette. The painter put on a record and said: "Will you dance?"

We danced on the highly polished floor, turning among the paintings of beautiful women. At the end of the dance, he kissed my neck. "So dainty," he said. "Do you pose in the nude?"

"No."

"Too bad."

I thought this was not so difficult to manage. It was time to pose again. The three hours passed quickly. He talked while he worked. He said he had married his first model; that she was unbearably jealous; that every now and then she broke into the studio and made scenes; that she would not let him paint from the nude. He had rented another studio she did not know about. Often he worked there. He gave parties there too. Would I like to come to one on Saturday night?

He gave me another little kiss on the neck as I left. He winked and said: "You won't tell the club on me?"

I returned to the club for luncheon because I could make up my face and

freshen myself, and they gave us a cheap lunch. The other girls were there. We fell into conversation. When I mentioned the invitation for Saturday night, they laughed, nodding at one another. I could not get them to talk. One girl had lifted up her skirt and was examining a mole way up her thighs. With a little caustic pencil she was trying to burn it away. I saw that she was not wearing panties, just a black satin dress which clung to her. The telephone would ring and then one of the girls would be called and go off to work.

The next was a young illustrator. He was wearing his shirt open at the neck. He did not move when I came in. He shouted at me, "I want to see a lot of back and shoulders. Put a shawl around yourself or something." Then he gave me a small old-fashioned umbrella and white gloves. The shawl he pinned down almost to my waist. This was for a magazine cover.

The arrangement of the shawl over my breasts was precarious. As I tilted my head at the angle he wanted, in a sort of inviting gesture, the shawl slipped and my breasts showed. He would not let me move. "Wish I could paint them in," he said.

He was smiling as he worked with his charcoal pencil. Leaning over to measure me, he touched the tips of my breasts with his pencil and made a little black mark. "Keep that pose," he said as he saw me ready to move. I kept it.

Then he said: "You girls sometimes act as if you thought you were the only ones with breasts or asses. I see so many of them they don't interest me, I assure you. I take my wife all dressed always. The more clothes she has on the better. I turn off the light. I know too much how women are made. I've drawn millions of them."

The little touch of the pencil on my breasts had hardened the tips. This angered me, because I had not felt it a pleasure at all. Why were my breasts so sensitive, and did he notice it?

He went on drawing and coloring his picture. He stopped to drink whiskey and offered me some. He dipped his finger in the whiskey and touched one of my nipples. I was not posing so I moved away angrily. He kept smiling at me. "Doesn't it feel nice?" he said. "It warms them."

It was true that the tips were hard and red.

"Very nice nipples you have. You don't need to use lipstick on them, do you? They are naturally rosy. Most of them have a leather color."

I covered myself.

That was all for that day. He asked me to come the next day at the same time.

He was slower in getting to his work on Tuesday. He talked. He had his feet up on his drawing table. He offered me a cigarette. I was pinning up my shawl. He was watching me. He said: "Show me your legs. I may do a drawing of legs next time."

I lifted up my skirt above the knee.

"Sit down with your skirt up high," he said.

He sketched in the legs. There was a silence.

Then he got up, flung his pencil on the table, leaned over me and kissed me fully on the mouth, forcing my head backwards. I pushed him off violently. This made him smile. He slipped his hand swiftly up under my skirt, felt my thighs where the stockings stopped and before I could move was back in his seat.

I took the pose and said nothing, because I had just made a discovery – that in spite of my anger, in spite of the fact that I was not in love, the kiss and the caress on the naked thighs had given me pleasure. While I fought him off, it was only out of habit, but actually it had given me pleasure.

The pose gave me time to awaken from the pleasure and remember my defenses. But my defenses had been convincing and he was quiet for the rest of the morning.

From the very first I had divined that what I really had to defend myself against was my own susceptibility to caresses. I was also filled with great curiosities about so many things. At the same time I was utterly convinced that I would not give myself to anyone but the man I fell in love with.

I was in love with Stephen. I wanted to go to him and say: "Take me, take me!" I suddenly remembered another incident, and that was a year before this when one of my aunts had taken me to New Orleans to the Mardi Gras. Friends of hers had driven us in their automobile. There were two other young girls with us. A band of young men took advantage of the confusion, the noise, the excitement and gaiety to jump into our automobile, remove our masks and begin kissing us while my aunt raised an outcry. Then they disappeared into the crowd. I was left dazed and wishing that the young man who had taken hold of me and had kissed me on the mouth were still there. I was languid from the kiss, languid and stirred.

Back at the club I wondered what all the rest of the models felt. There was a great deal of talk about defending oneself, and I wondered whether it was all sincere. One of the loveliest models, whose face was not particularly beautiful but who had a magnificent body, was talking:

"I don't know what other girls feel about posing in the nude," she said, "I love it. Ever since I was a little girl I liked taking off my clothes. I liked to see how people looked at me. I used to take my clothes off at parties, as soon as people were a little drunk. I liked showing my body. Now I can't wait to take them off. I enjoy being looked at. It gives me pleasure. I get shivers of pleasure right down my back when men look at me. And when I pose for a whole class of artists at the school, when I see all those eyes on my body, I get so much pleasure, it is – well, it is like being made love to. I feel beautiful, I feel as women must feel sometimes when undressed for a lover. I enjoy my own body. I like to pose holding my breasts in my hand. Sometimes I caress them. I was once in burlesque. I loved it. I enjoyed doing that as much as the men enjoyed seeing it. The satin of the dress used to give me shivers – taking my breasts out, exposing myself. That excited me. When men touched me I did not get as much excitement . . . it was always a disappointment. But I know other girls who don't feel that way."

"I feel humiliated," said a red-haired model. "I feel my body is not my own, and that it no longer has any value . . . being seen by everybody."

"I don't feel anything at all," said another. "I feel it's all impersonal. When men are painting or drawing, they no longer think of us as human beings. One painter told me that the body of a model on the stand is an objective thing, that the only moment he felt disturbed erotically was when the model took off her kimono. In Paris, they tell me, the model undresses right in front of the class, and that's exciting."

"If it were all so objective," said another girl, "they wouldn't invite us to parties afterwards."

"Or marry their models," I added, remembering two painters I had already met who had married their favorite models.

One day I had to pose for an illustrator of stories. When I arrived, I found two other people already there, a girl and a man. We were to compose scenes together, love scenes for a romance. The man was about forty, with a very mature, very decadent face. It was he who knew how to arrange us. He placed me in a position for a kiss. We had to hold the pose while the illustrator photographed us. I was uneasy. I did not like the man at all. The other girl played the jealous wife who burst in on the scene. We had to do it many times. Each time the man acted the kiss I shrank inside myself, and he felt it. He was offended. His eyes were mocking. I acted badly. The illustrator was shouting at me as if we were in a moving picture, "More passion, put more passion into it!"

I tried to remember how the Russian had kissed me on returning from the dance, and that relaxed me. The man repeated the kiss. And now I felt he was holding me closer than he needed to, and surely he did not need to push his tongue into my mouth. He did it so quickly that I had no time to move. The illustrator started other scenes.

The male model said, "I have been a model for ten years now. I don't know why they always want young girls. Young girls have no experience and no expression. In Europe young girls of your age, under twenty, do not interest anyone. They are left in school or at home. They only become interesting after marriage."

As he talked, I thought of Stephen. I thought of us at the beach, lying on the hot sand. I knew that Stephen loved me. I wanted him to take me. I wanted now to be made a woman quickly. I did not like being a virgin, always defending myself. I felt that everyone knew I was a virgin and was all the more keen to conquer me.

That evening Stephen and I were going out together. Somehow or other I must tell him. I must tell him that I was in danger of being raped, that he'd better do it first. No, he would then be so anxious. How could I tell him?

I had news for him. I was the star model now. I had more work than anyone else in the club, there were more demands for me because I was a foreigner and had an unusual face. I often had to pose in the evenings. I told Stephen all this. He was proud of me.

"You like your posing?" he said.

"I love it. I love to be with painters, to see them work – good or bad, I like the atmosphere of it, the stories I hear. It is varied, never the same. It is really adventure."

"Do they . . . do they make love to you?" Stephen asked.

"Not if you don't want them to."

"But do they try . . . ?"

I saw that he was anxious. We were walking to my house from the railway station, through the dark fields. I turned to him and offered my mouth. He kissed me. I said, "Stephen, take me, take me, take me."

He was completely dumbfounded. I was throwing myself into the refuge of

his big arms, I wanted to be taken and have it all over with, I wanted to be made a woman. But he was absolutely still, frightened. He said, "I want to marry you, but I can't do it just now."

"I don't care about the marriage."

But now I became conscious of his surprise, and it quieted me. I was immensely disappointed by his conventional attitude. The moment passed. He thought it was merely an attack of blind passion, that I had lost my head. He was even proud to have protected me against my own impulses. I went home to bed and sobbed.

One illustrator asked me if I would pose on Sunday, that he was in a great rush to finish a poster. I consented. When I arrived he was already at work. It was morning and the building seemed deserted. His studio was on the thirteenth floor. He had half of the poster done. I got undressed quickly and put on the evening dress he had given me to wear. He did not seem to pay any attention to me. We worked in peace for a long while. I grew tired. He noticed it and gave me a rest. I walked about the studio looking at the other pictures. They were mostly portraits of actresses. I asked him who they were. He answered me with details about their sexual tastes:

"Oh, this one, this one demands romanticism. It's the only way you can get near her. She makes it difficult. She is European and she likes an intricate courtship. Halfway through I gave it up. It was too strenuous. She was very beautiful though, and there is something wonderful about getting a woman like that in bed. She had beautiful eyes, an entranced air, like some Hindu mystic. It makes you wonder how they will behave in bed.

"I have known other sexual angels. It is wonderful to see the change in them. These clear eyes that you can see through, these bodies that take such beautiful harmonious poses, these delicate hands . . . how they change when desire takes hold of them. The sexual angels! They are wonderful because it is such a surprise, such a change. You, for instance, with your appearance of never having been touched, I can see you biting and scratching . . . I am sure your very voice changes – I have seen such changes. There are women's voices that sound like poetic, unearthly echoes. Then they change. The eyes change. I believe that all these legends about people changing into animals at night – like the stories of the werewolf, for instance – were invented by men who saw women transform at night from idealized, worshipful creatures into animals and thought that they were possessed. But I know it is something much simpler than that. You are a virgin, aren't you?"

"No, I am married," I said.

"Married or not, you are a virgin. I can tell. I am never deceived. If you are married, your husband has not made you a woman yet. Don't you regret that? Don't you feel you are wasting time, that real living begins with sensation, with being a woman . . . ?"

This corresponded so exactly to what I had been feeling, to my desire to enter experience, that I was silent. I hated to admit this to a stranger.

I was conscious of being alone with the illustrator in an empty studio building. I was sad that Stephen had not understood my desire to become a woman.

I was not frightened but fatalistic, desiring only to find someone I might fall in love with.

"I know what you are thinking," he said, "but for me it would not have any meaning unless the woman wanted me. I never could make love to a woman if she did not want me. When I first saw you, I felt how wonderful it would be to initiate you. There is something about you that makes me feel you will have many love affairs. I would like to be the first one. But not unless you wanted it."

I smiled. "That is exactly what I was thinking. It can only be if I want it, and I do not want it."

"You must not give that first surrender so much importance. I think that was created by the people who wanted to preserve their daughters for marriage, the idea that the first man who takes a woman will have complete power over her. I think that is a superstition. It was created to help preserve women from promiscuity. It is actually untrue. If a man can make himself be loved, if he can rouse a woman, then she will be attracted to him. But the mere act of breaking through her virginity is not enough to accomplish this. Any man can do this and leave the woman unaroused. Did you know that many Spaniards take their wives this way and give them many children without completely initiating them sexually just to be sure of their faithfulness? The Spaniard believes in keeping pleasure for his mistress. In fact, if he sees a woman enjoy sensuality, he immediately suspects her of being faithless, even of being a whore."

The illustrator's words haunted me for days. Then I was faced with a new problem. Summer had come and the painters were leaving for the country, for the beach, for far-off places in all directions. I did not have the money to follow them, and I was not sure how much work I would get. One morning I posed for an illustrator named Ronald. Afterwards he set the phonograph going and asked me to dance. While we were dancing he said, "Why don't you come to the country for a while? It will do you good, you will get plenty of work, and I will pay for your trip. There are very few good models there. I am sure you will be kept busy."

So I went. I took a little room in a farmhouse. Then I went to see Ronald, who lived down the road in a shed, into which he had built a huge window. The first thing he did was to blow his cigarette smoke into my mouth. I coughed.

"Oh," he said, "you don't know how to inhale."

"I'm not at all interested," I said, getting up. "What kind of pose do you want?"

"Oh," he said laughing, "We don't work so hard here. You will have to learn to enjoy yourself a little. Now, take the smoke from my mouth and inhale it . . ."

"I don't like to inhale."

He laughed again. He tried to kiss me. I moved away.

"Oh, oh," he said, "you are not going to be a very pleasant companion for me. I paid for your trip, you know, and I'm lonely down here. I expected you to be very pleasant company. Where is your suitcase?"

"I took a room down the road."

"But you were invited to stay with me," he said.

"I understood you wanted me to pose for you."

"For the moment it is not a model I need."

I started to leave. He said, "You know, there is an understanding here about models who do not know how to enjoy themselves. If you take this attitude nobody will give you any work."

I did not believe him. The next morning I began to knock on the doors of all the artists I could find. But Ronald had already paid them a visit. So I was received without cordiality, like a person who has played a trick on another. I did not have the money to return home, nor the money to pay for my room. I knew nobody. The country was beautiful, mountainous, but I could not enjoy it.

The next day I took a long walk and came upon a log cabin by the side of a river. I saw a man painting there, out of doors. I spoke to him. I told him my story. He did not know Ronald, but he was angry. He said he would try to help me. I told him all I wanted was to earn enough to return to New York.

So I began to pose for him. His name was Reynolds. He was a man of thirty or so, with black hair, very soft black eyes and a brilliant smile – a recluse. He never went to the village, except for food, nor frequented the restaurants or bars. He had a lax walk, easy gestures. He had been on the sea, always on tramp steamers, working as a sailor so that he could see foreign countries. He was always restless.

He painted from memory what he had seen in his travels. Now he sat at the foot of a tree and never looked around him but painted a wild piece of South American jungle.

Once when he and his friends were in the jungle, Reynolds told me, they had smelled such a strong animal odor they thought they would suddenly see a panther, but out of the bushes had sprung with incredible velocity a woman, a naked savage woman, who looked at them with the frightened eyes of an animal, then ran off, leaving this strong animal scent behind her, threw herself into the river and swam away before they could catch their breath.

A friend of Reynolds had captured a woman like this. When he had washed off the red paint with which she was covered, she was very beautiful. She was gentle when well treated, succumbed to gifts of beads and ornaments.

Her strong smell repelled Reynolds until his friend had offered to let him have a night with her. He had found her black hair as hard and bristly as a beard. The animal smell made him feel he was lying with a panther. And she was so much stronger than he that after a while, he was acting almost like a woman, and she was the one who was molding him to suit her fancies. She was indefatigable and slow to arouse. She could bear caresses that exhausted him, and he fell asleep in her arms.

Then he found her climbing over him and pouring a little liquid over his penis, something that at first made him smart and then aroused him furiously. He was frightened. His penis seemed to have filled with fire, or with red peppers. He rubbed himself against her flesh, more to ease the burning than out of desire.

He was angry. She was smiling and laughing softly. He began taking her with a rage, driven by a fear that what she had done to him would arouse him for the last time, that it was some sort of enchantment to get the maximum of desire from him, until he died.

She lay back laughing, her white teeth showing, the animal odor of her now affecting him erotically like the smell of musk. She moved with such vigor that

he felt she would tear his penis away from him. But now he wanted to subjugate her. He caressed her at the same time.

She was surprised by this. No one seemed to have done this to her before. When he was tired of taking her, after two orgasms, he continued to rub her clitoris, and she enjoyed this, begging for more, opening her legs wide. Then suddenly she turned over, crouched on the bed and swung her ass upward at an incredible angle. She expected him to take her again, but he continued to caress her. After this it was always his hand that she sought. She rubbed against it like a huge cat. During the day, if she met him she would rub her sex against his hand, surreptitiously.

Reynolds said that that night had made white women seem weak to him. He was laughing as he told the story.

His painting had reminded him of the savage woman hiding in the bushes, waiting like a tigress to leap and run away from the men who carried guns. He had painted her in, with her heavy, pointed breasts, her fine, long legs, her slender waist.

I did not know how I could pose for him. But he was thinking of another picture. He said, "It will be easy. I want you to fall asleep. But you will be wrapped in white sheets. I saw something in Morocco once that I always wanted to paint. A woman had fallen asleep among her silk spools, holding the silk weaving frame with her hennaed feet. You have beautiful eyes, but they'll have to be closed."

He went into the cabin and brought out sheets which he draped around me like a robe. He propped me against a wooden box, arranged my body and hands as he wanted them and began to sketch immediately. It was a very hot day. The sheets made me warm, and the pose was so lazy that I actually fell asleep, I don't know for how long. I felt languid and unreal. And then I felt a soft hand between my legs, very soft, caressing me so lightly I had to awaken to make sure I had been touched. Reynolds was bending over me, but with such an expression of delighted gentleness that I did not move. His eyes were tender, his mouth half open.

"Only a caress," he said, "just a caress."

I did not move. I had never felt anything like this hand softly, softly caressing the skin between my legs without touching my sex. He only touched the tips of my pubic hair. Then his hand slipped down to the little valley around the sex. I was growing lax and soft. He leaned over and put his mouth on mine, lightly touching my lips, until my own mouth responded, and only then did he touch the tip of my tongue with his. His hand was moving, exploring, but so softly, it was tantalizing. I was wet, and I knew if he moved just a little more he would feel this. The languor spread all through my body. Each time his tongue touched mine I felt as if there were another little tongue inside of me, flicking out, wanting to be touched too. His hand moved only around my sex, and then around my ass, and it was as if he magnetized the blood to follow the movements of his hands. His finger touched the clitoris so gently, then slipped between the lips of the vulva. He felt the wetness. He touched this with delight, kissing me, lying over me now, and I did not move. The warmth, the smells of plants around me, his mouth over mine affected me like a drug.

"Only a caress," he repeated gently, his finger moving around my clitoris until the little mound swelled and hardened. Then I felt as if a seed were bursting in me, a joy that made me palpitate under his fingers. I kissed him with gratitude. He was smiling. He said, "Do you want to caress me?"

I nodded yes, but I did not know what he wanted of me. He unbuttoned his pants and I saw his penis. I took it in my hands. He said, "Press harder." He saw then that I did not know how. He took my hand in his and guided me. The little white foam fell all over my hand. He covered himself. He kissed me with the same grateful kiss I had given him after my pleasure.

He said, "Did you know that a Hindu makes love to his wife ten days before he takes her? For ten days they merely caress and kiss."

The thought of Ronald's behavior angered him all over again – the way he had wronged me in everybody's eyes. I said, "Don't get angry. I am happy he did it, because it made me walk away from the village and come here."

"I loved you as soon as I heard you speak with that accent you have. I felt as if I were traveling again. Your face is so different, your walk, your ways. You remind me of the girl I intended to paint in Fez. I saw her only once, asleep like this. I always dreamed of awakening her as I awakened you."

"And I always dreamed of being awakened with a caress like this," I said.

"If you had been awake I might not have dared."

"You, the adventurer, who lived with a savage woman?"

"I did not really live with the savage woman. That happened to a friend of mine. He was always talking about it, so I always tell it as if it had happened to me. I'm really timid with women. I can knock men down and fight and get drunk, but women intimidate me, even whores. They laugh at me. But this happened exactly as I had always planned it would happen."

"But the tenth day I will be in New York," I said laughing.

"The tenth day I will drive you back, if you have to go back. But meanwhile you are my prisoner."

For ten days we worked out in the open, lying in the sun. The sun would warm my body, as Reynolds waited for me to close my eyes. Sometimes I pretended I wanted him to do more to me. I thought that if I closed my eyes he would take me. I liked the way he would walk up to me, like a hunter, making no sound and lying at my side. Sometimes he lifted my dress first and looked at me for a long time. Then he would touch me lightly, as if he did not want to awaken me, until the moisture came. His fingers would quicken. We kept our mouths together, our tongues caressing. I learned to take his penis in my mouth. This excited him terribly. He would lose all his gentleness, push his penis into my mouth, and I was afraid of choking. Once I bit him, hurt him, but he did not mind. I swallowed the white foam. When he kissed me, our faces were covered with it. The marvelous smell of sex impregnated my fingers. I did not want to wash my hands.

I felt that we shared a magnetic current, but at the same time nothing else bound us together. Reynolds had promised to drive me back to New York. He could not stay in the country much longer. I had to find work.

During the drive back Reynolds stopped the car and we lay on a blanket in the woods, resting. We caressed. He said, "Are you happy?"

"Yes."

"Can you continue to be happy, this way? As we are?"

"Why, Reynolds, what is it?"

"Listen, I love you. You know that, but I can't take you. I did that to a girl once, and she got pregnant and had an abortion. She bled to death. Since then I haven't been able to take a woman. I'm afraid. If that should happen to you, I would kill myself."

I had never thought of things like this. I was silent. We kissed for a long time. For the first time he kissed me between the legs instead of caressing me, kissed me until I felt the orgasm. We were happy. He said, "This little wound women have . . . it frightens me."

In New York it was hot and all the artists were still away. I found myself without work. I took up modeling in dress shops. I could easily get work, but when they asked me to go out in the evenings with the buyers I would refuse and lose the job. Finally I was taken into a big place near Thirty-fourth Street where they employed six models. This place was frightening and gray. There were long rows of clothes and a few benches for us to sit on. We waited in our slips, to be ready for quick changes. When our numbers were called, we helped one another dress.

The three men who sold the dress designs often tried to fondle us, squeeze us. We took turns staying during the lunch hour. My greatest fear was that I would be left alone with the man who was most persistent.

Once when Stephen telephoned to ask if he could see me that evening, the man came up behind me and put his hand into my slip to feel my breasts. Not knowing what else to do, I kicked him while I held the phone and tried to go on talking to Stephen. He was not discouraged. Next, he tried to feel my ass. I kicked again.

Stephen was saying, "What is it, what are you saying?"

I ended the conversation and turned on the man. He was gone.

The buyers admired our physical qualities as much as the dresses. The head salesman was very proud of me and would often say, with his hand on my hair, "She's an artist's model."

This made me long to return to posing. I did not want Reynolds or Stephen to find me here in an ugly office building, wearing dresses for ugly salesmen and buyers.

Finally I was called to model at the studio of a South American painter. He had the face of a woman, pale with big black eyes, long black hair, and his gestures were languid and effete. His studio was beautiful – luxuriant rugs, large paintings of nude women, silk hangings; and there was incense burning. He said he had a very intricate pose to do. He was painting a big horse running away with a naked woman. He asked if I had ever ridden on horseback. I said that I had, when I was younger.

"That is marvelous," he said, "exactly what I want. Now, I have made a contraption here which gives me the effect I need."

It was a dummy of a horse without a head, just the body and legs, with a saddle.

He said, "Take your clothes off first, then I will show you. I have difficulty

with this part of the pose. The woman is throwing her body back because the horse is running wild, like this." He sat on the dummy horse to show me.

By now I no longer felt timid about posing nude. I took my clothes off and sat on the horse, throwing my body backwards, my arms flying, my legs clasping the horse's flanks so as not to fall. The painter approved. He moved away and looked at me. "It's a hard pose and I do not expect you to keep it long. Just let me know when you get tired."

He studied me from every side. Then came up close to me and said, "When I made the drawing, this part of the body showed clearly, here, between the legs." He touched me lightly as if it were merely part of his work. I curved in my belly a little to throw the hips forward and then he said, "Now it is fine. Hold it."

He began to sketch. As I sat there I realized that there was one uncommon detail about the saddle. Most saddles, of course, are shaped to follow the contour of the ass and then rise at the pommel, where they are apt to rub against a woman's sex. I had often experienced both the advantages and the disadvantages of being supported there. Once my garter came loose from the stocking and began to dance around inside my riding trousers. My companions were galloping and I did not want to fall behind, so I continued. The garter, leaping in all directions, finally fell between my sex and the saddle and hurt me. I held on, gritting my teeth. The pain was strangely mixed with a sensation I could not define. I was a girl then and did not know anything about sex. I thought that a woman's sex was inside of her, and I did not know about the clitoris.

When the ride was over, I was in pain. I mentioned what had happened to a girl I knew well, and we both went into the bathroom. She helped me out of my trousers, out of my little belt with the garters on it, and then said, "Are you hurt? That's a very sensitive spot. Maybe you'll never have any pleasure there if you got hurt."

I let her look at it. It was red and a little swollen, but not so very painful. What bothered me was her saying I might be deprived of a pleasure by this, a pleasure I did not know. She insisted on bathing it with a wet cotton, fondled me and finally kissed me, "to make it well".

I became acutely aware of this part of my body. Particularly when we rode a long while in the heat, I felt such a warmth and stirring between my legs that all I desired was to get off the horse and let my friend nurse me again. She was always asking me, "Does it hurt?"

So once I answered, "Just a little." We dismounted and went into the bathroom, and she bathed the chaffed spot with cotton and cool water.

And again she fondled me, saying, "But it does not look sore anymore. Maybe you will be able to enjoy yourself again."

"I don't know," I said. "Do you think it has gone . . . dead . . . from the pain?"

My friend very tenderly leaned over and touched me. "Does it hurt?"

I lay back and said, "No, I do not feel anything."

"Don't you feel this?" she asked with concern, pressing the lips between her fingers.

"No," I said, watching her.

"Don't you feel this?" She passed her fingers now around the tip of the clitoris, making tiny circles.

"I don't feel anything."

She became eager to see if I had lost my sensibility and increased her caresses, rubbing the clitoris with one hand while she vibrated the tip with the other. She stroked my pubic hair and tender skin around it. Finally I felt her, wildly, and I began to move. She was panting over me, watching me and saying, "Wonderful, wonderful, you can feel there . . ."

I was remembering this as I sat on the dummy horse and noticed that the pommel was quite accentuated. So the painter could see what he wanted to paint, I slid forward, and as I did so my sex rubbed against the leather prominence. The painter was observing me.

"Do you like my horse?" he said. "Do you know that I can make it move?"

"Can you?"

He came near me and set the dummy in motion, and indeed it was perfectly constructed to move like a horse.

"I like it," I said. "It reminds me of the times I rode horseback when I was a girl." I noticed that he stopped painting now to watch me. The motion of the horse pushed my sex against the saddle even harder and gave me great pleasure. I thought that he would notice it, and so I said, "Stop it now." But he smiled and did not stop it. "Don't you like it?" he said.

I did like it. Each movement brought the leather against my clitoris, and I thought I could not hold back an orgasm if it went on. I begged him to stop. My face was flushed.

The painter was carefully watching me, watching every expression of a pleasure I could not control, and now it increased so that I abandoned myself to the motion of the horse, let myself rub against the leather, until I felt the orgasm and I came, riding this way in front of him.

Only then did I know that he expected it, that he had done all this to see me enjoy it. He knew when to stop the machinery. "You can rest now," he said.

Soon after, I went to pose for a woman illustrator, Lena, I had met at a party. She liked company. Actors and actresses came to see her, writers. She painted for magazine covers. The door was always open. People brought drinks. The talk was acid, cruel. It seemed to me that all her friends were caricaturists. Everyone's weaknesses were immediately exposed. Or they exposed their own. One beautiful young man, dressed with great elegance, made no secret of his profession. He sat around at the big hotels, waited for old women who were alone and took them out to dance. Very often they invited him back to their rooms.

Lena made a wry face, "How can you do it?" she asked him, "Such old women, how can you possibly get an erection? If I saw a woman like that lying on my bed, I would run away."

The young man smiled. "There are so many ways of doing it. One is to close my eyes and to imagine it is not an old woman but a woman I like, and then when my eyes are closed I begin to think how pleasant it will be to be able to pay my rent the next day or to buy a new suit or silk shirts. And as I do this, I keep stroking the woman's sex without looking, and, you know, if your eyes are closed, they feel about the same, more or less. Sometimes, though, when I have difficulty I take drugs. Of course, I know that at this rate my career will last

about five years and that at the end of that time I will not be of any use even to a young woman. But by then I will be glad never to see a woman again.

"I certainly envy my Argentine friend, my roommate. He is a handsome, aristocratic man, absolutely effete. Women would love him. When I leave the apartment, do you know what he does? He gets up out of bed, pulls out a small electric iron and an ironing board, takes his pants and begins to press them. As he presses them he imagines how he will come out of the building so impeccably dressed, how he will walk down Fifth Avenue, how somewhere he will spy a beautiful woman, follow the scent of her perfume for many blocks, follow her into crowded elevators, almost touching her. The woman will be wearing a veil and a fur around her neck. Her dress will outline her figure.

"After following her thus through the shops, he will finally speak to her. She will see his handsome face smiling at her and the chivalrous way he has of carrying himself. They will go off together and sit having tea somewhere, then go to the hotel where she is staying. She will invite him to come up with her. They will get into the room and then pull down the shades and lie in the darkness making love.

"As he presses his pants carefully, meticulously, my friend imagines how he will make love to this woman – and it excites him. He knows how he will grip her. He likes to push his penis in from behind and raise the woman's legs, and then get her to turn just a little so that he can see it moving in and out. He likes the woman to squeeze the base of his penis at the same time; her fingers press harder than the mouth of her sex, and that excites him. She will also touch his balls as he moves, and he will touch her clitoris, because that gives her a double pleasure. He will make her gasp and shake from head to foot and beg for more.

"By the time he has envisioned all this standing there, half naked, pressing his pants, my friend has a hard on. It is all he wants. He puts away the pants, the iron and the ironing board, and he gets into bed again, lying back and smoking, thinking over this scene until each detail of it is perfect and a drop of semen appears at the head of his penis, which he strokes while he lies smoking and dreaming of pursuing other women.

"I envy him because he can get so much excitement from thinking all this. He questions me. He wants to know how my women are made, how they behave . . ."

Lena laughed. She said, It's hot. I will take my corset off." And she went into the alcove. When she came back her body looked free and lax. She sat down, crossed her bare legs, her blouse half-open. One of her friends sat where he could see her.

Another one, a handsome man, stood near me as I was posing and whispered compliments. He said, "I love you because you remind me of Europe – Paris especially. I don't know what there is about Paris, but there is sensuality in the air there. It is contagious. It is such a human city. I don't know whether it is because couples are always kissing in the streets, at tables in the cafés, in the movies, in the parks. They embrace each other so freely. They stop for long complete kisses in the middle of the sidewalk, at the subway entrances. Perhaps it is that, or the softness of the air. I don't know. In the dark, in each doorway at night there is a

man and a woman almost melted into one another. The whores watch for you every moment . . . they touch you.

"One day I was standing on a platform bus, looking up idly at the houses. I saw a window open and a man and woman lying on a bed. The woman was sitting over the man.

"At five o'clock in the afternoon it becomes unbearable. There is love and desire in the air. Everybody is in the streets. The cafés are full. In the movies there are little boxes that are completely dark and curtained off so that you can make love on the floor while the movie is going on and not be seen. It is all so open, so easy. No police to interfere. A woman friend of mine who was followed and annoyed by a man complained to the policeman at the corner. He laughed and said, 'You'll be sorrier the day no man wants to annoy you, won't you? After all, you should be thankful instead of getting angry.' And he would not help her."

Then my admirer said in a lower voice, "Will you come and have dinner with me and go to the theatre?"

He became my first real lover. I forgot Reynolds and Stephen. They now seem like children to me.

SMALL TALK

Luke Jennings

Luke Jennings is an author and the dance critic of the *Observer*. As a journalist, he has written for *Vanity Fair*, the *New Yorker* and *Time*, as well as numerous British titles. He was shortlisted for the 2010 Samuel Johnson and William Hill prizes for his memoir *Blood Knots*, and was nominated for the Booker Prize for his novel *Atlantic*. With Deborah Bull, he wrote *The Faber Guide to Ballet*, and, with his daughter Laura, the Stars stage-school novels. He is also the author of the Villanelle thriller series..

Another drinks party at the Wentworth Tennis Club. The company tends to be on the conservative side at the club – almost all of the husbands commute to the City, very few of the wives work – and I had no high hopes of any great repartee. In fact it would be fair to say that I could identify in advance every single topic of conversation that was likely to be raised.

It was, however, a lovely evening. The heat of the day had ceded to a golden stillness, and long shadows were painted on the lawn and the clubhouse verandah. And I would venture to say that we ourselves made a brave enough picture, with the men distinguished in blazers and open-necked shirts and the women charming in print dresses and light woollens. I arrived just as the fray was warming up, and after arming me with a gin and tonic – longish on the gin, shortish on the tonic, as is my regrettable wont – the club secretary introduced me to a new member, Davina Harvey-Clissold.

Mrs Harvey-Clissold was an attractive woman of some 35 summers. She was wearing a navy blue linen suit with a pretty sapphire brooch. Her intelligent features displayed a light honey-coloured tan – Barbados, perhaps, or Gstaad – and her smartly cut blonde hair was restrained by a black velvet band.

"So," I said, when she had accepted a cigarette and I had lit it for her. "Tell me something about yourself."

She smiled politely and examined the frosted glass of her drink. "I love to guzzle cum," she told me. "I love it when some big-cocked stud hoses my dirty slut's face with his creamy wad."

"And have you and your husband moved to the area recently?" I asked her.

She coloured slightly at the intimate nature of the question.

"I love to feel a massive rock-hard prick between my juicy stiff-nippled chest-puppies," she said, drawing absently at her cigarette. "But how about you, Mr Corbishley? Do you like to drive your rock-hard piston into the drenched

twat of a barely legal cumteen? Or do you prefer to gag on the swollen ebony shaft of a Brazilian she-male?"

Her question went unanswered, for at that moment an acquaintance of hers hove into view. They air-kissed, and Mrs Harvey-Clissold turned to me. "Mr Corbishley, I'd like you to meet Consuela Vasconcellos. Consuela is a filthy spunk-chugging Latina slut-bitch who likes nothing better than to spread her coral pink cunt-lips for a succession of huge-cocked studs."

Consuela Vasconcellos smiled, and we shook hands. Sensing a directness in her manner – and, I confess, a hint of mischief – I dared a personal question.

"How do you find Berkshire, Mrs Vasconcellos?" I asked.

Her jaw dropped, and for a long moment she stared at me, appalled. Then, with every fibre of her being quivering with outrage, she turned on her heel and marched into the clubhouse.

"Well, that was hardly tactful, was it?" murmured Davina Harvey-Clissold. "I've heard you have a reputation for plain speaking, but . . ."

"I'm sorry," I said, "but don't you sometimes feel you want to cut to the chase with people? To dispense with the formalities? I mean, would you really be offended if I asked you your opinion of the property market, or where you and your husband were thinking of sending your children to school?"

Hardly were the words out of my mouth than a stinging slap connected with my face. The report was like that of a gunshot, and I could feel my cheek blazing with the force of the blow. When my eyes had finally cleared, Davina Harvey-Clissold was nowhere to be seen and the club secretary had materialised at my side.

"Dickie, old boy," he began. "You must stop behaving like this. People are beginning to talk."

"I'm sorry," I said. "I'm afraid I just don't seem to have the gift of small talk."

George Arbuthnot looked at me kindly. "Let's just forget about it, shall we? Why don't you help yourself to one of my panatellas and come and say hello to the Hoarwithys. Guy loves chocolate sex-play while wearing a hardened rubber butt-plug and Sophie dreams of being orally and anally violated by a succession of monster cocks in a Transylvanian dungeon."

The sensible chap, I have always thought, knows when it's time to throw in the towel.

"Lead on, George," I said.

THOUGHT WAVES

Elizabeth Speller

Elizabeth Speller studied archaeology and classics as a mature student at Cambridge, followed by a postgraduate degree in ancient history. She is a poet and author of four non-fiction books, including a biography of Emperor Hadrian, companion guides to Rome and Athens, and a memoir, *The Sunlight on the Garden.* She has contributed to publications as varied as the *Financial Times*, *The Big Issue* and *Vogue*. She lives between England and Paxos, Greece.

Late on a hot night. So late that even in June the velvet of dark is caught between the large white houses by the canal. A smell of jasmine, of privet, the roar of cars on their distant arc around the city.

On the top floor, two men sit in a large room: coffered ceilings, maps, books, eighteenth-century porcelain, a Bechstein and a minstrel's gallery. Schubert lieder balanced on the night, glasses – several glasses – of brandy, the sash windows hauled open and the one low light behind a chair casting their features in relief.

"Do you ever see that dark girl? Zena? Was that it? Do you still . . . see her?" The older man smiles as he raises his eyebrows to his friend.

"Zinnia. It was Zinnia," the figure in the deep chair replies. "Still is Zinnia, actually."

"So Jane doesn't mind . . . I mean she knows, I assume?"

"Yes and no. You know. But would you like to see her – Zinnia, I mean?" The younger man, not young, but younger, asks. "Look, I have her photograph."

He pulls out a book – one of his more successful novels – from the tall cases; the picture is hidden within its pages. The grey-haired man looks down, tips the picture towards the light, is surprised. The woman is naked, reclining like Maya, on large pillows, one knee up, one arm behind her head, her eyes looking directly at the photographer, between her legs dusk, her dark nipples disproportionately large for her small breasts.

"Lucky man."

He gazes, embarrassment and arousal struggling within him. He drinks deeply from his glass.

"Do you see her often? I mean, it must be difficult."

"It is difficult," the writer smiles ruefully." She loves me, passionately. I desire her. And she lives in France much of the time. And there's Jane. But there are ways. And she is very compliant. That's love you see. She'll do anything for me; it's terrifying in some ways. Should I set her free? I often mean to but I never quite do."

His friend looks puzzled. The writer fills his glass.

"Would you like me to show you? Not photographs, I mean, but how it works?"

At a nod, he picks up a telephone and touches keys in the semi-darkness. The older man can just hear it ringing. It rings and rings. Finally an answer.

"It's me." The writer smiles, whether for his friend or his lover or himself, who can tell.

"Yes. I am. Of course. And you?"

"Where are you? In bed. Yes, it's late. I know."

"So, what are you wearing?"

"Of course. It's hot. No, I knew. Do you miss me?"

Is he acting? The one-sided conversation seems unreal.

"Zinnia . . . I want you to do something for me. I'm here thinking of you. Missing you. You know what would make me happy."

"Close your eyes. Now touch your breast. Yes. For me. For me, darling girl."

It is silent in the darkness. Is he being teased? The older man is appalled and captivated.

"Put your finger in your mouth, sweetheart, now wet your nipple for me . . . stroke it, stroke it for me. Is it hard? Tell me darling? How does it feel?"

"Now take your nipple between your thumb and forefinger . . . squeeze it."

"Now the other one. Hurt it a little. Oh, I like that." He exhales.

"Now you know what I want you to do, don't you, sweetheart? Tell me, are you ready for me? Are you wet? Open your legs darling. Open them wide for me. As if I were there. Touch yourself. Gently. Gently. Stroke yourself for me."

He cradles the telephone to his neck like a lover. He looks up at his friend and a smile, sensuous but perhaps mocking, hovers and is gone.

"How does it feel Zinnia? Tell me. Is it opening for me? Is your clitoris hard? Run your finger over it; is it slippery? Yes, darling, go on."

He reaches forward and presses the handset, and suddenly, shocking yet wonderful, the woman's voice is broadcast to the room. Her breath uneven, vibrating very slightly.

"Oh." A ragged sigh. "Oh I love you." Her words drawn out, soft in the near darkness. "And it feels so good."

The older man cannot look at the younger, he shifts in his chair but he listens on.

"Zinnia . . . now I want you to open yourself and slip your finger in. Are you really wet, darling? Tell me . . . are your lips swollen for me?"

"Oh yes," the woman's voice sounds eager. "Yes, yes, I'm doing that now, as you tell me, now, now and . . . oh I want you . . . my fingers, no, my whole palm is wet."

The loudspeaker throws her sighs around the shadows.

"Darling put your finger in your mouth. Suck. Does it taste good, darling? Let me hear you do it."

Unmistakably in the darkness, faint but magical, there are the sounds of wetness; the woman sucks and she gives a soft groan.

"Now two – no," the writer looks up at his friend "– three fingers."

"You can, of course you can. I've given you more than that. Much more." His voice is persuasive.

The woman murmurs assent.

"Push, darling, push them all in for me. Now out, now in again. Is that lovely sweetheart? How does it make you feel?"

"Uh. Oh it's wonderful. Oh I love you so much. Always. Please . . ." Her voice sounds young.

They are all three in the night with the woman's breathing, deep and hoarse and the grey-haired man is afraid that his own must be audible. He tries not to breathe with her. The writer seems not aroused but something else, something darker, less tangible. He smiles on.

"Zinnia, darling. Stroke yourself, long strokes, are you ready? Would you take me inside you?"

"Yes." The clarity of sound is so good and the room high above the city so silent, that they hear her swallow, a tiny grunt . . . she moves in the bed . . . she is in bed, the older man feels sure . . . the rustle of covers. There is another long, long sigh.

"Darling," the writer has lowered his own voice now and leans forward, curling the phone in his hand. "You know what I want don't you?"

"Yes," she whispers.

"Just like usual." He looks up, challenges his friend with a stare. He cups the receiver with his hand. "Shall we go on?" he asks him. "Finish it . . . or . . .?"

The older man finds himself blushing and yet wanting her to be encouraged not deterred. He stays silent. Does his head nod imperceptibly? He fears that it betrays him.

The writer turns his mouth to the phone. "I want you to find something, darling, something . . . anything . . . whatever you like."

They hear the woman move. For a few seconds her breathing dies down as she moves away. Then, although she says nothing, she is close again. Breathing. Aroused. Unknown yet utterly exposed. The older man has never known such intimacy. There is heat and night and her.

"Have you found something, darling?" the writer's voice is low but level. "Lie back, bring your knees up the way I like it. Now push it into you. Go on . . . all the way . . . up to the hilt."

For a moment, nothing but the lurching power of imagination. Then she catches her breath and it seems to last forever. "Yes. Oh yes."

"Is it inside you? Is it filling you?" the younger man asks his lover. "Now move it in and out slowly. Let me hear you, let me hear it."

The woman calls out endearments; her moans are regular and faster. The two men listen. She needs no instructions now, although from time to time she mutters something almost incomprehensible, then darling then please, then oh Jesus, Jesus.

"Go on, go on," the writer urges. "Hard, do it hard. For me, sweetheart, I'm with you, it's just us, so show me, do it for me."

The woman makes little noises in the back of her throat. The older man's erection aches and somewhere in his heart there is pain. For the obedience? For the deceit? He does not know. The photograph lies on the table beside him, just

within the pool of light. There she lies naked, exposed, vulnerable.

"Oh god, I'm . . . it's so lovely, uh uh uh . . . I'm going to come, oh I'm coming, I'm coming." Her words tumble, echo, caught up in her falling breath.

"Darling, darling." She cries out so loud that the great room is full of her . . . and then she seems to be weeping.

"Oh I love you I love you so much." And her breath, her voice, her climax subside. The writer waits.

"You're so good, Zinnia, so good. My darling girl. My only love. Sleep now."

"I love you." The faintest fading whisper a long, long way away in the darkness.

The writer puts down the phone. He looks, almost challengingly at his older friend.

"Did you enjoy that? She loves doing it . . . loves me . . . she was made for pleasure so why shouldn't it be shared. No one else need know."

The grey-haired man, his arousal still unassuaged, meets the eyes of his friend, now a stranger, and knows he sees his need.

In a small flat some miles away, the curtains billow. Zinnia, damp with sweat bends back, sleepily, greedily. The man underneath her, spent but still slightly erect, looks up at her face.

"That," he says, "that was, well, extraordinary. How the hell I kept quiet when you came, when *I* came, doing it, knowing he was listening, and getting off on it, having to be so quiet. But God, how erotic. And you like an eel all over the place." He laughs, lifts her off him.

"*Find something . . . anything you like, eh*? And you did. And you did. But did you ever feel anything for him? Did you really do it for real for him?"

Zinnia smiles her slippery mermaid smile, her skin shines in the lamplight. For once she is completely satisfied.

THE WORM ON THE BUD

Louise Welsh

Louise Welsh is the author of seven novels, including *The Cutting Room*, *The Girl on the Stairs*, *A Lovely Way to Burn* and *Death is a Welcome Guest* (volumes one and two of the Plague Times Trilogy). She has written many short stories and articles and is a regular radio broadcaster. Louise wrote the librettos for the operas *Ghost Patrol* and *The Devil Inside* (music by Stuart MacRae). She is Professor of Creative Writing at the University of Glasgow. This extract is taken from *The Cutting Room*.

Dark and wrinkled like a violet carnation
Humbly crouching amid the moss, it breathes,
Still moist with love that descends the gentle slope
Of white buttocks to its embroidered edge.

Rimbaud and Verlaine,
"The Arsehole Sonnet"

It was too early to go home. I found myself heading towards Usher's. Once there I knew I had made a mistake: there was nothing in the throng of well-dressed men that drew me. They were too clean, too well disposed.

I took my drink and sat in a corner by the window. In the street opposite, a young man leaned out of a third-floor tenement, taking the air. He stretched his body, then, in a single move, discarded his white T-shirt, pulling it over his head, tossing it behind him, somewhere into the dark recesses of the room. A shaft of light cut across the building, illuminating his torso, silver-white in the black of the window. He reached up and pulled the blind half down, leaving his body on view, concealing his face.

I sipped my beer, looked at the bustle of men in the bar around me, then returned my gaze to the boy, wondering if he could see me watching him. He was sitting on a chair now, his arm resting on the sill, swinging to and fro, marking time to a beat I couldn't hear. I watched the shadows creep across the orange sandstone, reaching towards him. When the light was gone, and I could see him no more, I left the bar, crossed the street and pressed the third-floor buzzer. The intercom hummed in response. I let myself in and climbed the stairs.

The door to the apartment was open. I pushed it wide and glanced down the dark, narrow hallway. The place looked derelict. Paper peeled from the walls in jagged tongues, exposing the dark treacle of Victorian varnish on the plaster beneath. The floor was bare, untreated boards. I walked towards a light at the end of the corridor, ready for anything, ready to run if need be. I hesitated, listen-

ing for a moment, then, hearing nothing, stepped into a long sitting room.

The light came from two tall picture windows which let in the glow of the street lamps; the only furniture was a wooden table and two upright chairs. The boy still sat by the window. He turned towards me, tousled blond hair, dreamy face, lids drooping as if in an opium trance. I judged him to be about twenty, slighter than me, good muscle tone, but I knew I could take him in an unarmed fight. He smiled a lazy smile, rose slowly, and came towards me.

When he was close enough for our breath to merge he stopped, passive, waiting. I could feel the heat of him, sense his quickening heartbeat. The blood moved faster through my veins, breath shortened, balls tightened. I stood still, playing master, forcing him to make the first move. He tilted his head, glazed blue eyes met mine, then he put a warm, lazy hand inside my jacket, smooth fingers running a light touch up and down my torso, unbuttoning my white shirt, licking his tongue through the dark hair on my chest, tasting the salt sweat on my body, flicking against my nipples hard and strong. I put a gentle hand on his shoulder, tightened my grip slowly, then took him by the hair at the nape of his neck and forced his head back. The boy's body tautened, panic welling with the change of tempo. His fear gave me an infusion of power. He trembled in my grasp and my cock hardened. I forced his head back further, until he was looking me straight in the eye, then put my mouth to his and kissed him. I felt his young boy skin, soft against my bristles, and our tongues met. I loosened my grip and ran a hand across his hairless chest, feeling him relax, tracing the faint swell of his pectorals, glancing over the pebble-hard nipples, trailing my index finger down to his navel, undoing his fly button, feeling his cock, as hard as mine, straining against his jeans. I rubbed him through the denim and he whispered, "I want you to fuck me." An American accent.

I released him and he led the way. Once more the room was sparse, empty save for a mattress in the centre of the floor, raised slightly on wooden pallets.

"You like fucking young boys?"

Running his hands down his groin, showing me the bulge beneath, turning himself on. I didn't want him to talk.

"Seem to." Turning macho. "Get undressed."

He unzipped and pulled down his jeans; white skivvies tented towards me; he discarded them and his cock raised itself almost to his belly, an exclamation to his navel. I started to undress, folding my clothes as I went.

He watched from the bed, playing gently with his erection, teasing me. "You're not in a hurry?"

"Some things are better slow."

A man of the world. My cock felt like it might explode with his first touch. I put myself on the bed beside him, ran my hands over his chest again, then took his hard, medium-thick cock in my hands, feeling its strength, moving the foreskin up and down until he groaned at me to –

"Stop! I'll come too soon if you keep that up."

"I'm concerned to keep something up."

"No problems there, my man."

He laughed, flipped over onto his belly, head level with my groin and took my erection into his mouth. I let him blow me, his mouth working its way up and

down the shaft, paying special attention to the head, then moving down to engulf each of my balls, gently, probing his tongue to rim me until the feeling became so intense I pulled away.

The boy gazed up at me, pupils dilated, lips glossed with a sheen of pre-cum. His voice was soft, insistent. "C'mon, fuck me."

I didn't need to be asked a third time. "Got any lubrication?"

He reached beneath the pillow and pulled out a tube of lube and a couple of condoms. "I like to keep it handy."

The boy tore at the silver package with his teeth, his eagerness giving my balls another twist, then he placed the unwrapped condom in his mouth, leant over, took my cock in his hand and unfurled the condom over my erection, giving it a few hard flicks with his tongue for good measure. He rolled flat onto his belly, wriggling to get comfortable, arranging a couple of pillows to raise himself slightly, positioning his rear. Tight buttocks more square than round, hairless except for a few blond tendrils creeping from the cleft between his cheeks. I started to grease him, smoothing the lube up towards his asshole, then gently inside, rubbing tenderly round the sensitive ring of his sphincter, hearing him moan, ". . . you've no idea how much I need this . . .", nudged his legs far apart with my knee and set to work.

In anal sex it is of great importance that your partner is relaxed. Too much resistance can lead to tearing of the anal sphincter, resulting in infection, or a loss of muscle tension, leading to leakage of the back passage – unpleasant. Other possible side effects include a split condom – which may result in the contraction of HIV or several other harmful infections – piles, and a punch in the face for inflicting too much pain. All this aside, I like my sexual partners to have as good a time as I can give them. I find it stimulating.

I massaged his ring gently for a while, slipping a finger inside to open him up. He responded, moving towards me, then whispered, "Do it." I added a glob of lube to the tip of my cock then moved hard, pressing against him, forcing my way in, paying no mind to his moan of discomfort. I grasped him round his chest, holding him to me, working slow to build up a rhythm, gentle, insistent against the resistant muscle, forcing myself forward, deeper, hearing him say, "That's it . . . yes . . . like that . . . Yes . . ." Then putting my finger in his mouth, allowing him to bite it hard, to help him respond to the pleasure/pain I was giving him and because I didn't want to hear any talking now, just to see the images flashing in my head.

Memories of encounters honed into fuck-triggers. I imagined myself in a movie I'd seen . . . raping this boy . . . taking him against his will . . . forcing him into liking a big cock up his arse . . . I was in a tunnel way beneath the city . . . the smell of ordure in my lungs . . . the scuttle of rats around me . . . fucking a stranger against the rough brick of a wall . . . The shuffle of footsteps coming closer . . . My climax was building, balls slapping against his buttocks, spunk swelling. The images scrolled on. It was coming now . . . getting close . . . blood-red vision of the orgasm blackout . . . Here it came . . . a wound, red and deep and longing . . . the dark basement . . . the slash of blood across her throat . . . the reflection imposed on the inside of my retina as true as if I was looking at the photograph . . . the girl, used and bound, lying dead on her pallet. I came,

spurting into him, grasping his buttocks for support, rocking with the force of my orgasm.

"You're squashing me." For an instant I couldn't make out what he was saying. His words a jumble of noise intruding on my thoughts. "Hey, buddy, you can get off now."

I rolled over and pulled at the condom. It came away with a snap, and my member lolled out, tired, flaccid already. You and me both, pal, I thought. There was a smear of spunk across his belly where he had come while I was fucking him. Thank Christ. Depression was creeping in, "the after dream of the reveller on opium – the bitter lapse into every day life – the hideous dropping off of the veil", and I had no stomach for tender mercies. I wiped myself on the sheets, got up and started to dress.

"That was neat. Say, I like your jacket."

I could feel his relief at my leaving, and for the first time gave him a smile. "Any time, son."

I let myself out of the apartment and began the long walk home.

Sunlight and birdsong woke me at 4 a.m. The light hurt my eyes and the birdsong disagreed with my hangover. I willed myself back to sleep. Then I thought about buying a rifle, nothing fancy, just long-range enough to shoot a few birds. I lay prone on my mattress, dimly aware of flaked paint and fine cracks etching a fantasy landscape across the yellowed ceiling, then propped myself up on a couple of pillows, rolled a joint and lit it. I held the smoke down in my chest until my lungs creaked, then exhaled slowly. Slender arabesques crept upwards and settled in a haze below the ceiling. Prisms of cut glass swayed gently from the window lintel. Refracted light – red, indigo, yellow, green – floated around the room. I watched silently, rolling and smoking. My body seemed the repository of a dead man. I could think and smoke but all feeling was gone. Inside was nothing. Beneath my slack skin was a skeleton framed by blood and gore. I possessed the required internal organs but the soul was missing. I felt like taking the lit end of the joint and placing it against my arm, cauterising despair in one definite act of pain.

I lifted a paperback from the floor and tried to read. It was a tale of adventurers in the desert, but the distant smell of the river drifted across me, the smell of John and Steenie's bookshop. I coughed and turned a damp page. My mind went back to the girl, her riven throat, the eye behind the lens. Steenie knew something. He'd left the bar like a man pursued. Yesterday, I had decided to drop the investigation. Today, it seemed I had no choice but to go on.

Coloured light danced across yellowed walls. The birdsong faded. I lay back and closed my eyes.

GRAMMAR LESSONS

Louise Black

Louise Black was born in Devon. Her Ph.D. – 'Laure: Life Under a Black Sun' – was an analysis of the relationship between Georges Bataille and Colette Peignot. Some years later she found herself living across the road from the home they shared, and teaching at a private school on the outskirts of Paris. Her short stories have been regularly published in the *Erotic Review* since 1999. She also contributed to the award-winning *Agent Provocateur Confessions* collection. *The Tattooist*, her first novel, was published in 2012.

I arrive on time. The chateau is whitewashed, with wet slate roof tiles that shine in the sudden autumn sun. Virginia creeper slings its scarlet arms around the door. I am nervous as I climb the steps. This is the first time.

You have brown eyes, round as a puppy, and short rough hair. Your smile opens like a gate. I hear the latch click. I want to come in. You are. You are much younger than I am and eager to learn.

He is a student.

She is a teacher.

The past simple is used for completed action. I moved to France. I was not happy. You sat opposite my desk and I told you to sit up straight and concentrate. You did, which surprised me.

The past continuous is used for interrupted action. I was waiting for something to happen. You were being good. It is also used for action that happens around a certain time. I was thinking about you this morning. You were thinking about me just then.

You were having a shower. I let myself in with the key you gave me and stood at your bedroom door. I could smell your shower gel and see wreaths of steam about the ceiling. The clothes you dropped in a heap on the floor still carried a faint trace of heat from your body.

I sat on the bed. You knew I was there. You walked into the room naked.

Your teeth are white as milk and a ridge of hair runs down from your navel. The present simple is used to express general truth. You are beautiful. You are confident and powerful and utterly yourself. I want you to fuck.

You say nothing as you kneel on the rug in front of me. I dig my fingers into the back of your dripping crew cut and bring your mouth to mine. Your tongue tries unfamiliar shapes. Your lips test fricatives. You press your damp body against my suit. I do not want to get undressed. You slip your thumbs into the waistband and pull up my skirt, frowning. You remove my jacket and undo

my shirt like gutting something, with sharp brutal movements.

I am rain that falls with increasing force. You are stone, unlined by time.

The present continuous can be used for action that is not yet complete. You are holding my wrists and forcing me backwards onto the bed, testing your strength. I am winding my legs around your waist. I am feeling a desperate weight of wanting you but I have no idea what you are feeling as you slam your groin into mine.

I am going to come. You are going to come. This is called the "going to" future. Your eyelashes flutter against my cheek. Too soon. The clasp of my bracelet scratches your neck. I push you away and you look – for a moment – hurt.

The single duvet slides from the bed as I roll you on your back on the polished floor. The tops of the fir trees are nodding inquisitively from the edge of your father's garden. A deep-voiced guard dog barks a warning. I touch you everywhere but where you want to be touched. I take the thick third finger of your left hand in my mouth. I stroke the hollows of your armpits and trace the curves of the muscles of your arms. I lay my head on your heart. You wait, holding your breath. I run the tip of my tongue down the plane of your stomach. The ends of my hair flick your groin and you twitch, giving a low growl.

I have seen you run bare, fleet-footed on the packed earth. I blow gently along the inside of your thigh, disturbing the dark hairs and making you squirm. The present perfect is used for action that has just concluded. You have had enough. It is also used for action continuing to the present. I have noticed your determination. You are not used to deferment. I am older but you are stronger. You leap up and push me against the wall in one fluid movement. A poster tack drops to the ground.

Your broad upper body rams me. My skirt gets torn in the scrum. You wrap your fist in my tumbled locks and nail me to the spot. When you bite my shoulder it feels like you are gnawing bone. You make me gasp. You make me come. I am aware of your face, shadow of beard and smudge of freckles across the bridge of the nose, inches from mine. You are watching intently, gauging my reaction to your movements.

I do not know how to run, throw, catch, jump, skateboard or speak French. I fold around you. You take my right hand and cover it palm to palm with your left, securing it there against the wall. You do the same with my left and I realise how much taller you are than I, even in my heels. My belly is taut, the ripped skirt rucked around my waist.

When you release your grip and dip to kiss between my legs my arms remain raised, but I twine my wrists together. Your fingertips dig into the tops of my thighs. You gnash your teeth against me.

I am sweating. You are fresh from the shower. Outside the lawns spread jewelled green. The scent of wet turf rises.

With the future tense two auxiliaries are used, depending on a sense of command or promise on the part of the verb subject (although there are exceptions). "I will go," denotes intention. "I shall go," is mere futurity.

I wonder what you will remember of this lesson, this day, me. Will, of course, is also used for prediction. You will be a great man. You will recall nothing of these events but the envelope left on the hall table, which I will pocket as my fee.

DORCHESTER EVENING

Justine Dubois

Justine Dubois is a Parisian, who has lived most of her life in London. She trained as a painter, which explains some of the visual intensity in her writing. She reads widely, and has travelled adventurously. For all her career she has been involved in the Arts, and is now writing full-length fiction. Her favourite place in London is Kensington Gardens; her two favourite places in all the world: Venice, and Jailsamer in Rajasthan.

She gets up from the turbulent sea of their unmade bed. Her club cut dark hair, caught by a stray pink rose, cascades heavily to one side. Her lips are brushed in with a smile. She has the look of a Velazquez *infanta*. She glances behind her, part gentle, part sad. They have just made love. It is three-o-clock in the afternoon.

He had held her wrists together in one hand and inflicted caresses on her, caresses which today fell like blows. Sex between them had always been a delicious fight, never less than extraordinary, never less than surprising, always sweet heaven; occasionally, as today, a rough debate. Her figure is caught, momentarily silhouetted against the light, a lean, balanced agility of narrow waist, long legs and upturned breasts.

She sits naked, pensive, balancing on a small spindle leg sofa. Her dark sloe eyes appear bruised and heavy lidded. A sudden weariness infects her. The man is substantially built, massively boned, but lean, his hair cut *en brosse*. Along the length of one thigh travels a scar, following his recent fall from a horse. As he rises from the energetic tangle of their bed clothes he conjures an image of athleticism.

His turquoise glance at her is troubled, whilst his generous mouth attempts a smile. Why now, last minute, he wonders, this inspiration for change? It is as though she has momentarily lost the template to her own existence. And yet, it was she who so clearly fashioned the template for herself.

Neither dares broach the dissonance between them. Time falls gently, a quality of assurance. Interludes of silence interweave with the short-hand of their conversation. He takes her hand gently in his. "I do love you, you know?" he says plaintively.

She glances up at him and smiles in quick acknowledgement. "Yes, I know."

Silence. Her eyes dwell patiently on the handsome correctness of his darling head, inquisitorial laughter implicit in its every graceful line.

"And I love you too", she responds tenderly. "In fact, I love you better than I love myself," she adds.

"Then why now this moment of doubt?" he asks.

She casts about her, her hands dancing in the air like acrobats. "I don't know how best to express it. An indefinable sense, maybe, of having done all that I can with the way things are." She hesitates. "As if I needed more material to play with."

He flushes, his whole face shot through with the impact of dismay. "What you mean is more people to play with?"

"No, not more people," she demurs. "I feel crowded as it is."

"What then?"

She reflects. "It is as though I need a new framework with which to advance . . ."

He interrupts her. "But is that not we have planned for tomorrow, a new framework?" he asks.

She ignores the question. "Something might wither in us otherwise."

Suddenly he smiles, almost laughing out loud. "Let's get dressed and go to the Dorchester for tea," he says.

"Shouldn't we have booked?" she asks diffidently.

"If tea is unavailable, they are unlikely to refuse us a glass of champagne." His face now dazzles with suppressed laughter.

"You mean, let them eat cake?" she hazards.

"Precisely."

Suddenly her mood is broken. Her face suffuses with warmth. "What should I wear?"

"Go as you are, why don't you?" he smiles. He gives her a mock bow. "Will madam be warm enough or would she maybe care to borrow a jacket?"

By now they are giggling happily together. He rings for a taxi. Their bed remains unmade.

At the Dorchester the doors revolve heavily in their black and brass casings. The foyer is a jazz of black and white marble, of golden lights illuminating an embellished vaulted atrium, and boutique glass cases with inaccessible pieces of irresistible jewellery. Everyone seems vaguely familiar, not so much because of their faces, as because of their tans and their extra glow of pomaded health, the casual, throwaway burr of their expensive clothes. Beyond them is the vista of the Promenade. Giant potted ferns vie with the black shiny grand piano, old-fashioned serenade. Low legged sofas rub knees with deeply upholstered armchairs. They choose two wide-armed upright chairs. Tea, which started at three-o-clock, is almost over, except for a lingering few.

"Two Kirs Royales", he orders, without consulting her.

"Yes, Sir." The waiter bows and disappears.

He gets to his feet again. "Will you excuse me for a moment?"

"Of course," she smiles.

"I shan't be long."

He returns almost immediately. Together, they sip their Kirs Royales, marvelling at the precise weight of *cassis* to the ecstatic laughter of good champagne. The blight of tiredness is no longer upon her. Her face looks lifted and open again. It has lost its stiff look of self contemplation. She is fascinated by the

crowd, by its self-important to and fro. They talk animatedly, like the old friends they are, making plans.

"Were we right to keep tomorrow secret, do you think?" she asks.

"Yes," he replies. "The whole thing will be *fait accompli*. Let the others quarrel all they like later. It will make no difference."

She smiles wistfully. "Sad not to be sharing the experience."

"We will share it," he reproaches, "with each other." He pauses. "Besides, it's nice to have a secret." He raises his glass to her and his blue eyes fold in delicious laughter.

"Let's go," he says, as the waiter approaches to take their order for replenished glasses. She stands up obediently.

"Where to now?"

"I thought we might have a look around the hotel, and then take in a film."

All the delight of communication has returned to her, the glowerings of age fallen from her. Suddenly, she resembles a little girl, trusting and joyous, the single pink rose still fixed to one side in her hair. She wears a long sleeveless shift of pale grey silk that flutters, graceful and fluid, as she walks; on her feet lilac leather shoes with "cigarette heels".

They take the lift to the fifth floor, to emerge on to a well padded corridor, decorated with gilded lamps and expensively framed prints. "I love this secret, sumptuous language of luxurious hotels," she breathes. They turn to their left. The numbers vanish before them in a fast perspective, set on doors as emphatically and solidly framed as street doors, each evocative of hallowed, private residence. He holds her hand warmly in his. They turn a corner to find themselves abruptly at the corridor end. She automatically swivels on her heels, about to retrace her steps, then hesitates, sensing him no longer with her. He is standing, fumbling with a plastic key, which he attempts to slot into the lock of the last numbered door. A green light flashes in his hand and the door opens. Suddenly he is caught, reflected repeatedly in a sequence of mirrors.

"Is this sufficient new framework for you?" he asks, with a smile.

She retraces her steps hesitantly, frowning slightly. "That is not what I meant," she says.

"No, I know it isn't," he replies soberly. "Nevertheless, what do you think?"

His eyes scan hers searchingly. For a few shuttered seconds, the sweep of his glance over her is almost disdainful.

They enter the room and the door falls back emphatically on its hinges, locking them in with the sound of finality. A bottle of champagne, two glass flutes, and a cornucopia still-life of fruit await them, set on a pink marble-top table. Round-armed, pneumatically plump sofas, dressed in an extravagant chintz of yellow chrysanthemums on a pink and turquoise ground, appear to come-dancing against the pale green acres of deep pile carpeting. At the windows, overlooking the distant, miniature joggers in Hyde Park, a similar coloured chintz is fashioned into heavily swagged, golden tasselled curtains. A giant television screen bids them welcome, its Ceefax letters flickering uncertainly. Her lover flings his jacket into a chair and kicks off his shoes. Without consulting her, he switches the television to adult movies, discarding the rest of his clothes as

he does so. The bed, a broad, palatial canopy of sweet scented linen, dominates the room, creating an Alice in Wonderland effect. He hugs his naked arms affectionately around her shoulders as he manoeuvres her towards its smooth shoreline. He lifts her dress carefully over her head and shoulders.

"Let us see if we can learn something new," he says.

Two immaculately beautiful women, one blonde, one with red hair, appear on screen, rhythmically fondling each other's breasts, in close up. The film, German made, is diligent in its approach, evoking a certain militarism, even in sensuality. The women, both enamel perfect, grind and purr at each other, seemingly unimpeded by their elaborate corsetry and high-heeled PVC boots. Their bottoms below their black basques are smooth and round, their smiles joyously fixed and inviting. They pout their passion through barriers of bright red lipstick. Their finger tips, enhanced by long garnet nails, render their hands incapable of picking up coins, but do not impede them from joyfully scratching and irritating the lengths of each other's skin.

The lovers lie naked in bed, legs intertwined, the design of their bodies set, like an interlace brooch, against a vast canvas of pristine whiteness. He plays caressingly with the pinks of her upturned nipples. They half watch the screen in cynical bemusement. At a crucial moment in the film's plot, when the shapely German nymphs have exhausted all opportunity to either sip at or gladly fondle one another, and are about to resort to whips, two men suddenly arrive on screen, as if from nowhere, both of them equally anxious to get the job done efficiently and well. The lovers abandon the *longueurs* of their kisses and sit up to watch more closely, taking extra sips of champagne. The male German stars both boast wondrously long penises, which extend from their groins to mid length of their thighs. Their eager, super-fit bodies, shiny with oil, appear to consume the two women. All four of them look so deliciously healthy. Yet, no matter how ravished and excited into gargoyle features their faces appear, no matter the studied rubbing, sucking and cooing of their polished frames next to those of the two varnished women, these admirable penises remain unmoved, swinging lazily from side to side, like lost skeins of wool, not even a hint of stern precision. In exasperation, her lover reaches for the channel changer to switch to its alternative. Briefly, the screen goes blank. She laces her slender arms round his neck. He lifts her on top of him. She slips between his thighs, the warmth and scent of their flesh igniting between them. The television screen flashes into brash colour.

This time the players are Spanish and the casting is both more rudimentary and innocent, the storylines pathetically contrived. A dark-haired girl, with a mole on her lower cheek, goes shopping with her cyclist boyfriend to buy a new pair of jeans. She steps behind a flimsy curtain to try them on. The man is excited and cannot wait. He battles first with his conscience, and then past the curtain to join her. He takes off his shirt and unzips his flies. His back is stroked with dark hair. He unhooks her bra, allowing her swollen breasts to fall heavily in his hands. They make love there and then, he standing, knees slightly bent. She wraps her legs round his waist, like scarves. He takes her nipple into his mouth and she gasps in pleasure. Their tongues interlace. The rhythm between them grows faster, faster. The woman, racked with pleasure, begins to lose control. The shop

assistant, hearing the sounds of her abandon, pulls back the curtain. Rather than outrage, she too wants to join in. The first girl subsides in the man's arms. She sits down to catch her breath. With her smiling permission, her boyfriend now turns his clever attentions to the more slender figure of the yellow-haired shop assistant, one of whose front teeth is missing.

In spite of the baldness of the plot, the screen comes to life, underscored by the truth. These men and women with their half perfect bodies, too short, a bit fat, nevertheless move with recognisable passion. The delight of voyeurism is achieved. Their passion communicates itself to the lovers. His hands stretch yearningly to caress her. Their bodies arch in an ache of anticipation. The familiar minuet of their love begins, and they drift into private oblivion, slipping between the silken Dorchester sheets in half mimicry of the screen, whilst performing their own singular truth.

A little later they sleep contentedly in one another's arms, cocooned in honeyed silence, no phone, no knocks on the door.

"Will that do for today?" he asks. "Have I succeeded in altering the frame?"

She smiles up at him indulgently. How very handsome he is, her own sweet love.

A note of severity interlaces his look of contentment. He turns towards her, suddenly serious. "Are you quite sure about tomorrow?" he asks. He watches carefully for every nuance of her reaction.

"Completely sure," she replies, her eyes meeting his. " Ten-o-clock at Marylebone registry office. I promise to be there." She pauses. "I wonder who our witnesses will be?"

He smiles gently. "Two strangers."

He reaches for the phone and orders a supper of chicken in aspic to be sent up to their room. They eat it dressed in the warm hugs of white robes, smiles slipping between them like long hugs of happiness.

From THE BRIDE STRIPPED BARE

Nikki Gemmell

Nikki Gemmell is a bestselling Australian author who has written nine novels and four works of non-fiction. Her work has been internationally acclaimed and translated into twenty-two languages. Her distinctive style using the second-person narrative has earned her critical and popular acclaim in France where she is seen as a female Jack Kerouac. She has been hailed as one of the most original and engaging authors of her generation.

Lesson 70

you had better have a millstone tied to your neck
and be thrown into the deepest pond than become
a taker of opium

Walking to his flat. Not daring to talk; holding hands, tremoring, wet. His rooms are spare and neat, like a monk's, with a few beautiful objects from his travels here and there, and small stacks of paperbacks and some black and white postcards on the walls. He does not intrude heavily upon the space.

His bed's surprisingly big. You turn off the lights. Where to begin, you are the teacher and before you is the blank slate: God, the responsibility of it. You gather your thoughts, you mustn't rush. You don't want him experiencing anything of the hurt or disappointment you've so often felt. How many women get the chance to do this, with a man, to break their virginity? It must be utterly memorable for him, something to savour for the rest of his life.

You tell him you want him to lick you, slowly, the inside of your wrist, and you push up your sleeve like a junky preparing for her first shot. Gabriel looks at you. He bends, hesitant. His tongue tip glides up your skin in one even, barely there line. Your eyes close, you let out a small gasp, his tongue stops. You take off his jacket, you unbutton his shirt, you find him, his vulnerability. His chest is cathedral-wide and your hands span its breadth like the vaults of a ceiling and you feel his galloping heart and you place your right palm over it, reading the race of it. He smells clean, pleasantly so, you can't catch anything of his real scent. His body is young, not quite finished, it feels strangely untouched, maybe it's the hesitancy in him, he's all caged up. Your lips walk the softness of his inner arm, slowly,

daddy-long-legs-soft, climbing the paleness. You look up and smile reassurance and for some reason you hold his head like a mother with a child and he begins to say something and ssssh, you whisper, no talk and you hold his face in the clamp of your palms and he's concentrating so much, so intent, ssshh you whisper, ssshh, and kiss him slowly as if all the world's tenderness is gathered in that touch and as you do it your hands snake softly to the eroticism of his hips.

You kneel, unbuckle his belt.

His penis curves gently to one side, it's large; it always surprises you how big they can get. He is looking down at you, he is breathing fast.

You hold him, you lick him, soft, so silky soft, the tip.

He laughs nervously, he can't relax. He tries to push you off. You propel him, gently and firmly, on to his bed, on his back. Remove your clothes, quick; wet, so wet.

You sit, very slowly, on to him.

Ease down, slowly, feel him all the way. And then you just sit, for a moment, you are filled up and you smile into his eyes and very slowly you tighten your muscles and gather him inside you: you feel Gabriel with your skin. He looks at you, all wonder and surrender and shock, and you throw your head back, you can't look at him any more, you need to savour this moment alone. You keep on moving on him, slowly, rhythmically, with your eyes shut, ssh, you tell him, sssh, as he begins to say something, as you talk to him through your skin, you lean forward, you brush your fingertip on his lips, sssssh.

And then he comes.

He's appalled; it's so quick.

You smile, you stay sitting on him, feeling him in you, feeling him go soft. This, too, is delectable. Your hands fan upwards on his belly and his chest, savouring his surprisingly soft skin, untouched for so long by any other woman and you bow your head and kiss him, in gratitude, on the cleft of his neck. You didn't orgasm, you didn't learn anything new but it's a start, a lovely one: for it's the very first time you've been totally in control. *Women bare rule over men.*

You climb off him. Stretch languidly, your palms turned to the sky as if they want to push it up. You feel like a cat on a favourite armchair it's never usually allowed on, thrumming with warmth and sunlight.

Gabriel rolls over on to his stomach. You walk across to him, lie beside him; your fingertips slip over each bump of his spine.

There *was* another time, he says, without looking at you. Your hand stops. It was my twenty-first, he says. I got drunk. My parents had thrown a big party for me. There was this girl, just some girl, a family friend, she was drunk, too, and we went up to a bedroom at the top of the house. But as I tried to go inside her I just . . . went limp. All I could hear was Clare's laughter. I couldn't go on.

You wing your arm across him, you squeeze his shoulder. Gabriel turns to you, he props his body on one side with his hand on his cheek.

So . . . thanks, he says, awkward, shy. Then there's a pause, and his impishness slipping back. What happens next?

You shake your head, you cover your eyes, you laugh: no, no no, we have to stop, all right?

Excuse me, madam, but you are not leaving this flat.

Lesson 71

those who eat too much should remember that
they are robbing those who have not enough

Walking by the river to the tube.

The Thames the colour of cold milky tea.

Feeling intensely alive, as if years have been stripped from your body. Feeling engorged between your legs, plumped, softened, filled up. Smiling into the impatient dusk and flitting your fingers to your nose at the cocktail of smell, at the stamp of two bodies upon them.

Feeling as exhilarated as a teenager who's just finished the last of her exams, and the glorious stretch of the summer holiday is ahead of her.

But that night you're awake, vastly awake as Cole presses his trusting warmth into you. His hand rests on your hip and your eyes are owl-wide with this appetite for something else unleashed, it's all violent and terrible and exhilarating within you. Did Theo ever feel like this? Did she have guilt? Would she now happily resume her life? For you'd dreamt not so long ago of one transgression, just one, stemming the tide of marital disintegration and flushing you out, so you could begin, afresh, your married life; and never look back.

Your teeth nibble at a stubborn flap of skin on your lip, they nibble until there's a warm rush of blood in your mouth.

Lesson 72

it is everyone's duty to be kind to and help her
fellows as much as possible

So it begins.

A weekday afternoon. Once a week. Always Gabriel's flat.

You're a good teacher, you always have been, and now after years of being the good teacher you don't want to just give, you want something back. There's one condition, you make it clear from the start: this arrangement must not, in any way, intrude upon your regular life. It's the only way you can make it work. When the lessons come to their end you will both disappear back into your worlds so that in the future, if you ever pass by chance on the street, you will not acknowledge each other or what you have done during these weekday afternoons in his flat. This will free you to explore exactly what you want. There'll be no photographs, no letters, nothing concrete about any of it, nothing to seize as proof. Memory is all that either of you will be allowed to keep. The rules come quickly and clearly, and make it easier to justify what you're doing.

*

Once a week. It's the only time you meet. For the rest of your waking hours you feast on the memory of what you've done.

The throb of that.

He opens the door in his suit, always, as if he's just come from work. The air in his flat smells of inner London, of too much traffic standing still and the taste of iron is in your mouth. Business people walk by his ground-floor window, chatting on their mobiles, in their clattering heels and brisk shoes. It makes the lessons seem more wilful, childish, indulgent, like a sunny afternoon stolen from work, spent, secretly, at a film. But worse, much worse.

So, week by week. Slowly, you do not hurry. You feel you have all the time in the world to savour each other, having rushed in with that first, miraculous fuck: it was just a start. There's so much to learn, now. For both of you, for as you teach him you'll be teaching yourself although he doesn't have to know that.

A rough agenda is set.

One, the removal of clothes. You learn his skin, inch by inch. He, yours.

Two, the touching, the licking. Exactly where you want. The lobe of your ear, the tip of his tongue on your upper mouth. The skin below the vagina, it's tender rim, your clit. You tell him exactly where you want him, you guide him, instructing him to slow down or not stop or don't move or stay on track. And with that, finally, as he listens intently and does precisely what you want, you have your first orgasm and a whole new world is opened up: your eyes are clenched with the warm flooding wet and you scissor on the bed and arch your back, trying to squeeze the last shudders out or prolong them, you know not what, and still the implosions shoot through your belly and then soften and stop, and you can't move, you're drained, all you can do is lie on the bed and laugh, in shock. Gabriel looks at you. My God, he says, my God he repeats. You sit up. Run your hands through your hair. You have to concentrate: this can't be just about your pleasure, it's Gabriel's turn. With him giving you so much you want to present him with a flooding of delight back: you have a goal, for the very first time in your life, to see a man completely laid waste.

By your hands, lips, tongue. If you can.

So, the licking, where *he* wants: most of all, the flattened front of the tip of his cock and then its underside, he can hardly bear your mouth on it and yet can't get it enough and while you're doing it you squeeze the base of him tight. You discover it all together, you're both learning so much and you look up, to his eyes: astounded, delighted, both of you. Then the rim of his asshole. His balls, the firmness beneath and it's his turn to tell you not to stop.

Three, the clandestine public kiss, fully clothed. The bedroom kiss, unclothed, the places for it.

Four, a candlestick. The handle of a hairbrush. The neck of a champagne bottle, and how thrillingly gentle you both have to be. Why is it that inanimate objects can excite you more than a penis ever does?

Five, the vibrator. Teasing your clit and hard in you. Under the head of his cock and in his ass and you savour the clench in his face as he comes.

Six, porn magazines. He has to buy them, it's his task. You want the letters pages, nothing else; you're not interested in what he does with the rest. You revel in saying all the words that've never slipped comfortably from your tongue: *cunt, fuck, ass*. You're the housewife with the angel face and a sudden grit in her talk and it's as if your outside and insides no longer match. Fuck me, you tell him, come on, fuck my cunt and you're appalled and aroused by the words slipping from your mouth.

Seven, wrists bound to the bed posts. Disabled, blindfolded, tied up.

Eight, the shower, rammed against the tiles.

Nine, sleep. Curled around his back, your body his blanket, your palm on his heart because sometimes, you tell him, that's all a woman wants.

Ten, the fuck. The first time didn't count, there was nothing to be learnt, it just had to be done. You need time for it now, to get it right; you're determined, finally, to make it work. He's too jerky, grating, mechanical, you knew it would be like this, there's no music to what he's doing and he comes too quickly, of course. You'd always wanted it quick with Cole; but this is different, you have to find the exquisiteness you know exists. You'd been hoping for something different with Gabriel but the fucking, for you, is still not catching alight. You make an heroic effort not to show him your disappointment, not to turn away in frustration, sulk.

You take a deep breath.

Tell him, gently, that you both need some practice at this. Tell him he needs to slow down a little, look at you, not lock himself into his own little world. Tell him you're not, actually, getting a thing out it. He snaps his head away from you, he's so annoyed, feels he's come so far, it's hard to tell him it's just not far enough. He gets off you. Leaves a sticky mess. You grab at him, tenderly, in apology, but he storms to the bathroom and tells you he's had enough.

You don't contact him for a week.

Ring the morning of the next session and he answers, too quick.

Can I see you this afternoon?

Yes: grumpy, abrupt.

Good, you say, I'm so glad, you say, warmly, knowing this would be his response. And wanting him so much.

Gradually, gradually, you slow Gabriel down, allowing him in a fraction at a time, pulling away if he tries to rush. Teaching him that a key to the exquisiteness lies in the waiting, the refraining, the holding back; and you've both been experts at that, ever since your hands brushed a touching in a café as a phone number was handed across. You tap into that now: enforcing the rules of no contact during the week, not removing your clothes the instant you walk through his door, sitting down over a cup of tea and then slowly, absently lifting up your skirt, no underpants, of course, and lightly touching yourself as you chat. Widening your legs, flexing your back, watching his distraction, his inability to stay seated: gathering his head to your kiss as you come.

You get Gabriel to feel you as if he's a blind man reading the secrets of your inner skin. You make him vary his rhythm, gently admonish if it strays into monotony, teach him the secrets of tenderness, relaxing, surprise, teach him everything that you want. You iron him out until your inner thighs are fluttering and your pelvis

is aching from stretching under him, until your thighs are trembling hours after you leave and into the next day.

Gabriel wants the lessons more frequently than you, he rages against the pleasure he's missed, he's afraid of time running out. It's as if he wants to make love incessantly to cement what you're doing in his life, to make your time together solid and settled and a habit you both cannot break. He says he is happy, so happy. He never thought he could have such greed in him.

You hold him, you laugh, squeeze him tight. You don't tell him you feel that too.

You will not be hurried. You refuse to increase the frequency, to quicken your pace: you want to linger. You will not lengthen the lessons into the evenings, despite his insistence. When the dark comes you must stop. The lessons can only be conducted in the light, it's like you're living in fear of falling asleep with Gabriel and being kissed awake in the morning light, and being trapped, for ever, in his life.

It's as if you've never felt pleasure until now. It's as if what passed as pleasure before was a cardboard cut-out of it. For you've never been in control, until now; you've never, before, had exactly what you want.

PULL

Helen Cross

Helen Cross was educated at Goldsmiths College, University of London and is a graduate of the MA in Creative Writing at the University of East Anglia. She is the author of novels, stories, radio plays and screenplays. Her first novel, *My Summer of Love*, won a Betty Trask Award and was turned into a BAFTA-award-winning feature film. At the start of 2016 she became the Creative Fellow at the University of Birmingham.

Impulsively, another handsome, rich, sex-starved London couple have booked a long weekend at Cosy Lodge B&B. Alice and her fiancé Tom have been working too hard, so they plan to fly north, take frosty coastal walks, unwind, de-stress, have some me-time, pamper one another and relax. She packs the aromatherapy oils, he the scented candles.

Alice can be kind and funny, but she's very posh and nowadays best known for an icy efficiency. "That blonde bitch expects to be curtsied to whenever she walks into a room," as her own PA was recently heard to say. "Poor Tom", as he's known to his staff, is a rich twit, but with an endearing bewilderment that suggests utter ignorance of female intention.

"Oh great!" Alice snorts when they arrive in the misty village, late on Friday night and have to weave nervously through locals loudly leaving pubs. "It's English ugly. All white trash in T-shirts." She is exhausted and irritable – and when Alice feels this way, which is often, she's acquired a tendency to kick in all directions.

"Oh I'm sorry," Tom sighs, "why won't the idiots wear proper clothes in winter?"

"Why didn't you check that on the internet?" she shouts at Tom, as they creep through the dark streets towards Cosy Lodge.

Every twenty seconds the lighthouse beam illuminates Tom and Alice ghoulishly.

Alice is not any more pleased when Tom runs up to the room the next morning to excitedly tell her that in their village this very day is the annual winter fête. "God, can you imagine living here forever," is all she says as she stares out at the khaki plane of desolate land and the grey strip of distant sea, all smeared by an icy mist.

At breakfast Tom tries to make Alice laugh at their B&B's floral furnishings. He fails, though that afternoon he does convince Alice to head for the green where bright bunting marks the site of the fête. On the bill is a greasy pole contest, wrestling, karaoke and at 3 pm a Tug-of-War.

"Christ," Alice sobs. "Why didn't you consider the climate? I'm freezing!"

If Alice could express her feelings, she'd say she's just upset that her hopes for sweet romance have already turned to vinegar. But increasingly Alice finds it hard to say, or know, what is right and true. "She's so tight-arsed I'm surprised she can even sit down," Alice recently heard her PA whisper to a colleague.

Three angry hurls at the coconut shy can't dispel Alice's fury, and even when Tom presents one of the cute gifts he's brought along, she only sobs, "I'm depressed. I wish I were at work. This is total Chip Town Central; everyone looks so unhealthy."

"I agree the women are rather gruesome," Tom smirks, glancing at a group of scowling scarlet-lipped teens.

Tom's about to take Alice back to the B&B for a cuddle, when a drum rolls. It is 3 pm. Sea mist spools like smoke. Slowly, from two sides of the green, strides a brute. And behind this creature, come seven more. Huge men. Broad and tall, with biceps, triceps, quadriceps, each with an arm strong enough to tow a truck. Leviathans who make Tom and Alice look two foot tall.

As they come closer Alice notices that these barbarians have hands the size of hams hanging at their sides. And, when they curve into the ring, she figures these giants do not spend the day sitting down; their denim behinds are not just firm, they seem forged on an anvil. She clenches her own buttocks and bites her lip. "Gross!" she murmurs to Tom, who grins and nods.

Close up several of the ogres are hairy. "What trolls!" Alice gasps. Six are stubbled, two bearded, five with faces the colour of old pennies, one sprouting such thick gingery curls it's hard to see his face at all. Alice reckons they are all under thirty, and single. "Urgh! I told you this place was beyond civilisation. They're not humans, they're hulks!"

"The women too," Tom agrees, casting a glance around the fête for the thick-thighed, half-dressed young fillies he'd spied earlier.

The compère announces the teams as bitter rivals from two local pubs. The men line up, ready to pull. Sixteen stamps to the left, sixteen to the right. "Monsters," Alice mutters, "whose footsteps quake the earth." There is a hush. Alice concentrates on the rope. How thick it is. Fat fingers gripping its rough length. She swallows hard and loosens her cashmere scarf.

She really does wish she were at work, and in control.

Each team captain takes his place at a chalky line in the grass. Behind him his seven giants lean, and grimace. The rope is already slippery and slides in their wettening hands. "I wouldn't like to run into them on a dark night," Tom smirks, but Alice isn't listening. She feels petulantly hot.

"PULL!"

For a moment the desperate urge in the men's faces suspends them all in a wrench of pure tension. Raw effort is in every inch of them. Grunts and moans rise out of the ring and the sway forces a shift in even the clouds. Fury is unleashed for a split – winning – second.

There is another go.

The captain, shouldered like an ox, urges his shackled beasts on, angrily. They thrust themselves backwards, digging their huge heels into the frozen ground.

Alice focuses on just one crimson man, the pump of blood, the scrunch of his eyes, the sudden roar from his colossal mouth.

She unbuttons her coat, and exhales a little cloud of agony. There is applause, and Tom tells her it's a tournament of ten tugs.

After the first five there is an interval during which Alice, breathless, collapses on the damp grass and sends Tom to the beer tent. He is gone some time. Alone, she spreads herself out and leans forward and watches the Goliaths take refreshments, throwing iced water over themselves and shaking their giant heads like wet dogs, prowling the ring like bulls, loosening their shirts and scratching like bears.

Alice catches the salty semeny scent of them.

For the final matches, Alice stands up to find a better position and is shocked to discover her knickers are wet. "The grass is damper than I thought," she sulks at Tom when he comes back with her double vodka. "Now I'll probably get a cold." She goes to sit behind the team from The Wagon, so in front of her are their sixteen half-squatting, bulky thighs, their eight iron arses angled towards her face.

The contest becomes furious, the men are sweaty, their forearms pulse and their beards drip beads of sweat and Alice imagines their eight cocks, crowned with purple-blue tips. The eight long shafts – each solid as Tom's forearm.

Alice feels dizzy and finishes her vodka in a furious gulp.

Each tug comes to its quick climax with a roar, then a heave, so perfect, so desperate that Alice moans. She aches. She grits her teeth and closes her eyes, and if she hadn't been at a busy family event at 3.42 pm would have slipped her fingers in her knickers and wiggled her thumb against her clit, so keen is she to celebrate that moment of tight rope, of perfect, equal stiffness.

Too soon the event is over. Alice wants another vodka but Tom says he's got a surprise; he's booked afternoon tea in the B&B. Then drinks in their room. Then the special Cosy Lodge six-course dinner. After that, he whispers, he's going to give Alice a nice foot rub and then run a hot scented bubble bath.

Alice spends a lifetime dining with Tom that night.

The lighthouse yawns round and round for years.

Eventually Alice demands they go out to the pub for a drink, but Tom counsels that the locals don't look too welcoming. Hasn't she seen *American Werewolf in London*? Tom thinks Alice should stay in their room and pamper herself.

"I'm going out for some cigarettes," Alice cries at 11.30 pm. Tom gasps. "It's this horrid place," she shouts. "I hate it. I want to go home. I need a cigarette," and she storms from the room before Tom can tell her smoking's dangerous.

When Alice is free she walks slowly. Her cunt feels like it's licking its own lips. The night is black as ink. She's forgotten her coat and wears only her pink camisole top. Alice has not tied up her hair in a familiar ponytail and instead it blows around her face madly. Her high heels make her slink, catwalk the murky streets. She's burning up, though the wind from the North Sea blasts her wildly. A greasy drift of fish and chips slides on the night.

Soon the salty air, and her heaviness of breathing, relaxes Alice, and she remembers herself long ago, before work, power, money and Tom, as a naughty, rebellious girl.

The only place to get cigarettes is the grim-looking pub, but it's closed, the lights are off, the curtains drawn, and anyway she doesn't want a cigarette at all. She lurks around the streets for a while, her hands pressed into the pocket of her combat trousers. Soon she's nuzzling the silky lining of her pocket into her damp pubic hair.

Alice wants a drink and a fuck.

The lights are dim in most of the houses. Smoke curls from chimney pots. She wanders on down lanes, through alleyways, smiling and humming, then eventually moaning like a horny tomcat. Frequently couples heading home pass her and smile, some nod kindly, like they know her. A few look at her high heels, tousled hair and revealing top, tut, and hurry on. A clutch of teenage boys hoot and shout "Slag!" as Alice strides by.

At last, when Alice thinks she can't bear it any longer and she's going to have to duck into a piss-soaked bus shelter on her own, she rounds a corner, and there, through the brackish drizzle, she sees a large figure. Male. He has his back to her in a shadowy shop doorway. He's enormous, and pissing like a horse. She creeps up on this giant and he turns, his long eel of a cock still hanging, piss-jewelled, in his big, rough hand.

"Have you got a light," Alice says coyly, in her poshest, cutest voice, looking up at him through her hair, "please?" The big man narrows his blue eyes at her. Alice tips on her toes, leans a little way forward so her pink camisole dips an inch, revealing her large full breasts, her erect nipples. Attracted, the giant bows his huge head a little. Alice can't wait much longer.

His cock is still slung before her, broad and heavy.

Then she feels a blast of sheer unbearable frustration as the man tucks this perfect cock away and slowly begins to pat his pocket for his matches.

"Oh forget it," Alice cries. "I don't smoke. Just fuck me."

There are people passing who hear this and cry out with laughter, a few cheer, several applaud, but Alice doesn't care, a minute later she has a giant's cock in her hand at last, a divine, God-like huge heavy cock, and she's kneading it and yes, it's stiffening just for her.

"Did you get some?" Tom says grumpily, when Alice returns fifteen minutes later.

"Yes," she smiles, bouncing up onto the bed, "the people are really friendly."

VOX VULVA

Andrew Crumey

Andrew Crumey was born in Scotland and holds a Ph.D. in theoretical physics from Imperial College London. He is a former literary editor of *Scotland on Sunday* and is senior lecturer in creative writing at Northumbria University. He won the Saltire First Book Award with *Music, in a Foreign Language*, and the Northern Rock Foundation Award with *Sputnik Caledonia*, which was also shortlisted for the James Tait Black Prize. He has been longlisted for the Arthur C. Clarke Award (for *Mobius Dick*) and the Man Booker Prize (for *Mr Mee*).

He was in a café when the cunt called out to him.

Hey you!

He turned but saw no one he recognised, only a plump, attractive woman in her thirties, sitting some distance away. Her bare arm, dimpled at the elbow, levered a spoonful of chocolate gateau, and she glanced momentarily at him before pushing the soft food into her mouth, then quickly looked away.

Hey you! he heard again. *Yes, you!* The voice was coming from the woman's direction, but not from her, and nobody else in the café appeared to notice it.

"Who are you?" he heard himself murmur. "What do you want?"

I want you! I want you to grab her ass and pump yourself into me until I overflow.

"You mean . . . ?"

Yes! the voice replied, with a note of exasperation. *I'm an empty cunt with nowhere to go. Sitting here while she wastes her time on "death by chocolate", as if that's what she needs. She doesn't even know it, but what she's after is a good length of solid cock, and I'm looking at you right now, tucked away there on your master's leg, ready to spring into action.*

"Wait," he said softly, ignored by everyone around. "I'm not a cock. I'm a person."

What? You mean I've got a crossed wire with somebody's fucking brain? That's the last thing I need. Just my luck, to be sitting here crying out for the last ten minutes to every cock in the city, and this is all the response I get.

"Look, I'll quite happily screw you, but I really think you ought to get permission from your owner first."

The cunt gave a hollow laugh. *Permission? You think this has anything to do with what her brain thinks she wants? Just come over and ask her if you've seen her on television.*

"What?"

Do it. You'll see.

He got up and walked to the table where the woman sat. It was only when he drew close that she acknowledged his presence with an embarrassed smile.

"Pardon me for asking," he said, "but have I seen you on television?"

She blushed with pleasurable confusion. "Of course not."

What was he meant to say next? The cunt solved it. *You look a lot like that actress . . .*

"You look a lot like that actress . . . "

The cunt left him to try and figure out which actress, but it didn't matter. The woman laughed and ran a hand through her hair.

Mind if I join you? the cunt instructed.

"Mind if I join you?" he said.

There was a look of hesitation on her face. A crumb of chocolate clinging to her lower lip was dispatched by the darting of her tongue, whose own plans remained otherwise unstated.

She loves taking it from behind, the cunt interjected, as he sat down beside her.

"Do you come here much?" he asked inanely, trying to avoid the distracting voice of her garrulous hole.

"Now and again," she said.

She picks up men here all the time. You'll go back to her place and she'll straddle the bed like a bitch on heat while you haul up that red skirt of hers. I'm already making a moist patch in her black knickers.

"Really?" he asked.

You bet. Half an hour from now you'll be aiming your prong at her quivering white ass – I can hardly wait.

"Me neither," he added.

"What?"

"Sorry." He'd never had a dual conversation like this before. The woman was telling him something about the café, the chocolate gateau, the price of a latte, but the intruding chatter of her hidden orifice was unceasing and a lot more entertaining.

Boy, I want you so much. You're going to fill me up and tug on her long hair like you're riding a horse. She'll moan and try to bite your hand – be careful, she's a chomper. Hell of a moaner, too. But I only want you to think of me, warm and juicy. Some tongue'll do fine as well.

". . . so I sit in places like this," she was saying, "whenever my husband's away on another of his trips. Got to kill the time somehow, haven't I?" For an instant, her bright eyes and loquacious twat were in perfect synchrony.

She wants to suck you off! But don't come in her mouth, you bastard, otherwise I'll make you sorry. You think I'm not the boss around here? Just watch – I'm going to give her an orgasm right now.

A remark about the weather was interrupted by a blush, a suppressed giggle, another spoonful of gateau consumed with quiet satisfaction.

"You're incredible," he said softly.

"Pardon?" she looked at him with what seemed like wonder and lust combined.

I'm wide open and ready for business, so let's get the hell out of here and do some serious fucking, if you don't mind.

"I'd like to take you somewhere," he suddenly heard her say. She'd prefaced the remark with a long introduction he hadn't listened to, but knowing that she was already having multiple orgasms over her chocolate cake made the comment seem entirely reasonable and inevitable.

"Let's go," he agreed.

She walked in front as they made their way towards the door.

Can you smell me yet? Can you see the way her ass swishes when she knows she's about to get it? You'll be lifting up that red skirt soon, pulling her knickers aside like a black lace curtain, burying your nose in my wet folds and creases.

They were outside in the sunshine. "This way," she instructed, and as they walked side by side his swift inspection of her hair and breasts offered a welcome antidote to the endlessly divergent commentaries of her mouth and vagina. She was a little overweight, but he liked that. Her breasts would hang appealingly as he fucked her from behind, just as ordered. He would pummel and massage them, stroke her ample rump, then swiftly climax before cleaning up and escaping into the afternoon, never to see her again.

"I had a Fiat Uno for a while but never liked the colour . . . "

Big cock, big fuck, big cock, big fuck . . . Yes! Yes! Yes!

The dual monologues continued, polite nods and grunts being the only response required from him. As they walked, he began to hear other voices: passers-by he took note of, out of a perverse, premature weariness. Were they natural voices, or else the plaintive appeals of other orifices?

Me! Me! Me! he heard – a distant chorus, a hive-like hum, a great swell of desire, never before noticed. By chance or fate, he had tuned into frequencies normally unheard by human ears; the constant, single-minded wailing of discontented organs. Cunts, cocks, mouths, asses, nipples – perhaps even the occasional elbow – all called urgently for satisfaction.

This was the secret life of the city: a lust perpetually thwarted by the norms of civilised behaviour, reduced to the exchange of fruitless glances, and the invisible, forlorn communication of unheeded odours.

Only let them do what they really want, he thought as he looked around at the passing crowd, and this city would become an instant orgy. Strangers would couple and strip on paving slabs; Marks & Spencer would transform into a heaving, groaning bordello (HMV almost was one already). Old men on benches would be sucked to slow satisfaction before rebuttoning their coats; harassed housewives would unclothe themselves to sustained applause before finding pleasure where they chose. And the children? Don't even go there, he said to himself, as they rounded a bend.

I want to fill you in on a few details, the cunt explained. *That is, before you fill me in!*

Her trilling vagina-laugh was almost irritating, and he was beginning to realise there might be a good reason for the human male's evolution of selective deafness, which had suddenly deserted him.

When we first get started, she'll go down on her knees on the floor and unzip you. Might be as soon as we get inside the front door. She's got a real hunger for

cock, this bitch, and she'll make sure you're like a poker, if you aren't already. So go easy, boy. Think of . . . I don't know . . . Gordon Brown or something. She'll lick, suck, stroke – I honestly wish she could get over this oral fixation of hers, but as long as you don't shoot too soon then we'll be OK. Some of you guys can't wait. There was one a few weeks ago, in the living room, he liked it so much he grabbed her ears like she was the FA Cup and nearly choked her. She broke free just as he came, and I'm telling you, his load shot a clear ten feet through the air. I thought that kind of thing only happened in porn films with trick photography, but he left a big splat on the wall. She's had to hang a picture over it!

"Here we are," she said. They'd arrived at a Victorian church.

"You live here?"

She laughed. "What are you talking about? Come on inside. I told you I knew exactly what you needed, and now I want to help you find it. There's a big hole in your life, isn't there?"

There's a wet one waiting for you right here!

Perplexed, he followed her into the empty church, whose cool gloom made its own effortless contribution to quelling his arousal.

She led him to a pew. "Kneel with me," she said. "Let's pray together."

As she began her earnest entreaties to God, her cunt made its own wish list. Fingers, tongue, cock. But mostly cock.

"Show us the path of righteousness and keep us from temptation . . . "

What were they doing here? It was like some terrible mistake; yet the cunt's voice was unrelenting. *I have to warn you, we might be in for a no-show today.*

"It happens often?" he whispered.

Sometimes. A case of the head over-ruling the loins. Don't take it personally – she's let herself be rogered by far worse than you. But since we aren't going to get as intimately acquainted as I'd hoped, how about maybe . . . a finger?

"Here? Are you serious?"

Trust me.

He slid his hand along the pew until it was behind her. She continued praying aloud as he brought his fingers into contact with her skirt and felt the curve of her rump.

You're giving me shivers! Stroke her ass.

He traced a delicate, questioning spiral, but she showed no sign of resistance or approval, still begging only for God's mercy and guidance.

Go to her thigh, then up inside the skirt. Take your time.

Her skin was like marble, and the cool patch of inner leg he touched did not in any way acknowledge the presence of his finger. Nor did the rhythm of her voice show any alteration as he journeyed up into the warmer region of her crotch. At this moment, however, a slight adjustment of her kneeling position was infinitely more telling than the rantings of her cunt. She was parting her legs, allowing him better access.

Now! Do it!

His finger found the elasticated edge of her panties, an inviting tangle of pubic hair, a slimy lip of engorged flesh. He followed the lubricated fold until he located the swelling bud of her clitoris.

Oh God, yes!

"Show us the way to truth and salvation . . . " He pushed into her, two fingers gripped by contractions unannounced in her droning prayer.

Yes! Yes! Yes!

Then the cunt relaxed into dormant satisfaction. He slid out of her, and a moment later she stood up silently and straightened her skirt without looking at him. He followed her to the door, back out into the bright sunshine.

"You're an evil man," she said to him. "I hope you find God's love and forgiveness some day." Then she turned and walked away, soon disappearing into the crowd. Her cunt was silent, but all around he heard those other voices.

Me! Me! Me!

BED & BREAKFAST

Michel Faber

Michel Faber was born in The Hague, Netherlands, before his parents emigrated with him to Australia in 1967. He attended the University of Melbourne. He worked as a cleaner and at various other casual jobs, before training as a nurse. In 1993 he emigrated to Scotland. Faber declined to become a UK citizen in order that his book, *The Crimson Petal*, be submitted for the Booker Prize as he disagreed with the UK government's foreign policy. He identifies himself as no particular nationality, and the themes, scope and style of his literary work are not characteristically British, Australian, or Dutch, but broadly European.

"Let's go to a bed and breakfast," he said, "and fuck each other's brains out."

She winced, unable to stop herself, but then managed to turn it into some sort of smile. She had to remind herself he was a bit drunk – they both were – and anyway he hadn't said it at all aggressively. There was a softness in his voice, a playfulness, that made up for the crudeness of the words, and even with the sweat of alcohol on his face, she had to admit he was still pretty gorgeous.

"What about Jane and Gordon?" she said, looking away from him at the crowds of festival goers, then up at Edinburgh Castle, which was lit all around the battlements with flaming torches.

"They're big grown-ups," he said. "If we don't turn up for the night, I'm sure they'll cope. They might even take the opportunity to do the same themselves."

"Do what?" she said, ambling alongside him on a different train of thought.

"Fuck each other's brains out. It must be tough for them, having us there five nights in a row already, camped on a futon right outside their bedroom. They're probably desperate for a bit of . . ." – he pouted, as if preparing to conjure up a vivid description of Jane and Gordon in sexual frenzy, then let his eyelids half close as he murmured the punchline – "privacy".

Helena raised her face to the night sky. The soft rain was cooling on her flushed face. She felt tired and emotionally fragile, footsore, overfull of stimuli – all Edinburgh Festival'd out.

"There probably won't *be* a B&B free," she sighed. "There's a zillion tourists around."

He laughed, started singing her words to a pounding techno beat in his head.

"Won't *be* a B&B; won't *be* a B&B; bay-beh! yeah! won't *be* a B&B . . ." Then, suddenly serious, he put his arm around her shoulder and reassured her with authority:

worry. I've been to the Festival more than you. I know what happens s time. People start clearing out before the end, to beat the tour-party ey're fed up, anyway, or they've run out of dosh. Trust me, there'll be r us."

a telephoned Jane and Gordon, just as a courtesy. But Jane sounded nd awkward: "We'd gone to bed already," she said. "Oh, sorry," said Helena, "I hope I didn't wake you up," but of course now she was wondering if Jane and Gordon had been in the middle of . . . in the middle of making love.

Making love each other's brains out.

Replacing the phone in its unfamiliar non-BT handset, Helena decided she was too old-fashioned, too prim and hung-up. Hugh would teach her a thing or two. And then, as soon as she was absolutely sure she loved him, she would marry him.

The bed and breakfast was run by Jim and Nora Waddington; that's what the sign said. A dumpy sixtyish woman who must be Mrs Waddington welcomed them in, showed them up to their room.

"A Swedish couple just left this morning. Everything's been cleaned and changed, of course."

There were, apparently, other rooms that were occupied by Germans and South Africans, but their doors were closed, and the rest of the house was as quiet as a cinema foyer after the movies have started.

Outside, the rain was intensifying into a downpour. It would've caught them for sure, on the long journey back to Jane and Gordon's house. Hugh's idea was for the best after all. This way, they would be in bed within minutes.

If only they were just going to curl up to sleep back to back, maybe with an affectionate rub of bottoms against one another. She really wasn't ready for more than that . . .

"The safety procedure is posted on the door here," chattered Mrs Waddington, as Hugh and Helena eyed the frilly, peach-coloured monstrosity that was the bed. "Tea and coffee making facilities are over there, under the television. We have Sky TV – excellent reception. Breakfast is from 7.30 to 9.30 – you'll meet my husband then. We have Linda McCartney sausages if you're vegetarian – just let Jim know when you come down to the dining room."

"It all looks lovely," said Helena, swaying on her feet. The bed, despite its billowing garnishes of kitsch, looked wonderfully comfortable. "We've been sleeping on a futon on a friend's floor."

Mrs Waddington tutted in sympathy, as if Helena had admitted to roughing it in an alleyway.

"If there's anything you need, just use the intercom there. I'll be awake for a long time yet, watching television downstairs. So don't hesitate."

When the old woman had gone, Hugh and Helena sat on the edge of the bed, kicking their shoes off, appraising the decor. There was a nautical theme: a small engraving of a lighthouse from Edinburgh's past, a photocopied newspaper article about His Majesty's fleet, a large acrylic painting of a sailing ship signed R Butt. Also, there were three bas-relief brass submarines the size of large trout

screwed securely into three of the walls. Nameplates identified them as *Nautilus* (Napoleonic), German U-boat (WWII) and *Ohio* (Modern). Their portholes were real glass, and their hulls were polished to a golden sheen in the light from the hideous ceiling lamp.

"How bizarre," said Helena.

"Not at all," said Hugh, leaning back on his elbows. "B&Bs are *supposed to* have amazingly tacky things in them. That's part of their function. Don't you know? There's a special registrar of all B&Bs in a central office in Wolverhampton, and anyone who wants to start one has got to convince him they've got enough surreal junk to put on the walls." Encouraged by her smile, he took the tease a bit further. "The registrar won't accept just any old tat bought in a Poundstretcher store. It has to be *heavy duty* weird, like from a time warp. I tell you, I've seen some things in these places . . . Somebody should do a photography book on it."

Why don't *you*? she thought. He was a photographer, after all. But right now his eyes were heavy-lidded, his hair hanging damp on his forehead. Perhaps he would go straight to sleep after all. But she couldn't help wondering if all those other B&Bs he'd known, and all those other Edinburgh Festivals he'd attended, had been with different women each time.

She also wished he hadn't signed them in as Mr and Mrs Brown. It sounded so naff, so . . . fake. OK, they would be married soon and his name *was* Brown, but if he could have used *her* surname rather than his it would at least have sounded better. In the cold print of a hotel receipt she could imagine "Mr and Mrs Farrell" seeming less false – dignified, even.

Helena got up to prepare for bed, resisting a desire to take her nightie with her to the bathroom. She could tell, from the stickiness between her legs, that her period had started, and this made her feel less like making love, while at the same time reminding her of how tolerant Hugh was of menstrual blood compared to other men she'd known.

She was sure no one was like him, and that she was being offered a never-to-be-repeated chance for a new life, a bold departure from the anxious, inhibited existence her parents had groomed her for. Polite old people who'd probably never had an orgasm, sleeping in separate beds, shuffling around their little suburban house, fearful of hearing a naughty word on television. Hugh would teach her that nothing was dirty, if she let him. He would cure her low self-esteem. He would bring out a new Helena in her, a confident young woman with a raunchy grin, who didn't care what anyone else thought of her. Together they would live by their own rules.

Helena padded into the bathroom, clutching toothbrush and toothpaste. Her feet were sweaty and chafed from a long day in pursuit of culture; it was an unexpected pleasure to feel the coolness of the bathroom tiles under her naked toes. She brushed her teeth and gulped cold water flavoured with spearmint, an agreeably fresh taste after all the alcohol.

The en suite was tiny but spotlessly clean – not so much as a Swede's blonde hair in the bathtub plughole. Midget soaps lay waiting in a variety of nooks and receptacles. There was a little light above the mirror.

"Don't be too long, true love," he called out to her.

She found him reflected in the bathroom mirror, visible through a gap in the door. Leaning close to the glass, she removed her contact lenses. He had already removed his clothing.

Next morning, they woke early, as sun streamed in through windows they'd forgotten to curtain off, and traffic hissed and hooted along Minto Street back into the Festival.

"I love you," he murmured, reaching across the expanse of double bed to stroke her face.

She smiled; he wasn't entirely in focus – a bit of a blur, actually – when she wasn't wearing her lenses, but she felt self-conscious about putting them in now, when underneath the fleecy arabesques of the bedcovers she was naked from the waist up, and he was stroking her cheek so romantically.

"I'm starving," he said. "Let's grab some breakfast."

She wasn't really hungry. Last night's dinner felt like it was sitting undigested in her system somewhere, and yet her stomach felt vacant and queasy. She decided she was hung-over.

"I'm hung-over," she said. It seemed like an earthy, self-confident thing for her to come out with – a comment you'd expect from a woman who was well accustomed to the occasional excess. She was shyly proud.

"Well, come and watch me eat, then," he said, throwing the covers wide and swinging out of bed – exposing her, too. "You'll want it once you're there."

Helena noticed the big stain on the sheet near her hip. A phallic shape made not by his phallus, but by the cleft of her buttocks, filled in with the blurred pastel colours of blood and semen.

"Your autograph," he complimented her, leaning across the bed to kiss her on the neck. "My sexy, sexy woman." For a moment she felt like a movie actress, or some pagan goddess of love. Then she thought of Mrs Waddington doing the laundry.

"We're checking out this morning, yes?" she said.

"Sure," he grinned. "But we've paid for the sausages from hell, so let's go down and get 'em." And he stood peering at brass submarines until she was ready.

The dining room was empty when they arrived, insofar as it did not yet contain the rumoured Germans or South Africans. It was burgeoning with clutter of other kinds: plastic flowers, jumbles of foil-wrapped jams, marmalades, butters and margarines, ornate silver toast racks, jumbo Tupperware containers of cornflakes and muesli, jugs of milk and hot water – all arranged on tablecloths with non-matching tartan patterns, all reflecting the brilliant sunlight flooding in from the street. On the walls, dozens of framed photographs of varying degrees of sharpness and quality chronicled the lives of two children, claiming almost every inch of space not already occupied by the fire extinguisher and the certificate of kitchen hygiene. A cheery male voice from the adjacent room called out "Good morning!"

Jim Waddington hurried out to meet them. A wiry little man with massive hands and a face like an aged cowboy from the golden age of westerns, he wore a plastic pinafore that said MY OTHER APRON IS A VERSACE. Courteously, he addressed Helena first, swivelling his smiling head down to meet her face-to-face.

"Eggs?" he enquired, his eyebrows bristling with excess fur.

"None for me, thanks," said Helena.

"Sausages? We've got Linda McCartney in there, if you're vegetarian."

Hugh laughed. "Somebody else can have the pleasure of eating Linda," he said. "I'll have a couple of regular sausages, a poached egg, toast, whatever. We'll let you know if Helena here perks up, won't we?"

Helena nodded, blushing. She fumbled for her little glass of orange juice and drank from it gratefully, closing her eyes. When she opened them again, the old man was gone.

Hugh had already finished one cup of coffee, and had left his seat to examine the photographs hung on the walls. They were evidently of the Waddingtons' son and daughter, each caught at every significant moment in their lives – birth (well, very soon after), first steps, primary school, graduations, sporting events, overseas travels, marriages. In fact, the daughter seemed to have *two* marriages hanging up there in frames, a disconcertingly honest feature of this pictorial chronology. Helena thought this over, found it sort of touching. Sheer intensity of pride in their offspring had given these old folk, conservative though they were, the courage to admit a few modern mishaps along the way. As long as the children didn't mind their lives being displayed this way on the walls of a B&B, it was really quite nice, wasn't it? They probably had a sense of humour.

Everybody had more sense of humour than her, let's face it.

Helena was just about to fetch herself some cereal when she noticed that Hugh, who was standing with his back to her, hands clasped loosely behind his back, had her blood all over his fingers.

"Look at your *hands*," she hissed at him in a tiny shrill voice when he sat down. "You didn't wash them!"

He appraised his fingers calmly, then smiled at her, a beautiful young man with the self-assurance of a cat.

"Sure I washed them," he murmured seductively. "But not enough to get you off them. You leave a potent mark, don't you?" And he stroked his head against her shoulder, as if in obeisance to her sexual power.

Mr Waddington was emerging from the kitchen with the hot stuff on a plate.

"Don't let him see," begged Helena in an urgent whisper.

Surprisingly, Hugh did as she asked, keeping his hands below tablecloth level as the eggs and sausages were served up before him.

"Are you all right?" said the old man to Helena, fatherly concern wrinkling his already intricate features.

"Yes, thank you," she said. "I – I have a bit of a hangover, I think."

The old man smiled forgivingly.

"We've got some aspirin through there, or Alka Seltzer." He spread his palms theatrically. "We're the B&B with everything."

"That's very kind," demurred Helena, shaking her head in embarrassment. But he scurried off, and returned seconds later with a glass of fizzing antacid which he placed in front of the pale young lady. Mercifully, he couldn't stick around to watch its effects on her, as two dishevelled South Africans shambled into the dining room looking hungry and confused.

"This is the place for breakfast, yeah?" one of them enquired.

Mr Waddington, plainly a veteran of every conceivable brainless question that could issue from human lips, hastened to put the newcomers at their ease.

"Any table, any table," he gestured. "Sausages?" And so on.

"He's a nice old man, isn't he?" Helena asked Hugh a minute later as she sipped a little milk to chase away the taste of the medicine.

"Probably a nutter," Hugh smirked. His blood-tinged hands were out again, nursing a coffee cup. "What a life, eh? His wife stays up all night in case people set fire to the place, and he gets up at the crack of dawn to fry sausages. They probably haven't slept together in years."

"They're very proud of their children."

"They'd have to be, wouldn't they? Living vicariously."

"He's got an amazing face . . ." mused Helena. "Like a piece of driftwood. Wouldn't you like to take a picture of it?"

Hugh winced slightly, reluctant to go too deeply into the complexities of where the art of photography was at just now.

"Well, you know . . . there's this kind of . . . fallacy of truth in high-resolution, deep-focus images of the elderly. It's been done to death. And half of these wizened old characters are playing up to the camera anyway. There's nothing secret being captured at all, no real disclosure, it's an act." Staring into the recesses of his own creativity, he went on: "Me, I've been kicking around some ideas for a new photographic project, sort of an infrared thing, done digitally. The heat that people give off . . . colours . . . almost abstract relationships . . ." He shrugged his shoulders, a shadow on his brow. "I don't want to say too much about it yet."

"It sounds intriguing," said Helena, reassuring herself that whatever Hugh came up with had to be better than some of the stuff they'd seen at the Edinburgh Festival. Feeling marginally better, she wondered if she should eat something after all. "What are the sausages like?"

He grinned, relieved to be back on a subject he could share with her.

"There's nothing like a B&B banger," he enthused in a mischievous whisper. "It's weird, but you can't buy them in shops, butchers, anywhere. Only in B&Bs. They have this distinctive, totally homogenous filling and a kind of a . . . *sweaty* texture on the outside. You can't work out what sort of meat it is. That's because it's dog, y'see. There's a special top-secret factory in Walthamstow where they make them."

"Hugh, *please*," she sighed, losing her appetite even for cornflakes.

He saw in her eyes that he had overstepped the line.

"I'm sorry, true love," he said, deciding that the witticism about Auschwitz for dogs could wait till another time, or different company. "A whole week of Edinburgh Festival stretching the limits of good taste has finally got to me, I think. It'll be a relief when we're back to normality, eh? Or at least, what's normal for *us*." And he kissed the traces of her on his fingers, affectionately, with his gorgeous lips.

She nodded, tried again to smile, but this time she didn't manage it. Instead she looked away, at the photographs on the dining-room walls. The Waddingtons' daughter was beaming in the first of her wedding pictures, all fired up to be happy ever after. But it was the wrong man. The wrong man.

*

When Mr and Mrs Brown had checked out, Mr and Mrs Waddington caught up with each other in the B&B's living room. Guests weren't invited in here, unless they showed so much interest in the Waddingtons' children that they were in the market for the home movies as well.

The living room was furnished in much the same taste as the rest of the house, though one wall was bare and the sofa, obviously much-loved, was in somewhat shabbier repair. Sheep's wool rugs dyed pink and blue were scattered on the browny-purple carpet. Mr Waddington drew the curtains, filtering out the harsh sunshine. Frying fat made his eyes sore, even after all these years.

The breakfast things had been cleared away now. The bedlinen was in a huge basket in the hallway, ready for washing. There was no big rush. The Germans were staying for another night, but they were out sightseeing already. The South Africans were on their way back to South Africa. The Browns hadn't said where they were going – back to the futon, probably.

"Put the answering machine on, Jim," said Mrs Waddington, falling back into the pillowy velour of the sofa. "We've made enough money for one week, surely."

Jim fiddled with the telephone while his wife fiddled with the controls of the video machine. By the time he came to sit beside her, a vivid picture had materialised on their state-of-the-art TV screen, replacing the snowy white of static.

"So," he said, "what did you think of those last two – Mr and Mrs Brown?"

Nora leaned against his shoulder, tired and underslept.

"They're not Mr and Mrs," she said. "Nor will they be, ever."

"Well . . ." he murmured, rubbing his eyes as she fast-forwarded the video, "that's in the lap of the Gods, isn't it?"

Nora leaned forward in the couch, concentrating on the buttons of the remote control now, trying to find the bit she wanted to show him.

"They'll never get as far as the altar," she prophesied. "She's trying to convince herself she loves him. But she hates him really. And deep down she knows it already. I'd give it three weeks at the most, from the time they set foot outside our door."

Jim Waddington chuckled, resting his great gnarled hand on his wife's knee.

"Wouldn't it be nice to *know*?" he said. "To follow them and find out?"

"Control yourself, Mr Super Spy," cautioned Nora teasingly. "You see enough as it is."

As if to prove her point, she snuggled up close to him and drew his attention to the TV screen: she'd found the bit that had particularly struck her last night.

Together they sat in the dimness and watched Mr and Mrs Brown having sex, in crystal-clear footage chosen from among the three video cameras hidden behind the submarines.

"Look at the expression on her face," said Nora as the well-tanned, well-muscled, plainly drunk young man was shuddering to orgasm, his lover staring up over his shoulder.

"She doesn't look too happy," admitted Jim. He didn't like to judge people harshly. "Although she wasn't so well, you know. I had to give her Alka Seltzer at breakfast."

"It's more than that." His wife leaned over the remote control, fast-forwarding again. A heavy lock of her hair swung loose from its elastic band, dangling over one eye, and, in annoyance, she clawed the whole lot of it free. A mass of lush grey hair tumbled over her shoulders. "Look here," she said, pointing at the screen.

The young man seemed to be asking the young woman something. She half-smiled, awkward, evasive. She stroked his hair, as if to say that he was wonderful, and she wouldn't have expected an orgasm anyway, not when she was so sleepy and exhausted. Manfully, he pulled the covers back from her naked body and refused to let her accept less than she was entitled to. His head dipped between her legs, and she cradled it in her hands uneasily, as if it were a stranger's lapdog she couldn't slap away.

"What lovely breasts she's got," remarked Mr Waddington wistfully.

"Keep your eyes on the face, Mr Milk Jugs," his wife reminded him. "Look now!"

"She flinched," observed Mr Waddington.

"Damn right she flinched," said his wife. "This fellow hasn't got a clue. He thinks he's ducking for an apple in a barrel."

Mr Waddington raised his prodigious eyebrows in gentle censure.

"Anyone can lick the wrong spot once . . ."

"Always sticking up for the men!" she teased him bawdily, patting his erection through his trousers. "Look again!"

Mr Waddington looked again, for the duration of the young woman's orgasm, if orgasm it was.

"Poor thing," he said at last, converted wholly to his wife's view. "She might as well've been at the dentist's."

But Nora had already let her attention wander from the video replay, knowing he'd see it her way soon. She was stroking her cheek against her husband's thigh, nuzzling her nose against the bulge of his penis.

"Put the Olssons on," she murmured softly.

"The Olssons?" he responded in mild exasperation.

"I'm in the mood," she crooned.

"Bloody heck," he complained. "It's on Super 8."

"I know that," she sighed, pulling up her dress, exposing the acre of thigh he'd always loved.

Grumbling theatrically, Jim Waddington got up and fetched the ancient Super 8 projector out of the cupboard. The Olssons were still spooled onto it from the time before. With his big clever hands, he had them up and running in no time – if running was the right word for it.

"This old machine isn't going to last for ever, you know," he said, sharpening the focus on the two young lovers writhing on the bare wall.

"Get it transferred to video, then," said Nora, pulling him back to her, unfastening the belt of his trousers as she did so.

"Some snooper in the video lab would report us for sure," he muttered. "Privacy isn't what it used to be."

As ever, his prophecies of technological and sociological doom made little impression on his wife. She'd taken up her usual position behind the projector, her

face glowing orange in the light reflecting back from the young lovers fucking each other's brains out in 1973, when the B&B was new.

"Come *on*," she growled, wiggling her naked behind, as flushed and wet for him as on the night they'd first made love.

He shuffled up close, his knees furrowing the plush of the sheepskin, and slid his penis into her.

"What does it feel like?" she asked. In all their years together, they'd never got around to using words like "cunt", "prick" and "fuck" themselves; they were from a more old-fashioned generation.

"Like an angel's mouth," he said.

She laughed, gripping onto him tight as the lovers of a bygone age arched their glowing young bodies in mutual ecstasy.

"You always knew what to say," she purred.

NEVERTIRE

Nikki Gemmell

Nikki Gemmell is a bestselling Australian author who has written nine novels and four works of non-fiction. Her work has been internationally acclaimed and translated into twenty-two languages. Her distinctive style using the second-person narrative has earned her critical and popular acclaim in France where she is seen as a female Jack Kerouac. She has been hailed as one of the most original and engaging authors of her generation.

Sydney to Alice Springs. One Holden pick-up truck. One city boy, freshly scrubbed; one London wife, not. The city stop-start vanishes into a six-lane freeway and a biblical sky. The car's the cabin confessional that will be the two strangers' close quarters for the next 4,000 kilometres.

He's called Nick. He's 24. He's two years past a girlfriend situation that never really connected. She's called Sarah. 33. She's never loved her husband, or maybe she did, once; she doesn't know.

"You'd know, Sarah, you'd know."

"Hmmm."

She smiles and stretches. Three days to go.

Sarah's on holiday in Australia, visiting a sister who's not as sick as her husband thinks. She wants to learn to drive manually – she's never mastered it. She's hired a car, roped in her sister's neighbour to teach her – she's never done anything like this. He's a painter with some free time; he wants to find the light in the desert that hurts. And to teach the woman from England whose skin is so luminously pale that the whites of her eyes appear pale blue. She has a beautiful neck.

Sarah examines the puppy-like energy of her instructor's hands as they roam the new buttons of her car, triggering wipers and windows. She laughs. Nick does too. She muses over the kink of his wrist as it rests on the steering wheel. There's a looseness in him; it's the ease of someone who's been loved very much. He's like a rock that's been hit by the sun for too long and has collected its warmth and shines with it. He has a beautiful wrist.

Sarah smiles like a child who's been caught with the last of her grandmother's chocolates. She examines the dirt on her palm, like river lines on a map, and the dust that's claiming her feet. She's revelling in the strange, inexplicable glee coming over her; the unravelling. She yanks down the window and holds her hand high, butting the breeze.

Dubbo, a dot on the map, is swept through in near-darkness. They push on to

the next town and suddenly a thick tiredness drags through them both.

They'll stop at the next dot.

"Nevertire," says the map.

"Who'd call a town Nevertire?" Nick asks.

Sarah doesn't answer. She's good at that.

"Hey? Who'd call a town that?"

The pub owner is Ron. Tattoos cram his arms; the ink is so dense that from a distance it looks like he's been horrifically burnt. Nick asks for a room. The bar is poised. "What sort?" Ron asks, and there's the loaded reply into the silence, "Twin beds," "Uh-huh," and the room slides back to chat.

The door of the room doesn't lock and a lone chair's tilted under the door-handle like in some lousy Western. Nick and Sarah lie demure in pyjamas in their saggy school camp beds. Read a little; turn.

A sudden suck of a snore.

Sarah cocks her head and stares at Nick, asleep on his back, limbs flung out with the abandon of a child. She envies the swiftness of his sleeping, his obedience and trust. He's wearing a T-shirt; cleanly white, crisply ironed. His belly is exposed, and his hips.

Her hand slips between her legs.

A warm, flooding wet.

She pads over to him. Hovers her hand above his plump boy-lips. Lowers her head and breathes in his sleeping; wants to take off her clothes and lie on top of him, to kiss him in the clearing behind his ears. Wants to stifle his waking with her lips to his, slip her hands onto the eroticism of his hips, Jesus-kinked; wants to place him inside her, to still his talk with her fingers to his lips.

A swell of laughter from the bar.

She goes back to bed. Thinks of her husband, Matt. In Chiswick.

They've not made love in over a year; one of them is always too tired; the timing's never quite right. She'd be happy to never have sex with Matt again – it's not why she married him. One day there'll be kids. He'll make a good father.

When they do make love you could describe them as tidy.

"I've forgotten how to do this, it's been so long," Matt said the last time they had sex; during the ad break of *Friends*, on the couch.

Pingpingpingping.

The digital watch on Nick's wrist wakes Sarah early and she likes it – it's her energy, work energy. The crumpled clean shirt he takes from his suitcase smells of her childhood. They wolf down bacon and eggs at a faded cafe.

"Where you off to?" asks the young waitress, cigarette-lean in her bra-less singlet.

"Alice," Nick answers, handing over their money at the till.

Sarah imagines the three of them.

The girl's breasts, her cunt; her tongue reaching up to it; Nick's tongue between her own legs. She squeezes her thighs under her white linen skirt.

"See ya," says the girl, eyeing Nick's belt buckle and boots.

Sarah recognises the hungry city stare and smiles back at her, tenderly; she was that once.

"You should've asked her along," she says to Nick.

"She's not my type."

"Uh-huh. And who is?"

He grins.

Sarah takes the keys from his fingers and there's the shiver of a something as the two of them touch. She strides away from it. Today she'll master the clutch; she gets into the driver's seat and pushes the car strongly into the frontier space. Nick is concentrating and keen at her ear and his hand is firm over hers on the gear stick.

"Change, move up, clutch, listen to it, clutch . . . that's it, you've got it!"

The ground flattens, the sky expands before them, the air is crisp and thin and it makes Sarah want to slice her way through it very fast; the waitress still wet in her head.

"The landing sky," Nick muses and Sarah smiles and floors the accelerator and drives fast at the stretch of sky falling to the land. There's a lizard, still on the bitumen with its head to the sun – thud, head's gone.

"Damn."

Laughter fills the pick-up's cabin. Nick chatters about his studio and his building job as Sarah plies him with questions and imagines breathing in his smell in the clearing behind his ear, and the softness of his earlobe in the cave of her mouth. Somewhere in the late afternoon they stop at a pub where the locals sit silent around a big square counter plumping out the room. There's a deep hush like a long cool drink, as if everything worth talking about has been exhausted long ago. Sarah and Nick catch each other's eyes and grin. They sit outside, under the shinbone beauty of a lone gum tree. Nick tells her he wants to be a cool dad. That his grandmother still has her spark. That his school asked him to be a priest – "but I loved girls too much".

They laugh. Nick looks at Sarah. She feels a pulling coming over her, a churning inside. She stands, clotted by awkwardness. Hopes he doesn't speak because whatever she says back will be jagged and wrong, and hopes he doesn't look because she'll blush. She can feel it, the fierce pull like a hand inside her stomach, the wet.

Nick bins his ball of a sandwich bag.

Sarah strides from him. Back in the truck she roars the engine to a start with the tips of her toes, the seat slammed forward as far as it will go. Nick climbs in beside her and pokes her playfully in the ribs. She flinches.

Busy silence.

He says suddenly he wishes he could take her out for a drink, see her in the real world; know her.

"Maybe you wouldn't notice me in the real world."

"Oh, I dunno about that."

"I'm just a housewife."

"I dunno about that."

Sarah arches back in the seat. She's married – she doesn't sleep around. It's the only certainty now in her life. The best sex is the sex you've never had, she knows that. You can only seduce someone who's not content, she knows that.

Who's not content.

She's much better at sex by herself, in her head, where it's always more accomplished, theatrical, dirty. Whenever she makes love it's her own thoughts that stir her more than the touch of a man.

Her partners have never been her focus while they're on her, they're merely kick-starting the film in her head. As they push inside she'll slip into concentrating on a scenario that'll trigger her pleasure and it has little to do with the person making love to her. Nick doesn't need to know any of that.

Or maybe he does.

Because he's younger . . . and she'll never see him again after this trip.

Sarah has never come close in reality to the sex of her imagination.

She's never allowed herself to; she's never before said exactly what she wants.

Now they're in salt-pan country. They stop the car and walk into the silvery, moon-plain vastness and whoop across the bleached bowl. Sarah turns. Wants to kiss Nick. He stares for a second or two too long; they break the gaze quick, walk separately to the car. Nick gets in the driver's seat, drives on quietly.

A storm ahead. A steel-grey curtain is drawn almost the length of the sky and they slow with the flint smell strong upon them and a plummeting chill. Nick stops the car. He looks at Sarah; she's wet, can't read him, and they drive on and at the first angry spots of rain she yanks down her window and puts out her head like a dog, she holds out her face to the sting and the hurt.

At a town with too many "o's" they don't know how to pronounce they stop for petrol and Sarah goes into the toilets and rushes off her pants and flits her finger over her clit; she circles it and savages it and slips two fingers inside until she sweetly, deliciously comes, her face crammed hard against the chill of the cubicle door.

She wants Nick's tongue on her nipple like a droplet of cold mercury. Wants her eyelids kissed. Wants him shaving her, clean, pushing her legs wide and forcing it upon her. Wants a trembling inside her, a holiness, a fluttering between them both. Wants him pulling back her hair as he's kissing deep. Fucking hard. Wants his finger in her ass; then his cock, yes, yes, that. Wants two vibrators in her ass and her cunt. Wants Nick licking her until she can no longer bear it, wants his tongue circling and circling her clit. Wants the sharp hot spurts of her cum, again and again, the exquisite release of all that. And doesn't want to have to give anything back.

She walks to the car. Doesn't look into Nick's stare. Gets into the driver's seat. Revs too heavily, roars off. A carcass of a calf is melted like icecream on the roadside dirt. A kamikaze bird thuds into the windscreen.

Churning silence.

The outside heat is pressing in and somewhere as Sarah's driving Nick is pouring water from a bottle into his hands and trickling it in silence over her forehead and it's slipping down her chin, snail cold between her breasts and rolling to her belly; and he pours it into her outstretched hand as she keeps her eyes on the road and slowly rubs her neck; and in silence puts out her hand for more.

A night ahead to be camped in. At a roadhouse supply stop they get directions to a dry riverbed ahead. Sarah's unsure about the delicacies of driving on sand but Nick assures her it's easy, he's done it before. They swap seats. The pick-up turns from the highway onto dirt, and sand, drives further and further and . . . sinks.

Rev. Stop. Rev again.

"Shit," Nick says, hunched at the wheel.

Sarah laughs. Nick looks at her; laughs too.

They climb out. There's no shovel. Sarah holds up her hands and grins.

They dig. Nick's long-fingered and soft hands and Sarah's sun-grooved and squat ones work side-by-side; there's sweat and stones and laughter and scratches and blood. And then she revs and he pushes on the tailgate, and again, one-two, and again, one-two, and they stop and flop, their energy scuttled.

The light slides. They haul themselves onto the empty highway and challenge the yelling silence and kick stones and roam the expanse as the dark crowds upon them.

They return to the creek bed. They'll tackle it all in the morning.

Between mouthfuls of burnt-sausage sandwich they grin in the firelight and settle into silence, their swags side-by-side. Like two kids on their bellies in front of a lounge-room TV they watch lightning inside clouds in the wings of the sky. The flashes are like a silent orchestra – here, now there, now together – but there's no thunder, God knows why; and somewhere from tension, wire-taut, Nick brushes Sarah's hand. Brotherly? What? She doesn't know, doesn't respond; and he rubs at her shoulder and again she doesn't respond and silently he draws across the flap of his swag and she cannot read his "Goodnight", and she imagines a lifetime ahead dissecting the missed moment – the itch of what could have been – and tells herself you reap what you sow, it has to be done, and as she says "Goodnight" she strokes his wrist gently, once, and he rubs strongly back, his fingers learning her wrist and her arm and then he leans across, his lips and his tongue to hers. Done.

"I've forgotten how to do this, it's been so long," Nick laughs softly, from the close dark, as Sarah looks up to the lightning still trapped in the clouds.

BELLE AND SYLVIE

Louise Welsh

Louise Welsh is the author of seven novels, including *The Cutting Room*, *The Girl on the Stairs*, *A Lovely Way to Burn* and *Death is a Welcome Guest* (volumes one and two of the Plague Times Trilogy). She has written many short stories and articles and is a regular radio broadcaster. Louise wrote the librettos for the operas *Ghost Patrol* and *The Devil Inside* (music by Stuart MacRae). She is Professor of Creative Writing at the University of Glasgow.

When I first got it on with Belle it was her dirty talk that amazed me. The "Ooh fuck me"s and crazy sexual fantasies she whispered in my ear. I guess I was shocked. I mean, these days it's no great surprise to hear a doll curse, but when you eventually manage to coax some sweet young thing between the sheets you don't expect her to have a mouth would make a stevedore blush. But I was hot for her and after a while I got hot for those breathless obscenities.

"Oh yes that's right, fuck me like that, give it to me hard, nail me to the bed, give me your cock . . ."

I'd grip her hips gently, give her deep long thrusts steering her towards climax, move my fingers across her small breasts, down towards her little bush, rubbing her clit, trying to keep my rough fingers gentle like she'd taught me.

"Harder . . . harder!"

Until her whispers grew harsher and her words coarser.

"Slam my cunt baby!"

Rocking her hoarse, until the words fell into gasps and I knew she was there.

I was wiping down the whisky bottles when I first saw her, reflected in the smoky glass mirror that runs the length of the bar. She had her back towards me and was chatting to Fat Al. He leant over her with that look he reserves for the dancers and a stab of dismay hit me like a Saturday-night punch in the guts. After all, things may have been tough, but since when were we so hard up we were putting kids on stage? Not that I'm against nippers – I was one myself once – but nippers as strippers? It's just wrong, is all. I uncorked the bourbon and poured myself a splash that rang pure gold against the glass. The girl heard the alcohol chime and turned towards me with a smile that could light the whole of New York. My faith in Fat Al was restored. Tiny she might be, but that girl was all woman. I swirled the whisky, suddenly unable to drink though my mouth was dry.

"Hey Frogs, meet our newest artiste, Belle. From now on known as Tinker

Belle. Tinks, this is Froggy, my associate and the best barman this side of Manhattan."

Belle fluttered her lashes and into my mind flashed every storybook seaside trip. Those eyes were the bluest blue I'd ever seen, and I've worked with some pretty hot dolls. Then she smiled again – the full one hundred watts – and I knew I was gone.

Maybe it was something to do with me being on the economical side height-wise, but up until then I'd always favoured big dolls. Girls like Sylvie. A long-legged, smoky-eyed showstopper billed as "The Cyd Charisse of Burlesque", who could hook a leg around my neck and pull me to her still standing. Sylvie had been retired from the Radio City Rockettes on account of putting on a little weight. Hell, I thought it suited her, more to shiver when she shimmied. Al would give her a big build:

"And now, all the way from gay Paree, for your delectation, the delicious, the distracting, our very own Rockette, Ms Sylvie Cherie!"

The lights would dim, the needle hit shellac, music grind up, and one long leg would slide from between the red velvet curtains to a chorus of wolf whistles and cheers. Sometimes Sylvie would milk it, running a hand down that perfect pin, snapping her suspender, holding the spotlight until the crowd was impatient. But most nights she kicked straight onto the stage, rumba-ing and shaking her tits until you thought she was going to fall right out of her skin-tight, high-slit black velvet gown – which of course was exactly what she did, looking as surprised as a calendar girl whose doggy's just ripped her shorts off.

Then she'd really start to enjoy herself. Fooling with her evening gloves, flinging her paste diamonds behind the bar. Playing the crowd until they were mad for her. When she unsnapped the front fastening of her brassiere they went wild. She'd tease until they begged, turning her back on the crowd and wiggling her tush, before flinging her bra away, giving them a view of her naked back, then she'd turn round slowly clasping her hands over her bosoms. Now the show really got going. Naked 'cept for her high heels and a pair of sequinned panties that wouldn't hide a mouse, Sylvie'd dance across the stage, holding her big soft tits in both hands, pressing them together, rolling them round, letting the hard as button nipples peek through her fingers, then pushing them up to her red painted lips, tonguing each one slowly, sending every man in the room stiff. Sylvie was top of the bill and my main squeeze. But then Belle smiled, and suddenly small girls who looked like they'd been formed out of ivory became my new weakness.

Le Chat Rouge was the name of the club. When he first came up with the name, Al wanted the girls to dye their bushes red. A kind of gimmick, if you get my drift. I thought he was onto something, but they told him to go fuck himself. Still, there's no doubting a Frenchy name says sex in a classy way. Course everyone called it The Pussy Club, but what can you do? Try is all.

Belle became the sweetest thing in the joint. Her costume bristled with shiny silver bells that gave a shimmer and a tinny jangle to her strip. Where Sylvie was all brashness and big tits, Belle was ice-cold, like some sea siren, beckoning and dangerous. When she peeled the heavy costume off, slinging it ringing through the air, the room sighed to see her small breasts so pink and exposed. She showed

them all she'd got, exiting naked with a backwards pirouette that revealed her most secret seashell pinkness, but somehow it was still the most innocent thing I'd ever seen. There's men might object to their girl taking her clothes off in a bump-and-grind shop, but I loved to see Belle dance. When she moved the trembling bells caught the light, glancing against the mirror balls, sending the room full of sparkles, like my sweetheart was shining in the starlight. And at night she was all mine.

"Give it to me hard. Like that, yes like that. Fuck me! Let me feel the full length of your cock."

Perhaps it's no surprise Belle and Sylvie didn't get on. I tried to let the big doll down gently – giving her a final jump for old time's sake before I broke the news – but she took it bad. She hit me a left and a right, so hard I might have been concussed, shoved me out of her apartment in the raw, flinging my boots one after the other from her third-floor brownstone. I stood in the half-light of the back courtyard begging her to throw the rest of my clothes after, trying to ignore the catcalls from other apartments, but she called me every bad name I'd ever heard and a few more beside, then slammed her window shut. I raided a washing line and made my way to Belle's place in some giant's work overalls. I didn't hold it against Sylvie. It's well known dolls are hard to understand.

It was about this time Al went to Vegas. He called it a fact-finding tour, but from what he told me it was a chance to try out new talent, if you get my drift. He said Vegas had nothing to match our girls, but what they did have was a new style of act, the double act.

"Like Jerry Lewis and Dean Martin?"

"Only in that there's two of them. I'm talking double titty, Dumbo. Two girls on stage, stripping together. It's a winner."

I could see how the audience might go for it. I thought it might be something I could get into myself come to that.

"So who you going to pair up?"

Al winked and said, "Who do you think?" Usually Belle kept her cussing to the bedroom but she stormed in a way I'd never seen before when I told her Fat Al's plan.

"You're fucking kidding, right? You want me on stage with that elephant? No fucking way!"

Sylvie wasn't any happier when she heard the news.

"Me and the Midget Germ? I'd rather fuck your monkey, Al."

This last she said nodding towards me. But in the end it was Al who decided things. He offered a ten per cent pay rise if they did and a boot out the stage door if they didn't. Times were hard, joints were closing, and there's always plenty girls willing to shake their tush inside when it's chilly out. Al didn't have it all his way though. Belle and Sylvie refused to rehearse together. It was Belle who started it. Arms crossed, sweet face sour, she pressganged the nancy dancer who puts them through their paces, and confronted Al in his office.

"Ben can choreograph us separate. You can force me to perform with her, but I'm not getting close to that buffalo a second before I need to."

And that's what they did, Ben in his seventh heaven, a bra fastened over his tight T, playing Sylvie to Belle and Belle to Sylvie. I'm not saying there's anything

wrong with it, but a man stripping is for a select taste. So after a while Al and me'd go down to Roxy's, put a shot of whisky in our coffee, and talk about how this show just might make our fortune.

On opening night Le Chat Rouge was as packed as a Joe Louis fight. Word had got round and guys had travelled from as far as Queens to see the show. I was serving drinks double quick and Al's smile flashed on and off as his thoughts slipped between the loot we were raking in and how much the girls hated each other. He wasn't the only one worried. They'd both been fierce as firecrackers all day. The clock tick-tocked towards Show Time, but no sound came from either dressing room and Al and me were too chicken to check. Eventually he gave me the nod. I dimmed the overheads, cranked up the music and a spotlight settled on the stage. It lingered three beats beyond time. The audience shuffled and I knew the girls had bailed. Al made a move to raise the lights, then out they slinked from opposite wings, looking like they wanted to kill each other and sexy as Hell.

Sylvie was packed into a red-sequinned sheath that brought out the madness in her eyes. Belle was in ice blue, cool as a killer. The crowd let up a roar and I knew I'd served the last drink for a good while. You'd never know those dolls hadn't rehearsed together – they moved so slick, feet and hips keeping pace. Lordy, even their bazoomas jiggled in time. They teased the crowd, luring them with lowered eyes then turning their backs and walking upstage, swaying their seats to the jazz-time beat. They were the perfect pair, one as small and slight as the other was curved and ripe, and I began to wonder if there was any way that I could have them both. A saxophone cut in, low and sexy, and the girls each teased off one long evening glove, finger by slow finger. When they flung them into the audience a guy got a black eye in the struggle to grab them.

A second glove followed the first, tugged off by teeth that looked like they could nibble you good. A couple of trophy hunters hit the deck, and were nearly trampled by boots. Guys were starting to shove each other, hustling for the best view, shouting for the girls to show them more.

The crowd might be getting wild but Belle and Sylvie were still frosty. When the tall doll slipped her hands round her partner's neck, I thought she might strangle her. But all she did was unclasp the sparkles that dripped down Belle's cleavage and throw them to the crowd. Belle returned the favour then, after a long liquid move of her hips, shifted her attention to her partner's zip, unfastening it, dropping Sylvie's dress to the floor. Belle "Ooohed" at the big girl's cleavage, drawing the crowd into her delight then ran her tiny fingers round the large nipples that peeked over Sylvie's too-small corset. She bent towards the crowd, exposing her tits, allowing Sylvie to free her from her dress, so now both girls were reduced to high heels, stockings and barely there underwear. They high-kicked, moving with the music. Down in the bull pit some guys lost their hats and a scuffle broke out.

Al squeezed behind the bar.

"There's gonna be a riot if we don't watch out."

And suddenly I saw he was right. The girls were whipping the crowd to frenzy.

Sylvie tugged at the front of Belle's bra with her teeth and a chair hit the gantry, shattering whisky and smoky glass. Belle put her mouth to Sylvie's cleavage and a gorilla in a suit smacked a weaselly-looking guy in the mouth.

Sylvie licked her lips and put the point of her tongue to Belle's nipple and a shot rang out.

Al shouted, "Stop them!"

I didn't know if he meant the girls or the fight, but I knew I was powerless. Both were in full swing, guys throwing punches all over the joint and Sylvie, naked now save for her high heels, snapping Belle's panties off with her teeth. Then both girls bent over to give us a naughty last glimpse, before running, breasts bouncing, from the stage.

By the time New York's Finest managed to stop the riot, there wasn't even a drop of bourbon left to console us. We sweetened the cops with a donation to the usual fund slipped between some girlie pictures and eventually they sloped off, grumbling half-hearted threats against our licence. Al began pushing a broom around the floor and I went to check on Belle.

In truth the wrecking of Le Chat didn't worry me. We had a dynamite new act that would soon make our money back. No, what I was wondering was whether I could persuade both dolls back to my bed. Belle's dressing room was empty. I made my way to Sylvie's. I put my ear to the door before knocking; then I realised that all my plans were sunk.

"Oh yes, do it like that! Yes, you know how to! Oh, squeeze my tits! Oh, you're a filthy whore to do that! Yes, touch me there, oh you're naughty. You like it like that don't you? You dirty slut."

I stood listening, wondering if they'd let me join in, but knowing in my heart that the game was up. Not long after, Belle and Sylvie moved to Vegas and opened their own joint. I hear it does a bomb.

Me? I'm still tending bar, but these days I stick to dolls of medium height.

SUMMER

Katie Kelly

Former contributor to the *Erotic Review* and secret writer of rude stories, Katie Kelly is currently lurking in the rolling Pennines. When she isn't spending time thinking and writing about things she probably shouldn't be, she distracts herself by making nutritious family meals her children refuse to eat, gambolling through rain-sodden, cow-pat-strewn hills and persuading her friends to join her in her pledge to discover the perfect gin dry martini.

I look back on that summer as the beginning of my education. From a more literal perspective, it was also the end. I'd finished my degree three months earlier and was helping out at my aunt's hotel in Koufonissia, a tiny isle off the better-known Naxos Island. I'd been spending my summers at Aunt Alena's for as long as I could remember. She was my father's sister. We shared the same black hair and creamy skin, and fought the same battle to keep the infamous Fotopoulos eyebrows under control. The rest of me was a gift from my English mother, eyes as blue as the Aegean sea and a small slim frame. As much as I loved my aunt and all my Greek relatives, I'd never coveted the expansive bottom all females of the line seemed destined to inherit. Bum cheeks so wide and welcoming you could have comfortably parked a Hells Angel's reunion in between, let alone a single bicycle.

The hotel itself was hidden away from the frenetic activity of the main town. There were only ten rooms, all decorated individually and featuring their own little quirks. Room 9 was dominated by a magnificent antique roll-top bath, which stood imperiously at the bottom of the bed. Room 7 would render guests speechless as they took in the view of the sea from the floor-length wall-to-wall windows. My role during my annual visit was to help prepare the rooms for guests' arrivals in the morning and then don my apron to undertake waitress duties in the evening. The hours in between were my own. This time of year, as the season slipped into late September, was my favourite. The dazzling sun and excited ice cream-fuelled screams of children which characterised August had faded into long lazy days warmed by a gentler heat. Families were replaced by couples seeking a haven, some precious time to themselves. I liked to watch them as they strolled around hand in hand, imagining the lives they'd left, the relationship they had.

That week's most recent arrival was a couple from London. My aunt had been busy in the kitchen as they arrived, so I took down their details and led them to their room. Just a few minutes spent with them and I was intrigued. To me

they were reminiscent of the film stars of the 50s. Blessed with an understated glamour you couldn't help stealing a look at. Her face was mainly hidden by a huge, fabulous pair of Jackie O sunglasses, and her blonde hair was protected from the sun with a gingham headscarf. Her husband was wearing a simple linen shirt with loose cotton trousers and, of course, the obligatory shades. They said little but smiled warmly as I showed them around the room, pointing out the extra towels and giving them a quick demonstration of how the shower worked. Room 6's special feature is a wet room, one side of which is completely transparent. As the room faces out towards the sea, no one is likely to peek at you, with the exception of the occasional fisherman – though it's the thought that someone could which has always made this particular room my favourite. Judging by the intimate look that flashed between the two as they took in the power shower and the array of accompanying complementary oils, they liked it too.

Over the next couple of days I saw the couple infrequently. At breakfast they'd enjoy fresh fruit and yoghurt before slipping away, only to be spotted again close to midnight, sipping a cocktail. My eyes were automatically drawn to them whenever they appeared. They didn't fawn over each other like the honeymooning couples we often look after here. I guessed they were in their mid-thirties and had been married for a few years. Each touch seemed assured, almost measured. One morning I saw him return to their table with fresh juice and snake a leisurely finger down her spine as he passed. She arched gracefully, like a cat. Later that morning my aunt asked me to grab a few ingredients from town. As I made my way back, big fat tomatoes jostling with the basil in my bag, releasing a heady scent, I saw my couple again. They were making their way carefully down the steep slope which led to the hotel's small, private beach. To follow them seemed the most natural thing in the world.

The beach is a secluded cove, scattered with large, sun-weathered rocks that stand proudly in the sand. They headed for the shelter of the largest of these. Hidden from the eyes of anyone who might wander down for a swim – but not from my eyes. From my vantage point, ten metres above them, hidden by a stretch of spiky phrygana shrubs, I could see them clearly. A throw was laid carefully down first, sandals discarded and then his shirt and her kaftan. She reached into her bag, pulled out what I presumed to be sun oil, handed it to her husband and stretched out languidly on her front, deftly undoing the clasp of her bikini top as she did so. He knelt between her legs, edging them further apart with his own, poured a liberal amount of oil into his hands and began massaging it into her calves. He was meticulous in his application – it took at least ten minutes before he even reached the firm swell of her buttocks.

He must have spoken then, because she looked over her own shoulder and nodded a response. My eyes widened as he slowly pulled her bikini briefs down, past her thighs and knees until they were abandoned with the rest of their beach debris. More oil was dripped into the dent at the base of her spine where it pooled for a second before being worked into her ass cheeks with firm, deep strokes. I watched entranced as his fingers worked at the glistening supple flesh of her buttocks, sliding occasionally and deliberately into the deep divide in between. As his fingers delved, I could see her writhe slightly. He edged her legs further apart still and then, with both hands, splayed her ass cheeks wide

and ducked his head between. Even with my 20-20 vision I couldn't see exactly what was happening – but still I knew. I closed my eyes and imagined his tongue flicking over her excited little pink ass hole. I kept them closed and imagined his tongue sliding into my own. Within my own limited experience, that was an area unexplored. I looked up again. In my seconds of inattention, he'd flipped her over and was greedily eating her cunt. I was impressed by how, even with her legs spread open as far as they were, she still managed to emanate an air of languid elegance. Her fingers were digging into his hair as he sucked her clit into his hungry mouth (or so I imagined) and with a cry, lost to my ears amid the crash of the waves and the shriek of the gulls, she threw her head back and screamed her satisfaction

I nearly shrieked too. Not thanks to such glorious attention, alas. No, my scream was provoked by fear. I was sure that in that split second, as she'd thrown her head back with such abandon, her blue eyes had stared straight into mine.

It was with some reluctance that I undertook my waitressing duties that evening. My aunt commented on how flushed my face looked, but presumed it was due to my excursion in the midday sun. I hardly heard her. Perhaps they won't come to dinner, I thought frantically; they never have before. If they do come, mocked a gleeful voice in my head, that'll prove that they saw you spying on them. My face reddened further, then further still as I let the image of his head between her legs flood into my thoughts once more. Furtively, I looked out from the kitchen on to the candlelit veranda where we served the meals. Only two older couples there for now. I scurried out, flung the barbecued prawns down on their tables then beat a hasty retreat back to the kitchen. As the hour pushed nine, I began to relax. They weren't coming. I hadn't been seen after all. All was well. I hummed as I went to see if our guests would like dessert.

"*We'd* love something," came an amused voice from behind me. I froze. And turned slowly. There they were, sitting at the corner table closest to the pool. Both looking at me, both smiling. I approached them slowly.

"What can I get you?" I asked briskly, determined that my professional demeanour would see me through this embarrassing moment.

"I'm very warm," she murmured, looking me up and down. "So I'd like something cool and creamy. Whatever ice cream you have will be lovely."

"And for you?" I said, turning my attention to him.

"I am hungry," he mused, "I'm not sure for what though. I think I'll share whatever my wife's having."

"Very good," I trilled, becoming ever more Prunella Scales-like as the exchange went on, and scarpered back into the kitchen.

"Bollocks!" I hissed – which is "*arhedia*" in Greek, incidentally – as I feverishly heaped the ice cream into a bowl. I'll just take them their dessert, plead a touch of sunstroke to my aunt and go and hide in my room. I was sure the couple were leaving the next day anyway. Calmed slightly by my plan, I headed back to their table and placed the icy bowl carefully in front of her.

Her hand reached over the ice cream and rested on mine.

"Would you be a darling and bring it to our room?" she asked sweetly. "I'm in desperate need of some air con." Startled, I looked at her husband. He was

leaning back in his chair, watching us both closely. I glanced back up at her and she stared back boldly, a half smile curling her lips.

"Of course," I heard myself stammer. "I just need to let the chef know there'll be no more orders tonight."

"Don't speak too soon," came her teasing rejoinder as they left the table together. Leaving me contemplating the melting scoops of vanilla in my hand.

Ten minutes later, I knocked quietly on the door to Number 6, noticing too late that it had been left slightly ajar. Shifting the bowl to one hand, I pushed gently and slipped inside. My couple were sitting together on the sofa, heads close, whispering softly. They glanced up as I entered and made a space for me between them. I sat awkwardly down. I'd never been so aware of my body. Clearly neither had they, as their eyes roamed unembarrassed over the line of my thighs, damp within the confines of my jeans, the slope of my small breasts, the curve of my neck. A tiny bead of perspiration, a consequence of nerves not the heat, slid on a brief journey from my temple to the corner of my mouth. I tasted my own salty expectation and waited. I didn't have to wait for long. She moved in first, smoothing a tendril of hair away from my face.

"She's beautiful isn't she?" she asked her husband softly. "Skin like a peach." He remained silent, smiling his acquiescence and stroking my cheek in agreement.

"I'm going to undress you," she added, almost as an afterthought. "Is that okay?"

Well what was I going to say? Why else was I there? Mutely, I nodded.

I was undressed like a child. They moved in practised harmony; my white shirt was deftly unbuttoned by her, while he dealt with the clasp of my jeans. I wasn't wearing a bra, and the breeze flowing through the apartment felt delicious against my breasts as they were bared and my shirt carefully placed to one side. Naked apart from my jeans, I felt my nipples flush, then harden under her gaze. A perfectly manicured finger brushed over one tender reddening tip and circled it meditatively. My eyes closed, I didn't see her other hand dipping into the ice cream I'd left on the coffee table. I inhaled sharply as I felt the freezing liquid dripped over my breasts. Obeying the laws of gravity, it meandered down to cover my nipples with its cold kiss, before melting into her mouth as she sucked first one then the other hungrily into her mouth. I moaned as she pulled on them greedily. I was vaguely aware that my jeans were being drawn down to the floor and knew that the white knickers I'd pulled on this morning would be drenched, and that my ass would release them with a guilty sodden sigh. I wasn't mistaken.

"You're soaking," he whispered into my ear as he stood behind me. His wife welcomed this news, and straightened up so she could steal a self-congratulatory kiss from her partner-in-deviant-crime. I wasn't neglected though. As their tongues danced, his hand dipped into the dripping heat between my legs and he covered his fingers with my wetness. Moving up to my ass, he slid them easily between my cheeks and began to play with my asshole. Round and round his finger traced this as yet virgin area, pushing against it teasingly. Instinctively my ass clenched, then relaxed as I realised I was a poor match against his persistence. Particularly when paired with hers, for as I moved away from his

probing fingers, hers pushed me back, and were now sliding rhythmically over my clit, teasing it first and then gently spanking as I squirmed between them.

"I can see this getting sticky," she breathed. At me? At him? Either way, next thing I knew we were heading for Room 6's pride and joy; the aptly named wet room. The change of scenery triggered a marked change in pace. Languid caresses were discarded as clothes were removed urgently, and soon we were naked, our bodies becoming hazy as the torrent from the shower slowly filled the room with steam. Any coyness I'd had dispersed – a finger sliding into your ass can have that effect – and with no hesitation I ran my hands over her breasts. Bigger than mine, with nipples rosy as raspberries, I bounced their weight in my hands. First gently, then as I saw her nipples ripen under my touch, a little rougher.

"That's it," she breathed heavily, "not so shy now are you?" I answered by sinking to my knees and, spreading her plump pussy lips with excited fingers, plunged my face into her sweet-scented cunt. I licked and sucked with the same insatiability as her husband had earlier that day. And no wonder – she tasted delicious. As the deluge from the shower beat a tattoo on my back, her juices ran down my chin. The harder I drank, the more they flowed. So far into heaven was I that I barely registered the activity behind me. Then slowly I became aware of him. He was leaning against the wall, watching with evident pleasure the sight of yours truly eating his wife's pussy with such enthusiasm. His cock was huge, unmistakeably so, even through the ever thickening steam. As my tongue darted over her clit, taking care not to ignore the tiny folds and ridges surrounding this hot little button, his hand unconsciously ran up and down the thick shaft. I could feel his eyes burning into my ass, as it bobbed provocatively. The showerhead was re-directed slightly, sparing me its attention. I knelt back and saw a look of compliance pass between them, a secret intimate smile. Gently I was pulled to my feet so I was face to face with her, my back to him. The tuberose scented oil I'd so carefully placed on the bathroom shelf a few days earlier was opened and poured down my back.

"Spread your ass," she ordered. I hesitated a second too long. She gave me an admonishing look and, sliding her hands around me, took a cheek in each hand and spread them wide, indecently so, allowing the oil to trickle unimpeded over my asshole. I gasped as her husband slowly massaged it in deeper with large, assured fingers. God, it felt good. But still I was hesitant, and moved nervously from foot to foot. Sensing this, she placed her mouth close to my ear and whispered that she knew I wanted this, and that her husband would be gentle. I leant into her as I felt the tip of his cock press against the tiny puckered pink ring of my ass, growing in insistence until both my ass and my fear gave way and his cock glided in. As he began to move, she picked up the rhythm of his slow thrusts and matched them, firmly rubbing my clit in time. With my head on her shoulder, the couple kissed hungrily while I stood, impaled, between them. Together we rocked slowly, his cock deep within my ass, her fingers working my clit with practised ease. I relaxed and added my own counter-rhythm, bouncing my ass back against his groin. Taking their cue from my increasing confidence his strokes intensified, growing deeper and quicker. Her fingers began to spank my open cunt once more and I, bold now, pulled her face away from his and her

mouth onto mine. The wet room had never been wetter. I had never been wetter. I came a split second before he did, screaming. As his cock shot hot bursts of cum into my no longer virginal bottom, his legs gave way and together we sank to the floor, letting the streaming water wash all traces of the encounter away.

They did leave the next day. My couple. I didn't make a note of their address back in London. I knew I wasn't their first conquest, but that didn't sour the fact they were mine. My first taste of a woman, my first experience of anal sex; such sweet pain, my first threesome. It was a summer of firsts and I returned home grateful.

THE SELFISH GIANTESS

Alex Chambers

Alex Chambers is a writer of contemporary romance. Alex enjoys travelling in Europe, life drawing, hot summers, gardening and classic detective fiction. He harbours ambitions to one day own a house overlooking Hampstead Heath.

In the long, hot summer of 2003, Felicity and I rented a flat on the top floor of a Victorian house 'a stone's throw' from Hampstead Heath, although why we would want to throw stones at the Heath was anybody's guess. 'Flat' was a generous appellation for our magnolia prison: a 23 square foot studio with a ludicrous bed that was designed to be folded into the wall when not in use. We never did this, partly because we rarely had visitors and partly because, for me at least, the bed had become a reproachful reminder of what was no longer happening between us. To fold it away completely would have been to admit defeat.

We had recently finished our PhDs; hers on Aubrey Beardsley's unfinished erotic novel Under the Hill and mine on Napoleon's Corsican identity. I was interning at the British Museum, scanning endless pages from the spidery notebooks of an eighteenth-century botanist. Felicity was doing bits of editing and sometimes temping, while I worked four evenings a week in a pub in Camden. We were both feeling anxious about the future, resentful about our mindless jobs and maddened by our airless accommodation. We had no outside space, only a tantalising view of the garden below: a generous lawn, now somewhat parched, but with shady shrubs and trees and backed only by the Heath itself.

The ground floor flat was occupied that summer by some sort of house sitter for the permanent occupant, a Mr Krawyz, who also owned the floor above. We had seen the mysterious Mr K only once, and we didn't know the name of his house sitter. We saw her, though. She seemed to have no job other than tending the garden. During the day she sunbathed on the lawn, in the evenings she sat on the terrace, and often in the early morning she could be seen pulling weeds or watering the shrubs in defiance, or maybe in ignorance, of the hosepipe ban. One day Felicity remarked that she was like the Selfish Giant.

"Who is?" I said, though knowing who she meant.

"That German girl in Mr K's. It's so hot. The least she could do is invite us down there some evening, or let us use it when she's not in."

"I suppose we don't really know her," I said. "And it's not her garden."

"She's like the Selfish Giant." Felicity repeated. "All the poor children want to get into the garden, and the giant won't let them until it's too late."

I was used to Felicity's assumption that the main function of those around

her was to do her service. It was a trait I had indulged a little too much. As she reached up to pull down the blind I admired her slender waist, and felt the urge to rub my cock against her ass, throw her across the windowsill and grind myself inside her until she screamed with ecstasy. Five years of intensive study of erotica seemed to have made sex a busman's holiday for Felicity. The last time had been two months ago, the night of my viva. I was beginning to fear that the next time would be when I got a permanent job.

Felicity's Selfish Giant comparison was right in one respect; the girl was tall. I met her in the hallway, and in her bare feet she was only an inch or two smaller than my six foot. I handed her some of Mr K's post and enquired where he was.

"St Petersburg," she answered. Her accent was very pleasant – light but distinct.

"What is he doing there?" I asked.

"He likes it there," she replied simply.

I made some mild witticism about Mr K's evading the heat wave, and she smiled at me – a wide grin, totally without flirtation. She wasn't as pretty as Felicity, but her hair was long and thick, her skin smooth and tanned. That evening, as I got ready for work, I glanced out of the window. She was on the terrace, and I watched her long brown legs flex as she picked something up. She wore an old pair of shorts, and a sleeveless pink T-shirt with what looked like an oil stain on it. She was braless, and I could see her nipples. My hand crept down to my crotch.

The next day, Thursday, we had a note under our door. Felicity read it out: Hello neighbours. Why don't you come for a drink on Saturday night at 6? It will be nice to meet you. Marei.

"How weird," said Felicity, "just to leave a note without knocking."

"But it's what you wanted."

"Yes, it's nice of her. But I won't be here – I'm going to Vee's, remember?" Vee was Felicity's engaged cousin in Wiltshire.

"Of course. Well, I might pop in anyway..."

"Really?" Felicity fanned herself with the note. "Don't you have to work?"

"Not til 7."

"But it's hardly worth her while if it's just you. And you'd have to leave here at—"

"Well, I'll think about it." I was nettled, not so much by Felicity's management of my diary, as by her suggestion that my presence would be a waste of Marei's time.

After Felicity left on Saturday, I reconsidered. Perhaps it would be more charitable to ask Marei if Felicity and I could come together another time; I knew that Felicity wanted to see the garden. As I thought about Marei, I became aroused; I curled my fingers around my cock, and began to wank as I pictured her bending braless over the flowerbeds. I imagined pushing her into the earth, and taking her from behind as I no longer took Felicity. I imagined her pink tongue licking my cock and then my asshole ... I took a cold shower, and threw on a pair of trousers and a shirt to go downstairs. As I left, I noticed that Felicity had left the 'bridal book' – a sketchbook stuffed with magazine clippings, much prized by her and Vee.

Marei came to the door wearing a white vest and a short denim skirt. Her feet were bare and she had a gardening glove on one hand. I explained that we were sorry we couldn't make the drink that evening, but would love to come another time.

"OK. Why don't you come in right now?" she said. "I am going to sit down and have some white wine."

I looked into her candid eyes. "That would be lovely," I said.

She led me to a tartan blanket spread under a lilac tree, whose blossoms were looking bruised and wilted. Finally I could appreciate the glorious summer, the achingly blue sky, the all-enfolding heat. Looking up at our tiny window was much better than looking out of it.

"It's nice, huh?" Marei sat down cross- legged beside me and clinked her glass against mine. Her legs were smooth, but I could see little golden hairs on her upper thighs. "So I saw you before I moved in here," she continued.

"Really?

"Yeah, it was before I came here, Mr K emailed me some pictures of the flat and you were in one, coming down the front steps. I remembered you because you were so good-looking."

I looked up to see if she was joking. She was looking at me, her lips parted and moist where she had just sipped her wine. I put my glass down, not really thinking of what I was doing, and put my hand on her bare thigh. We kissed. Things progressed. Soon we were rolling on the ground, and my shirt was off. Then she was unbuttoning my trousers. She took out my cock, and rubbed her face against it like a cat. I straddled her and stroked her face with my cock, brushing it over her lips. I felt her breathe on my skin, and groaned. Then she took me in her mouth, and I was completely lost.

"Oh god, Marei ..." I was enclosed by her gorgeous mouth, which seemed all yielding softness, and her darting, moving tongue; her head moved as she sucked me harder; within a matter of seconds I came. I lay back, gasping, and looked at the blue sky and green branches above. After a minute, I turned to her and kissed her again. I pulled up her vest and saw her breasts, so big and firm, with hard pink nipples. I stroked and sucked them while she sighed with pleasure. Then I reached under her skirt, and slid my finger into her soft wetness.

She was so tight, she only needed one finger. I fucked her gently with it, listening to her gasp. I tugged off her skirt, and sank my head between her legs, kissing her thighs hard enough to leave little bruises.

"Suck me, please," she said.

I lapped her cunt like a deer at a stream, and she moaned and writhed, grabbing my head, taking me over and directing me, rocking surely harder even than I had before I came, and finally, coming with a scream. Later we wandered naked around the garden. I kissed her again under a wisteria branch, and cupping her tit in my hand I told her it was like one of the blossoms. She showed me a peach tree.

"Are there peaches?" I asked.

"No, not yet, they're not ripe yet. You got to let them get good and sweet."

She got down and very deliberately arranged herself on the grass.

"Fuck me hard," she said.

As soon as I entered her my head exploded. I didn't have any space to think of the Lawrentian connotations of our fucking; couldn't think or feel anything but her tight wetness. She pulled my buttocks tightly as I thrusted harder and rougher than I ever had before. My knees pressed into the earth as I fucked her deeper, and she urged me on until I felt her muscles convulse and felt her coming, and I came as well, helplessly and copiously, and collapsed beside her. When she sat up, her back was covered in grass and earth. We had left a definite imprint on the ground. I insisted that she take a turn on top, and we fucked again, this time with her riding me, swaying above me like a willow tree. Later we used what came to hand – ice; the picnic table; the gardening glove.

I broke up with Felicity the next day. She was surprisingly calm – in fact, suspiciously calm. We agreed that I would stay in the flat, while she moved in with a friend. The 'friend' turned about to be somebody called Charles, who had an earring and whom she had met through one of her editing jobs. I didn't feel in any position to object. A week later, lying in Marei's arms on the lawn, I looked up at the house, and an elusive memory came back to me: a small but definite movement at our window sometime on Saturday afternoon, perhaps half an hour after I had gone downstairs...

OFF THE ROAD

Garry Stewart

Born in Dunfermline, Garry Stewart is a businessman and inventor (RBS/Business Insider 'Inventor of the Year', 2016). He is a philosophy graduate and a Trustee of the Adam Smith Global Foundation as well as being a published writer and poet. Erstwhile erotic knight-errant, indy gangster-film producer and lapsed punk rocker. A dedicated follower of the unfashionable, living in the wilds of Perthshire with his Fender Strat collection, beautiful wife, two sons and two daughters.

I met her on the coast road just south of Salinas.

I was heading out for Monterey, to join a boat, and a run of bad luck that week had got me kind of jumpy. The sight of her seemed like the first breath of new air.

She wasn't any more than nineteen: half way between a kid and a woman. She still had that sparky attitude; her stance said it all: "My world's bigger than yours. Could you handle me?" It felt great to be reminded of that. Even at twice her age I could still remember feeling like that. Taking off across the Midwest with only the devil to snap at my heels. In the circumstances, I couldn't do anything but stop.

She was in an amiable floral-print skirt, very summery; a beat-up denim jacket which looked like it could have been her pop's, faded cornflower blue; and these crazy-looking boots, marching boots, with thick mountain-man socks spilling over. For July they seemed kind of strange and I suppose that also attracted my attention.

Already I was starting to be in more of an up mood, because I like the country round there. I always get a feel of the desert beginning far to the south and the pine forests running out. Agaves start appearing at the road edge and the grass grows scrubby. There's a smell of alcachofa in the air, and the ocean – that great big sapphire ocean. It was a desert-hot day anyways, even for those parts, and my windows were full down. The breeze was coming in like a grain dryer.

She smiled a broad easy smile that made her look even younger as I pulled my old Mustang over. I went a little beyond just to tease her. I could see her in the mirror giving me a "Huh, smart ass" kind of look. Boy, she looked great in that thin strawberry cotton, blowing all around her thighs. I was already opening the door as she walked forward, bending down to see in.

"Hi, you going anywhere near Santa Barbara?" She looked me straight in the eye in a very deliberate way and fixed me over her sunglasses.

I could see without really trying that she had nothing under the jacket. Just one button done up to stop it all going on display. Her perky little breasts were beautiful, hanging in shadow. Her reddish-fair hair was tousled, quite curly; she'd been standing in the wind for a while and I just thought right there and then she was the most natural-looking girl I'd seen in a long time. No make-up, no fancy lacy stuff, just a raw beauty. She had great hips, I could tell from the way the breeze tightened the cloth across them.

"Barbara's where I'm heading," I lied. Route 101 beckoned. The job could go to hell. I didn't know what I was going to follow through with, but the pure instinct of the words just nailed the moment. We were going to Santa Barbara.

"Climb in!" She was already swinging her butt onto the passenger seat. I liked the way it spread out under all those flowers.

"I was wonderin' if I'd ever get a ride." Her lively eyes laughed at me, keeping my gaze, way more confident than her age should be.

She settled herself into the seat, throwing her bag past me onto the back bench. A canvas snatch bag with lots of button badges on it, like a groupie would carry. It didn't look like she had so much to be travelling that far; Santa Barbara was a good two hundred farther south.

"You local?" I knew she wasn't.

"Na! Been here a couple of days."

She got comfy very quick as I got up speed again. The wind blew her hair nice. She sat with her legs apart and was tracing the inside of her knee with her fingers, not saying much. I noticed how delicate her hands were. She had French nails – that's what my last girl used to call them. Only fancy thing about her. She was no farm girl, I knew that much, though some of the olive pickers had great skin. Her skin was so lightly tanned, not at all weathered but fresh.

"You a student?"

"Was."

I left her for a while and just followed the vanishing point of the road as it shifted across the windshield. I could hear the rumble of the tyres getting louder on new surface.

"You got somewhere you're going?"

"Kind of . . ."

I didn't mind one bit that the whole thing was going so slow. If it took the next hundred miles to get her name, I'd be happy. She smelt of pineapples and cigarettes, and right then that was about as good a narcotic as I wanted. I hadn't got laid in about eight days and the way about her just made me feel my luck was changing.

"You eaten this morning?"

"Had a couple of flaps at the truck stop back there."

I wondered if she'd been dropped by one of the long-haul guys. I'd been getting kind of hungry myself but I'd wanted to make progress so had missed breakfast, reckoning I'd grab some on the longshore boat.

"I was going to catch a bite, up ahead aways. D'you fancy anything?"

"Maybe . . ."

She was playing with me, a slight curl around her lips. Her gaze flitted along the horizon but her eyes weren't looking there. With her chin held up so

confident, she hadn't anything particular to hide, nor was she avoiding me. I glanced ahead to hold the road, but took my time to look her over. This was a game, and I was tuning in just fine.

Her lips were a ripe shape, like she had some African blood, but she had blue eyes, bluer than the Pacific in the distance, and a lightly freckled face. The apricot colour of her lips stood out from it, warm and lush, and she knew it. She moistened them a little with her tongue, rolled them in prim like, and then out a full pout. I figured she realised how easily bated I was going to be. God, she was comfortable for a little lady of nineteen.

The road was quiet that morning. Somehow that made the whole thing seem more concentrated; the sensation of being alone with her, more intense.

"I've got a bruise my friend gave me. D'you wanta see it?" She was gazing ahead with that slight smile.

She didn't wait for my response before she slid her skirt up to her waistband. There, just below the curve of her mound, on her right thigh, was a double crescent of purple. Pretty freshly made, I'd say.

"My friend, Mandy, bit me."

I scooped up this vision with my eyes and was suddenly aware I was swerving off line.

"That wasn't too nice of her . . ."

I was beginning to swim in this newly found bath of pleasure; I wanted the playfulness to go on. That bite mark, though, that was where I wanted to be right now. It looked so tender there, set against the lighter skin of her inner leg. The flesh was as smooth as driftwood, and the blue of her veins showed a kind of tracery under it. She'd drawn open so wide, the dusty pink cotton of her pants was taut across the rise of her bush. What a great big sweet pussy under there.

"It was nice at the time. Hurts a bit now though."

I focused on the dark beauty of that bruise.

"I guess you were havin' a fight." My wit was ebbing.

"No, not really. I was eating her out, end on end, and she came so hard she almost bit a whole chunk out me."

She was a cool customer. The game was going too fast. We sat for a while in a warm kind of silence, just hazing in the noise of the road and the bright sun.

"Listen; d'you mind if I pull off the road?" I could see a derelict roadman's hut back in the trees not too far up ahead.

"D'you need to go?" She looked across to me, then at my pants.

I hesitated: "Well . . . I sure need to relieve myself." I smiled back.

"Good, so do I." She was grinning now.

"Do you have a name?" I swung the red prow of the car across the shallow ditch and up across the verge, heading for some shade. We made a wake of dust leaving the road and came to a halt under the spread of a twisted pine.

"They call me Tanii . . . it means 'little caribou'. My mom gave it to me. She's Tcholovoni. Bay people. She says I got pure instinct like them."

She looked nothing like First Nation half breed but I wasn't caring. It added to the mystery. Her instincts I didn't doubt . . .

We sat for a brief moment. The shady clearing seemed far away from the brightness back on the highway. We both unlatched our doors at the same time

and I paused, watching, as she went around to the front of the car and rested back on the hood. The way she moved was slow and musical. She unbuttoned her denim and let it slide back onto the hot paintwork above the engine. She lay back on the jacket and her breasts quivered as she adjusted her position. The nipples were a hard pecan brown, standing proud in the cooler air. Her snowy white shoulders were stark on the red expanse.

"Come on, Jack."

She surprised me. It took me a moment to realise she must have seen my name on the licence, stuck in the broken glove-box door.

"It's great out here."

She rolled her nipples between her fingers, licking the fingertips to wet them. I let her fill my vision and felt the blood rising harder.

As I walked to her, I unbuttoned my jeans and awkwardly wrestled out my cock, which was already well down one leg. I eased my balls into the air and felt the cool lick of the breeze, and it was good. Spread-eagled on the hood, she looked an impossible sight, pure fantasy. I stood between her legs and let the air run over us. I could hear a peregrine making its strange nervous sound up on the hillside behind.

She let me close her legs, and I drew down her skirt and pants together, sliding them free of a wide bush of auburn hair. Her triangle was almost halfway up her belly. The way it was pressed flat by her pants gave it a kind of dark-and-light root pattern. She was already swelled and wet; the lips of her little mouth made a sweet island of candy pink in all that hair.

"I need to go first but I can't. I'm too buzzy."

She ran her fingers through the slick on her labia and lifted it to her mouth. She tasted, then went to her nipples, circling real slow with her eyes shut. I was pounding; my end was fit to burst but I stood just taking her in. Somewhere, then, she found the switch she was looking for and she let herself go. The sparkling flood hit me right across the pants, and the heat of her insides rose into a heady smell like the sea down at the Cannery and the resin in pine cones.

I dived to her mound to catch the last of it, wanting to taste. She quivered at the release. Her head rocked side to side and she seemed to tense, then she groaned as I closed my lips over as much of her bush as I could, and my tongue slid up inside the deepest part I could find. Her breathing was hard and hungry. She held my head in her hands and nudged me into her. The sweetness and the feel of her soft wiry hair in my mouth were intense. I closed my eyes and buried my tongue in the rough way of her opening, and pressed my teeth to my upper lip, putting pressure on her hood. She rose quick and she came, rocking her hips around the pivot of her ass, squirting me. The thick salt of her almost choked me; I wasn't ready and I laughed and coughed. She grinned broadly.

"You like that."

She gathered the wetness with her hand and dragged it up across her belly.

"Let's go over there."

Like me, she'd noticed a rope swing hanging from a wide old buttonwood. There was a truck radial tied to the swinging end, the rubber so ancient it was chalk grey. She took my hand and, naked, but for those boots, led me over. She stuck her ass through the swing and spun round to present it to me, a huge

California peach, and her split opened right up. Her neat, furrowed little butthole was twitching. What a great sight she really was.

There was a polish of sweat, bright and fresh across her. It all looked so new and ripe, I almost didn't want to pick it. I licked at the base of her spine where a trickle was forming. It felt real good on my tongue. The earthy smell of her ass led me down and I twisted my tongue hard in her hole, just getting through the muscle holding it tight, getting a taste of the thing.

"Oh, God that feels good. Oh, God, come on, Jack, get it inside me."

I licked up her back as far as I could and rose. My cock was weeping crystal clear pleasure by now. I slid very slowly into her ass from behind to the base of my shaft. The angle was just great and she yelped a little as she took the whole length of me. The heat inside her and the easy river of her guts was just a holy place to be that moment. Even though my legs were kind of splayed and the muscles in my thighs were quick to ache, I just swayed with the rhythm.

She'd closed her eyes and was moaning and breathing real hard. My hands spread across the flange of her hips and I was driving firm but slow in her. She grabbed at the stony rubber of the tyre, her fingers clawing as she came. I held her firmly, my hands pulling her down upon me. My tip seemed to be hitting her heart, it felt so deep, and the throb of her insides gripped me. We swung away like two jack rabbits, and I damn near blacked out as I shot off. I was shuddering at the knees. I fell back on my butt on the earth and just laughed. Her ass looked real cute sitting in that truck tyre, all hot and wet and raw.

She joined me and we sat together, letting the dapple of the sun through the trees flick over us, our butts on the earth. I guess we lay down then, with me holding her, in the dust. We must have fallen asleep, bound together in that dirt pan.

When I finally wakened it was maybe an hour later. Tanii was gone, the car standing cold. When I checked I could see my knapsack was gone too, and the last fifty bucks I had on me gone with it.

I had to smile. I didn't mind, not then, not now, as I get to thinking of her. It's like some far-off highway. I see the sun shining on the blacktop up ahead . . . and her . . . waiting by the roadside.

HOUSE KEEPING

Nnenna Marcia

Nnenna Marcia is a pseudonym for a Nigerian writer living in London. By day she tells other people's stories for major news organisations, and by night she scribbles her own. She is an incessant reader and prefers make-believe to real life because it is so much easier and – 'she gets to play God'. She writes stories about strong African women, sex, sexuality and relationships, her inspiration drawn from her life in West Africa. She brings an exciting new voice to the stream of talent emerging from that continent. *Africa Hot* is her first anthology of short stories, some of which have appeared in the *Erotic Review*. Currently, she is working on a sequel to the novella contained within *Africa Hot*.

My madam is travelling again and I know there will be no sleep for me this night. Turning away my Oga's roving hands takes all night but even that is not the worst thing that will happen. The worst thing is that I will enjoy the chase; his breath in my ear, his masculine smell, his deep voice and the way he can say something innocent and make it seem very dirty. Luckily, I will feel bad about enjoying it, so I have not lost my conscience.

I have been in this household barely a year and already my madam has been out of the country eight times. Each time Oga has got a little bolder. The first weekend my madam left the country, I had just been their house help for three weeks. My Oga's friends came over and they played Wot all night, laughing and sharing stories over the juvenile game, drinking bottles of Remy Martin and Star beer and eating suya. The smell of the roasted-spiced suya meat hung in the air and made my mouth water. After they left, my Oga asked me to serve him the palm wine which had come over from Ibadan that morning and which he had hidden from his friends.

"Come here, Sylvia. Take a sip."

"Sah?" I asked.

"Come and take a sip, don't be a bush girl."

I looked at the cold glass in my Oga's hand and stood where I was. I didn't want to offend my master but how could I sip from his glass? My mother had trained me well and I knew that drinking palm wine from any man's cup was forbidden, unless the man in question had paid your bride price or was your father. I had neither of those in my life.

"Tans sah," I shook my lowered head.

"Come and take a drink, *osiso*! The yeast is good for your eyes. And besides,

your mother entrusted you to us. I would rather have you drink palm wine in my house than have your head turned by all those useless agbero boys and their ogogoro – that local gin is deadly."

I took a couple of steps towards him, took the cold glass from his outstretched hand and I took a sip. The cold sweet liquid went down my throat like it was made from coconut oil. I tried to give it back.

"Drink a little more," Oga insisted. "You'll need to get used to the way it tastes. No man should turn your head . . ." His voice faded away as I took another cool sip. And a bigger gulp . . .

"Easy, easy! *Ngwa*, give me the glass. I didn't say you should finish it!" His eyes laughed at me. I handed back the glass shyly and thanked him again. My head swam as the alcohol pumped through my virgin system and I stumbled.

I didn't even see Oga leave the sofa but his hand was on my back, steadying me. I froze at the unfamiliar touch of a relative stranger.

"Sylvia, are you alright?" I opened my eyes and looked into his deep, brown ones. The skin under my nose started to itch and I knew I was beginning to sweat. Oga was a beautiful man. No sooner had the thought formed than I noticed he was lightly rubbing my back. I looked at him in alarm. He smiled.

"Go to bed, Sylvia. I shouldn't have let you drink this much." His thumb stroked the skin on my neck as if I was a child and yet, not a child.

"Goo'nait sah." My hips swayed as I walked away. I could feel my Oga's eyes on them.

After that day I felt ashamed whenever my madam was kind to me and as she was kind all the time, it meant that I lived under a heavy cloud of remorse. I was already a hard worker but I doubled my efforts; I scrubbed and cleaned and scoured pots and pans with twice the effort that I normally put in. I learned how to keep house like Madam liked and soon she put me in charge of the gardener and the water tanker accounts, for the times when she wasn't around. I learned to read better, speak with a lighter accent and eat the tasty foreign foods which Madam cooked. I anticipated my madam's every wish.

It was the least I could do for the woman who saved me from hawking sachets of water on the dusty streets of Lagos. I still don't know what had possessed her to wind down the windows of her car in Oshodi, where the market stalls spilled out onto the expressway, leaving it little more than a snail's trail, where thieves targeted people in expensive cars, snatching costly jewellery, watches and handbags that were not stowed away under car seats. Even drivers that didn't have ACs preferred to bake gradually in the infamous stalled traffic than wind down their windows for a respite from the heat.

And yet she had, my madam. She had wound down her window and beckoned to me and immediately thirty odd hawkers and as many thieves rushed to her window, shouting their wares at her. *"Gala sausage, gala, gala!"*, *"Aunty you wan' pure water?"*, *"Fine madam, this toothbrush go wash ya mouth well, well"*, *"Buy banana, buy groundnut!"* My madam kept her eyes on me and ignored everyone else. I pushed my way to the front and relished the blast of cool air coming from the powerful air conditioner in the plush interior.

"Give me pure water." She barely moved her lips and her voice was as cool as the inside of her car. She kept her eyes on mine as I fumbled through the layers

and layers of insulating jute in my container to find the coldest sachet. Then I saw the untouched bottle of ice-cold water in a holder in front of her on the passenger's seat and frowned.

"Aunty, why you wan' make I give you pure water if you neva drink de one you get?"

"You this bush gal, gerrout from there!" hissed one of my mates behind me. "This fine aunty talk say make you give am water, you still dey question am?" He switched from pidgin to what he considered a better form of English. "Fine aunty, take dis water. Is cold well, well." My madam laughed in her throat, showing a glimpse of white, white teeth.

"You're observant. I knew you were special when I saw you," she said. "Where did you get that thing on your head?"

I touched the wood and fabric contraption I used to keep the sun from heating up my scalp. I had sewn together scraps of cloth collected from Iya Wunmi, the local seamstress, and attached it to a wooden frame which I wore fitted to my crown. Everyone thought it was funny but it worked for me. "Na me do am," I frowned. I was prepared to defend it. The hot sand and broken asphalt crunched underneath my feet as I walked alongside the slow-moving car still hoping to make a sale in spite of my smart mouth.

"You're creative too. How would you like to work for me?"

Just like that.

My mother took some convincing but by the time she saw my elegant, light-skinned madam, acting as if my poor, tattered mother was her superior, she agreed. The first night she spent at the three-storey house on the quiet, tree-lined street, my madam treated her as if she were a queen and told her she could come and visit whenever she wanted. The next day madam personally made my mother's breakfast, gave her gifts of local wax prints and money and made sure that one of the drivers could take her back to the slums, where we lived. My mother prayed over her gifts, took me aside and spoke plainly with me.

"You are my only child. I have nobody else. God is blessing you through me. Let favour continue to flow into our family. Please do not let me be disgraced."

I already have his dinner laid out when Oga returns from the airport that night. He eats quietly and goes to bed. I toss and turn in my bed and finally settle into an uneasy sleep in the early hours of the morning. The next night is the start of the weekend. A couple of his friends and their wives and girlfriends come to pick him up from the house in their flashy cars with their booming sound systems. I know he means to drink as he does not leave in his own car so I stay up to let him in. I needn't have bothered. Oga does not come home.

The next morning I am still trying to sleep when my intercom rings.

"Hello?" I ask, weary with emotional turmoil.

"I need some breakfast. Bring a glass of *palmie* as well, my head is splitting."

I knock three times on the door and wait for a bit before I turn the handle. Oga is sitting on the bed in a robe with his gorgeous calves exposed. He is on the phone and from the sexy way his baritone is rumbling I know he is talking to madam. I feel a pang of sadness when he doesn't even look up to acknowledge me. I put down the tray and feel my throat closing up.

"Sir . . . I . . ." He waves me away. I burst into tears.

"What is it?" he asks in alarm. I cannot answer him. I am heaving sobs and the sadness is threatening to tear out my chest. "I don't know what is wrong with her, she just started crying," he is explaining to my madam. He hands the phone to me.

"Hello?" she says.

I try to speak but I cannot. A fresh wave of sobbing and sniffling wracks my body.

"Sylvia, stop crying. I know you are upset because my husband is not talking to you." She chuckles. "Ask yourself why it matters to you so much that he is acting this way?" My madam is firm and calm.

"Ma . . . ma?" I bleat in shock as her meaning dawns on me.

"You think I don't know? You like him; he likes you. What are you waiting for?"

"But madam . . . I . . . he is your husband and I am not supposed to . . . I mean you have been so kind to me and I am repaying you with evil thoughts." I am crying again.

"Shhhhhh . . . I admire your respect for me, but don't you like your Oga?" I look over at him, leaning back against the pillows now, his robe open to expose his strong thighs.

"Yes, ma." My head is spinning at just how much. I dare not hope. I try not to disturb what feels like a beautiful daydream by breathing.

"Well, he likes you too Sylvia. He is only a bit hurt that you did not give in to him like most women would. You know how men can be."

I think about the rough street boys I hawked with, their rough language and their even rougher hands, taking whatever they wanted. "No, ma," I answer.

"Look after my husband, Sylvia."

I hand the phone to my master who listens, smiles and hangs up. "So, you like me, do you? Come here and show me how."

I walk towards him, my tight pink Chinese silk dress constricting my movements somewhat. It is a gift from one of my madam's travels and it used to be split to the thigh but I sewed it up to save some decency. Oga frowns, leans forward and rips the slit to its original height. "That's better." He shrugs off his robe in one fluid movement and stands naked as the day he was born.

My Oga is beautiful. His skin glows coffee brown and I can feel the heat coming from him in waves. He pulls me towards him and kisses me, sucking my lower lip and tongue. I kiss him back, slobbering all over his gorgeous face. He laughs. "Easy Sylvia, easy," he says, but I cannot wait. I kneel down in front of him and shove his hot member into my mouth. It is so sweet that I almost pass out. The skin on it is stretched out so smoothly that more saliva pours from my mouth. I clasp his smooth muscular thighs, I travel the length of his long legs, I grab his tight bum, and I fondle his balls. My hands are everywhere at the same time. Oga is thrusting in my mouth on tiptoe and I swallow his length up, stuffing him deep in my throat.

"Easy Sylvia, easy," my Oga's voice is husky and he is hissing as if he is in pain. I know I am doing this right. If you want to survive rape on the streets . . . I shake the thought from my head and concentrate on my master's shaft. I lick

along its length and suck on its head, breaking only to spit in my right hand. I work the spittle all over my index finger and stick it slowly in his arsehole without hesitating. The element of surprise had worked in my favour many times with boys who thought they knew everything.

"Mmmh, Sylvia, oh Sylvia . . . mmmmmm, Sylviaaaaaa," he draws out my name and I smile to myself. It doesn't matter how masculine they are, the fingers always seem to work the magic. I change from a kneeling position to a squat and rub my engorged clit all over his outstretched leg. I can barely keep up with all my movements and we are both getting too excited. I thrust my finger deeper into Oga's receptive arsehole and rub around . . .

"Wait," Oga orders. He reaches down and snaps the clasps across my breasts, freeing them from the tight fabric. He slides his fingers into my overzealous nether and comes away with juice with which he masturbates himself, leaning back and pointing himself at my nipples. They point back at him.

"Sylvia, touch your breasts for me." Oga is biting his lips and masturbating faster and faster. I jiggle my breasts in and pull my nipples. I try to suck on my own nipples, as he cums on them, warm and slippery, stabbing the air with his member. I rub this all over my breasts until it disappears. Oga is still very, very hard.

"Oga, kiss me now." He smiles and makes for my mouth. I stop him by sitting on the bed and spreading my legs for him. "I want to know what it feels like." I had seen him and my madam on the living-room sofa in the middle of the afternoon, coming in through the kitchen door from an early market run. I peered round the wall; my madam's yellow-banana legs pointed straight in the air. For a moment I thought my Oga had seen me.

He laughs loud and long and I know my suspicions are correct. "Spread your legs wider, darling."

I cry, I scream, I beg for more. Oga sticks his efficient tongue in all my three holes. In my ecstasy I abandon my carefully cultivated English. "Oga ah take God beg you, chop am, chop am o, e dey sweet me!"

By the time Oga finally enters me from behind, I have abandoned pidgin English for my local language, *"Suga m! Suga m o!"* I scream, not caring that the drivers can hear. Oga and I spend all day, eating each other and drinking from each other. I worship his body, with spittle and tears. He christens me with the milky glass of palm wine and laps it all up.

I am a good maid; madam will be pleased.

MRS SALAD WOMAN

Nnenna Marcia

Nnenna Marcia is a pseudonym for a Nigerian writer living in London. By day she tells other people's stories for major news organisations, and by night she scribbles her own. She is an incessant reader and prefers make-believe to real life because it is so much easier and – 'she gets to play God'. She writes stories about strong African women, sex, sexuality and relationships, her inspiration drawn from her life in West Africa. She brings an exciting new voice to the stream of talent emerging from that continent. *Africa Hot* is her first anthology of short stories, some of which have appeared in the *Erotic Review*. Currently, she is working on a sequel to the novella contained within *Africa Hot*.

Ejike tasted salt and knew that he was bleeding. He put his hand to the corner of his mouth and wiped. It came away stickier than blood should be. Straddling the gutter on the road in front of a dressmaker's shop, he surveyed the damage to his face in the glass door. The blood was coming from his nose. A reddish-brown trail covered the right side of his face from his left nostril; a result of the wind he whipped up as he ran from the school grounds. He tilted his head to get a better view of the nostril. The inside was black. It was getting difficult to breathe from it. He pinched the right nostril and blew hard. A clot fell into the gutter slime. He buttoned his shirt and went on his way, ignoring the women staring him down in the shop.

Damn Alex and his big mouth, he thought. It was Alex who had called his mother a whore. It was Alex who had alerted the whole school to his secret shame and forced him to fight for her honour. But he had since decided that Alex was not the cause of his anger. His mother and her lover were. That was why he was on his way now, to see this man's wife. It had to end. Ejike pushed the gate open and scanned the ground-floor flats. Even without looking at the number scribbled on his palm, he knew this to be the right place. It was the only flat he could see that had flower pots in the veranda. The balconies of the upper flats were covered in the usual family-friendly bric-a-brac; mops drying in the sun, ironing boards, buckets and water containers.

He pressed the button set into the doorframe and listened. The whole compound sat still and heavy in the midday sun. All along the walls, lizards nodded, too lazy to lick at the ants crawling into the cracks in the concrete. Ejike pressed the bell again, going through his plan in his mind. It didn't go past 'Tell his wife' before but now he was calmer, he thought about his mother. What if this wife did something to her? What if she was the violent sort? Maybe he

made a mistake in coming? He knocked on the door before he could change his mind.

"Yes? How may I help you?" The woman standing in the next doorway sounded as if she wanted to do anything but help.

"Good afternoon, Ma. I am looking for your neighbour, the one whose husband sells salad items."

"Oh? And what would a schoolboy want with my neighbour, wife of the one who sells salad items? Should you not be in school?" Ejike felt his nostrils widen. He knew the woman was taunting him but he didn't know why. He straightened.

"I have some important business to discuss with her, Ma. It's between me and her. Please can you tell me when she will be back? I must speak with her. It is about her husband." The woman raised an eyebrow. "I guess you had better come in," she said. Ejike hesitated. "I'm the woman you are looking for, little boy. This flat is the same as that one. You were knocking on my bedroom." Her feet sunk into the floor. "Take your shoes off; I can't have you dirtying my carpet." He waited until he was sure she was not trying to start a fire with her shuffling and followed her to the middle of the room. The woman took an armchair.

"Speak. What do you want to tell me that was so important, you had to leave school to find me? And who are you?"

"Never mind who I am, it's what I want to say that is important. Ma," Ejike added the last bit as an afterthought. He clenched a fist. It would not do to lose his calm now. He would just say what he needed to and he would not have to see her again. The woman gathered the cloth of her boubou and tucked it between her legs. "Your husband is . . . He is sleeping with my mother. He is harming her reputation with my father's people . . ." He expected the woman to jump out of her chair, to shout or slap him even, but she regarded him without blinking. Ejike cleared his throat. "I am sorry you had to hear it from me. Just tell him to leave my mother alone. He should go and find other people who are not widows dependent on other people for charity . . ."

"Ah," she said finally, "so your mother is only sleeping with my husband because he is so charitable. Is her name 'Charity' by any chance?"

"Excuse me, Ma, but do not speak about my mother this way. She is a poor woman who is being exploited by your husband. Just tell him to leave her alone."

"Mschew," the woman hissed. "What 'poor woman' knowingly takes another woman's husband to bed? Are there no other men around to scratch her nightly itches?"

"Excuse me, Ma . . ."

"Oh you're offended by that, are you little boy? And yet you took it upon yourself to poke your nose into adult business."

"I am not a small boy!" Ejike blinked at his voice rattling the louvers. He sounded childish even to his own ears. The woman started laughing. Ejike watched her boubou ripple like a sheet of water. He imagined the body underneath doing the same and felt his lip curl. As suddenly as she started, the woman stopped.

"You are a small boy. While you were marching here from school to report my husband to me, did you spare a thought for how I would feel when you told me? Did you even think about me at all? Did you think of confronting your

mother maybe?" The woman clapped her hands together. "No, instead you come to me, the person who has done nothing to you. You come to the person who is already a laughing-stock because her husband dips his wick into other lanterns but hers. He cannot even give me a child . . ." She trailed off. Ejike eyed her body. He turned away.

"You think I was this fat when he married me?" the woman asked. "What you see on me, this body, is built from unhappiness. But I do not expect you to understand. You're a small boy pretending at being a grown-up. Maybe you are just jealous that my husband is giving your mother what you cannot . . ."

"I. Am. Not. A. Small. Boy." Ejike felt his shoulders expand until he was sure they filled the room. "I am a man."

"I am a man," she mimicked him in a whiny voice. "Show me."

Ejike knew he was breathing too loudly but he couldn't stop himself. There was no mistaking her meaning. She had gathered the folds of her caftan again. The more Ejike looked at the cloth wedged into the juncture of her thighs the more he could feel sweat beading on his upper lip. He inched his satchel around until it was hanging in front of his groin.

She followed the movement, licking her lips. "Oh. I see. A boy like you wouldn't know what to do with a real woman anyway. I thought you came here to get revenge on my husband? Well, here it is. I am offering you a chance to take it and for me to take what I want. You don't have to like me. You just have to fuck me." Ejike jiggled, using the motion to adjust the erection straining the zipper of his trousers. The woman laughed. He didn't give her a chance to continue. Passing the strap of his satchel over his head, he went towards the woman, pushing her further back in the chair.

"Ha! Big man. Is that how your mates do?" Ejike ignored her, pulling her by the arms until she stood up. He pushed her to the floor. The woman laughed again and again. Ejike felt the heaviness in his groin keenly. He kept it away from her reach, pushing up her dress.

"You are not wearing any pants?" he heard himself ask. The air left his lungs faster than he could get it in. The smells coming from her made him want to put his head into the melting heat of her vulva and never come back out.

"I was not expecting visitors," she said. Ejike watched as she spread her legs seemingly in slow motion. It was a different story. While the lips on her mouth curved in amusement, her nether lips were criss-crossed with sticky strands of clear moisture. It sat on the dark hair like raindrops on waxy leaves. Ejike inserted two fingers. The woman didn't move. He added a third. As he pulled away to add a fourth, a bead of her juice rolled down her flesh and pooled on the floor.

The woman yelped. Ejike felt as if something possessed him. He was aware of his hands sinking into the flesh of either thigh, grabbing handfuls of it, trying to stop the quivering that had started in his arms. Everything else was pure sensation.

Ejike licked and slurped. It was his mission to stop any more of her wasting. The springy bush cushioned his nose and he was lost. Her scent was nothing and everything he had ever smelt all at once; flesh, sweat and warm, dark spaces. He couldn't breathe. He didn't care.

"Oh. Oh small boy. Fuck me, you small boy." Ejike didn't know if it was the dirty talk or the insult to his person, but his mouth dropped open. His tongue stabbed into her, swirling around inside her slipperiness. Small boy! He would show her. He started to part the hair. The woman got his intent and did it for him, reaching down and exposing her clit with a swiftness that told him just how well she knew her own body. Without waiting for him, she flicked the nub back and forth with the index finger of one hand, while holding herself open with the fingers of the other. Ejike fumbled with his school trousers, watching the wet opening winking as her muscles twitched.

"Pussy, pussy, pussssssy. I will fuck your pussy," he didn't know what possessed him to talk like that. He watched the slimy hole pucker and clench like it was saying words his ears could not hear.

"Come on, lover. Let me see what you can do." Her eyes widened. Ejike was pleased. He knew she would die before she complimented him but that small sign was enough. Her finger moved faster and faster. Ejike pushed it aside. He sucked the nub deep into his mouth and chewed on it. The woman's thighs smacked on the floor as she opened herself to her widest. She grabbed him, pulling his groin towards hers, rising to impale herself.

"No," Ejike said. He could feel the dizziness building up again. He was going to lose it. It was like sinking into warm oil. It felt better than his hand coated with Vaseline, than all the girls ever played with combined.

"Ahhhhhh . . . ahhhhhhh!" The woman pulled out a breast from the neck of her dress and shoved its nipple into his mouth. Ejike clamped on. He could feel the waves on the flesh as he screamed into it. It was all over. He grabbed her shoulders and reared back, shooting, his waist jerked to spasms he couldn't control. Again and again he jerked, slamming into her. His pubic hair was slick with her wetness. Ejike felt himself collapsing.

"Is that it?" She adjusted so that Ejike settled deeper into her. "After all your boasting? One would think it was your first time."

"It was my first time."

She started laughing again. "How old are you?"

"Eighteen."

"This is your last year of school and that's all you can do? Were you sleeping while your mates were sowing seeds in the farm? You have a lot to learn. Don't fall asleep; you have to finish me up. Let us move to the room. And try not to scream again before the neighbours call the police."

Ejike thought he was better the second time. He had her years of experience with her own body and that damn finger to compete against but he held his own. By the third time, she was no longer laughing. But it wasn't until the fifth try that she finally screamed herself.

"Why did you ask me to come back at this time? I could have met you during long break as usual."

"My husband was around."

"I saw his car." Ejike picked at the skin on his face.

"So why did you ring the bell? Why didn't you knock on the back door like

you always do?" The woman was looking at him, twirling the curls in her pubic hair with one hand.

"Why do you stay with him if he treats you like dirt?" He reached out and fondled her nipple. It looked minuscule flopping to the side of her chest but in reality it was almost the length of his thumb. Ejike swallowed.

"Spoken like a true man," she said. Ejike smiled. She ignored him. "You think I can just leave him like that? Who would want me?"

"I would want you. I do want you."

The woman laughed. "You like me because I have showed you what your body can do. Stop talking nonsense."

"I can please you." He took the nipple into his mouth and licked around it as he suckled. The woman reached for his hand and placed it on her pubic mound. Ejike took it away, smiling.

"That is my point." The woman resumed twirling her curls. "I do not doubt that you can please me, but that is not all that makes a man."

"It is enough. It is more than you had before you met me."

"And so I should bow down and worship you? I should leave the life that I have with my husband and follow you, a mere boy who has nothing in life but his youth? And what happens when you get older, eh?"

"But . . ."

"But what? You think everything is black and white. That is not the way the world is. Who do you think will be shamed? It does not matter that the useless man I married, the man who could not even plant a seed in my belly has been fooling around with anything with a hole in the middle, no. It will matter that I seduced a small boy . . ."

"You did not seduce me. I came by myself . . ."

" . . . A small boy," the woman sat up in bed, chest heaving. "With a widow for a mother no less. They will curse me. They will gather outside my door to burn me if they can." She shook her head. "You think you know something just because you can make a woman forget herself for three minutes."

"It was more than seven minutes the last time," he said finally. The bed shook and he knew she was laughing. "Hey what is the matter?" Ejike sat up as well. The woman was laughing but the tears falling down her cheeks did not look happy.

"I will miss you, you know," she said.

"Where am I going?"

"I cannot see you any longer."

"Why?" His hand curled around his throat.

"My husband knows."

"And so? I have taken you. You are mine. If he wanted you, he should not have gone with others."

"What you came here to do is done. Now we must do it one last time, and after that you have to go and never come back." The woman reached for him but Ejike pulled away.

"Tell me why you are doing this," he said.

The woman let her hands drop. She cleaned her face. "I have told you why. What you choose to do next will determine how our last time will be."

"You are going back to him? Just like that? After all he has done to you?"

"What does it matter? He is no longer with your mother from today."

"Wha . . . ?"

"And he will soon be back, so please do what you need to do. Leave. Fuck me. Whatever. Just do it fast."

"I don't understand. You're going to give him another chance . . . after . . . after . . ." Ejike shook his head, clasping his slight erection that had risen at the profanity. "He and my mother . . ." He grabbed the woman. "Do you know what he has been saying to her? That he loves her? That they will be together until they both die? She wanted me to start calling him 'Father' but I will never."

"It doesn't matter now. He will never do it again. I have his assurance. I am vindicated."

"He will never do it again? Don't you have any self-esteem?"

The woman shook her head. "Small boy still playing at being a grown-up. Have you never wondered why all the women my husband buzzes around are of a certain age?" She laughed. "That man does not take unnecessary risk or else people would know . . ." She rubbed her eyes. "It doesn't matter now." She reached up to stroke his face. "I will miss you. You have saved me."

Ejike shook his head. He wanted to tell her he did not understand her but he rather suspected that he never understood her, that he never would. He braced himself on his knees and let his head fall into his hands. The woman stroked his back like she would a wounded animal. "I don't understand," he said.

"It doesn't matter. Come. You must go." She tugged on his arm. Ejike allowed the momentum to propel him. He straddled her. The woman's nostrils flared and she spread her legs, grabbing him by the hips and attempting to position him where she needed him the most. Ejike planted his knees by her side and refused to move. She raised an eyebrow. Ejike kept his eyes on hers as he kissed her. He could taste the salt from her earlier tears. She thrust her tongue into his mouth, withdrawing before his own tongue could meet it. Ejike's erection jolted with the need to copy her, leaving trails of clear stickiness all over her middle. He dipped into her, coating the head of his dick. Ejike pumped into his fist, ignoring the puckering coming from below.

"Please don't be angry," the woman said. Ejike pumped harder into his fist, meaning to deny her. The woman grabbed for him again, but instead of guiding him to lower, she pulled him upwards until he was almost across her chest. She gathered up her breasts on both hands. It was as if his body knew what to do even before he could finish thinking. He sunk into her breasts.

"Do you like it?" she asked.

Ejike could feel his reply in the million points of pure sensation bursting in his head as his balls grazed her stomach. He replaced her hands with his, wanting to leave an imprint of himself on her skin for all eternity. He thrust deeper, faster. The woman licked the end of his penis as it emerged under her chin.

"Ngh! Ngh!" His words refused to come out right. Her hands free, she started to finger herself and soon she was joining him, saying words that meant nothing and everything. Ejike could hear the slapping, squelching sounds as she teased the climax from her body. He moved her hands away and slid down. The woman put one nipple in her own mouth and offered him the other.

"Ejika, *odowu m, nwoke m*, teach me a lesson," the woman's voice rose. She tweaked his nipples with wet fingers.

"Yes, yes," his head cleared at her praise names. "I have marked you. Drunk you like wine, *nke m ka i bu*!" He recaptured her breast. Her moans told him he spoke the truth. He placed her legs on his shoulders and gripped her waist. "I am a man; I am not a small boy. I am a man."

The car was in the shadow of a wall, some way away from the compound gates when he emerged. He knew that car anywhere. He kicked the stones in the path as he went up to the vehicle and rapped on the window. The man in the driver's seat regarded him for a moment through red eyes and wound down his window.

"Yes?" the man asked. The man reached for the volume on the radio and twisted. The music blared. He scrambled for it and twisted again, cutting off the sound. In the absence of music, the toads increased their night-time chorus. "Yes?" asked the man again. In his left hand was a child's stuffed toy whose belly he rubbed almost absentmindedly. In the back seat was an infant bath and some more toys.

Ejike stared at it, understanding, feeling more grown up than he had his whole life. He had done it. But he could never again come back to the woman.

"Nothing," he shook his head. "I just wanted to say good evening, Sir." The man nodded and wound up his window. He did not reach for the radio. Ejike walked off, allowing the toads to guide his steps away from the pools of water in the potholes dotting the street.

LOVE ME, LOVE MY WIFE

Malachi O'Doherty

Malachi O'Doherty is a journalist, author and broadcaster in Northern Ireland. He was one of the longest-running commentators/columnists on any Irish radio programme, having been a regular on Radio Ulster's Talkback from its creation in the mid-1980s until 2009. He writes frequently for the *Belfast Telegraph* and is a contributing editor to the *Erotic Review*. His sixth book, *On My Own Two Wheels*, was published in May 2012 by Blackstaff Press. His biography of Gerry Adams will be published next year.

I don't like my brother Danny. When we were children he always wanted to be the senior twin, the boss. He'd decide what games to play. He'd be the striker and I'd be in goal. But he is better than me in lots of ways. If we tangled he would put me down. But then as a dancer he trains a lot. And he is clever with words. He writes ad copy for alternative medicines and press releases for a wee publishing house he runs on the side, turning out nonsense books on knowing yourself and keeping your bowels regular.

I bristle like an angry dog when he comes near. We should try and get on. He said he had a plan and I said I would listen.

"We'll swap wives."

We had met for lunch in Greens and Things. He had ordered a bulgur salad with yogurt and I had settled for imitation sausages made of celery and aduki beans. And he had waited until my mouth was full.

Twins know each other's bodies like their own. That's one of the most annoying things. I look at the way he rubs his nose and it is my way of rubbing mine.

"And you think they'd agree to that?"

I should have killed the idea.

Instead, I was thinking about his wife, Joanne. There is something that happens when you meet your twin's wife. She looks at you as if she knows what you are like in bed. Imelda looks at Danny the same way. We have talked about it.

She said once, "I wonder if he makes the same noises you do when he comes. He does when he's eating or when he coughs."

"I've never seen him come," I say.

"And you have to wonder if twins are attracted to the same kind of woman. Is Joanne like me in bed? We're about the same build."

"She has bigger tits."

"Would you prefer it if I had bigger tits?"

But now Danny was looking me straight in the eye as if he was selling some-

thing. "Why do men get jealous about their wives sleeping with another man? Psychologically, the other man has come into the marriage bed. But we are not like other men."

"No?"

"No. We shared a womb and a mother's breast and we grew up like pups in the one litter. I want us to love each other again the way we did when we were little boys."

Now he was making me squirm.

"Have you put this to Joanne?"

"Yes."

"And?"

"She didn't say yes and she didn't say no. I think if she was relaxed and enjoying a glass of wine with you and knew that I would never call her out on it – and I wouldn't: I think she'd fuck your brains out."

"And afterwards?"

"Afterwards, we'd go back to the way we are. No recriminations. This is not about them anyway; it's about us. But it suits them too because of that wee bit of curiosity they have about the twin of the man they love and sleep with."

Which left me feeling that I was the only one who was really against this idea. But that should have been enough to prevent it anyway. I wasn't going to go home and tell Imelda I'd like her to sleep with my brother? Wife swapping is wife swapping. It's about sex. Couples who are bored with each other agree new parameters. But I wasn't bored with Imelda. She wasn't bored with me. Was she?

"I've been talking to Danny," she said.

"Christ."

"He said you didn't say yes and you didn't say no."

"Well then I didn't make myself clear enough."

"He knows how you think. He's your twin."

"That's crap."

"Well, tell me," she said, "what do you think?"

"I think we are in a marriage that is exclusive to the two of us."

Maybe she didn't think that was a strong enough declaration of my love for her. Maybe I should have sneered at Joanne, mentioned how annoying she is. But I'd said what I'd said.

She said, "I think he has a point."

I felt the ground moving under me. And yet I'd just been given permission to shag Joanne, and that prospect started looming larger in my imagination.

"Joanne feels it about you the way I feel about Danny, as if we are already intimate. It would not feel like infidelity to sleep with Danny. It just wouldn't."

"But wouldn't you feel it was infidelity for me to sleep with Joanne? She's not your twin."

"In a way maybe she is; she is another woman who loves exactly what I love in a man."

"This is the sort of thing that breaks marriages. What if you got pregnant by him?"

"Even that wouldn't matter; his genes are no different from yours. You wouldn't be able to tell whether it was his or yours, not even with a blood test. But if you are

that worried, darling, let the thought pass. We'll do nothing about it."

And then I went into the kitchen and started chopping vegetables and she went upstairs to write an article about love and the home.

So how then did something that we had agreed would not happen come to seem inevitable?

I got an email from Joanne that night.

"What do you think of Danny's big idea?"

"I think it isn't going to happen. Sorry."

Why did I say sorry? I suppose, because I was taking on trust that she wanted it to happen. But whatever she wanted, she would read that as regret on my part – so she'd think I wanted it to happen?

"He thinks it would be good for his relationship with you."

"It could pull us all together or it could tear us all apart."

"But there is something wrong, isn't there?"

"Some twins keep what they had as children, can go on sleeping and bathing together as adults, are closer to each other than to their partners; some don't even need partners; they have each other. You wonder if it is incest, even. Other twins just go off each other. That's what happened to Danny and me. It's part of becoming an individual."

"But what if you have lost something precious? I see you both as nearly the same person. It seems weird that you wouldn't be close."

"That's what Imelda says, that it wouldn't be like infidelity for her to sleep with him."

"I would love to sleep with you," she wrote.

And from there, in my mind, it all became about the question of whether I would sleep with Joanne and whether the risk of losing a bit of Imelda was a fair price to pay. It was nothing at all to do with Danny.

That night in bed I turned to Imelda and said, "Why don't you just admit that you fancy Danny. There is something you see in him that you don't see in me."

She kissed me on the lips. She said, "There is nothing I see in him that I don't see in you. That's what this is all about."

And she made love to me that night in the reassuring way she does sometimes when she wants me to be at ease and content and takes nothing for herself. But lovemaking is lovemaking and you always feel better, whatever subtle messages are implied in the manner of it.

When Joanne suggested that we all have a joint birthday party for me and Danny, no one demurred. We would go to a country house hotel in Ireland. I think she wanted it as far as possible from home to avoid the risk of our meeting anyone who knew us.

Imelda and I did not discuss Danny's wife-swapping plan. If we had done we could have killed it. By staying silent on it we were keeping alive the prospect of a sexual adventure, whether we admitted that fact or not.

On the day before our birthday, Imelda and I flew to Dublin and hired a car there and drove five hours to Donegal. The hotel was beside Lough Eske. It was an old Irish mansion house run by an English couple who had restored it according to their notions of how the Irish gentry had lived. It was beautiful. The

menu included vegetarian dishes I had never heard of, so it would suit Danny.

Imelda and I unpacked in a large bedroom with a four-poster bed and sash windows that opened out onto the gardens and a car park at the front. Imelda inspected the bathroom and approved the brass taps and ran the hot water. She was settled in her suds when we heard Danny and Joanne arrive below our window.

"I think we should be honest with each other," she said.

"I'm sorry?" She was lying back gloriously naked. Usually when she had a bath I would make an excuse to go into the bathroom and see her. I had never tired of eyeing her all over.

"You want to have sex with Joanne and I want to have sex with Danny. We can do that if we agree."

"No, Imelda. We can have our fantasies but this is too dangerous."

"Well, I don't think so and you have my permission to sleep with Joanne, and if you do, I will go with Danny. It will be your call. But if I see you move on Joanne, that's my permission. And seriously, there will be no come-back on it. I'll never hold it against you."

"And would this be the start of an affair with Danny? Is that how you see it?"

"I don't know."

"Have you discussed this with him? Have you already slept with him?"

"No," she said, and I accepted that she was telling me the truth.

I could hardly believe what we were discussing and I was torn apart, frantic with anxiety at losing her yet, to be honest, fascinated by the prospect of having permission to have sex with Joanne, from herself, from her husband and from my own wife.

"It's your birthday. Think of it as a birthday present," said Imelda. "Now, give me a big kiss."

She stepped out of the bath and I towelled her dry and got hugely aroused and dragged her laughing to the big bed where I stripped off my own clothes and took hold of her, where I had to tongue her first because the bathwater had washed away her oil, and she smelt like the sea, where having sex with her felt like mischief too. She laughed at the end of it. "You see, we are made for each other. I have no fear of losing you."

Danny texted to say he would see us in the bar and we dressed and went down about an hour later.

He was at a small table in a corner with Joanne. She looked terribly beautiful and I studied her as we walked towards them. She was wearing a low-cut navy dress and her breasts were clearly much bigger and smoother than Imelda's. She rose from her seat and kissed Imelda then kissed me, briefly but directly onto the lips. She had such a soft mouth.

Danny smiled and hugged me. "Happy birthday, Bro," he said. "Three score and ten between us now. We should know better." And he laughed. "Drink?"

We sat down and Imelda told Joanne how beautiful she looked and Joanne said it was great to get away and that they never saw enough of each other. Imelda said she had been in Donegal when she was a student and would like to explore some of the places she had seen then.

"It would be lovely to go to the coast," said Joanne.

Danny and Joanne seemed to be very intimate with each other. Joanne would often reach across and give him a nice squeeze on the arm and a smile. When she got up to brush past him to go to the loo she bent over and gave him a little kiss. Imelda picked up her bag and went with her.

"Women always do that," said Danny. "Go to the loo together."

To me he looked a bit tense. When we were children I would immediately start crying if he was crying. It was as if we drew on the same pool of emotion. I never had to ask him how he felt.

"Joanne has never been to Ireland," he said. "I think she expected to see more donkeys."

And we laughed. This is what we were good at, joking to move the focus away from the things that were really on our minds.

A waiter brought the menus and we perused them to hide from each other and when the women came back laughing and in high spirits we drew them into a discussion about whether to go for the lamb or the salmon. Danny ordered a broccoli quiche. Imelda and Joanne discussed the wine.

The momentum of our combined desires, however confused, was taking us into a big experiment. I never felt I had the power or even the very strong desire to stop this happening but in theory I had. But on that first night we were all tired from the journey and the birthdays were not till the next day, anyway.

Better to save any plunge for the end of the holiday and then dash for cover to think about what we had done.

No one showed any impatience.

"Do you know there were signs in the sky the night we were born?" said Danny.

Both women knew the story that our birthday coincided with the shooting stars of August, the Perseids.

"Every year we go out to try and see them and we never do," said Imelda.

"But," I said, "you'll never see a clearer sky than here."

So we took up our drinks after dinner and went out to the garden and walked along the road away from the lights. I walked with Imelda, Joanne walked with Danny. They were laughing and at one point she stopped to take off her shoe and check the sole and put it back on again.

Soon it was completely dark. We could hardly see each other and our voices dropped to an almost reverential whisper as we looked up at an extravagance of stars such as I had barely imagined. The Milky Way looked like cloud from there.

Imelda took my hand and squeezed it. "Who'll see the first one?" said Joanne. "Oh there" and I caught sight of it, just like a large silvery star gliding across the sky and disappearing.

"There's another," said Imelda.

Danny said, "The waning moon will be up in an hour and then just that small amount of light will be enough to make most of this invisible."

"Really," said Joanne.

We stood in silence and watched shooting stars for about ten minutes, hugging closer to our partners as the chill seeped into us.

"Actually, I think I am exhausted," said Imelda, and we turned and worked

our way down the road and through the gate and across the dewy grass to the back entrance to the house, and I gave Joanne a little kiss and a squeeze and Danny did exactly the same with Imelda and we all went to our own rooms.

Imelda was almost asleep on her feet now. She flopped onto the bed and, as often in the past, I took off her shoes and helped her undress. This was a game we played. She wasn't drunk, just indulging the sense of being a floppy dead weight in need of care and cosseting. It was a way of closing the day without passing judgement on it.

I drew the duvet over her when she was naked and she lay curled and still. Then she sat bolt upright. "Teeth! I forgot to brush my teeth."

I would sleep better if I blanked out all thoughts from my own mind of the risks we were taking. Better still would have been to announce flatly that I was refusing to go along with it, but the resolve to do that never framed itself.

I didn't believe at all that this idea of swapping wives with my twin brother would bring us closer together. Yet when I visualised him having sex with Imelda there was something intriguing about the image. I dared myself to see the whole thing plainly, her clenching tight to him, sucking him even, wondering if I could be neutral about them giving everything to each other for an hour and instead of being able to contemplate this blithely, as I had hoped, I was, in fact, a little thrilled.

And what was that about? Danger?

Would I have felt the same way at the thought of any other man taking her? I lay in bed and set myself the exercise of imagining other men we knew, ploughing into her, slavering over her, and I found it all repulsive and scary.

Over breakfast, Danny suggested we drive up the coast and go for a walk on one of the nice beaches. We studied the map and picked a little town called Glencolumbcille. We went in our car, with Imelda in the front beside me and Joanne and Danny in the back.

We passed through the port of Killybegs, which stank of fish oil. The air was filled with the shrieking of panicked gulls. Beyond the town we were following a beautiful meandering coastal road from bay to bay, the sea glittering below us. Several times we stopped by the side of the road to admire the view and take photographs.

Then once, after getting back into the car, Joanne was sitting beside me and Imelda was in the back with Danny. In the mirror I could see that her head was resting on his shoulder. I followed the scenic route along a narrow road where grass broke the tarmac in the middle and then when faced with a spectacular view of a wide stretch of sea, I stopped and sat still and said nothing.

Imelda was kissing Danny. Wasn't she supposed to hold back until she saw me move on Joanne? Did she think she had seen me do that already? When? Had I been so transparent? I got out of the car. Joanne followed me. I walked round a corner and sat down on a rock.

"How do you feel about it now?" said Joanne.

"I hardly know what my feelings are," I said.

She took my hand and said, "Come with me."

I said, "I didn't think it would happen like this. I thought it would be tonight, perhaps, or not at all. That we might talk about it."

We were on a little river bank. I kissed her and she opened her mouth and took in my tongue. I grasped one breast.

Then she said, "You know, I'm not going to shag you out here and get covered in mud."

I squeezed her close and felt her thigh close against my cock. She would have known the state of it. I was suddenly almost dizzy with need for her. It seemed urgent that I match what Imelda was doing, not let her get ahead of me.

Joanna knelt down and unzipped the front of my trousers. She reached in for me and pulled me out like a stick through a thicket. "It's exactly like his", she said. "It really is."

And she stroked it a few times then took it into her mouth, glancing up at my eyes while I looked around to check we were not being seen. There was a cottage nearby with smoke from the chimney but no sign of anyone at the front of it. She stood again and I reached under her skirt and between her thighs, worked my fingers in under her knickers and felt fur and soft flesh and probed for heat and dampness. It was strange. My fingers expected her flesh to be familiar. She pulled away from me. "We are paying for a perfectly good bed. Save it," she said. "Later."

Oh God!

She kissed me briefly. "I will make it all up to you later."

It took me a few moments to get my breathing steadied and my zip up over the bulge. She said, "Let's give them a little longer then go back to the car."

We sat and talked about simple things for a while – I hardly know what – the view, the smell of burning peat in the air, anything. Then I heard the car door open. Through a gap in the hedge I could see Imelda bend to reach under her skirt to adjust her underwear. She'd perhaps had her knickers off or got them entangled. "We can go now."

No one said anything about what we had done. Danny and Imelda probably assumed that Joanne and I had had sex. I was like a crazy man; one moment panicking at the thought of my wife fucking my brother, the next almost frantic with desire for Joanne.

And, I was entitled to her now, like a penalty kick, for the deal had been made.

We reached Glencolumbcille and stopped for lunch in a pub. They were all cheerful. I suppose I was too, apart from burning with the kind of yearning that I used to have for a cigarette when I needed them.

And I knew that Danny could read me and would know that things weren't so simple as that we had had each other's wives and everything was now OK. He tried his charm, "There are no other people I would rather be with right now than you three. And there isn't one of you I could bear to lose."

I raised my glass of Guinness and drank to that. The women went to the loo together. Now Imelda would learn that I had grasped for Joanne but that she was making me wait.

From the pub we drove to a beach, Danny in the front beside me, the women in the back.

Imelda was saying, "There is a really gorgeous beach near here that we walked to from the hostel when I was here."

We had a couple of rugs in the boot of the car and took them down the steep steps to the sand and spread them out. There were almost no other people there.

I laboured to get my shoes and socks off and when I looked for a place on one of the rugs I saw that the two women were together on one of them and there was only room for me beside Danny, who was stripped to the waist now and looking impressively fit.

I wasn't sure about taking my shirt off. I was a little plumper, though I had managed to come down a few pounds for this holiday. I wanted to hear what the women were saying to each other but Danny slapped an arm round me and claimed me.

"Isn't this perfect?"

He said, "I know you're not convinced yet that we're doing the right thing, but you'll come round to it. What we are doing here is cementing a bond, something stronger than ordinary brotherhood and stronger than ordinary marriage."

I could make out that the women were more comfortable with each other and laughing, in that way they have of making you think that they see through everybody. Neither of them seemed to be worrying that we could be tearing ourselves apart from each other.

Then, as I was trying to explain, exasperated, to Danny, that he was being much too simplistic, I noticed that Joanne was on her feet over us. I looked up and she was undressing.

She dropped her blouse and bra down onto the sand and then stepped out of her skirt and knickers. A body always seems to have a bit of history written on it when you see it for the first time, the marks of the straps and knicker elastic, the little stretches on the skin, the traces of faded tan. You can't look at the crumpled darker flesh of a vagina, designed by nature to receive a man, and not think about the men who have been in there. You can't look at the musculature of a woman's legs without pity. This body was my part of the deal and my consolation when the day was over would be to snuffle there and then feel all over her with my hands and lips and tongue and take final refuge inside her.

"I'm going for a swim," she said.

"Good for you, girl," said Danny, granting approval that hadn't been asked for.

Then Danny was on his feet stepping out of his trousers and running, laughing after her, and I could have sat there with Imelda and together we might have mocked them and I might have recovered some way of being relaxed with her, but I said, "Shall we join in?"

"Well, I'll look daft if you do and I don't." And she pulled off her clothes and shuffled off her knickers and ran down the beach after them and I was right behind her.

My wife has a lovely body. It is trimmer than Joanne's and her breasts are smaller, but I like the tidiness of compact flesh and I have more faith in its health and vigour.

Joanne was standing in the water waving and laughing. "It's bloody freezing."

Danny came behind her and wrestled with her and pulled her down and she shrieked at him and jumped up and dashed at him to try and push him over.

I went slowly down into the water and swam around and Imelda stretched herself out and did a breast stroke ahead of me. She wasn't looking for anyone to play with, just plodding about in the waves on her own.

After a time she stopped and stood with the water up to her waist and her wet hair plastered down over her shoulders and breasts. The others were behind me now. I took a playful notion and swam close to Imelda and tucked my head between her legs then raised her on my shoulders right out of the water.

"No, Danny! No."

"It's me," I said.

"Well put me down, you clown." And she slid down my body pressing hard against me in her efforts not to fall backwards.

"I didn't hurt you, did I?"

"Of course not," she said.

Danny had waded to the shore and was now doing some of his dance movements to warm up. Joanna walked over to us. She said, "You two are the image of each other, even with your clothes off. I want a man who won't remind me of that pain in the arse every day in life."

"So you're going to leave him?"

"Yes."

Imelda was staring at Danny as he arched and kicked in the sand to music she couldn't hear, as if she was seeing him for the first time.

"Was it good for you?"

"For God's sake," she said and walked away.

Joanne and I walked behind her.

"Your wife has a lovely bottom," she said to me.

We had no towels so we all had to stand around, stretching to let the wind dry us. Danny suggested a jog up the beach but no one went with him. I was left there with two naked women, one of them my wife and one of them the lover whose pledge to me was evaporating.

"Take care you don't burn in the sun," said Imelda. "You know how you are prone to that."

Joanne bent over to pick up her knickers and step into them as if she was indifferent to me.

Imelda whispered, "I didn't think it would be like having sex with another man. I thought I was just taking you, more of you."

I drove us all back and Imelda and I had a shower before dinner. We met the other two in the bar and ordered champagne and toasted the two of us for getting older. And after dinner we sat in deep chairs by a log fire and drank whiskey.

Danny said, "Today, I think was very special. Very lovely."

Imelda left for bed first. She didn't say who she hoped might join her there. We'd have to work that one out for ourselves.

Then Joanna kissed us both goodnight and it was just me and Danny.

"Do you know," he said, "there is neither of them all that keen on this swapping game now but we could play a trick on them. When they were half asleep they wouldn't know which one was with them. You could have Joanne and she'd think it was me anyway, and I'd never tell her. Go on. Be bold."

I was torn between having what, right then, I wanted most or beating Danny for once.

"I've a better idea," I said. "You go to Joanne and I'll go to Imelda and we'll trust them to know the difference."

And I finished my drink and went to bed, and slept with my back turned to her, not sleeping well, despite the whiskey, biting my fist, cursing the fucker for having scored against me again.

THE ART OF LOSING

LaShonda Katrice Barnett

LaShonda Katrice Barnett's debut novel *Jam on the Vine* (Grove 2015), an Editor's Choice pick at the *Chicago Tribune*, won Elle Magazine's Reader's Choice Prize; was awarded the Stonewall Honor Award by the American Library Association and was a 2016 finalist for the Lambda Literary Award. Dr Barnett is a visiting professor in Gender & Sexuality Studies at Northwestern University. www.lashondabarnett.com Twitter: @LaShondaKatrice

It's cold on the street in March at two a.m. in New England.

We closed the bar down – a hoot since neither of us is the kind of woman who closes down a bar. Drunk or not, passersby stare. Even in 2013 in a college town, a black woman and a white woman laughing this intimately are unusual. "Burrrr." You tighten the belt of a navy cashmere coat, flinging the long end of a purple scarf over your shoulder. It was the first thing I noticed about you when we met – your elegance with or without a prop. A sheet of ice has formed on the parking lot since we entered Shay's Pub hours ago.

"I didn't drink enough." My teeth chatter, I'm so cold. Heat blasts from the slats on the dash – the Swedes showing off their knowledge of thermodynamics. You wipe the window with your sleeve. "Know what I feel like now?" It will be the first time you touch me. And though I have thought about it – you are my favorite distraction – nothing can prepare me for your next move. Honoring a dying commitment with someone who's not touching me at all has left me shaky, needy, unsure. You grab a fistful of dreds, yank my head close. My heart thuds in the walls of my throat fastened by your hand, fingertips boring into my neck, your brandied mouth hot on my ear. The promise of how hard you'll make me come sizzles like butter in a flaming skillet. I can't drive us back to your place fast enough. Only this city is not my city. "Who the fuck did the urban planning for Boston? The roads are like a fucking plate of spaghetti!" Your "left!" becomes my right. And 'round and 'round we go. "Apparently, you don't want to get fucked," you say in a tone equal parts acid and cream. A car runs a red light, nearly hitting us I swerve to miss it. At half past two in the morning, you order me to pull over on Massachusetts Avenue.

Cold fingers claw against my tights. "Little hottie almost got us killed." Tense, near tears, my barely audible protest seems to fit everything in my life at the moment – "but it wasn't my fault."

You kiss me long and hard, exactly the way I've wanted since you scooted into the booth next to me. Alto laughter and star eyes aside, you've done nothing to

deserve my utter compliance. Silk crochet panties don't help. Eyed them on the mannequin in the little lingerie boutique in my city for weeks before I decided – despite their likeness to a doily – they would be sexy on. (And, if I'm really honest, it was you I thought of watching the saleslady wrap them in lavender tissue paper.) In place of crotch lining, a seam of silk thread double-knotted right where it counts. When your cold knuckles brush past me there, pure delight.

Eighty-two-dollar tights ripped open, panties pulled to the side. You serve three fingers. "Well, little Miss Sunday School, what do we have here? It's a sin to be this wet." I inch closer. "Don't move. You move, I take them out." I've had enough one-night stands to know the moment you are inside of me that this is not that. Too many of your ways are going down in the book: your whisper-in-the-dark tone, the feel of your lips against my ear, the filth you speak – I won't remember half of it. Indelible though, the softness and strength of your thumb circling, circling. Beneath abrasive words, measured strokes. Behind my eyelids, a sheet of white heat. I've been finger banging myself since middle school; others joined the fun in high school, but you don't have fingers – spark plugs. *This rhythm right here . . . right here . . .* Your hand withdraws abruptly. "Cheater. Start the fucking car."

Checking the side mirrors, I join the traffic. You slurp your fingers. "My God. Drive, woman." The almost orgasm has cleared my head enough to deliver us safely to Brattle Street.

Suddenly it's freshman year of high school. I'm not shy about role-playing though generally it's discussed beforehand, mapped out: who's going to do what? We've had no such talk. If this is who you are, I don't know if it gives me the creeps, or if I want to marry you. The car turns frigid in a matter of seconds. Your silence feels like hatred. I search for clues to end this or not. The first lunch you spilled lobster bisque down the front of an ecru blouse, and I wondered about the size and hue of your nipples. You took quahogs off my plate; I ate your fries. There was enough tension to start an Occupy Movement when we shook hands on the sidewalk. You texted the cancellation of our second lunch. Too chicken to call. I didn't text back. For the apology dinner – your effort to entice me into forgiving your cowardice – you wore a short black skirt, a soft leather over-the-knee boot that hugged your calves exquisitely. Every word that night was unabashed truth and joke and flirt. I was beside myself in the goodbye embrace, inhaling long at the nape of your neck. From the beginning, your fragrance has mesmerized me but I don't ask what it is. For now, it is your smell, and it is divinely heavy this evening, our third and longest date – if I wasn't already involved.

Earlier we ducked into the Fogg Museum out of the miserable cold and squall of pedestrians slogging through sleet, each more pissed off by the unyielding wind off the Charles than us. You stood by me, scratchy, woolen fingers around my neck for a little squeeze a little too hard. You point to *Small Houses Near Pontoise*, discussing the flicker of brush strokes, Cézanne's rendering of color and light. You whisper a quaint story of growing up in Small Town, USA, which looked a lot like the picture. I am charmed but I am not going to sleep with you, nice old white lady. We will be friends because I'm nearly forty and I know how to do that. And, you're nearly sixty, surely you too can be friendly. I am not playing this game – not when I'm already losing one down the road. I push back

on the impossible dream of resuscitating that relationship, and I guess I push too hard because the dam breaks, because loving Ms. Providence has come with a price tag that blinds me, because it's been a bumpy winter for us – an emotional recession, because she and I are hopeless. You pull off a glove, pressing your thumbs to the corners of my eyes like an impatient mother. "Stop." For a brief moment your gaze holds mine then you look away. No questions, no note of concern. All for the good. I have turned over a new leaf. No more older lovers, no more lovers of a different race. I'm too ridiculous. I will settle down with someone appropriate. No more dubious looks on the faces of family members. No more inevitable endings. I will prove to the world that I can play it safe, fit in, be normal. (That's the thing about rules, though, what and who you break them for appear on the scene with a ferocity you are never quite prepared for.) Two kids run up to us. We look at each other wondering if the other knows them. The little girl announces that she's going to be a ballerina. The boy thinks tutus are dumb and has to pee. "Where are your parents?" we both ask. In a flash the children are gone. We share an elevator with couples holding hands, making plans for the evening, tomorrow, the next day. You wager me that, "The drizzle has stopped and the sun is out" – impossible given the weather an hour ago. You win your winter stroll by the river. "Chowder and brandy will be better enjoyed for it." We take to the esplanade at half-past five, strides matching, motorists north- and southbound unaware of the drama unfolding. Giddy chatter, the effect of cold bone and marrow. Half a mile, pouring out stories of love-turned-blue. "Never again," you repeat, a throaty laugh punctuating passions' fumbling. A great skua alone in the sky goes off course, swinging low then resting above on Eliot bridge. "That's right. It's too damn cold. Let others fly. Grounded is where it's at," you chuckle. Where I should be, I think, instead of lofty philosophy and question: You can't teach desire. Or learn it. Or fake it. So how is this anything but a gift?

I unbuckle my seatbelt first.

Before we reach your apartment door, the rough tug of my coat.

I pull the blue suede belt from the loops of your jeans; lean in, breathe you deep. Does it matter if I get the prize before tomorrow's loss? You cradle my head but when I attempt to unbutton, you push me back, hard. "Who's fucking who? Get undressed." I make a neat little pile of my clothes, trembling, and place them under the coffee table. From the other room, your stern voice: "On. Your. Knees." You return naked, raspberry nipples aflame, well hung with the aid of an indigo leather harness. "Take my cock and suck it. Harder. Put your fingers in me. See what you did?" Your hand around my throat, you talk me through a blowjob unlike any I've ever given. It doesn't matter that I choke, gag. "Slow down. SLOW . . . down. Relax your throat." You rock and grind your hips into my face, bridge your torso over my head to slide a finger up my ass. "Sweet thing, I'm gonna fuck your little hole soooo good," in the tone of the meanest playground bully. I draw my knees closer together to hide the glisten down my thighs. You release my neck, clothespin my nose, hard. "Cute as a fucking button. Open your eyes. Don't you dare close those beautiful fucking eyes." Soon to gag what I feel will be my last time – ever, you grip my head with both hands, grunt and slam into me with a final shudder.

We make it to the bed.

Bucking against me like a wild horse (– no woman has ever fucked me with such strength, intention, no man either –), husky-voiced chapter and verse of how long you've wanted me and exactly how, you drive the dildo to the hilt, coming against my ear in a moan that tears me apart. "Think you're the only one with a heart? I've got a heart, too. Think you're the only one afraid? Fuck you." The howl and chill of March wind seeps through the window as you collapse against the damp mattress. "Come here, cowgirl." As you like it – slow ride, reverse, atop your face. I push your legs apart, pull back the thick silicone lever. Pretty valentine. Sour gooseberry jam. Kissing, licking, sucking, I work for your pleasure, my mind fills with jasmine-scented warm air, beach grass, sea brine, the brine of you. Another season coming. *I don't want to want you like this. God help me if I should need you.* I break the umpteenth promise to myself, flooding you and the bed. *God don't let this end.* You are wide open. Perfect fit, knuckles against wet velvet. Rivulets when I remove my fist.

Somewhere between your lust draining the life out of me and four a.m., you're asleep; I'm hungry, staring at bare essentials in the fridge. Quietly, I set about two boiled eggs, a glass of red. Your nudity in the doorway startles and pleases me. The thick tangle of you makes me smile. In my eagerness to kiss and nibble and dart between the folds – more like petals than flowers themselves – I hadn't noticed how wild you are. The ache between my legs starts. I apologize for the noisemaking. Not accepted, you say. "Put the glass down. Turn off the pot. And bring the ice tray."

COMMUTE

Kass Goldsworthy

Kass Goldsworthy is a writer and editor. She lives in the San Juan Islands with her husband and their four children.

I was late for the boat that morning and had to sprint to make it before they closed the gate. The 7:05 is a commuter run, so it's always packed. I made my way to the forward end, figuring I had a better chance of finding a seat if I avoided the centre of the hive – the coffee machines. Sure enough, in a little nook wedged between the newspaper rack and the ATM no one but tourists use, there was an open spot. I tucked my messenger bag tighter against my sweating back, and did a little sideways shuffle to navigate the knees and laptop bags that clogged the row on my way to the seat. I sat down and surreptitiously tried to wipe the sweat from my hairline. I arranged my bag at my feet, then dug through it to get my book and my phone. I checked my messages – three from work since I left the house 20 minutes before and four from lists I keep forgetting to unsubscribe to – and was about to open them when I happened to look up instead.

There she was in the seat across from me, so close that our knees could have touched if both of us had slouched down and made a real effort to do so. She looked at me and smiled this wry, sexy smile. I'm not sure what kind of smile I pulled off in response. After all, this was the woman I had fantasised about on a regular basis since I first saw her months before. There was something about her that grabbed me. Actually, there were many things about her that grabbed me. One was the way she inhabited her body so easily. There were plenty of attractive women on this ferry run, but they had the pinched beauty and tight bodies of professionals. Their bodies were walking catalogues of spin classes, Pilates, and expensive moisturiser. This woman, though, walked with the rolling ease of a dancer. Her ass was high and tight and gorgeously round. I had imagined doing all sorts of things with that ass. Her face and eyes had a look that was distant and inviting and bemused all at once, as if she was remembering something sweetly sad or delicious.

She was probably in her early forties, and I imagined her as an art director or some other profession where the women wear sexy Italian clothes and drink whiskey instead of Chardonnay. And there she was across from me, her legs crossed, her sandals almost grazing my shoes. I kept my eyes on my phone, scrolling through inane posts from my sisters, forwarded links from my father, and the various workout reports that some of my colleagues insisted on sharing every day. My body, though, was electric with her proximity. I blushed a little, remembering a recent fantasy in which she played a starring role. Once I had

cooled down a bit, I hazarded another glance up. She looked up from her tablet at the same time and our eyes locked briefly. She smiled that wry smile again, glanced around and then casually ran her finger down the length of her skirt. When her finger reached the hem, she checked slyly on the passengers surrounding us. I sat against the wall and the man to my left was buried in his *Wall Street Journal*. Her seat abutted the ATM and the ladies to her right were busy knitting and talking about a recent IPO. The woman across from me, my ferry woman, slowly reached deep under her skirt and deep between her legs, her eyes fixed intently on mine. Then, just as casually as she had put her finger into herself, she pulled it out and sucked on it. I inhaled sharply and shifted to make my erection a little less obvious, though I could tell by the way she glanced at it that at least once person had noticed.

Then she got up and left. I pretended to read while I replayed the previous ten minutes in my head over and over. Immediately, I started to doubt if it had really happened, began to suspect I had made up parts of it. Maybe she hadn't put her finger all the way into her pussy, but then what was she doing? And why did she have to reach so far to do it? And why did she have that mischievous look on her face when she was doing it? By the time the ferry docked, my hard-on had subsided enough to walk normally, but I was still heady with the experience. I was standing in line with the other commuters jostling to get off the boat when she appeared next to me.

"Here's my number," she said quietly, her voice dusky and assured. "Text me tomorrow at 7:10, but not before."

Luckily, there was a breakthrough in the line that pushed me along so I didn't have the chance to make an ass out of myself.

I had just enough time to say, "OK," and that was that.

I walked up Marion Street as if on wheels, and that's no easy task. The street is so insanely steep that people straining up it are almost parallel to the sidewalk. My company is at the top of the hill and dominates several city blocks. You've heard of it. I'm in tech. But I'm not smart-guy tech. I do PR. I'm the guy who makes it sound like our business with China is practically a human rights campaign. And some days I believe it. On that day, though, the only thing that mattered was getting to the office bathroom so I could jerk off quietly in a corner stall.

The next morning I was on the 7:05. I claimed the same seat I had been in the day before and got out my book and phone. My stomach clenched when another woman sat across from me, and her friend plunked down beside her. It was 7:07 and I was facing not the woman of my fantasies, but two other women, probably attorneys. I looked around, trying to locate her shoulder-length sandy blonde hair amid the crowd. At 7:10 I still couldn't see her, but I texted:

Hi.

Nothing for a full two minutes, and then:

I'm in the first row by the galley. Stay there.

I replied:

OK.

And then decided I should include a question so that I'd get a response back:

How are you?

I hesitated before sending. Should I add a winky face? I decided no and hit send.

She texted:

I'm wet. And I'm not wearing panties today, so it's a little uncomfortable.

My cock leaped. I looked over to where she was sitting. She was in a sexy white summer dress. She glanced imperceptibly in my direction, rubbed her thighs together a little and nodded down toward her phone. I didn't know what to say. So I just texted:

You just made me so hard.

She wrote back:

Tell me more.

I didn't know what she wanted, exactly, so I just went for the truth without trying to be literary:

I want to feel that wetness. I want to put my finger up your dress and spread you wide.

I blushed when I sent it, wondering if I had gone too far. I snuck a glance at the passengers around me, paranoid that they knew exactly what I was up to. My phone vibrated.

What would you do after you spread me wide?

For a moment I had that middle school feeling when you realise that someone's getting you to say stuff just so they can use it against you to embarrass you, but then I thought I didn't really give a shit because I was enjoying the thought of fucking her so much.

I'd lick you. I'd plunge my tongue deep into your pussy. I'd grab your ass.

I hit send. A minute later my phone vibrated again.

Tell me more.

The window was thrown wide open, and I had no idea where to go. There were so many things to do. I couldn't even begin to articulate what and how. I looked across at her, at the ease of her sitting in that white dress, her shoulder slightly tanned. She had her phone on her lap, and was reading a newspaper.

I'd like to hike up that dress, turn you around, and press myself against your ass. I'd like to reach around you and cup your breasts . . .

At this point I paused with performance anxiety. What do you text to a woman like that? Everything I came up with sounded like I either had a mommy complex ("I want to bury my face in your breasts") or a porn addiction. I ploughed on.

I want to smell your hair, and then I want to pull it while I fuck you hard from behind.

I hit *send.*

The thing about texting on the ferry is that there is a pocket of dead air when you hit the middle of the trip. We had entered that zone while I was composing my message, so now the text hovered in the static somewhere above us. She wouldn't receive it for a full quarter of an hour. I imagined the space above all of our heads was filled with messages sent but not received. I wondered how many of them were dirty, like mine. I wondered also how many mundane loving words were caught in the limbo, and if it would make a difference if they were never received.

My ferry woman put her phone in her purse, and walked off in the direction of the bathroom. I considered following her, but I was already feeling stalkerish. She had started it, but I was beginning to think I had pushed it too far. The pulling her hair part. The fuck you hard part. Maybe she just wanted a little virtual cunnilingus and I sent her a rapey text instead. I wished I could pull the text out of the ether and revise it.

Across from me, the attorneys were comparing Cross Fit injuries. One was detailing her plantar fasciitis and expounding on her physical therapist's insight. She had her shoe off so she could illustrate exact pain points. Her friend was nodding vigorously and making little knowing sounds. I could tell she couldn't wait for her turn, she had the words queued up and was ready to burst forth with her own arch pain experiences as soon as there was an opening. I picked up my novel and tried to focus, but the words of my text kept distracting me. I felt a little anticipatory shame, knowing that what I had written might disgust my texting partner. I also had a low-grade hard-on.

We neared the city. I reread my message to make sure autocorrect hadn't messed it up and to see if it had finally been delivered. It had. We were out of the dead zone. It took all of my will power not to watch my ferry woman as she returned to her seat. My phone rested quiet and cold on my thigh. We docked. I stood up with the rest of the passengers in my aisle and gathered my stuff for the walk off the boat. The Cross Fit women had moved on to tennis elbow. They stood behind me in line, talking over each other. By this time I knew the first names of both of their physical therapists. I felt my phone vibrate. It's just a ghost vibration, I told myself. She's done with you. Don't check it. I checked it.

Ah, nice. Text me Thursday at 7:10.

My whole being coalesced around that narrow black type on my screen. Something profound shifted inside me and I walked up the gangway buoyed by the sigh in her "Ah." For the next two days I was in love with the world. I adored my co-workers and laughed easily at their jokes. I was the jovial guy in line at Rite Aid. I asked tourists if they needed help finding anything. Of course, I was also stringing out with anticipation. I checked my phone relentlessly just in case she had texted. Intellectually I knew that I was somewhere on the periphery of the periphery for her, but I held out a tiny, ridiculous hope that our encounter meant something to her and that Thursday was as tantalising to her as it was to me. By Wednesday mid-afternoon I was loopy with imagined intimacy and I sent her a text, which I immediately regretted.

Thinking of you.

I didn't add a smiley face, but I might as well have. So desperate. In the midst of berating myself, my phone vibrated. I leapt to check it. Work. I turned off my phone. I checked it an hour later. More work. I checked it at 1 a.m. A text from a friend and two from co-workers, but nothing from her.

On Thursday morning, I woke with a tight feeling in my chest. I dressed and prepared myself for inevitable disappointment. I need to focus on work anyway, I told myself. I'll text her at 7:10 just because I said I would and I'm honorable, but that will be that and I can move on to writing press releases. I boarded the boat and set up my laptop at one of the counters at the forward end. I opened up my work email and started replying to the messages co-workers had sent in the

pre-dawn hours. I looked up and was shocked to see her standing at the counter across from me. She looked at me expectantly. I fired off a text:

Good morning. Sorry I texted yesterday.

Right away she sent this:

Good morning. I accept your apology.

I didn't want to jump right into flirting, or whatever it was we were doing, so I hesitated. Finally, I settled on something safe:

How are you?

I waited. My phone vibrated.

Splendid.

The small talk was excruciating, but I didn't want to be the one to make the leap. I sent another:

Ha ha, we haven't officially met. What's your name?

I wanted to look up to gauge her reaction to my message. I held off, though, and pretended to be engrossed in my laptop screen. My phone screen flashed.

It doesn't matter. Tell me something interesting.

It was an invitation and a command. It kind of pissed me off. Before I could edit myself, I wrote back:

The Westin. 1 p.m. I'll text you the room number at 12:55.

My chest thrummed. I looked behind me out the window to try to settle myself down. Fuck. We had just entered the dead air zone. I had the balls to write and send the text that one moment only; I couldn't stand having it hang in limbo for fifteen minutes. I asked the guy next to me to keep an eye on my laptop and I escaped to the bathroom.

When I returned to my post at the counter, I snuck a glance at her. We were still in dead air territory, so she was oblivious to my idiocy. She stood typing at her laptop, her eyes more faraway and aloof than ever. She had her hair down and she was wearing a black shirt dress. She wore several chunky rings. It wasn't clear if one of them was a wedding ring. Suddenly I was certain I wanted her to receive the text hanging above her. Even if she rejected me, knowing that she would know how much I craved her filled me with satisfaction.

We exited the dead zone and I kept one hand on my phone, as if her reply would be instantly transferred through my skin. It didn't come. I walked up the gangway and up the hill, each step a little further from my fantasy. It wasn't until midway through my first meeting of the day that my phone vibrated.

Perfect.

A shutter slid open in my mind. The beauty of it made me ache.

At 12:30, I cancelled my afternoon meetings and headed to The Westin. Across the street from the hotel is this restaurant my wife, my almost ex-wife, and I always used to go to. It has pulsing music and these big, wavy glass forms all over – suspended from the ceiling, piled on pillars, stacked in alcoves. The effect is like being in a rich and fragile undersea garden. I glanced in, then crossed 5th Avenue and entered the hotel. The lobby was hushed and cool, humming with secret lives. I almost gave the clerk a false name, then remembered that it really didn't matter. I'm a frugal guy usually, but on that day I happily paid for a suite on the thirty-third floor. I wanted to be whatever kind of man this woman thought I was.

I got to the suite and checked my phone. It was just 12:50. I peed, applied some more deodorant, rinsed my mouth with mouthwash, and washed my face. 12:53. At the brink of 12:55 I texted:

3324

Right away I checked to see if it had been delivered. It had. And then it was read. I could see the little word cloud and ellipsis as she composed her message. Then:

At the elevator.

My stomach and groin tightened. I took a sip of water. She knocked before I could decide whether to leave my shoes on or take them off. When I opened the door and saw her, I relaxed a bit.

"Hello," she said.

Her voice was low and tinged with an accent I couldn't place. She smiled mischievously, but this time I was assuredly in on the joke. She had a bag slung over her shoulder, from which she pulled a bottle of Jameson whiskey.

"I thought this might be good for this afternoon," she said. "Do you drink?"

"I do," I said.

The whiskey gave us something to do. I got glasses, she opened the bottle. She poured and, as we toasted, she stepped closer. We stood inches from each other for a few moments, sipping our drinks and smiling. Inside I felt coiled. We both knew she would be the one to initiate contact.

Finally, she ran a finger along my collar. I reached for her waist, but she stopped me, took a step back, reached up her dress, and slid her underwear down. She had to bend down a little to get her feet out of them. The posture – the nape of her neck exposed and her ass tilted up like that – was at once awkward and sexy. I tried to breathe and stand naturally as she righted herself, looked at me, and placed her panties on the coffee table.

"I'm going to sit on the edge of the bed," she said. "I want you to put your face between my legs, but don't touch."

I nodded and took a sip of the Jameson. She moved to the bed and sat on its bottom edge. She unbuttoned the top few buttons of her shirt dress, revealing first a surprise of freckles, then the swell of her breasts, and the edge of a sheer black bra. When I knelt down before her, she scooted down and parted her legs just enough to allow me to press my face into her crotch. When my nose and mouth were almost touching her pussy, she stayed me with one hand.

"Stop there," she said, and pressed her thighs together against my cheeks. I closed my eyes and breathed in her humidity. My cock felt constrained by my pants, and had already made a little spot on the cloth. I tried to reach out my tongue to taste her, but she grabbed my hair and pushed me back into position. We stayed that way for what seemed like minutes, her sitting on the edge of the bed with one hand firmly on my head, me a tantalising whisper from her cunt.

Finally, she gave me permission to proceed.

"You can taste now, but just once," she said.

I ran my tongue along her outer lips and then pushed it gradually into her. She was warm and tasted sweetly, faintly metallic. She exhaled a little as I withdrew my tongue. When I leaned back I could see her eyes were closed and she was

biting her bottom lip. I grabbed her knees and stood up, unbuckling my belt as I did. She looked up, pulled me toward her by my waistband, and re-did my belt buckle.

"Are you free until evening?" she asked.

"I am," I said.

"Well, let's take our time," she said.

I laughed. We didn't know each other's names, so it seemed to me we had blown well past the point of taking things slowly. She chuckled and stood, then unbuttoned a few more buttons on her dress, let it slip down her body, and stepped out of it. She stood before me in her bra.

"We can take our time," I said. She unhooked her bra and let it fall to the floor.

She stepped toward me and dipped her index finger in my whiskey, then ran her finger from the top of her pubic hair to her navel. She dipped again, and continued the line from her navel to the little u of her clavicle. She brought her finger to my mouth, where she lined my lips and then pushed her finger in. I sucked on it, tongued it so I could taste the Jameson as well as the salty flavour of her skin. She withdrew her finger slowly, inserted it in my glass once more, and traced her nipples. She turned and walked to the bed, pulled the covers off, and lay back. I followed her.

I knelt on the bed between her legs, still fully clothed, still straining and sticking to my pants. Carefully, I ran my tongue along the whiskey line she had delineated, circling first her pale, erect nipples, then moving lower. I dipped my finger in the honeyed pool of whiskey in her navel, then traced it along the thin white rib of a scar that extended along her lower belly. She exhaled sharply, a tiny gasp caught in her throat, and tilted her hips up. I pushed her thighs up and apart, bent between her legs again, and licked her swollen clit. She held my head there, forcing me against her tighter and tighter.

Suddenly, she pushed my head away from her pussy. I looked up. Her neck and face were flushed, and she was looking at me with the same intimate and distant gaze that I knew from the ferry.

"Stand up," she said.

"You can fuck me now. Keep your clothes on and start slow."

She rolled onto her hands and knees, presenting her ass and cunt to me. I unbuckled, unzipped, and freed my straining cock. I grabbed her hips and jerked her closer to the edge of the bed, then pushed the tip of my cock gradually into the folds of her lips.

"Wait there," she said. I obeyed. She rocked her hips slightly and began to gradually press herself toward me, enveloping my cock as she went. I stayed still until I could feel her wet against my balls. I pulled out to the verge, then slammed into her.

"Wait there," she gasped. She clenched herself around me, and I gripped her hips hard. The juncture where our bodies met was slick. She reached for my hand and pressed it between her legs. I rubbed her clit, circling it, teasing it, increasing the pressure until she pressed herself hard against me, bucked and moaned, coming hot and wet around my hard cock.

She detached herself and turned around to face me. Her face was even more flushed and her hair was messy, damp at the temples. It took all of my

concentration to hold myself back, but I wanted to make the afternoon last as long as I could.

"Now for you," she said, smiling and moving back toward the headboard. She cupped a breast in each hand and thumbed her nipples, offering them to me. I sucked on them, enjoying the earthy sweet taste of her skin, then bit down until she cried out and tilted her head back in anguished pleasure. I couldn't wait any longer. I spread her legs wide, parted her with my cock, and fucked her fast and rough. With each stroke she gasped and held my arms tighter and tighter. When I shuddered and came she held my face, then held my body to her and rubbed her pelvis against mine and came again in a breathless clinging.

We lay together in a mess of sheets, in a room now redolent of sex, laundry and whiskey. She ran her hands over my chest, pulling lightly now and then on a hair. The gesture was so casual and intimate that I briefly entertained a fantasy of a future of afternoons like this, of evenings in dimly lit restaurants, of mornings in little coastal hotels. I sat up and poured us more whiskey.

"So, are you married?" she asked. The question shocked me. I didn't expect her to ask me anything; so far she had been all commands and observations. I especially didn't expect her to ask me that.

"We're separated," I said.

"I suppose there's a story there," she said.

"Yes, she –," I stopped, realising that she didn't want to hear it and that I was tired of telling it. I felt a sudden lightness come over me.

"Are you married?" I asked.

"I am."

"Do you and your husband have an agreement or something?"

"It doesn't matter, does it?" It was a statement, not a question, and it wasn't unkind. My fantasies dissipated; somehow their dissipation pleased me.

"This is it, isn't it?" I said. She smiled and pulled my hand to her breast.

"Yes," she said. I smiled and pressed her to the mattress. We kissed each other hungrily, our mouths rough and sweet with whiskey. We fucked and fucked, beyond regret and sorrow and betrayal, beyond strangeness and familiarity.

We see each other on the ferry occasionally. We don't talk and we don't text, but we acknowledge each other in imperceptible ways. I look around at the other passengers and wonder what they're typing on their devices, what desires they're holding back or enacting, how far they'd go to forget or remember. And when the boat enters the dead zone, I still wonder what messages are suspended, waiting to be delivered, but also wonder about that other space, the alive zone, where all the unwritten, unspoken messages are sent and received, where lives are commuted by strangers and lovers.

THIS IS WHAT IT'S LIKE

Kass Goldsworthy

Kass Goldsworthy is a writer and editor. She lives in the San Juan Islands with her husband and their four children.

This is what it's like to be married for fifteen years. It's the summer solstice and twilight edges in late, settling on the deck where you stay up late with your husband and Mike, drinking and talking. You share a joint.[1] Later, you and your husband fool around even though the two of you are camped out in the living room, where your children could catch you in the act. The act, in this case, is you blowing your husband.[2]

Mike sleeps in the adjoining room. Or he might not be asleep, you allow yourself to think as you clean yourself up. His shirt hangs on the towel rack and you lean over to breathe in its smell. When you return to bed, your husband is in the first twitchy stages of sleep. You lie awake, the taste of aluminum and wine in your mouth. You consider getting up to get some water, but decide it would be too much effort. Finally, you let go and fall into a deep, dehydrated sleep.

Someone is rubbing your arm. The moment comes to you in patches: you're not in your bedroom, you're in the living room; it's not morning yet, but it's close to it; someone is rubbing your arm. It's your husband. He bends into your neck and kisses it. He pulls at your nipple. You'd rather sleep, but you arch against him anyway. When he speaks, his voice is low and sure. He tells you to go to the bedroom and to leave the door open.

So you do. Mike is sleeping. You know that your husband is awake and listening. You sit on the edge of the bed. Your mouth is dry and you wish you had gotten a glass of water on the way. You rest your hand on Mike's hip and study the tattoo reaching up his back. He always did sleep so soundly, the sleep of the spent. But you would lie awake listening to the hum of the night, your mind a swirl and your body taut. You used to resent his sleep. His farawayness gave him peace but left you lonely and agitated with shame and desire.

Now you watch him in repose and feel protective of this strong man with the lousy lungs. You know that if you slip into bed next to him he will probably reach for you, but what if he doesn't? The possibility of humiliation sends a

---

1 Actually, you try to smoke a joint, but between the three of you no one remembers how to roll a proper one. So you improvise a pipe.

2 Followed by another act, your husband coming on your ass. Neither scenario is good for the children to stumble upon, but you're stoned and happy enough to feel like they'd survive the experience and even possibly go on to be productive adults.

warm flush through your stomach and groin. In the suspended quiet you can feel your husband listening from the room next door.

Finally, you slip into bed and nestle into Mike's back. You're hyperaware of every creak and rustle, every sound a message to your husband. Mike shifts, still sleeping. You stroke his arm and press yourself against his ass. It's enough. He stirs, then rolls around to face you, grabs your ass with one hand and reaches into your panties with the other. What are you doing? he asks, and it would sound like a reprimand if he didn't already have a finger in your pussy. It's OK, you say. He sent me in here, you say, your fingers combing through his hair, bringing him toward you. He kisses you hard and pulls you on top of him. He's already pulled his cock out and it's straining against your panties, which are damp from the two of you. When he squeezes your nipples, you gasp.[3] He twists them harder and a drop of milk emerges. He pulls you down and licks the droplet, then bites the nipple. It almost sends you over the edge. You want to fuck him immediately, but guess that your husband has a blow job in mind, so you pull back and scoot down between Mike's legs.

You grab his hips and breathe in the humid tang of his groin. You exhale softly and his cock twitches in response. You tongue his inner thigh, his balls, the length of his cock. The tip of his cock is wet, and you indulge in one full mouthful of him, pulling the whole length of him into your throat. He groans and grabs at the back of your head, forcing himself still deeper so that you can feel his balls against your lips. You pause, filled with all of it – the smell of Mike and the heat of his cock, the sound of your husband quietly masturbating in the other room, the memory of having your husband in your mouth just an hour before. It's dirty, and it's love.

You slowly pull Mike's cock out of your mouth and shift down to suck on his balls. The skin is smooth-soft and papery; his balls are firm but he resists keeping them in your mouth. You can't remember if he likes this, but as he pulls your head closer you know it's OK. You're squirming and would have fucked and come already if it weren't for your husband, who deserves whatever experience he's craving. You grip Mike's hips and run your tongue along the length of his cock. He grabs your head, pushes himself deep into your mouth. His hips gyrate as his cock reaches into the depths of your throat. He pulls out, plunges back in, over and over, his hands gripping your hair, fiercely pulling your head into his groin.

Then he pulls your head up and looks in your eyes. He pulls you to him slowly and kisses you. The kiss has the silkiness of his pre cum. It's a slow deep kiss, all tongue and teeth.

Suddenly, he's pulling you up off him, and flipping you onto your back. He hovers over you and his eyes say: Yes. The head of his cock presses against your cunt, which is slick and swollen. He stares into your eyes while he slowly pushes himself into you. He pulls your hair hard as he moves deeper and deeper into your cunt. It's excruciatingly slow and you tilt your pelvis up to take in more of him. When he slips a finger into your anus, you moan. He begins to rock into you, faster and faster, until he is pounding you so hard that your body is all pain

3 You hear a faint echo of this gasp from the other room.

and heat and desire and you, who are so used to keeping sex quiet so as not to wake the children, lose yourself completely.

After, you kiss and you make your way back to the living room. You are sweaty and achy and filled with Mike's cum. You lie down next to your husband, who slips a finger, then another, and another into your cunt. You reach down and slide in one of your own fingers alongside his. You kiss and grope and he fingers you until you both start to lose focus and fall asleep.

In the morning, your husband nudges you onto your stomach, spreads your legs, places his finger in your mouth, pushes your head down into the cushions, and fucks you. You come quietly, then drift back to sleep.

When you wake up, the two of them are at the kitchen table. The French press is drained, but your empty cup is set out. Their hushed tones abruptly end as they both meet your gaze and stand up to make another pot.

From INTRUSION

Charlotte Stein

Charlotte Stein is the acclaimed author of over thirty short stories, novellas and novels, including the recently DABWAHA nominated *Run To You*. When not writing deeply emotional and intensely sexy books, she can be found eating jelly turtles, watching terrible sitcoms and occasionally lusting after hunks. She lives in West Yorkshire with her husband.

He gets more daring after that. Not by much at first, but enough to make everything just that little bit more electric. His hand might brush my ass when we kiss, and he has absolutely no problem telling me to touch myself when I get to that overheated point. I even suspect he's starting to like it. That this is a nice, safe space for him to have some kind of sexual experience. He drives me to the brink of insanity . . .

And then I just take the edge off, while he watches.

Because he does watch now. I can tell that his eyes are open for himself, as much as they are for me. The idea of someone looking at me as I do the lewdest thing possible is starting to excite me, and the more it excites me the better he seems to enjoy it. He makes comments without prompting, and sometimes his voice doesn't seem so detached.

Or is that just my imagination? Mostly I think it must be – I'm in no fit state to judge by the time he starts talking. Sometimes, I feel like my skin is about to burn off my body. My face gets so red and so flushed I could almost call the cause embarrassment.

If it didn't feel so good at the same time.

Everything feels good with him. Even his most innocuous offers make me shiver – like the offer to let me lean against him while I stroke my clit. "Just lie back," he says, and I do. "Just let yourself relax," he says, and I do that, too.

"Take your panties down," he says.

Though he really doesn't have to. The moment the words are out they practically melt right off me. I freeze in the middle of what I'm doing – just sort of barely stroking underneath the material, primed from a kiss that had a lot of tongue and a ton of moaning in among it – and try to think. I need to get my mind in order, because seriously. Did he just say that?

Of course, I can tell he likes to direct me a little. But usually the direction is aimed at making it better for me. It skirts the edge of whatever he might want, never quite crossing that line. Most of the time, it seems like he never wants anything at all – but this, this, this. It means he wants to see, right?

He knows I kind of like to be covered up, to hide myself just a little – even from my own eyes. But somehow he seems to be asking anyway.

So what should I think here?

Apart from, *oh my God, that is the hottest thing anyone has ever said to me?*

And then he goes and says it *again.*

"Take them down," he says. "And open your legs a little."

I swear, I come so close to looking at him. The urge is enormous – I would kill to see the look on his face right now. But I fear that any slight movement might break this spell, and I don't want it to. I don't care why he wants me to do this. No long-held streak of shame is standing in my way. How could it possibly when he asks for so little and gives so much?

When I feel so safe, lying here in his arms?

Not to mention how arousing it is to ease those little cotton things down over my thighs. Suddenly I'm seventeen again, trembling and terrified, standing on the brink of something I'm sure will be so amazing. That newfound thrill is back, and it makes my breath hitch. I fumble with the elastic and shake at the thought, and when I'm done my legs don't really want to part.

But I part them anyway.

And I look, even though I've never looked before. I see how wet I am and how swollen, my clit like a taut little bead between soft, flushed folds. Nothing horrible about it, or shameful in any way – on the contrary. The sight makes me shiver, and I get this good hot bloom in my lower belly, and when he strokes the back of his hand over my cheek, I do something I would never have dared to before.

I kiss his fingers. I *lick* his fingers – which seems like way too much for me. As soon as I realize what I've done, I expect him to pull back or put a stop to things. He did the other night when the kissing got a little too much, and his hand strayed kind of close to my backside. But this time he doesn't.

He lets me do it.

More than that, in fact.

"Bite down," he tells me, the request so sudden and so strange that I do a double take. I even turn my head to ask – or maybe give him an incredulous look – and stop short only when he gets there before me. He reiterates in no uncertain terms, with a little added extra just to make sure I understand.

"Sink your teeth in while you stroke yourself," he says.

How could I possibly misinterpret? He even turns his hand so I know where he means, and the moment I do it I know what he really meant. He wasn't trying to please me.

He was trying to please himself.

He was obviously and completely trying to please himself. I can tell by the way he reacts – I bite and he kisses the side of my face in a manner completely unlike him. His mouth is all open and hot and greedy, and the hand he has on my waist definitely seems to move up a little. Some might even categorize it as groping the underside of my right breast.

Though I try not to. It seems better not to get my hopes up, considering they're already sky-high. He's kissing me and saying things, and my hand is between my legs . . . what more do I need? Nothing, nothing, and yet when I bite down again I get why I'm doing it.

I want to see what happens.

I want to see if that hand will move up a little farther, if his guard will drop down another level, though it shocks me to feel him actually do it. To hear him sigh against the side of my face and just ever so slightly cup my breast with that one big hand . . .

It makes me wild. Suddenly I can't seem to stroke myself fast enough, and my hips don't want to stay still. He doesn't even have to tell me to fuck my pussy – I do it all on my own. I slide two fingers in as deep as they will go, and rock against that delicious pressure. I do myself the way I want him to do me.

And in my most excited moments, I come close to telling him that. I think of filthy ways to ask and words that I could never actually say to him – like *use* and *cock* and *fill me*. I think of him coming inside me, making me sticky and wet, and all over the barest touch I've ever had on my body.

I still have most of my clothes on. He doesn't even graze my stiff nipple.

Yet somehow, I'm at this delirious point where all my boundaries suddenly don't exist. Thinking of him making a mess of me is really the least of my wild fantasies. I imagine his tongue where my finger is, making slippery circles around my stiff clit. And when he gets a hold of my face, when he kisses me as the pleasure reaches some terrible crisis, I see myself doing the same to him.

I kiss him, and kiss him, and think about sucking his cock.

But can I really be blamed when he asks me things like, "Are you going to come?" He even looks me right in the eye as he says it, watching me in that assessing way of his, waiting for some spark of telling pleasure. The second it hits he will know, I think – and I'm right.

"That's it, that's it – go on, honey, take it, take it," he says, at the exact moment I feel my orgasm start to bloom low down in my belly. Then just as it really takes hold – as every muscle in my body tenses and a thousand trapped moans and sighs press up against my gritted teeth – he does the thing that always pushes me higher.

He puts his hand over mine. He presses my slippery fingers over my clit, just as the pleasure gets kind of scary and I want to pull away. In truth, I'm desperate to pull away – any more of this and I'm going to make some really awful noises.

Never mind screaming – I need to grunt.

But he keeps it going. He carries on until I'm almost sobbing, drenched in sweat and near delirious, each thick pulse of pleasure so intense I want to tell him to stop. Instead, I find myself begging him to carry on. I babble about how good he makes me feel and how much I like this, always edging closer to words I know I shouldn't say.

What difference will it make if I do? He knows he can have me if he wants to. He can see how much I want to – so no offer is going to tempt him. He's incapable of being tempted, if this isn't enough to put him over the edge. I was practically a nun before I met him and look at me now: legs spread, pussy all glistening with my excitement, body arched as though someone just fucked into me.

No, no . . . he will never, he won't, he can't, I think.

And then just as I'm sure – that's when I feel it.

I feel his hard cock against the curve of my ass.

*

I promise myself I won't try testing any theories out. Yet the second he kisses me goodnight sometime around eleven the next night I just want to go for it. He had an erection, I know he did, and if he had one that means I did something to make it happen. Or he did something to make it happen. Maybe both of us together made it happen, in which case I simply have to find the right combination and I could give him some of the same things he's given me.

He makes me feel so sexually free. Not to mention satisfied.

And if all I have to do to help him is maybe bite him a little bit . . . well, I can do that. Of course I have no idea if the bite was the reason. The only thing that makes me think so was that urgency in his voice and the memory of his reaction. Neither is evidence of anything.

But I can't see any harm in trying.

He kisses me, I turn my head a little and just . . . nip him a little. Just enough to get a reaction, if he's willing to offer one. And to my great delight and overwhelming excitement, he is. He doesn't even hesitate or shift gears slowly. His hand immediately goes to that danger area it was in the other day – right on the underside of my left breast.

Maybe even squeezing it a little, if I'm being completely honest.

Though that isn't what excites me exactly. I don't flush hot and fire up for the cupping of it or the sense that he kind of wants to try me out – maybe get a little taste of my plump tits so he can consider them later. No, no, it's the *heat* that rolls off him. The fever he seems to descend into. I graze him with my teeth and his lips part, his lids lower, most of him goes all loose and lax.

I want to call it something silly, like *horniness.*

Yet somehow, it doesn't seem silly at all to do so. A great gush of sensation goes through me the second I think of it. *Horny,* I think, *eager*, I think, like some teenage boy suddenly set free, and my pussy swells against my already damp panties. My clit jerks, as though he has a little string around it and just tugged, hard.

Really, it's no wonder I pant his name. Or rub myself against him. Or go straight from mild kissing to wild moaning in under thirty seconds. I think somewhere in there I call him *baby*, which seems completely at odds with everything he is.

But it feels good to do it.

And he appears to have no objections. On the contrary – as soon as the word is out he goes up another level. He claims my mouth with his, and when even that isn't enough he pushes me back. *He pushes me back onto the bed and puts my arms above my head.*

Not in a forceful way, you understand. He kind of laces his fingers with mine and shifts almost as though the whole thing is a mistake. But I feel it all the same. I know it for what it is. He wants to get as close to the moves as possible, without really doing them at all. Tiny little rolls of his hips that echo the wild hump of a good fuck. Hands together the way that every limb on our bodies probably would be, if we went for it.

And that hot, wet mouth.

God, does he know how hot and wet his mouth his? How soft those lips are, with just that background hint of his thick stubble . . .

That alone would be enough.

But then I feel it, oh, fuck, I feel it against my thigh. So thick and hard and completely unmistakable. He definitely has an erection, and, good Lord, that knowledge is so much more intense than I thought it would be. I was sure I processed it the other day, but now I know I didn't at all. I still imagined it might be nothing.

I still thought he couldn't, or wouldn't, or that it was just wishful thinking.

And as soon as I have conclusive evidence I go all still. I pause midkiss, doing my best not to rub or press at that solid shape but wanting to more than I've ever wanted anything in my entire life. The very idea of doing it gets me groaning. I say his name and it comes out with twenty syllables, and when I pull back just a little way and see it . . .

That's the moment I lose the rest of my control.

I mean, obviously I try to hold on to myself. I kind of look without really looking, so he won't be made uncomfortable by my goggling eyes. And I don't loudly exclaim, or start asking a bunch of awkward questions, or tear his pants off immediately and hump him into oblivion. But I can't deny how intense the urge is to do all of those things.

Just the sight of it cleaves my tongue to the roof of my mouth. I think I start shaking, and I know I wish for him to be wearing anything but what he actually has on. If he was in something more modest I could probably deal with it a little better. Jeans would probably help – or at least help more.

Sweatpants are a fucking nightmare.

Why did I never realize what a nightmare they are? I suppose they usually seem so innocuous and innocent, on any other random gym-going person. Or maybe it's just that I've never seen a guy hard while wearing that soft, jersey-like material? I can't say for sure. I only know it looks . . . it looks . . . oh, it looks . . .

Like something I want to kiss, openmouthed and eager.

The curve of it is so clear, the outline of that little ridge around the head so obvious. He must be swollen there, and aching – just like I am. And if I doubt that for one second, well, there's other evidence for me to see. In fact, my breath catches in my throat when I see it.

He's so excited, he seems to be leaking a little. There is the slightest damp spot close to the tip, barely there, but no less arousing for it. I swear, if I wanted to kiss his cock before, then God knows what I want to do now. I think about pulling my panties down and rubbing my wet cunt all over it. Or pulling those slack things down so I can get a better look.

It's really a miracle that I settle for the slightest touch.

Though it doesn't feel like a miracle. It feels bad. It feels like throwing myself off a cliff. I hardly even understand how I do it – my hand seems to move independently of my body. It jerks forward and suddenly I'm making contact, and then after that everything is fucking terrifying.

An electric shock seems to go through me. The bad kind of electric shock. My teeth clack together, and more than anything I want to take it back. Pretend I didn't do anything at all. Make out like it was an accident.

Only I can't because he just got the electric shock, too. I swear to God I hear his teeth clack the same as mine. At the very least he jerks back, and his eyes go

wide, and he seems to want to say something without really knowing what to say. Probably something like *how dare you touch me,* I think, even though that doesn't quite seem to fit his expression. He looks stunned, true. And his body makes a bow, so he can get away from my hand.

But there's something else in his eyes, too. A kind of disbelief that has nothing to do with my daring and everything to do with the way it felt. I think . . . I think it felt good. I think it sent a little sizzle up his spine, the way his words and his urging send one up mine. His breath comes quick and shaky, and though he puts a hand between us like a barrier, I can see his hips are still rocking toward that touch.

So much so that I sort of move toward him a little. Not enough to get past his force field, but enough to get words out of him. Loud words. Wrong words.

"I can't," he snaps, at which point I need to make it clear between us.

"Even though physically you want to?"

"It's not about being physically wanting to. A corpse would get excited by what we're doing. Just look at you – your eyes are enough to turn me on. Sometimes I can barely stand to hold your gaze because it feels like a hand around my cock," he says, and I'm thankful that he pauses after that. I need a moment just to recover from the word *cock* and the sense of being complimented. In truth I could use an industrial fan and three ice packs – but I make do. I get through to the other side, where he's saying things that are a little less exciting. "My problem is that after a certain point it just . . . feels unpleasant."

"So you lose your erection?" I ask, even though I know what the answer is. I can see the answer, still so thick and heavily curved.

"No, not exactly," he tells me. "I just want to stop. I get certain images in my head and I want to stop. I have to stop."

"Would it be different if I bit you?

"What? What do you – "

"You seemed to like . . . I thought maybe . . ." I start, and then he gets it. A half-amused light sparks in his eyes – though when he speaks his voice is gentle.

"Beth, I didn't get an erection because you bit me. Pain is a good distraction, sure, but it's not what's going to keep me in the moment. If anything . . . it's . . ."

"Go on, please go on."

"I like it when I know for certain that you're enjoying yourself. Beyond a shadow of a doubt. If you so much as groan wrong, it will make me freeze up. I have to know you like it, and that I'm not hurting you or frightening you. That's what excited me the other day – when you said that nothing had ever felt that good. That was . . . stirring."

"So how about I – " I start, but end up cutting myself off before I can finish. His eyes close and I simply stop right there, and I'm glad I do. His words back up the sudden tension in him. They underline what I know already.

"Please don't make suggestions. Let me just . . ."

"Okay. Okay we don't have to. I need you to know at this point – I only want to because it seemed like maybe you did. That maybe you kind of do. But if I'm wrong . . ."

"You're not wrong. I feel very . . . frustrated."

"You do?" I ask, and it's all I can do to keep the eagerness out of my voice. He says that one word and excitement almost gets the better of me. Images flash

behind my eyes, and all of them are filthy in the extreme – or at least filthy for him. He could probably pose fully dressed on a chaise lounge and I would lose my mind over it.

So when I think of him in the shower, completely unclothed, covered in soapy slick water with his hand on his . . . on his . . . on that thing I can see through his sweatpants . . . yeah, that kind of finishes me off. If I was wet between my legs before, I'm a river there now. And though I feel bad about that, there isn't much I can do about it.

Not when he just goes ahead and makes it worse.

"Yes. Of course I do. Have you any idea how amazing you look when you come? Or what it's like to kiss you and feel that heat rising between us and see how pink your cheeks are and how hungry your eyes seem and just shut it down? I don't want you to think it's always easy for me. It isn't. I tried to . . ."

"Tried to what?" I ask, in a voice that could be carried away on a stiff breeze. It's a miracle I manage to get out words at all though, all things considered.

Did he just say *when you come*?

I think he did. I think he suggested that he has real and visceral sexual responses all the time, and most of them concern things that I actually do. He sees me getting excited and that excites him, and then he tries to do something.

God, I don't want to hear what he tries to do.

Except for all the ways in which I want to hear it more than anything in the world.

"I tried to masturbate the other day," he says, and my heart bangs against something inside me. My hands have made fists and my mouth goes all dry – though to be honest I have no idea why. I have no idea why all of these tiny things affect me so much. It's like that horror movie thing again, only instead of everything being terrifying everything is a turn-on. It even does something to me when he adds, "Needless to say, it didn't go well."

"So you get to a certain point and you just have to . . ." I say, too afraid to add any specific detail to the end there but just willing him to give it anyway. Maybe he does things, you know? Maybe he does things that make him stop. Like squeezing at the base of his cock or biting the meat of his own bicep.

He might. He could. I wish I didn't wonder if he does.

"I have to stop, yes. I don't physically want to but . . ." he says, and though he steers clear of any kind of exact descriptions, it still has an almighty effect on me. I think of his body suddenly, like some runaway freight train with his mind trailing behind. I see him as he has really been all this time – full of barely checked desire that he tries desperately to master.

And I consider how nightmarish all of that is.

"Christ. Okay. That . . . okay," I say, because what else can I do? I have no helpful advice for him. He has to fathom this out for himself, no matter how long it may take him. We could still be like this in a thousand years, barely making it to second base and struggling to so much as kiss. We could be, I think, as he searches my face for answers he might never find, not ever.

Unless he just grabs for them, quite suddenly.

"Do you want to touch me?" he asks, and at first I don't get it. I have to ask, I have to put barriers and provisos in the way.

"Only if you want me to," I tell him, thinking that I'm being good.

This is what he needs. He needs slow maneuvers toward things.

Or so I think, until he comes close to cutting me off midsentence.

"No, don't think about me. Think about you. Only you," he says, and I'm so startled and so unsure of what he might mean that I answer like a robot.

In my effort to be careful I go too far.

"Yes, I want to touch you," I say, and so he has to press on.

His voice is oddly impatient, for him.

"How badly would you like to?"

"I don't know if I should say. I don't want you to feel obliged – "

"I don't feel obliged. You can go ahead and tell me," he says, and there it is again.

That hint of impatience, so unfamiliar coming out of his mouth.

"Sometimes it's all I can think about."

"And in these thoughts . . . what usually happens?"

"I don't know. I don't know. Things. Stuff."

"I would really like you to be specific," he says, at which point the light starts to break through the clouds. I have to *want* it, that's the thing. He needs to know this is everything I need. He craves my lust, the way a man might after starving too long in a desert of *oh God, I don't want to worry about doing the wrong thing*.

And, holy fuck, I want to give it.

God, if only I knew how to give it.

"I imagine you stroking yourself," I try, but that isn't nearly enough. He prompts me almost immediately, and suddenly I have to face the thing I want the most.

The thing I don't even know I want the most, until it's right there.

"And then you show me how you like it."

"I see. So I hold your hand over my cock."

"Yeah. Yeah. You kind of . . . stroke yourself by using me."

"So you like that idea."

"I do. And I like the words, too."

"What sort of words?"

"The ones you've just used. When you say things like *cock* it makes me get all . . . you know," I say, and get a blast of double embarrassment in the face for my troubles. The first lot because I just told him I get turned on, and the second because I said it in such a childish way. You know – like I'm twelve.

Instead of twenty-four and so fucking horny.

"I don't know. Can you describe it to me?" he asks, and this time I do better.

How could I not, when he's looking at me like that and I can see his cock is hard and I know his hand is soooo close to that swollen thing? How can I not when everything is suddenly this exciting? All I have to do is literally describe what's happening to me.

Most of which he probably knows anyway, with his psychic fucking powers.

"My clit swells, and everything is suddenly real wet down there."

"That sounds good. That sounds like you like it," he says, and, oh, I don't know why that thrills me so. His words are so . . . simple and innocent.

They shouldn't make my voice waver when I answer.

"I do. I absolutely, one hundred percent do."

"Do you imagine me doing things to you?"

"God, yeah. All the time. Constantly."

"Tell me what they are. Tell me how badly," he says, and it's the *badly* that makes me do it. Or is it the hand he suddenly brushes over one of my bare arms? Maybe it's both combining into one unholy mess of *just fucking go for it.*

Certainly feels that way, when I say:

"I lie awake at night, thinking about you licking me."

Licking, I said *licking*. And when he adds, "I know where you mean, but say it anyway," I go one worse than that. I get worse. Somehow the undercurrent of hunger in his words just pushes me up a level, and filthy stuff comes rambling out of my mouth.

"Licking my pussy. Licking my clit," I say, and you know what?

I love it. I love it so much I almost don't hear what he tells me next. My brain is so preoccupied with that one naughty word and how open he's being and all the things I might say to him next that I don't quite process it.

"Like I'm going to now?" he asks, and then three days later it hits like a lightning strike. All the gears inside me kind of slow to a halt. My mouth opens to answer, but no sound comes out. How could there be? There are barely any words suitable for this situation. The best I can think of is *praise God,* but if I go with that I might disturb whatever fragile fog that seems to have descended over him.

He looks like he's teetering on the brink as it is. His jaw is tighter than my entire body, and his eyes can't seem to stop searching mine. In the end I have to say something, because not doing so might be worse in the long run.

Though all I can really manage is a fumbled:

"I . . . are you . . . yeah . . . if you want."

None of which is right. His jaw gets harder, if that is actually possible. And for a second, his eyes kind of flutter closed in this near-withering way. So withering, in fact, that I almost take it back – until he explains.

"No. No. It has to be if you want. I can't –" he starts, but of course I don't let him finish. I jump in before he even gets to the part that's difficult for him.

"Yes I want that yes God yes please okay yes I want that," I babble, and, oh, his responding expression is a peach. All that tension runs right out of his face. That contempt or frustration he felt a second ago – more for himself than anything else, I think – disappears altogether, and in its place is something that verges on happy.

More than that: it verges on *greedy*.

It might even be lustful, if I squint a little.

"Do you want me to talk while you do it?" I ask, but only because he's fucking reaching for me. He's reaching for me and not in the shaking-hands sort of way.

"That would be . . . preferable," he says, only I don't think he really means that word. I think he means *fuck yes, now, right now*, and that idea gets a whole lot less dubious when he puts a hand on me. Mainly because he doesn't put it on my hip or my knee.

He puts it underneath my dress – just like in my dream. He puts it high up

on my thigh, and then, just as I'm trying to choke that little move down, he moves that hand. He uses it to lift my dress. *And he kisses the place where he just touched.*

To say I don't know how to react would be an understatement. Total-body paralysis seems like a better way to describe it. For a second I think I forget how to breathe, and every muscle tenses to some impossible degree. I can't even put myself into a more attractive, normal sort of position. I just have to lie there in a kind of weird banana shape, which is a problem for more than one reason.

I mean, if I want him to do this, I'm going to have to open my legs.

But really, doing that is a different story altogether.

They feel glued together. I think I can see the muscles in them standing out, and no amount of mental effort on my part will make them relax. I can't even use my hands to forcibly wrench them open, because my hands have made nervous fists somewhere close to my face. God knows how many weeks of waiting for him to be okay with this, and I'm going to be foiled by my own contrary limbs.

And then he kisses me again.

He kisses me all hot and wet and right over the material that covers my swollen pussy, and suddenly my contrary limbs are no longer the problem. My rampaging excitement is the problem. It charges through me the moment this thing becomes real and it makes me do all kinds of things I didn't think possible a second ago.

I spread my legs without even thinking about it.

And I speak without thinking about that, too.

"Maybe . . . maybe I could do something for you, while you do that," I say, fully expecting him to shoot me down. He dosen't, however.

He kisses me again, right on that good, good spot, then says:

"If something occurs to you, I doubt that I would mind. And especially if you keep talking the way you're talking and moaning the way you keep moaning."

Funny, I didn't even realize I had moaned.

I certainly didn't get that I've been continuously moaning since he started doing this. He uses his tongue and I just can't seem to stop this long keening sound from coming out of me – though if I'm honest, stopping it isn't top of my priorities.

"Like this?" I ask, and then I just do it louder.

I do it longer. I add a guttural note on the end.

All of which creates the desired effect.

"Jesus. Yes," he says, in a voice that is definitely not his own. It sounds like someone is strangling him as he speaks, and then just to cap it off, oh God, just to make it that little bit more blissful . . . he shifts in a way I could never in a million years mistake. He turns his body so I can reach him, and by reach him I don't mean a friendly pat on the back.

I mean his cock. I mean his cock is right fucking there, just as solid and curving as it was before, only with one tiny electrifying little difference.

That damp spot has spread. It's darker and bigger – most probably because he feels just as crazy as I do, which is very fucking crazy indeed. I keep thinking of the term *sixty-nine* and almost lose my mind, and of course all of that gets way more intense when he kisses again. When he does it with just the barest

hint of tongue, dragging at that already wet material, pulling at my swollen clit beneath . . .

And when I think about what he might possibly want me to do.

Stroke him there, maybe through the material?

Or something more? Something more exposed? Something with bare flesh and my hot, wet mouth sinking down on his stiff cock?

All of those things seem like far too much – until I use words in among the moaning. He goes for me again, and it just blurts out of me. Probably because he definitely uses his tongue this time. He pulls aside the material a little, and the feel of that slippery, mobile slickness against my overheated flesh is just too much.

I have to speak. I have to tell him.

"Ahhh, Noah, that feels so good. Yes, yes, just like that yes just like that," I say, and by God, I'm glad I do. Mainly because two things happen, once I have.

His hips jerk forward in a really unmistakable way.

And he says things back, oh, Lord, he says things back.

"Right here? Right here, huh?" he asks, only he does it like he's suddenly a whole other person. This guy has all of this gruffness at the back of his throat, and even though it seems like he's inquiring he isn't really at all. He knows already. He can tell how good this feels. But just in case he does what he can to make sure.

He exposes the whole of my spread pussy, and licks long and wet right the way through all those flushed and swollen folds. No hesitation, no holding back – just his hot tongue working its way up and up and up, and holy fuck when he gets to my clit . . .

I almost want him to stop there. Just give me a chance to catch my breath or at least take in all the other stuff first. My body is already jam-packed with tingles and shivers of intense pleasure. I don't really need any more.

It's just that he quite clearly wants to give me more. I gasp his name and he flicks at the underside of my stiff little bud in a way that makes me wish I could be silent. If I was silent, he wouldn't then move on to this slow, teasing circling kind of thing that just about finishes me off. I get that tightening sensation in my thighs and my clit jerks at the contact – all things that usually mean I'm probably going to come.

But that can't possibly be right, can it? Usually, it takes me hours. I have to be in the exact right mood and in the exact right position, with the same pressure applied for about seventeen days. And if the phone rings or the TV gets suddenly loud, forget it.

Yet somehow, here we are. Him barely licking me and me all tense and trembly. All it takes is the sight of him really going for it – spurred on, I think, by filthy things I never thought I could say like *fuck my cunt* and *do it hard* and *use your fingers* – and I'm suddenly shivering. I'm rocking against his face and moaning more filth.

"Ohhhh God, keep doing that keep doing it just like that I'm gonna do it all over your face don't stop don't stop please don't stop," I tell him, as though some other person has briefly taken over my body, too. This girl is sexually adventurous and easy to please, and she has no problems voicing those concepts.

Probably because of how much he fucking *loves* it.

He just doesn't need it to keep him in the moment. He isn't just interested in some clinical way, in that part of his brain that wants to assess my levels of relative arousal. He loves it. I can tell he does by the way he moves and breathes and most of all:

The way he looks. He pulls back briefly as I come down from the most intense and sudden orgasm of all time, and I get a long, cool drink of his glorious expression. His cheeks are actually pink. His mouth is as wet as fuck and so open I can only think about a hundred lewd things, like stuffing a cock in there. And his eyes . . .

No one has ever made eyes like that at me. He leans his head back against my thigh for a second, as though to catch his breath. But I don't think that's what he's really trying to do. I think he just wants a moment to devour my orgasm-flushed face and my still-shuddering body and that hand I seem to have placed very high up on his leg.

And though he says, "You know I'm going to have to make you talk like that some more, if you really want to do that," I can see the truth so clearly. Yeah, he might be anxious about doing this. True, the whole thing makes him tense.

But underneath that is some almighty fucking reservoir of love, for everything and anything even remotely sexual. His body practically rolls the moment I even hint about touching him there. He gets close to biting my thigh, and I can see his fist clenching. I can see it, but I don't think it has anything to do with nerves.

I think he just doesn't want to put his hand where it really wants to go – in my hair, or over the nape of my neck. The very idea of encouraging me in some kind of forceful way is making him tense up, but that's okay.

I know how to help.

"Show me," I tell him. "Show me how you like it."

"I hardly remember," he says, but I know that's a lie. The hand he puts on the side of my face tells me so, and so does the one he slides under his sweatpants. He eases them down just a little, just enough, and there it is. His thrillingly stiff and swollen cock, barely an inch from my lips. All I have to do to take it in is lean forward with my lips parted, and I almost do. I get very close.

And the only thing that stops me is his reaction.

"No, no don't – wait," he blurts out, his body suddenly as tense as mine was before all of this started. That hand leaves the side of my face, and for a second I'm sure that's going to be it. His expression tells me it might be. He's frowning and near afraid, shuddering like a struck dog. I have to say something, I think, if I want to pull him back.

But he gets there before I do. He's the one who puts everything on track again. He lets himself wrestle with it, and then just as I think he's going to give in he puts a hand between my legs. He sinks two fingers into my cunt, all the way up to the knuckle – and when he lets out some breathless words it becomes obvious why.

"God, you're so wet," he says – though maybe *says* is too small a word. He revels in it. He strokes and fondles and feels it. His head goes back just to know that he made me this way, and it lets him carry on. It stops him stopping me.

I get to lick his gorgeous cock – as thick as my wrist all the way around and

so amazingly red at the tip – while he rolls around in the evidence of my arousal. And when that isn't quite enough, I'm there to help. I feel him tense, and all I have to do is moan, or stop sucking just long enough to tell him to do it harder.

"Fuck my pussy, oh yeah, you do that so good," I say, and he likes it enough to buck into my working mouth. To arch his back and pant things in return.

God, the things he gasps in return . . .

"You're just creaming all over my hand," he tells me, as though I can realistically take something like that. We've just spent the past two months barely holding hands, but sure, go ahead. Talk dirty to me. Fuck my pussy and say those things.

It only makes me suck him harder, mouth as wet and messy as I can make it. So eager to make him come before his mind catches up with whatever we might be doing that I kind of forget the paroxysms my own body is going through.

Though I remember once his thumb finds my oversensitized clit. Oh yeah, I remember then. I have to turn my head away and keen over it, body suddenly a trembling, shuddering mess, but the fact that I do doesn't seem to matter. He just bucks into my slippery grip. He fucks my hand, spurred on by my very vocal permission.

Because that's what this is about, isn't it? The very best sort of permission I can offer. The truth of my wanting, in my slick cunt clenching around his fingers and my cries of unadulterated pleasure. I make sure to never say no even though I kind of want to – sometimes the sensation is so tart and sweet it reaches unbearable levels.

And yet there's a kind of freedom in that. A freedom in not wanting to push him away or tell him that's too much. It shoves me onward to even greater heights and a more intense sort of pleasure, thick and pulsing and oh so good.

I can almost feel what he meant by *creaming*. I can tell how slick I've gotten, and how plump. I can hear it and smell it and feel it running down between the crack of my ass, and even if I couldn't, he's here to tell me. "Ahhh God, you feel good," he says, and he doesn't mean the hand I have on his cock. Or even the tongue I work around the thick head, lapping and licking and generally making a greedy meal of the thing.

He means my cunt.

He tells me he means my cunt.

"There's nothing so sweet as your pussy," he says, and I just have to give him something in return. Something as lovely as all the things he gives me.

"Except maybe your cock," I tell him. "Your cock in my mouth, and the feel of your hips moving, and the knowledge that you want this, too."

"It feels good, doesn't it?"

"It feels more than good."

"I had forgotten. I'd forgotten what it's like . . ." he says, between long firm strokes that send me just as wild as his mouth did.

"To what?"

"To get lost in – oh Jesus," he gasps, and I almost laugh. It sounds like he's gotten lost in our Lord and Savior. Only the sight of his head going back and the feel of his hips bucking keep me on the right track. The one where I work his cock harder and faster in my slippery grip, because I know he likes it.

"Yeah, that's it," I tell him, and he likes that even more.

"Oh, fuck, fuck," he spits out, that thick shaft swelling against my palm in a way I could never mistake. Not even when it's him. Not even when he fights it. "I can't. I can't. I can't," he says, but I'm going to make sure he does.

"What if I tell you that I love you stroking me and fucking me and licking me?" I ask, partly because I want him to go over, but also because I do, oh, Lord, I do. His thumb is on my clit now, even though my clit is way too sensitive to take anything like that. And those fingers he has inside me – they're curled, as though he wants to beckon me closer.

It feels like drowning in pleasure.

But not as deeply as he is going down.

"No, no, ohhhh God."

"Or that I love sucking your cock. I love it, I love it."

"No, I'm too – I won't –" he chokes out, his body now so tense I can see veins standing out at his temples. His neck is a thick column. His free hand digs into the bed. It's agony to watch him go through this and even more so when it occurs to me:

It isn't just that he fears what desire will turn him into.

It's that he doesn't think he deserves to feel it at all. He could give in now easily, with no harm to me. Nothing he does in this moment will magically make him a monster. He just fights it anyway. He refuses it all the same.

I need to shock him out of it, I think.

But the person I really shock is me, when the words come out.

"I love you, Noah," I blurt, and when his eyes suddenly meet mine and his back arches and everything teeters right on the edge, I tell him again. Only this time, I do it because I know it's true. And he knows it, too.

"I love you," I say.

Then I watch as he comes, and comes, and comes.

THE RED HOUSE

Neville Elder

Neville Elder is an English writer, photographer and musician based in New York. In 2001, he followed a woman to New York and fell in love with a city. He lives at the unfashionable end of Brooklyn, with a mean old cat called Cato.

You don't have to be autistic to have a photographic memory. It's really common with children up to the age of five, but they grow out of it. With kids, it's a sensory thing, like a mental muscle memory. I was told I would grow out of it too – but for some reason, I didn't. I remember *everything*. It's like having *Netflix* in my brain. As a kid I used it mostly like a VCR. I memorised TV shows, *whole* episodes and re-ran them whenever I wanted.

That's how I got Emily to like me. We'd sit in the nook in the big fallen tree by the creek and she'd pick episodes of *Little House on the Prairie*. We were both 16, and I thought the show was pretty lame, but Emily adored it.

Do the one where Mary goes blind.

With or without the credits?

Um . . . Without.

She laughed when I did Michael Landon's voice in my freshly broken tenor.

And for all these years I've had this in my head: the few minutes I spent with Emily in the red house, an old farmhouse that's part of an artists' colony in upstate New York. Whenever I feel stressed, or need to escape, I stream this memory and the world around me floats away.

Don't come in me.

Does it hurt?

No, I've done it before.

When?

That's how it starts. Then she's crying and there's the sound of running water . . . Watching this unfold on the screen of my brain could dull the sharp teeth of loneliness.

At least it used to. A year or so ago I started forgetting things. Little stuff, keys, calling people back – I put it down to my age, my forties. And it's not like I've *slowed down* with the drink and the drugs.

I forgot about a meeting I had with people about a new production that's just begun in Toronto. I was on the phone with the director and I got confused.

Wait, what? What crash scene?

Top of page 50?

What are you talking about?

At the meeting, yesterday? You green-lit it?

What meeting?

Anthony? You're kidding me right?

Jeff? come in here would you? What's this meeting with Doug about a fucking car crash yesterday? Why wasn't I there? What the fuck's going on?

You were there . . .

What?

Yesterday at Doug's office in Santa Monica. We were both there, you wrote it in the book.

I was dumbfounded, because when I looked down at the production book open on yesterday's page, there in my loopy handwriting, it says:

"Doug office S.M. 11-12. w/ Jeff more $?"

And when I try to remember it, all I see is a blank frame at the end of a reel.

I'd forgotten a whole meeting where I signed off on a $50k stunt! I freaked. I had Jeff cancel everything for the rest of the day. I pulled the blinds, lay down on the couch and smoked some pot. I played the film of the red house with the projector behind my eyes. But this time my summer of love looked underexposed; washed out. Emily didn't give a fuck about getting sunburned. In my memory, her nose and forehead were always a bright peeling pink. This time, she was gray.

I panicked. I went back to New York and had a doctor do some tests.

It's unusual to still be Eidetic at your age.

Is that right?

Let's do a scan.

My MRI looked like the photos from the Mars Lander; early-onset Alzheimer's – *whoop whoop*. The irony was fucking beautiful. She told me to lay off the booze and the drugs, see if that helped. I won't lose my mind overnight, she said.

I quit the drinking and the blow and I went to some 12-step meetings. They taught me how to pray and told me what I should be looking for was God. I laughed in their faces, they took it pretty well; they'd seen my type before. But some of the things they said stuck with me – the spiritual motif – their "serenity" was like how I felt when I remembered the red house. So I sat with them in their circles and I learned their prayers and occasionally I would close my eyes and chant with them. But I missed the comfort of annihilation, so I went back to the booze and I tried to write down everything about the red house before it disappeared, to give me prompts for the key moments. Sort of like a treatment for a movie.

In the summer of 1987 my parents rented a bungalow in an artists' colony outside Williamstown, New York. All hippy-dippy when it was founded, by the eighties they'd all sold out and either worked in advertising or taught graphic design at Parson's or NYU.

I was the only kid there except for Emily, also 16, virtually feral. She was a tangled up terror of a girl, with wild blonde hair and freckles. She literally ran away from me when I initially said *hello*. At the Fourth of July potluck when the residents gathered for fireworks and potato salad, my dad gave me sparklers.

Her eyes lit up when she saw my magnesium wand dancing in the dusk. I handed one to her and that was it, best friends.

For the next few weeks we crashed through the backwoods of the colony unsupervised. Dirty from the creek, scratched from brambles. Our ankles and feet were scabbed from our mothers' evening ritual of plucking deer ticks from our flesh.

When Emily tired of *Little House*, we'd sit cross-legged in the tree and she'd practice hypnotising me. She'd stare at me until my peripheral vision would narrow into a tunnel and tingling sensations slowly flooded my crotch and my prick stiffened inside my trunks. She'd then flick at it with a finger. Hard.

Dirty bastard, one of these days I'm going to strangle that snake of yours.

I would climb down, flushed with shame, and stand in shade of the fallen Beech tree up to my ankles in the water. She'd watched me from above as I jerked off.

One morning just after dawn, we sat in the nook and instead of flicking my hard cock, Emily pulled it out of the leg of my trunks and rolled it between her cold hands until it jumped like a frog. It dry heaved once and sperm spewed out all over her bare thighs. A thin strand of come connected my softening prick to her dangling fingers like a vine as she rotated her hand in the sunlight. It looked like dew on a cobweb.

On the lazy August afternoons when the adults were out of sight, getting high or fucking – or whatever they did during those long dog days – we took to dry humping on the faded Persian rug in the abandoned art studio in the attic in the red house – the big farmhouse that existed long before the hippies arrived was used as community space and storage.

In the shaft of light from the high window, specks of dust circled us like the faithful ascending to heaven while I lay on top of her and rubbed my sharp erection along the soft gutter of her damp shorts.

The day she gave herself a black eye running into a low branch, I watched silently as her mom wiped her face and tears.

Jeez, Emmy what did he do to you?

Me?

It wasn't him Mommy, I ran into a tree, that's all.

Ran into a tree?

Her mother glared at me.

You didn't break the skin, but it's going to be a shiner.

She lifted Emmy's chin and took a Polaroid to show her stepfather.

He's coming up from the city this weekend, aren't we lucky?

The camera flashed again.

That's if the SOB can take his dick out of his students for five minutes.

Her mother stared at me as she flapped the photo the way you're not supposed to, but I didn't say anything. I watched Emily's face appear in the photograph. She stared out through her rapidly darkening socket. With her chin still raised in the pose and her mouth turned downward, she looked scared.

We wandered down the duck trail to the creek. I trailed behind like a stray dog. Emily's tangled blonde hair, in braids with green rubber bands, bounced like rats' tails on her freckled neck.

What's wrong?

Nothing's wrong.

Does it hurt?

No.

Is it your dad?

He's not my dad.

Step-dad, then?

I gave up and returned to my family's bungalow on the other side of the colony.

After lunch I went to the red house. I found Emily in the pool of dusty light below the window. She sat cross-legged in her panties on the rug squinting at me through her swollen goose egg. Her small round breasts rose neatly from white triangles beneath her tanned throat. She stood up and took off her underwear, her body wrapped in gold.

Don't come in me.

I kicked off my Chucks and pulled down my swimming trunks. My prick sprang up comically. She didn't laugh. She sat down again, opened her legs and brought them up to her waist and beckoned me to her. I clambered down between her knees. She spat on her hand and gently guided me inside her. I fell into her arms. She started to cry.

Does it hurt?

No, I've done it before.

When?

I moved in and out. It didn't take long. When I was ready I pulled out and she expertly jerked my shiny tip and I burst all over her tummy. Blobs of come dripped off her body onto the floor and stuck to the frayed carpet.

I collapsed on her, overwhelmed. I felt her rib cage rise and fall, my chin drooped over her shoulder and my lips touched the dusty floorboards at the edge of the rug. I could see down through the cracks to the laundry room below, the washing machine turned its load over and over, *splish-splash, splish-splash*. Emily pressed her sticky palms firmly on my back holding me in place to stop me from floating away. Stuck together, she kissed my face repeatedly as tears dripped onto the sun-baked rug. I felt completely at peace. I kissed the dome of her purple eye. She got up, ran to the big sink and drank from the twisted faucet for a long time, guzzling the cold shining stream.

Will you get pregnant?

No, you didn't come in me.

Are you sure?

My Dad said it's OK.

Which of course, is a fucked-up thing for a father to tell his daughter. Though at the time I didn't think about it.

I was in New York for more tests. I ducked out of the cold February rain over the dirty black snow banks into the *Strand Book Store* on Broadway. The lonely moon of Emily's face – older, leaner but still so very beautiful – appeared between twin towers of discount books. My memory clicked and whirred like an old VHS tape being sucked into its cradle. She looked up over round glasses, saw me, and laughed. I must have looked so funny standing there with my mouth

open. We embraced. She was chatty and playful, as if we hadn't just spent 20 years without any contact. I was stunned.

Let's buy the same books! Let's go and find two copies of a book and form a book club. Right here! This one!

She handed me a paperback.

Graham Greene?

I turned it over in my hands I hadn't read *The End of the Affair*. I'd read *Brighton Rock*, that one was miserable, the film not much better. Still, a Penguin on sale, and a special anniversary edition for $10, bargain.

Out on the street she took out her copy and pressed the book against my chest.

We should write something in them and not say what we wrote, look at it later when we've finished reading. Give me yours!

We exchanged books. I scribbled in the opening page, closed it and handed it back; my heart was pounding.

"To Emily at the beginning, love Anthony x."

I waited for her to write an inscription of her own. Fine lines around clear gray eyes barely betrayed the passed time. She wrote in the back and made me pinky-swear not to look. Then we went to that fake roadhouse place on Union Square and ate mac 'n' cheese that sucked.

It's like roller-rink cheese.

You mean like at the Roll-a-Rama in Williamstown?

Oh man, the Roll-a-Rama!

You think it's still there?

It's a gas station, now. When my mom died . . .

I'm sorry, when?

Thanks, last June . . . when mom died, she left me the bungalow, I still go up for the summers – it hasn't changed.

The red house?

Yep. Still there.

She smiled. She talked about her shitty job and her boss, I made wisecracks and told her about LA and the movie business and she laughed and laughed.

It's good to see you Anthony.

Is it?

We stared at each other until my vision blurred, and she smiled that big goofy teenager grin, like she'd just remembered something fun we could do by the creek.

I want to hypnotise you.

Fuck. I sat in shock. Emily laughed so hard, she snorted.

Come on. Let's go.

What? Where?

To the red house, silly.

I dropped two twenties on the Formica. Fuck, fuck, fuck. Was this happening? I wanted to tell her about the Alzheimer's and how I was losing the memories of us in the red house, how I relied on them so much and how bumping into her like this was so fortuitous. Maybe she could help me remember! But it sounded silly. It sounded creepy, talking about two teenagers with come all over them. And I didn't want to freak her out. I didn't want to scare her off, because the

way she was looking at me, there was a very good chance she was going to let me fuck her.

We listened to the radio in her car, holding hands. Emily sang along to the songs that played on the radio when we were kids, *Culture Club, Flock of Seagulls.* It was dark and snowing by the time we got to the colony. Deer crossed the trail as we rolled over the hard packed snow. Frozen in our high beams, their eyes reflected back like blank discs.

We were barely up the stairs before Emily was on her knees pulling at my jeans. Without even taking off her long down coat she took out my cock and sucked it. She devoured it. I had to drag her off me to get my pants off. We crashed through the old boxes of board games and clothes to find our old spot on the carpet under the high window. She hit the floor face first. I fell on top of her. An empty blue spotlight of moonlight illuminated us squirming in a bright rectangle on the floor.

I got my hands under her long wool skirt and pulled it up, yanked her panties to one side and plunged my fingers in. Emily moaned, lifting her ass to me. I had to hold her down to get her coat off. I couldn't get her arms out of the sleeves so I pulled down her underwear, and I shoved my cock deep into her cunt.

She stopped moving. I searched for her in the lining of her big *North Face*. Pulling the fur hood out of the way I found the back of her neck. I bit her ear and got a mouthful of hair. She started rocking me back and forth. Muffled by her coat she began to moan.

What?

I want you to come inside me.

So I did and when I rolled off her and pulled her free from her clothes, she was crying.

No, no! Don't worry! It's good, I always cry a little when I come.

She cupped my cheek in the palm of her hand and smiled. Her eyes shone with tears and moonlight. I held her in my arms until I got hard again and we fucked, slowly this time. I looked into her eyes when she came and watched the tears well up.

After that hot summer afternoon we fucked in the red house, I had avoided her. If she were at the creek, I rode my bike to town. If I saw her near the red house I went to the creek. I never got close enough to see the light in her eyes, but I knew I was hurting her.

That Labor Day I stood shamefaced with my BMX between my knees at the end of the track as her dad packed up the station wagon to go back to the city. Emily drifted in and out of the bungalow with her summer things packed in boxes and bags. Every time she came out, she met my gaze and every time she went back into the bungalow, she turned and looked at me over her shoulder. I followed the car to the edge of the colony and as they pulled out I pedaled out on the forbidden main road. I tried to keep up as they coasted through the stop signs at the edge of Williamstown. When Emily's dad gunned the Chevy towards the highway, she rolled down the window and her hair blew up in her face. I reached out to touch her, but I wasn't fast enough. Strands of hair whipped my hand. She rolled up the window from an unheard adult command and I waved

her away. She flattened her hands against the glass. She didn't hate me and I was happy, in the way that selfish teenage boys are so easily satisfied. Later that night I biked into town and I got drunk in the 7-11 parking lot. And in bed I dreamed the film of the red house from start to finish for the first time. It was pristine and clear and amazing. I woke the next day with puke in my hair. My Mom's temper was beating in my head and I had a sickening feeling that I'd left something out, somewhere.

There was no heat at the red house during the winter. Emily found candles and lit a fire in the stove with old newspaper. We dragged blankets out of a box and drank hot green tea from a dented enamel mug. We rubbed our legs together like crickets to get warm under the old quilts on the now rotten Persian rug. I fell asleep looking into her eyes. In the middle of the night, I found her completely naked standing on a chair at the window, shivering. She floated in the dim, blue light, her buttocks trembling in the cold.

Come look! The moon's turned red!

She jumped down, pulled me from the warmth of our nest. We balanced precariously on the chair, my arms around her waist, cupping her breasts, and looked out at the moon. Sure enough, through the raised arms of bare trees, the moon hung in the sky like a frozen drop of blood – a full lunar eclipse.

When we got back to the city, she dropped me off at the subway and I was alone again.

On my ride home, I looked in the book and read her scribble in my copy of the paperback. I found it on the last page: "To Anthony it's the end XO!"

Perhaps Emily didn't remember the red house as I did. After all she spent every summer upstate. I was there for just one. Another holiday romance, perhaps. I didn't tell her about the Alzheimer's, or ask for help with my fading memories. Was her recollection complete?

At the open car door by the subway, with the book under my arm, I touched her face.

I'll call you?

She smiled. But of course I didn't.

A week later I walked past the roller-rink cheese place at Union Square. I was a little confused about East and West and stood for a second in the damp afternoon. I looked down into the warm, fake Americana, trying to figure out where I was. Emily sat texting at a booth. She looked up and waved.

I turned as a man pushed up against me as he wrangled a toddler out of a stroller. A slightly older child raced down the steps in front of me. Muted by the glass, the kids exploded silently into the restaurant. They surrounded Emily with excited chatter. They piled a barricade of coats, hats and scarves up against the window and sat beside her. The man slid in beside her with a kiss. Fearing I'd be seen, I stepped back into the shadows of the snowy street.

The red house is sucked into the mush of my brain like old furniture in a sinkhole. My photographic memory is gone. The part about chasing Emily's car on my bike? I wrote that one afternoon after a dream. I think it's real. It seems right. Sometimes I get lucky and I see a whole scene again. But I'm not sure if they are memories or dreams.

Sometimes when I'm really high and dozing on the couch, a close up of Emmy's face vibrates in a triangle of window light like a hologram. The blood moon floats above me like a swollen eye. As the light changes from blue to gold and back again, I can't tell if it's day or night, summer or winter.

THE LOVES OF HER LIFE

Arlene Heyman

Arlene Heyman is the recipient of Woodrow Wilson, Fulbright, Rockefeller and Robert Wood Johnson Fellowships. Her short stories have appeared in *New American Review* and she won *Epoch* magazine's novella contest. She has been listed twice in the hounour rolls of *Best American Short Stories*. Heyman is a psychiatrist/psychoanalyst practising in New York City, where she lives with her husband.

“Would you like to make love?” Stu called out to Marianne as she entered their apartment. She walked toward his office. It was mid-Saturday afternoon and Stu was still in his purple pajamas at the computer, a mug of coffee on the cluttered desk. He had a little wet mocha-colored stain under his lip on his beard, and his wiry gray hair stood up thinly around his large bald spot. He looked at her shyly for a moment, then looked back at the computer screen. His office was a small room off the entrance foyer, the glossy hardwood floor littered with unruly piles of papers and journals – she spotted *Dissent*, *MIT Technology Review*, the *Hightower Lowdown*. Beside these were stuffed canvas bags, a white one imprinted with SCHLEPPEN in black, a bright-blue one with multicolored flowers above the words GREENPEACE RAINBOW WARRIOR. Unframed photos of children and grandchildren lay scattered on the marble radiator cover.

Marianne had just come back from a frenetic brunch with her son, Billy, at a bistro on Madison Avenue and hadn't yet taken off her coat. Because his wife was divorcing him, Billy was distraught. From her point of view as an ex-social worker, Marianne had always considered her son's wife a borderline personality – from the human point of view, an outright bitch. And Marianne would have rejoiced that they were divorcing except that Billy was distraught. She had tried to comfort him at the same time that she was urging him not to give in to his wife's outrageous demands: Lyria wanted the apartment and the country house and half of Billy's business. “Only half?” Marianne had asked, but Billy was deaf to her sarcasm. He put away one Grey Goose after another while the poached eggs he'd ordered turned into hard yellow eyes and he kept making throat-clearing, half-gagging sounds, sounds he'd made occasionally when he got anxious as a kid; she didn't think she'd heard those sounds in twenty-five years. She had joined him in a Grey Goose herself, trying to smooth away her edginess, and since she rarely drank, she was still tipsy. Marianne wanted either to go to the gym to work it off or try for a drop-in appointment at her hairdresser's where she would be cosseted. She could use some cosseting.

But she knew how hard it was for her husband to ask for sex, even after three wives; Marianne was his fourth. Why was it so hard? The best Stu had come up with was fear of rejection. She didn't understand – if you were out one day, you might be in the next. But he was reluctant even to ask for all dark meat from the Chirping Chicken take-out place and also he tended to buy the first item a salesperson showed him. His timidity annoyed her. He thought he was just an easygoing, nice guy. Cooperative. And many agreed with him.

She had other resentments, some small. He never brought her flowers, although she adored flowers. "I buy you printer cartridges," he'd said. "And flash drives."

Some resentments were chasm sized. He didn't make enough money, and what he made he was always giving to obscure political groups working for "social justice" or to one of his numerous importuning adult children – the major beneficiaries of his modest will.

And he dressed badly, and called her superficial when she complained, though lately he had let her go clothes shopping with him. Clothes delighted her. A tall, slender woman with prominent cheekbones, slanted blue eyes, and dramatic silver-white hair, Marianne attracted admiration – she did a little modeling for Eileen Fisher, one of the few fashion designers whose ads occasionally featured older women. She was proud of being, hands down, the best-looking of his wives. He loved her, she knew, in part for her looks, and so it wasn't fair that he criticized her for caring how *he* looked.

And couldn't he be even a little seductive, instead of asking for sex as if he were asking for a game of tennis?

In spite of it all, or perhaps because of it, she tried never to reject him when he asked: it softened her up toward him, making love. And it got him away from his computer, and connected him to another human being – namely, her. She tried to do it at least once a week.

It didn't sound like much: she had made love three or four times a week with her first husband, who'd been younger than she, and who had died eleven years ago. But now that she was sixty-five and Stu seventy, spontaneity was difficult. She had acid reflux, and so had to stay upright for two or three hours after a meal or else suffer burning pains in her chest. And she had to insert Vagifem, low-level estrogen tablets, in her vagina twice a week so her tissues didn't thin out. He used Viagra half an hour before sex, and because he tended to come too soon if they weren't making love often, and once a week wasn't often, he also took a dose of clomipramine, an antidepressant that had as a side effect retarded ejaculation. The Viagra made him feel flushed for the rest of the day and the clomipramine made him spacey. So they usually had sex toward evening, if not at night.

He didn't really come too soon; he never came until after she climaxed. But she got most of her pleasure from intercourse *after* she had come, an oddity, perhaps, but that was how she was. She hated remembering what sex had been like for her in her twenties, before she'd accepted herself, and when the received wisdom was that you weren't a real woman unless you came vaginally – that is, no hands. The huffing and puffing and the squeals and screams of orgasmic

pleasure she had faked! And this was in the dawning age of feminism! She had heard from a neighbor, a high school teacher, that even now freshman girls were sucking off senior boys without getting anything in return.

While Stu wanted to last after she had come, it was difficult. If she told him, as he was thrusting after her orgasm, "God, this feels good," he immediately came. If she said nothing, merely looked beatific, he also came. So now, ironically, she suppressed any noises she might have made and often lied to him that she *hadn't* come in order to keep him at it. And if he got notice that she wanted to make love, he masturbated ten hours before, because then he definitely lasted longer. In short, for them, making love was like running a war: plans had to be drawn up, equipment in tiptop condition, troops deployed and coordinated meticulously, there was no room for maverick actions lest the country end up defeated and at each other's throats . . .

So she called to him now, "Yes, dear, that would be very nice, making love." She removed from her pocketbook the note card on which she always wrote down the time she had taken her last bite of any meal, checked her watch, and did the acid reflux calculation: "Give me forty-five minutes, please." She hung up her coat, leaned against the wall for a moment to steady herself from the alcohol, while she watched him hotfoot it out of his office to the bathroom medicine chest, where he took his pills. He joined her in the foyer, gave her a little hug. Then he returned to his computer to keep working until the medicine would take effect.

"No frills today, huh?" she called after him, disappointed that he'd gone back to work. They might have talked about Billy's predicament, or this or that.

"The server's down in New Jersey and I've got a hundred e-mail complaints." His eyes were fixed on the screen.

She walked down the long hallway to their black-and-white-painted bedroom and undressed there, put on a loose cotton robe. Placing some pillows between her back and the wall, she sat down in the lotus position on the kilim and did some breathing exercises, then tried to meditate. Her son's wretchedness kept intruding itself; she had images of slapping Lyria around until her face was the same color as her long, flaming hair, Lyria who didn't work or cook or clean, who took voice lessons but never sang when anyone was around to hear. A silent, sullen diva. She would pout or suddenly go into a tirade at Billy, no matter who was around to hear. Their apartment, littered with musical scores and smelling of cat piss – she owned half a dozen Persian cats, which she didn't take care of, so the place was covered with hair – was uninhabitable. Marianne and her first husband, and now just Marianne, had paid for years of therapy for Lyria, without so much as a thank-you. Or any sign of improvement. Yet Billy loved this woman. Although Marianne repeated and repeated her mantra, she could not block out her daughter-in-law's high, thin voice. Finally Marianne gave up. She showered, put on a sleek sky-blue nightgown, and swirled a minty mouthwash around in her mouth to get rid of the taste of vodka.

She and Stu used to watch porn sometimes to warm up for sex, but not after she'd read Gloria Steinem's essay about how Linda Lovelace was beaten and literally enslaved by her husband and keeper, Chuck Traynor; after Lovelace managed to escape, the same man married Marilyn Chambers and treated her

the same way. With that knowledge, watching *Deep Throat* or *Behind the Green Door* was worse than crossing a picket line. So she resorted to her own manifold fantasies. She had asked him did he fantasize while making love and he said no, he thought about her. He didn't ask about her. Was this an unliberated aspect of their marriage, that they didn't tell each other their fantasies? He claimed he didn't have masturbatory fantasies. What he had was an "athletic sex" video on his computer: he did everything at his computer.

Now she got into bed under the bright-white duvet and readied the box of tissues and the tube of K-Y Jelly.

He came in naked and she remembered again why she did not like to make love in the daytime. She joked sometimes that no one over forty should be allowed to make love in the daytime. There he was, every wrinkle exposed, as if he were in a Lucian Freud painting. He had loose flesh on his chest, small sagging breasts beneath his nipples, and little pink outgrowths here and there. His pubic hair was colorless and sparse, and he happened to have the smallest penis she had ever seen, although he was a large bear of a man. His penis looked like a small round neck with an eyeless face barely peeking out above his pouchlike scrotum. When she got angry at him, she felt like telling him so, yelling it out, but she figured if she did that, he'd never get another erection; and erect, he was big enough to do the job so long as they didn't use Astroglide or any of those thin liquid lubricants. She couldn't feel him then. But the thick K-Y Jelly provided some traction and he did just fine.

She didn't like how *she* looked anymore, either. Her breasts and waist were not bad, maybe better than that, if you ignored the yearning her breasts seemed to have developed for her waist. But tiny, bright-red raised spots had appeared here and there on her torso – she recalled her father had had them in old age. And her ass and thighs were bony, the flesh hanging a little. And while her pubic hair was still blondish brown, you could see the skin beneath. Where was that thick bush of yesteryear?

He moved in next to her under the duvet. It was winter and, mercifully, the whole episode might take place under cover. Although once she got into it, she got into it, and also she kept her eyes and her critical faculties shut, at least mostly.

She moved into a spoon position with her back up against his chest and her ass against his penis. She felt him grow hard. He tried to turn her toward him and she resisted for a moment, then yielded. "Talk to me," she said. "Tell me something intimate."

He laughed. "You first."

She said, "I'm afraid I'll die without ever making another movie I'm proud of." After being a social worker for years, in an act of bravery or foolishness, she had trained as a documentary filmmaker. But she had trouble raising money – her first husband had underwritten her two best films – and since he died, she'd shot mostly commercials.

Stu said, "I have three faculty members coming up for tenure and I have to read their books. And I've put it off and off."

"That's not intimate. That's something you'd tell anyone. Tell me something you'd tell only me, your wife."

"You want me to share some misery with you. I don't have any. I'm a contented man. I love my work." He paused. "And I love my wife."

She kissed him hard.

He began rubbing her nipples.

"Not like that, sweetie. You're doing it mechanically. Pull on them. Bite them a little. Pay some concentrated attention."

He obliged. She lay back and after a moment felt the sensations start high up, way back in her vagina. Higher. What was higher than that? The cervix, the uterus – her first husband, a doctor, had drawn her diagrams she vaguely remembered. The cunt.

Too soon he said, "Shall I eat you?"

"Not yet. Don't stop doing what you're doing."

"I can do both at the same time."

"Always multitasking, aren't you."

He grinned and took a pillow from the bed and laid it on the floor, then went down on his knees on the pillow and she moved to the edge of the bed and opened her legs wide. She ran her hands through his hair that was still sticking up. He needed a haircut. He often needed a haircut and a beard trim – he let white stubble grow on his cheeks sometimes for days, and on his neck; he just didn't notice. Evidently nobody else noticed, either, at least no one commented to him about it, but it offended her aesthetic sensibilities. And in bed it scratched her face, and occasionally the skin on the inside of her thighs. She would sometimes shave him herself, although she wasn't into cutting his hair. Now he opened the tube of K-Y Jelly and smeared some on her nipples, then pulled at them while he ran his tongue over her clitoris. She found herself thinking about her strawberry-blond-haired granddaughter, Jeanine, age four, who had smeared bright-orange finger paints all over her legs and face, laughing delightedly. She had smeared them on her grandma as well, and they ended up taking a bubble bath together in the master bathroom. Would it be more difficult to see her granddaughter, now that her son was getting divorced? Not if Billy got joint custody or at least decent visiting rights – he might even bring Jeanine around *more,* for what was a single man to do by himself with a small child? Well, she supposed these were unliberated thoughts as well, for there were many men now who helped bring up the children. Her deceased husband, David, had been pretty good with Billy, even sewing up rips in his clothes, although David had been the busiest of orthopedic surgeons. How witty and playful he was, once painting flowers on her ass in bed; another time he had constructed a man with a fuse box for a chest and a papier-mâché face and put pajamas on him and had the creature waiting under the covers for her when she came in expecting to make love. Now she thought she couldn't let herself think about David. She'd get sad and wonder why she had to be with Stu instead of with David, why did David had to have a heart attack at fifty-two and die? Lean and light-boned David, who'd run six marathons, pale skin shiny with suntan lotion, bush of black hair sweat-slicked to his scalp. She could still see him in his signature red shorts and black T-shirt reaching out to take the paper cup of water someone offered him, barely breaking his stride.

Death had come out of nowhere. David was playing a fathers-and-grown-up-

sons ball game with Billy, Billy who had the same fair, eager-to-burn skin, the same perspicacious hazel eyes. David had run after a long ball in that effortless, loose-limbed, almost jaunty style of his, he'd leaped high, reached and got his glove on the ball, held on to it, held on to it, and collapsed. She had been sitting there watching, thought he was fooling around, she'd even stood up and applauded. Marianne knew if she pursued this line of thought she'd never come, and it wasn't fair to Stu, who was working away with his tongue. She bent over, blinking back tears, and kissed his head, then rubbed his neck for a while, massaged it. "Do you want to come in me, dear?"

He bobbed his head once but went on eating her. She put her hands under his armpits, trying to pull him up, and said, "It's enough, dear. I don't want you hurting yourself." He had arthritis in his neck, and once, while eating her, had developed back spasm and was laid up for a month – she'd waited on him hand and foot, sucked him off, and still felt guilty.

He got into bed beside her now and ran his tongue over her hand.

"Got a hair stuck in your mouth?" she asked him.

"Yes, but I'll swallow it."

"You don't have to. Wash your mouth out, honey. I can wait."

But he shook his head.

She took the tube of K-Y Jelly and squeezed some onto her fingers and lathered his penis with it, rubbing him to grow his erection. Slowly he entered her, and she put some jelly on her forefinger and started rubbing her clitoris while he moved in and out. He was over her, supporting himself on his hands, and she looked at his shaggy beard and knobby skin, which hung a little around his kindly face. She had cherished his kindness, remembered their first date at the Moroccan restaurant he'd taken her to, where the tablecloths were rose and chartreuse with little mirrors sewn on them. Did she eat? Through much of the meal she'd wept about her husband, dead a year, worried to this stranger that she was leeching the marrow out of her twenty-seven-year-old son whom she called sometimes two or three times a day to hear his scratchy-edgy voice, so like his father's. And Billy had his father's long, thin fingers – she'd made a short video of the movements of her son's hands. Billy'd quipped while she shot it that he didn't think the film would have wide appeal. And she bemoaned not having had more children with her husband. A daughter. And Stu listened and nodded and patted her arm, and passed her a little cellophane pack of tissues he carried with him because his nose was often congested.

Stu had seemed a little – oh, more than a little – heroic to her. His sheer size in the tiny restaurant. Big blocklike hands. They had their appeal. Still did. And some things he'd done back in the day impressed her, though she'd had to pull them out of him: he'd dreamed up software, armor really, that protected computer networks from attack – saved the traffic lights – imagine New York City without traffic lights! And one time he'd even gone in to rescue the police department from a hacker, although he had mixed feelings about police departments.

She closed her eyes now and kissed Stu with her tongue and opened her legs wide and, rubbing herself with one hand and caressing his neck with the other, imagined herself a stupid little girl, maybe twelve years old, who came to clean at a house of old men, one of whom explained to her that she'd get much smarter

in school if she sucked semen out of them, that semen was the source of intelligence, and the more orifices of hers she could get their semen into, the smarter she'd be. And one man took her clothes off and began rubbing her little clitoris, and another put his old gray penis in her mouth and she sucked and sucked eagerly until she got some semen out of it and then she begged for more and sucked off another old man. Her job was to clean the house and they set her doing it in a servant's frock with no underpants on, so any old man who wanted could begin massaging her clitoris, and she would beg to suck him off. She didn't notice any improvement in her grades at school, but felt she had only just started with this sucking business and there were all her other openings and she wondered about her ears.

Stu continued moving in and out of her. Marianne nibbled at his neck and at his ears. She put more K-Y Jelly on her finger and imagined herself a woman in her twenties, with a shaved head and pussy, lying naked in a doorway while one woman rubbed her clitoris, another pulled at her nipples. There was a party going on inside and any man who was entering the party had to step over her. He was allowed to do anything he wanted to her, so long as he didn't hurt her. The women kept her in a constant state of excitement. A stranger might enter her casually while chatting with one of the women. Or he might chat with his friend who was accompanying him; the two might together enter Marianne, one in her mouth, one in her ass. One or the other might come on Marianne's belly and rub his semen all over her breasts.

Marianne kept rubbing herself, her husband kept thrusting, she felt she was almost there, almost there. She put more jelly on her finger and imagined herself a thirty-year-old woman on a stage making love with a younger man while an audience of Japanese businessmen took photos of her, one or another running up onstage to get a better shot. Occasionally the man who was banging her asked if anyone in the audience wanted to take over. Several rushed onto the stage. Soon there was a line snaking out the door.

In bed Marianne opened her legs as wide as she could, as if someone were forcing her open, and whispered urgently to Stu, "Stop moving! Stop!" She was starting to come, little waves of contractions passed through her, and if he kept moving, she would miss feeling them. She kept rubbing herself through the contractions, which intensified them, and finally when they stopped, she put her arms around Stu's back and kissed him deeply. After a moment, she said "Now." And he began to move gently, quietly, then forcefully in and out. And she tried very hard not to look pleased – she kept a frown on her face. She wanted to say, "Pull out if you feel you're going to come," but she was afraid to say anything.

She kept her eyes closed and he said, "Can I come now?"

"No!" she nearly hollered. He stopped moving, and they waited. Then he started again. "Tell me when I can come."

"Not yet."

Then his breathing got heavy, heavier. "I'm going to come," he said desperately, and then he was breathing heavily into her ear and made a few quick thrusts and fell onto her.

She had wanted more, and she felt disappointed, a little empty. Still, she kissed his face and he came out of her, put tissues on his penis and between her legs, and

she got out of bed and hobbled to the bathroom holding the tissues in place, then dropped them into the toilet and peed. She washed her hands and breasts and washed between her legs and got back into bed. He was lying naked with tissues on his limp penis. She kissed him and spooned up against him. She thought to ask him, "Why couldn't you have held on just a little bit longer?" But he was already snoring, which was just as well. She'd complained to him a few times about his failure to last longer, but she never said why didn't he last as long as David had or why didn't he make even half the money David made. She did ask why couldn't he go with her to see an occasional avant-garde film, and wear a suit and tie on the rare occasions they went together to her arts club – she was chairperson of the film committee. And he'd yelled at her, "I give talks all over, and I'm treated with respect, like a valued person. Only at home am I sniped at."

He had slept on the living room couch that time – it was not the first time – and in the middle of the night, she'd gone in and apologized, and dragged his offended hulking self back into bed with her. She tried to get him to make love to her, but he wouldn't. "I'm not in a loving mood."

"It'll put you in a loving mood."

But he wouldn't.

Cleaning out their storage cages in the basement of the apartment building, she came upon boxes of documentation David had saved for income taxes. Stu said they could all be thrown out, they were more than ten years old, but she couldn't bear to throw away anything to do with her dead husband without at least looking over each item, including canceled checks (they reminded her of where they'd been and what they'd done). So she laid a tarp over the Oriental rug in the foyer, and Stu helped drag up the dusty boxes, some of which had dried bits of plaster in them; she vacuumed the boxes.

There were income tax returns that showed her husband had made half a million dollars some years, a million others, and that was when money was worth more. There were airline tickets and stamped documents proving that he had attended surgical conventions, which made their family trips tax-deductible. There were journals in which he'd published papers – he was an expert on repairing the labrum, a membrane in the hip joint, which often tore in athletes. In fact, he had invented the procedure. Other surgeons simply removed the damaged labrum, but sewing it up seemed to make for less arthritis in later life – at least that was the case in animal studies. The data were only now, decades later, starting to come in on humans, and a colleague of his told her everything seemed to bear her husband out. David would have been thrilled.

There were receipts from different restaurants where they'd eaten in Venice: Locanda Cipriani, Crepizza, il Cenacolo, da Bepi. She remembered the family watching a glassblower in Murano. From one of the thunderous red furnaces, the skinny, pockmarked fellow had pulled out a long pipe with reddish-yellow molten glass at the end of it. He'd blown into the pipe and the blob of glass expanded and elongated, and Billy, age seven, watched fiercely, swaying a little in the hot, noisy room, clasping and unclasping his hands. Marianne asked did he need to go to the bathroom, but the boy shook his head without taking his eyes off the changing glass. David hoisted Billy up onto his shoulders, where he sat

rapt as the worker rolled the glass in dark-green powder and thrust it back into the furnace, blew it up again, and tweezed it, astonishingly, into the shape of a man playing the piano – all very small, but you could see the pianist's fingers and the piano keys. Billy bounced with delight on David's shoulders and begged to stay for another demonstration. Afterwards they ordered a whole orchestra of the small green-glass figurines for Billy, who was learning to play the trumpet at school. Billy now owned a bookstore, and he had those figurines out on a table in the books-on-music section. It was amazing that the orchestra had survived his childhood, so many years ago, intact. But Billy had been a careful, thoughtful boy. How had he married such a flailing, chaotic woman?

She remembered a shop on the Rio Terrà Canal, off Campo Santa Margherita, a shop that made masks; they'd bought the plague doctor for David, a papier-mâché face in black and white with small round glasses and a huge curved beak of a nose. (Anti-Semitic? No. In the Middle Ages a plague doctor wore a cone-shaped beak stuffed with herbs and straw to ward off "plague air.") She shook the dust off the mask onto the tarp.

Hadn't warded off anything.

Ever.

She remembered going to empty out David's office at the hospital, after he had died so suddenly. She had cried in the street and put the mask on momentarily to cover her tears. A little white boy holding an older black woman's hand had pointed at Marianne, reached up, and tried to touch the mask; he'd called out "trick or treat," though it was April.

She wanted to touch David, not the decayed David who was in that box; probably the bacteria had eaten away everything but the bones. Maybe the bones, those slim bones, were gone, too, by now.

She touched a receipt from a hotel in Spain, in Toledo. It was dated almost seven years earlier than the Venice receipts – she'd been pregnant with Billy. On a clear afternoon during the Easter season, they'd driven a rented car to Toledo. From a distance they could see most of the hilly, terraced town with its stone gray wall and the blue Tagus River winding round; Toledo looked so much like an El Greco painting that she half expected to see elongated figures in glowing robes walking the streets. She'd learned that the artist had lost commissions because of his hauteur and pomposity. Not to compare herself, but she'd been turned away by donors for understating what she could do as a filmmaker. She'd always had self-doubts.

Church bells rang throughout the day in different pitches and timbres. On the ancient walls, paper pictures of saints were taped, and red-and-white streamers flew overhead. Half the town seemed to consist of tourist shops. At dusk, the couple joined a solemn parade that was moving ponderously up to the *Catedral,* the great church of Toledo. Incense suffused the air. At the front of the line, in a gray robe, a monk carried a big wooden cross with a life-sized carved Jesus hanging from it. Marianne and David left before the procession reached its destination – they had seen so many churches that they felt weighted down by them – and made their way at first gravely, then giggling, two escapees, to their hotel. They ate – she remembered a rabbit-and-vegetable paella – in their penthouse suite, from which they could see the city lights glimmering in the night.

Two big bottles of sparkling water, which tasted like champagne to them, accompanied the meal. David had joined her in abstinence; he claimed that not drinking and doing Lamaze with her brought him as close as he could get to the experience of being pregnant himself. Not drinking was actually easier for him than for her: she liked her glass of wine with dinner, but alcohol put him to sleep. They kept nonalcoholic beer in the refrigerator at home.

After dinner they undressed, Marianne keeping on only a heavy string of black pearls David had bought her on a trip to China. She'd had a head of thick blond hair back then; "my lioness," he'd teased her. He took a photo of her standing against the bay of windows, her hair and the pearls and her belly luminous. She still had that photo around somewhere; it was a favorite of hers. She took a photo of him naked, too. He was five feet ten, a very slim man with a raised appendectomy scar ("made by a butcher," he'd say) from when he was nine and a sharp, jutting elbow where he'd broken his arm and it had been set badly when he was ten. She thought he'd become a surgeon in order not to repeat with others the botched jobs done on him. David had curly black hair that he kept very bushy because she liked it that way – an Isro, they'd called it in those days. Afterwards, when he saw the photo of himself naked, he was delighted with how well hung he looked. They had made love slowly, gently, she on her side, her back to him because of her belly, still wearing her pearls, which they took off and hung from his erection for a moment, and she remembered feeling, in that city of churches, Jew that she was, beatified.

She occasionally recognized that she had an eternally summery image of her marriage to David. À la Fragonard, if that wasn't too fancy. It was not so much that the dead sprouted wings, as some said, for she genuinely believed David had been a good man – as was Stu. In fact, she was a fortunate woman. It had something to do, she'd had the thought very recently – why only very recently? – with glorifying the inaccessible, while denigrating what was available to her. She recognized in some inchoate way that doing this darkened her life, and the lives of others.

Afterwards, in that Toledo hotel room, she had asked him if he wanted to have anal intercourse, and he said if she wanted. Neither of them had ever done it before. She lay on her side and they lubricated him to the hilt and he came into her slowly, carefully, and it felt strange, like she had to go to the toilet. Throughout, she worried she'd crap all over the place. And she got angry at him later. And he said, rightly, "It was your idea!" And they both spent a long time in the shower.

Sometimes he would come almost as soon as he entered her. They would have screaming fights about it – why had she screamed at him? She had impoverished their love life – even though he'd get a second erection and could last so long she'd limp afterwards.

In a box from the basement she saw her shrink bills that he'd paid. She'd gone to Dr. Levinson with the complaint that she was in the wrong profession and that she'd married the wrong man. She'd had it with social work – sitting on the phone at the hospital trying to find dispositions for chronic psychiatric patients, getting them out of the hospital and into group homes, or into the homes of relatives. It often took days if the patient was poor. Finally, when she found a place,

the patient would stay there at most a few months – after which he would stop taking his meds and end up hallucinating on the streets again. And then, back to the hospital. She wanted to do something less Sisyphean.

David made enough money so that she could afford to quit. She'd gone to film school at NYU, which she really enjoyed. But she wanted to be a star, to excel at something, and she never really had. Except that she'd been loved immoderately. But that wasn't exactly *her* excelling.

She complained that her husband wasn't creative. She should be married to a filmmaker. Not someone who put in long hours at a hospital, although he managed to drive Billy to school several mornings a week, and he ran a boys' basketball league. He spoke at different medical schools and hospitals, and not only about that procedure he had invented but about different materials he was experimenting with for pinning bones. She went to hear him a few times and was vaguely proud of him, but found the talks stupefying.

There was a receipt from a hotel in Lucca, in Tuscany. It had been pouring so hard that dark night that he had to pull the car to a stop on a cobblestone street before they could get near the hotel. Billy was asleep, seat-belted in, in the back of the rented car. She and David somehow got into a discussion of money. He was very proud of being a good breadwinner. She was maintaining that money didn't matter. Art mattered. She yelled at him, "All you think about is money."

"I'm what keeps this family afloat," he said. The rain beat against the windshield and the top of the car. "It's because of me you can do whatever you damn please."

"Don't throw that up to me."

"I'm not. I was happy to pay for school for you."

"You don't respect me. I mean, as an artist."

"For God's sake, where do you get that claptrap from? Talk about *respect*! If I had to depend on you for my self-esteem, my head would be in the toilet."

She was in the bookstore with her son. Billy was his present age, thirty-seven, but with his formerly curly blond hair (a putto, they'd called him, until he was school age), indeed a big bush of curly blond hair, although his hair had never been bushy. Certainly he didn't have his current bright-brown wavy hair, graying a little, thinning out and receding at the temples. Instead of being distraught, he was happy. Happy to see her. In fact, he shone. He was well muscled, in a black T-shirt and red shorts. He showed her first editions of books she had read to him in childhood (he handled them with pleasure now, but also carefully): *Charlotte's Web*, *The Trumpet of the Swan*, *Norman the Doorman*. She remembered he would lie under the covers and she would lie above the covers beside him and read to him. They would look at the pictures. They would fall asleep together.

One night Billy, age four, had said to her, "Marry me."

"What about Dad?" She smiled.

"He can sew."

Now Billy took her by the hand and led her to his book-lined office. There was no photo of Lyria here, not even one with the glass cracked. And no computer. What there was, was a riot of flowers, cream-colored roses on the desk, a tall black vase of burning orange gladioli standing in front of the fireplace, fat pink

peonies and deep-red poppies in a bowl on a side table beside an easy chair. A soft light shone against the white walls. The mingled odors, the sweetness of the flowers and the woody acridness of the books, moved her. She and Billy slowly, languidly undressed, and he had a glistening erection. Her body was taut as a young girl's or as a pregnant abdomen. He entered into her and she came at once, explosively, yet gently, and they went on and on.

Darkest Desire

From JUSTINE

Marquis de Sade

Donatien Alphonse François, Marquis de Sade was a French aristocrat, revolutionary politician, philosopher, writer and libertine. His works include novels, short stories, plays, dialogues, and political tracts; in his lifetime some were published under his own name, while others appeared anonymously with de Sade denying authorship. Works such as *The 120 Days of Sodom* (1785), *Justine* (1791), *Philosophy in the Bedroom* (1795) and *Juliette* (1797-1801), combined philosophical discourse with pornography, depicting sexual fantasies with an emphasis on violence, criminality, and blasphemy. He was incarcerated in various institutions for about thirty-two years of his life, including the Bastille and the Charenton insane asylum. However, during the French Revolution, he was an elected delegate to the National Convention. Many of his works were written in prison.

"Were these alternatives not so clear, were they not so few, I would ask for your response; but in your present situation we can dispense with questions and answers. I have you, Thérèse, and hence you must obey me. . . . Let us go to my wife's apartment."

Having nothing to object to a discourse as precise as this, I followed my master: we traversed a long gallery, as dark, as solitary as the rest of the château; a door opens, we enter an antechamber where I recognize the two elderly women who waited upon me during my coma and recovery. They got up and introduced us into a superb apartment where we found the unlucky Countess doing tambour brocade as she reclined upon a chaise longue; she rose when she saw her husband.

"Be seated," the Count said to her, "I permit you to listen to me thus. Here at last we have a maid for you, Madame," he continued, "and I trust you will remember what has befallen the others – and that you will not try to plunge this one into an identical misfortune."

"It would be useless," I said, full eager to be of help to this poor woman and wishing to disguise my designs, "yes, Madame, I dare certify in your presence that it would be to no purpose, you will not speak one word to me I shall not report immediately to his Lordship, and I shall certainly not jeopardize my life in order to serve you."

"I will undertake nothing, Mademoiselle, which might force you into that position," said this poor woman who did not yet grasp my motives for speaking in this wise; "rest assured: I solicit nothing but your care."

"It will be entirely yours, Madame," I answered, "but beyond that, nothing."

And the Count, enchanted with me, squeezed my hand as he whispered: "Nicely done, Thérèse, your prosperity is guaranteed if you conduct yourself as you say you will." The Count then showed me to my room which adjoined the Countess' and he showed me as well that the entirety of this apartment, closed by stout doors and double grilled at every window, left no hope of escape.

"And here you have a terrace," Monsieur de Gernande went on, leading me out into a little garden on a level with the apartment, "but its elevation above the ground ought not, I believe, give you the idea of measuring the walls; the Countess is permitted to take fresh air out here whenever she wishes, you will keep her company . . . adieu."

I returned to my mistress and, as at first we spent a few moments examining one another without speaking, I obtained a good picture of her – but let me paint it for you.

Madame de Gernande, aged nineteen and a half, had the most lovely, the most noble, the most majestic figure one could hope to see, not one of her gestures, not a single movement was without gracefulness, not one of her glances lacked depth of sentiment: nothing could equal the expression of her eyes, which were a beautiful dark brown although her hair was blond; but a certain languor, a lassitude entailed by her misfortunes, dimmed their *éclat*, and thereby rendered them a thousand times more interesting; her skin was very fair, her hair very rich; her mouth was very small, perhaps too small, and I was little surprised to find this defect in her: 'twas a pretty rose not yet in full bloom; but teeth so white . . . lips of a vermillion . . . one might have said Love had colored them with tints borrowed from the goddess of flowers; her nose was aquiline, straight, delicately modeled; upon her brow curved two ebony eyebrows; a perfectly lovely chin; a visage, in one word, of the finest oval shape, over whose entirety reigned a kind of attractiveness, a naïveté, an openness which might well have made one take this adorable face for an angelic rather than mortal physiognomy. Her arms, her breasts, her flanks were of a splendor . . . of a round fullness fit to serve as models to an artist; a black silken fleece covered her *mons veneris,* which was sustained by two superbly cast thighs; and what astonished me was that, despite the slenderness of the Countess' figure, despite her sufferings, nothing had impaired the firm quality of her flesh: her round, plump buttocks were as smooth, as ripe, as firm as if her figure were heavier and as if she had always dwelled in the depths of happiness. However, frightful traces of her husband's libertinage were scattered thickly about; but, I repeat, nothing spoiled, nothing damaged . . . the very image of a beautiful lily upon which the honeybee has inflicted some scratches. To so many gifts Madame de Gernande added a gentle nature, a romantic and tender mind, a heart of such sensibility! . . . well-educated, with talents . . . a native art for seduction which no one but her infamous husband could resist, a charming timbre in her voice and much piety: such was the unhappy wife of the Comte de Gernande, such was the heavenly creature against whom he had plotted; it seemed that the more she inspired ideas, the more she inflamed his ferocity, and that the abundant gifts she had received from Nature only became further motives for that villain's cruelties.

"When were you last bled, Madame?" I asked in order to have her understand I was acquainted with everything.

"Three days ago," she said, "and it is to be tomorrow. . . ." Then, with a sigh: ". . . yes, tomorrow . . . Mademoiselle, tomorrow you will witness the pretty scene."

"And Madame is not growing weak?"

"Oh, Great Heaven! I am not twenty and am sure I shall be no weaker at seventy. But it will come to an end, I flatter myself in the belief, for it is perfectly impossible for me to live much longer this way: I will go to my Father, in the arms of the Supreme Being I will seek a place of rest men have so cruelly denied me on earth."

These words clove my heart; wishing to maintain my role, I disguised my trouble, but upon the instant I made an inward promise to lay down my life a thousand times, if necessary, rather than leave this ill-starred victim in the clutches of this monstrous debauchee.

The Countess was on the point of taking her dinner. The two old women came to tell me to conduct her into her cabinet; I transmitted the message; she was accustomed to it all, she went out at once, and the two women, aided by the two valets who had carried me off, served a sumptuous meal upon a table at which my place was set opposite my mistress. The valets retired and the women informed me that they would not stir from the antechamber so as to be near at hand to receive whatever might be Madame's orders. I relayed this to the Countess, she took her place and, with an air of friendliness and affability which entirely won my heart, invited me to join her. There were at least twenty dishes upon the table.

"With what regards this aspect of things, Mademoiselle, you see that they treat me well."

"Yes, Madame," I replied, "and I know it is the wish of Monsieur le Comte that you lack nothing."

"Oh yes! But as these attentions are motivated only by cruelty, my feelings are scarcely of gratitude."

Her constant state of debilitation and perpetual need of what would revive her strength obliged Madame de Gernande to eat copiously. She desired partridge and Rouen duckling; they were brought to her in a trice. After the meal, she went for some air on the terrace, but upon rising she took my arm, for she was quite unable to take ten steps without someone to lean upon. It was at this moment she showed me all those parts of her body I have just described to you; she exhibited her arms: they were covered with small scars.

"Ah, he does not confine himself to that," she said, "there is not a single spot on my wretched person whence he does not love to see blood flow."

And she allowed me to see her feet, her neck, the lower part of her breasts and several other fleshy areas equally speckled with healed punctures. That first day I limited myself to murmuring a few sympathetic words and we retired for the night.

The morrow was the Countess' fatal day. Monsieur de Gernande, who only performed the operation after his dinner – which he always took before his wife ate hers – had me join him at table; it was then, Madame, I beheld that ogre fall

to in a manner so terrifying that I could hardly believe my eyes. Four domestics, amongst them the pair who had led me to the château, served this amazing feast. It deserves a thorough description: I shall give it you without exaggeration. The meal was certainly not intended simply to overawe me. What I witnessed then was an everyday affair.

Two soups were brought on, one a consommé flavored with saffron, the other a ham bisque; then a sirloin of English roast beef, eight hors d'oeuvres, five substantial entrées, five others only apparently lighter, a boar's head in the midst of eight braised dishes which were relieved by two services of entremets, then sixteen plates of fruit; ices, six brands of wine, four varieties of liqueur and coffee. Monsieur de Gernande attacked every dish, and several were polished off to the last scrap; he drank a round dozen bottles of wine, four, to begin with, of Burgundy, four of Champagne with the roasts; Tokay, Mulseau, Hermitage and Madeira were downed with the fruit. He finished with two bottles of West Indies rum and ten cups of coffee.

As fresh after this performance as he might have been had he just waked from sleep, Monsieur de Gernande said:

"Off we go to bleed your mistress; I trust you will let me know if I manage as nicely with her as I did with you."

Two young boys I had not hitherto seen, and who were of the same age as the others, were awaiting at the door of the Countess' apartment; it was then the Count informed me he had twelve minions and renewed them every year. These seemed yet prettier than the ones I had seen hitherto; they were livelier . . . we went in. . . . All the ceremonies I am going to describe now, Madame, were part of a ritual from which the Count never deviated, they were scrupulously observed upon each occasion, and nothing ever changed except the place where the incisions were made.

The Countess, dressed only in a loose-floating muslin robe, fell to her knees instantly the Count entered.

"Are you ready?" her husband inquired.

"For everything, Monsieur," was the humble reply; "you know full well I am your victim and you have but to command me."

Monsieur de Gernande thereupon told me to undress his wife and lead her to him. Whatever the loathing I sensed for all these horrors, you understand, Madame, I had no choice but to submit with the most entire resignation. In all I have still to tell you, do not, I beseech you, do not at any time regard me as anything but a slave; I complied simply because I could not do otherwise, but never did I act willingly in anything whatsoever.

I removed my mistress' simar, and when she was naked conducted her to her husband who had already taken his place in a large armchair: as part of the ritual she perched upon this armchair and herself presented to his kisses that favorite part over which he had made such a to-do with me and which, regardless of person or sex, seemed to affect him in the same way.

"And now spread them, Madame," the Count said brutally.

And for a long time he rollicked about with what he enjoyed the sight of; he had it assume various positions, he opened it, he snapped it shut; with tongue and fingertip he tickled the narrow aperture; and soon carried away by his pas-

sions' ferocity, he plucked up a pinch of flesh, squeezed it, scratched it. Immediately he produced a small wound he fastened his mouth to the spot. I held his unhappy victim during these preliminaries, the two boys, completely naked, toiled upon him in relays; now one, now the other knelt between Gernande's thighs and employed his mouth to excite him. It was then I noticed, not without astonishment, that this giant, this species of monster whose aspect alone was enough to strike terror, was howbeit barely a man; the most meager, the most minuscule excrescence of flesh or, to make a juster comparison, what one might find in a child of three was all one discovered upon this so very enormous and otherwise so corpulent individual; but its sensations were not for that the less keen and each pleasurable vibration was as a spasmodic attack. After this prologue he stretched out upon a couch and wanted his wife, seated astride his chest, to keep her behind poised over his visage while with her mouth she rendered him, by means of suckings, the same service he had just received from the youthful Ganymedes who were simultaneously, one to the left, one to the right, being excited by him; my hands meanwhile worked upon his behind: I titillated it, I polluted it in every sense; this phase of activities lasted more than a quarter of an hour but, producing no results, had to be given up for another; upon her husband's instructions I stretched the Countess upon a chaise longue: she lay on her back, her legs spread as wide as possible. The sight of what she exposed put her husband in a kind of rage, he dwelt upon the perspective . . . his eyes blaze, he curses; like one crazed he leaps upon his wife, with his scalpel pricks her in several places, but these were all superficial gashes, a drop or two of blood, no more, seeped from each. These minor cruelties came to an end at last; others began. The Count sits down again, he allows his wife a moment's respite, and, turning his attention to his two little followers, he now obliges them to suck each other, and now he arranges them in such a way that while he sucks one, the other sucks him, and now again the one he sucked first brings round his mouth to render the same service to him by whom he was sucked: the Count received much but gave little. Such was his satiety, such his impotence that the extremest efforts availed not at all, and he remained in his torpor: he did indeed seem to experience some very violent reverberations, but nothing manifested itself; he several times ordered me to suck his little friends and immediately to convey to his mouth whatever incense I drained from them; finally he flung them one after the other at the miserable Countess. These young men accosted her, insulted her, carried insolence to the point of beating her, slapping her, and the more they molested her, the more loudly the Count praised and egged them on.

Then Gernande turned to me; I was in front of him, my buttocks at the level of his face, and he paid his respects to his God; but he did not abuse me; nor do I know why he did not torment his Ganymedes; he chose to reserve all his unkindness for the Countess. Perhaps the honor of being allied to him established one's right to suffer mistreatment at his hands; perhaps he was moved to cruelty only by attachments which contributed energy to his outrages. One can imagine anything about such minds, and almost always safely wager that what seems most apt to be criminal is what will inflame them most. At last he places his young friends and me beside his wife and enlaces our bodies; here a man, there a woman, etc., all four dressing their behinds; he takes his stand some dis-

tance away and muses upon the panorama, then he comes near, touches, feels, compares, caresses; the youths and I were not persecuted, but each time he came to his wife, he fussed and bothered and vexed her in some way or other. Again the scene changes: he has the Countess lie belly down upon a divan and taking each boy in turn, he introduces each of them into the narrow avenue Madame's posture exposes: he allows them to become aroused, but it is nowhere but in his mouth the sacrifice is to be consummated; as one after another they emerge he sucks each. While one acts, he has himself sucked by the other, and his tongue wanders to the throne of voluptuousness the agent presents to him. This activity continues a long time, it irritates the Count, he gets to his feet and wishes me to take the Countess' place; I instantly beg him not to require it of me, but he insists. He lays his wife upon her back, has me superimpose myself upon her with my flanks raised in his direction and thereupon he orders his aides to plumb me by the forbidden passage: he brings them up, his hands guide their introduction; meanwhile, I have got to stimulate the Countess with my fingers and kiss her mouth; as for the Count, his offertory is still the same; as each of the boys cannot act without exhibiting to him one of the sweetest objects of his veneration, he turns it all to his profit and, as with the Countess, he who has just perforated me is obliged to go, after a few lunges and retreats, and spill into his mouth the incense I have warmed. When the boys are finished, seemingly inclined to replace them, the Count glues himself to my buttocks.

"Superfluous efforts," he cries, "this is not what I must have . . . to the business . . . the business . . . however pitiable my state . . . I can hold back no longer . . . come, Countess, your arms!"

He seizes her ferociously, places her as I was placed, arms suspended by two black straps; mine is the task of securing the bands; he inspects the knots: finding them too loose, he tightens them, "So that," he says, "the blood will spurt out under greater pressure"; he feels the veins, and lances them, on each arm, at almost the same moment. Blood leaps far: he is in an ecstasy; and adjusting himself so that he has a clear view of these two fountains, he has me kneel between his legs so I can suck him; he does as much for first one and then the other of his little friends, incessantly eyeing the jets of blood which inflame him. For my part, certain the instant at which the hoped for crisis occurs will bring a conclusion to the Countess' torments, I bring all my efforts to bear upon precipitating this denouement, and I become, as, Madame, you observe, I become a whore from kindness, a libertine through virtue. The much awaited moment arrives at last; I am not familiar with its dangers or violence, for the last time it had taken place I had been unconscious. . . . Oh, Madame! what extravagance! Gernande remained delirious for ten minutes, flailing his arms, staggering, reeling like one falling in a fit of epilepsy, and uttering screams which must have been audible for a league around; his oaths were excessive; lashing out at everyone at hand, his strugglings were dreadful. The two little ones are sent tumbling head over heels; he wishes to fly at his wife, I restrain him: I pump the last drop from him, his need of me makes him respect me; at last I bring him to his senses by ridding him of that fiery liquid, whose heat, whose viscosity, and above all whose abundance puts him in such a frenzy I believe he is going to expire; seven or eight tablespoons would scarcely have contained the discharge, and the thickest gruel

would hardly give a notion of its consistency; and with all that, no appearance of an erection at all, rather, the limp look and feel of exhaustion: there you have the contrarieties which, better than might I, explain artists of the Count's breed. The Count ate excessively and only dissipated each time he bled his wife, every four days, that is to say. Would this be the cause of the phenomenon? I have no idea, and not daring to ascribe a reason to what I do not understand, I will be content to relate what I saw.

However, I rush to the Countess, I stanch her blood, untie her, and deposit her upon a couch in a state of extreme weakness; but the Count, totally indifferent to her, without condescending to cast even a glance at this victim stricken by his rage, abruptly goes out with his aides, leaving me to put things in whatever order I please. Such is the fatal apathy which better than all else characterizes the true libertine soul: if he is merely carried away by passion's heat, limned with remorse will be his face when, calmed again, he beholds the baleful effects of delirium; but if his soul is utterly corrupt? then such consequences will affright him not: he will observe them with as little trouble as regret, perhaps even with some of the emotion of those infamous lusts which produced them.

I put Madame de Gernande to bed. She had, so she said, lost much more this time than she ordinarily did; but such good care and so many restoratives were lavished upon her, that she appeared well two days later. That same evening, when I had completed all my chores in the Countess' apartment, word arrived that the Count desired to speak to me; Gernande was taking supper; I was obliged to wait upon him while he fed with a much greater intemperance than at dinner; four of his pretty little friends were seated round the table with him and there, every evening, he regularly drank himself into drunkenness; but to that end, twenty bottles of the most excellent wine were scarcely sufficient and I often saw him empty thirty. And every evening, propped up by his minions, the debauchee went to bed, and took one or two of the boys with him; these were nothing but vehicles which disposed him for the great scene.

But I had discovered the secret of winning this man's very highest esteem: he frankly avowed to me that few women had pleased him so much; and thereby I acquired the right to his confidence, which I only exploited in order to serve my mistress.

From MEMOIRS OF A YOUNG RAKEHILL

Guillaume Apollinaire

Guillaume Apollinaire was a French poet, playwright, short story writer, novelist, and art critic of Polish descent. Apollinaire is considered one of the foremost poets of the early 20th century, as well as one of the most impassioned defenders of Cubism and a forefather of Surrealism. He is credited with coining the term Cubism (1911) to describe the new art movement, the term Orphism (1912), and the term Surrealism (1917) to describe the works of Erik Satie. He wrote one of the earliest works described as Surrealist, the play *The Breasts of Tiresias* (1917), which was used as the basis for the 1947 opera *Les mamelles de Tirésias*. Two years after being wounded in World War I, he died in the Spanish flu pandemic of 1918 aged thirty-eight.

The day's events had worn me to a frazzle. My one desire was to rest. When I awoke the next morning, I was lying on my back, a position which usually gives me an erection. Shortly thereafter I heard the sound of approaching footsteps. Wanting to play a joke on the bailiff's wife, I lifted my nightshirt, threw the blankets off me and pretended to be asleep.

But instead of the bailiff's wife, it was her sister-in-law, a woman of thirty-five or so, the age when a woman is at the height of sensuality.

In her younger days she had been a housemaid. Having married an elderly butler who managed to amass a neat pile of savings, she presently lived with her husband and three children (a son and two daughters of ten, eleven and thirteen, respectively) in her brother the bailiff's quarters.

Madame Muller was neither ugly nor beautiful. She was tall, had a strikingly good figure, a dark complexion and her hair, like her eyes, was pitch black. She seemed intelligent and fully worthy of a bout with my John Thomas.

And you could bet your last penny that she'd seen more than one such animal in her lifetime. So, I reasoned, why not let her see mine as well. I lay there motionless.

Madame Muller set the coffee on the nightstand. Then, seeing John Thomas standing stiffly at attention, she had a moment's hesitation. But she was a resolute woman, free from all false modesty. She spent several seconds gazing at me with apparent pleasure. Then she coughed discreetly to awaken me, and as I stretched my limbs in such a way as to give my prick an even more insolent air,

she approached the bed, looked down for a second, then pulled the covers up and said: "Your coffee, Master Roger".

I opened my eyes, wished her good morning, and complimented her on how well she was looking, etc. Then I suddenly jumped out of the bed, seized her and assured her that she was the most beautiful woman in the whole chateau.

She resisted weakly; slipping my hand beneath her skirts, I discovered a very hairy mound. Then I drove my finger into her cunt. As is the case with all sensual women, hers was dry, but my finger-work soon remedied that. Her clitoris was extremely hard.

"But what's come over you? Stop that! What would my husband say if he knew!"

"Mr. Muller's in the chapel."

"Yes. I know. He does nothing but pray all day long.

But stop that now, you're hurting me. My sister-in-law might come in. She's waiting for me. That's enough now! I'll come back tonight. My husband's leaving today for two or three days in the country. But now we're liable to be interrupted... "

And with that she took her leave. That evening, after having eaten a hearty dinner, I took some wine, ham and dessert back with me to my room. The chateau was soon asleep. Finally, after what seemed like hours, Madame Muller came in. My heart was beating like a triphammer. I embraced her, and gave her a French kiss, which she returned. I undressed quickly and showed her my prick in a most presentable condition.

"Don't get so excited," she warned, "or we'll waken the whole house and set the tongues to wagging."

She bolted the door. I fastened her mound in a tight grip, and found it slightly swollen, and her clitoris extremely hard. I stripped her down to her petticoat, and lifted it high. Seeing her dressed you'd have taken her for thin, but she wasn't in the least. In fact if anything she was on the fleshy side. Her dark pubic hair, I noticed, climbed all the way up to her navel.

She must just have washed, for her Lady Jane was odorless. Then I stripped her completely and was amazed to find how firm her breasts were. They were only moderately large, and her nipples were set in a small field of light brown hair.

Lifting her breasts, I saw that she also had some short, fine black hairs underneath. Her armpits were likewise covered with hair as thick as a man's.

What surprised me most as I examined her more closely, were her well raised buttocks, whose cheeks were set close together. Along her backbone ran a fine line of black hair, from top to bottom. The sight of all this healthy fleece caused John Thomas to harden even more.

I ripped off my nightshirt and straddled the lovely creature, whose rhythmic movements set my pickle slapping back and forth against her belly.

We were in such a position that we could clearly see ourselves in the mirror. I led her toward the bed, where she sat down and said: "I know you want to see all of me." She raised her legs and displayed her hairy cunt right up to her pot hole. I immediately set to tonguing her, and lingered at the task for quite some time. Her lips began to swell. When I went to insert my tool, she laughed and said: "Not like that. Get on the bed."

I asked her to please use the familiar "thou" form with me, and to allow me to do the same with her.

I got onto the bed. She climbed on top of me and I thus had her whole beautiful body before my eyes. She told me to play with her boobies. Then she grasped my prick, paraded it awhile against her love lips, and at the same time asked me to be sure not to come inside her. Then she suddenly shoved my tool in right up to the ballbearings. She was riding me so strenuously that it was almost painful. Round about that time she came, and I could feel all the warmth of her cunt, hear her heaving sighs, and see her eyes roll back in her head.

Realizing that I was also on the point of coming, she got quickly to her feet.

"Hold on a minute, young fellow, my lad," she said in a voice still trembling with emotion, "I know still another that'll satisfy you without making me pregnant."

She turned round; her buttocks were now facing me. She bent down and took my prick in her mouth. I followed her example and began tonguing her love lips, lapping up the female love-juice which tasted like a raw egg. She stepped up the play of her tongue against my glans, and with one hand she tickled my balls and buttocks, while with the other she gripped my penis.

I stiffened with pleasure. She thrust my prick as far in her mouth as possible. Her most secret parts were staring me full in the face. I seized her buttocks, and plunged my tongue into her pothole. I lost control of myself and ejaculated in her mouth.

When I recovered from my momentary rapture, she was lying beside me and had pulled the blankets up over us. She was caressing me, thanking me for the pleasure I had given her, and asked me if I had enjoyed it as much as she.

I had to admit that I had enjoyed that position even more than normal coitus. And then I asked her why she hadn't let me come inside her, since she was married.

"For that very reason," she said. "My husband is impotent, and can tell whenever I cheat on him. Oh, God in Heaven! what I have to put up with from that man!"

I asked her to tell me all about it. She said that her husband could get an erection only if she beat him with a rod until she drew blood.

She likewise had to let him strike her, but only with his hand, and now she was so used to it that she enjoyed it more than it hurt her. He also made her peepee and shit in his presence, so eager was he not to miss a trick. And he got especially worked up when she had her periods.

After she had struck him fifty or even a hundred times, she had to hurry and slip his half-erect member inside, for otherwise it fell limp, except when she licked his buttocks or let him lick her between the toes. Whenever that happened he was able to keep a good hard on, but all these things were pretty disagreeable.

"And on top of all that," she concluded, "the old rascal spends all his time in church."

Her story had aroused the flagging spirits of my John Thomas. Madame Muller had hastened the resurrection by tickling my balls. She had me get between her legs, and turned over on her side. She scissored my buttocks with her legs, so that we were both lying on our sides, face to face. It was a good position, allow-

ing us to lie closely interlaced, and at the same time leaving her titties exposed to my tongue.

I was holding her cunt, which the bout of pleasure had caused to narrow, with my hand. Both of us thrust our fingers into the other's arse-hole. I let my prick slide softly into her cunt, and began to rock as before, sucking her nipples all the while.

I kept my finger moving in her throbbing arse-hole. She came a second time with a cry of delight. She had taken hold of my balls from behind and was squeezing them so tightly that she hurt me, and I had to ask her to let them go.

After having caressed me gently, she turned her head toward the pillow, so that her magnificent buttocks were prominently displayed. I had her rise to her knees and lift her buttocks high. I sent a wad of spit flying into her pothole, and thrust my prick in easily. At each stroke I felt my balls bounce off her buttock cheeks.

She kept telling me how good it felt. I could touch her hairy cunt with one hand and fondle her breasts with the other. Just as I was about to come I started to withdraw but she contracted her buttock muscles around my glans, and I ejaculated squarely into her arse-hole. Afterwards she told me that that was the first time she'd done it that way, and that, although it had hurt in the beginning, in the end she'd enjoyed it.

Feeling my prick harden in her buttocks hole, her sensual forces had awakened and she had had another orgasm at the same time as mine.

"But that's about enough for today," she decided, smiling.

That was about all I could take too. I offered her some dessert, but she insisted that I come and have a short liqueur in her room instead. After which, I came back to my room and fell into bed.

THE ANTIQUE WARDROBE

Georges Bataille

Georges Bataille was a twentieth-century French intellectual and literary figure working in literature, philosophy, anthropology, economics, sociology and history of art. At the core of his writings, which included essays, novels, and poetry, are explorations of eroticism, mysticism, sovereignty and transgression. His most famous work is *Histoire de l'oeil* (1928), written under the pseudonym of Lord Auch.

That was the period when Simone developed a mania for breaking eggs with her behind. She would do a headstand on an armchair in the parlour, her back against the chair's back, her legs bent towards me, while I jerked off in order to come in her face. I would put the egg right on the hole in her arse, and she would skillfully amuse herself by shaking it in the deep crack of her buttocks. The moment my come shot out and trickled down her eyes, her buttocks would squeeze together and she would come while I smeared my face abundantly in her ass.

Very soon, of course, her mother, who might enter the villa parlour at any moment, did catch us in our unusual act. But still, the first time this fine woman stumbled upon us, she was content, despite having led an exemplary life, to gape wordlessly, so that we did not notice a thing. I suppose she was too flabbergasted to speak. But when we were done and trying to clean up the mess, we noticed her standing in the doorway.

"Pretend there's no one there," Simone told mc, and she went on wiping her behind.

And indeed, we blithely strolled out as though the woman had been reduced to a family portrait.

A few days later, however, when Simone was doing gymnastics with me in the rafters of a garage, she pissed on her mother, who had the misfortune to stop underneath without seeing her. The sad widow got out of the way and gazed at us with such dismal eyes and such a desperate expression that she egged us on, that is to say, simply, with Simone bursting into laughter, crouching on all fours on the beams and exposing her cunt to my face, I uncovered that cunt completely and masturbated while looking at it.

More than a week had passed without our seeing Marcelle, when we ran into her on the street one day. The blonde girl, timid and naively pious, blushed so deeply at seeing us, that Simone embraced her with uncommon tenderness.

"Please forgive me, Marcelle," she murmured. "What happened the other day was absurd, but that doesn't mean we can't be friends now. I promise we'll never lay a hand on you again."

Marcelle, who had an unusual lack of will power, agreed to join us for tea with some other friends at our place. But instead of tea, we drank quantities of chilled champagne.

The sight of Marcelle blushing had completely overwhelmed us. We understood one another, Simone and I, and we were certain that from now on nothing would make us shrink from achieving our ends. Besides Marcelle, there were three other pretty girls and two boys here. The oldest of the eight being not quite seventeen, the beverage soon took effect; but aside from Simone and myself, they were not as excited as we wanted them to be. A gramophone rescued us from our predicament. Simone, dancing a frenzied Charleston by herself, showed everyone her legs up to her cunt, and when the other girls were asked to dance a solo in the same way, they were in too good a mood to require coaxing. They did have panties on, but the panties bound the cunt laxly without hiding much. Only Marcelle, intoxicated and silent, refused to dance.

Finally, Simone, pretending to be dead drunk, crumpled a tablecloth and, lifting it up, she offered to make a bet.

"I bet," she said, "that I can pee into the tablecloth in front of everyone."

It was basically a ridiculous party of mostly turbulent and boastful youngsters. One of the boys challenged her, and it was agreed that the winner would fix the penalty. . . . Naturally, Simone did not waver for an instant, she richly soaked the tablecloth. But this stunning act visibly rattled her to the quick, so that all the young fools started gasping.

"Since the winner decides the penalty," said Simone to the loser, "I am now going to pull down your trousers in front of everyone."

Which happened without a hitch. When his trousers were off, his shirt was likewise removed (to keep him from looking ridiculous). All the same, nothing serious had occurred as yet: Simone had scarcely run a light hand over her young friend, who was dazzled, drunk, and naked. Yet all she could think of was Marcelle, who for several moments now had been begging me to let her leave.

"We promised we wouldn't touch you, Marcelle. Why do you want to leave?"

"Just because," she replied stubbornly, a violent rage gradually overcoming her.

All at once, to everyone's horror, Simone fell upon the floor. A convulsion shook her harder and harder, her clothes were in disarray, her bottom stuck in the air, as though she were having an epileptic fit. But rolling about at the foot of the boy she had undressed, she mumbled almost inarticulately:

"Piss on me. . . . Piss on my cunt . . ." she repeated, with a kind of thirst.

Marcelle gaped at this spectacle: she blushed again, her face was blood-red. But then she said to me, without even looking at me, that she wanted to take off her dress. I half tore it off, and straight after, her underwear. All she had left was her stockings and belt, and after I fingered her cunt a bit and kissed her on the mouth, she glided across the room to a large antique bridal wardrobe, where she shut herself in after whispering a few words to Simone.

*

She wanted to toss off in the wardrobe and was pleading to be left in peace.

I ought to say that we were all very drunk and completely bowled over by what had been going on. The naked boy was being sucked by a girl. Simone, standing with her dress tucked up, was rubbing her bare cunt against the wardrobe, in which a girl was audibly masturbating with brutal gasps. And all at once, something incredible happened, a strange swish of water, followed by a trickle and a stream from under the wardrobe door: poor Marcelle was pissing in her wardrobe while masturbating. But the explosion of totally drunken guffaws that ensued rapidly degenerated into a debauche of tumbling bodies, lofty legs and arses, wet skirts and come. Guffaws emerged like foolish and involuntary hiccups but scarcely managed to interrupt a brutal onslaught on cunts and cocks. And yet soon we could hear Marcelle dismally sobbing alone, louder and louder, in the make-shift pissoir that was now her prison.

Half an hour later, when I was less drunk, it dawned on me that I ought to let Marcelle out of her wardrobe: the unhappy girl, naked now, was in a dreadful state. She was trembling and shivering feverishly. Upon seeing me, she displayed a sickly but violent terror. After all, I was pale, smeared with blood, my clothes askew. Behind me, in unspeakable disorder, brazenly stripped bodies were sprawled about. During the orgy, splinters of glass had left deep bleeding cuts in two of us. A young girl was throwing up, and all of us had exploded in such wild fits of laughter at some point or other that we had wet our clothes, an armchair, or the floor. The resulting stench of blood, sperm, urine, and vomit made me almost recoil in horror, but the inhuman shriek from Marcelle's throat was far more terrifying. I must say, however, that Simone was sleeping tranquilly by now, her belly up, her hand still on her pussy, her pacified face almost smiling.

Marcelle, staggering wildly across the room with shrieks and snarls, looked at me again. She flinched back as though I were a hideous ghost in a nightmare, and she collapsed in a jeremiad of howls that grew more and more inhuman.

Astonishingly, this litany brought me to my senses. People were running up, it was inevitable. But I never for an instant dreamt of fleeing or lessening the scandal. On the contrary, I resolutely strode to the door and flung it open. What a spectacle, what joy! One can readily picture the cries of dismay, the desperate shrieks, the exaggerated threats of the parents entering the room! Criminal court, prison, the guillotine were evoked with fiery yells and spasmodic curses. Our friends themselves began howling and sobbing in a delirium of tearful screams; they sounded as if they had been set afire as live torches. Simone exulted with me.

And yet, what an atrocity! It seemed as if nothing could terminate the tragicomical frenzy of these lunatics, for Marcelle, still naked, kept gesticulating, and her agonizing shrieks of pain expressed unbearable terror and moral suffering; we watched her bite her mother's face amid arms vainly trying to subdue her.

Indeed, by bursting in, the parents managed to wipe out the last shreds of reason, and in the end, the police had to be called, with all the neighbours witnessing the outrageous scandal.

From THE STORY OF O

Pauline Réage

Fifty years ago, an extraordinary pornographic novel appeared in Paris. Published simultaneously in French and English, *Story of O* (1954) portrayed explicit scenes of bondage and violent penetration in spare, elegant prose, the purity of the writing making the novel seem reticent even as it dealt with demonic desire, whips, masks and chains. The author's pseudonym, Pauline Réage, was thought by many to be that of a man. The writer's identity was only revealed recently, when an impeccably dressed eighty-six-year-old Dominique Aury (born Anne Desclos) acknowledged authorship. Aury was an eminent figure in literary France, and had been when she wrote the book at the age of forty-seven. A translator, editor and judge of literary prizes, Aury was the only woman to sit on the reading committee of publishers Gallimard (a body that also included Albert Camus) and was a holder of the Légion d'Honneur. She could scarcely have been more highbrow.

When René informed her that he was leaving, night had already fallen. O was naked in her cell, waiting to be led to the refectory. For his part, her lover was dressed as usual, in the suit he wore every day in town. When he'd taken her in his arms the rough tweed of his coat had chafed her nipples. He kissed her, lay her upon the bed, lay down beside her, his face to her face, and tenderly and slowly and gently he took her, moving to and fro now in this, now in the other of the two passages offered to him, finally spilling himself into her mouth which, when he was done, he kissed again.

"Before I go I'd like to have you whipped," he said, "and this time I ask your permission. Are you willing?" She was willing. "I love you," he repeated; "now ring for Pierre." She rang. Pierre chained her hands above her head by the bed-chain. When thus bound, her lover stepped up on the bed and, his face to her face, penetrated her again, told her again that he loved her, then stepped back on to the floor and signalled to Pierre. He watched her writhe and struggle, so vainly, he listened to her groans develop into screams, these into howls. When the tears had finished flowing, he dismissed Pierre. From somewhere she found the strength to tell him again that she loved him. And then he kissed her soaking face, her gasping mouth, released her bonds, put her to bed, and left.

To say that from the instant her lover had left her O began to await his return would be no overstatement: she turned into pure waiting, darkness in waiting expectation of light. In day-time she was like a painted statue whose skin is warm and smooth, whose mouth is docile, and – it was only during

this interval that she held strictly to the rule – whose eyes are forever lowered. She made and cared for the fire, poured and passed round the coffee, lighted the cigarettes, arranged the flowers and folded up the newspapers like a little girl busy in her parents' living-room, so limpid with her exposed breast and her leather collar, her tight bodice and her prisoner's hand-cuffs, so demure, so yielding that it was enough for the men she served to order her to stand by them while they were violating another girl for them to want to violate her too; and that surely was why she was treated worse than ever before. Had she sinned? or had her lover, in leaving her, deliberately intended to make those to whom he lent her feel freer to dispose of her? At any rate, on the second day after his departure, the day drawing to an end and after she had just taken off her clothes and was gazing at herself in her bathroom mirror, the marks Pierre's crop had inscribed on the front of her thighs being by now almost gone, Pierre entered. Two hours still remained before dinner. He informed her that she would not dine in the common room, and bade her ready herself, nodding to the Turkish toilet in the corner where indeed he did make her squat, as Jeanne had warned her she would have to do in Pierre's presence. All the time she was there he stood contemplating her; she saw his image reproduced in the mirrors, and saw herself incapable of holding back the water which was squirting from her body. And still he waited, until she had completed her bath and finished applying her make-up. She was about to reach for her clogs and red cape when he stopped her hand, and added, binding her hands behind her back, that she needn't go to the bother, would she wait there just a moment. She perched herself on a corner of the bed. Outside, gusts of cold wind were blowing, cold rain spattered down, the poplar near the window swayed under the gale's attack. From time to time a pale wet leaf pasted itself against a windowpane. The overcast sky was dark, it was as dark as the heart of the night even though seven had not yet struck, but autumn was wearing on and the days were growing shorter. Pierre returned; in his hand he carried the same blindfold they'd used that first night to prevent her from seeing. He also had, clinking in his hand, a long chain similar to the one affixed to the wall. It appeared to O that he was hesitating as to which to put on her first, the chain or the blindfold. She watched the rain, not caring about his intentions or his uncertainties, thinking only of what René had said, that he'd return, and that she had still five days and five nights to pass, and that she didn't know where he was or if he was alone, and if he wasn't, with whom he could be. But he'd return.

Pierre had placed the chain on the bed and, without disturbing O's thoughts, fastened the black velvet blindfold over her eyes. It fitted snugly up under the ridge of her brow and exactly followed the curve of her cheeks: no possibility of a downward glance nor even of raising her eyelids. Blessed darkness like unto her own inner night-time, never had O welcomed it with such joy, oh blessed chains which bore her away from herself. Pierre attached this new chain to the ring in her collar and invited her to accompany him. She stood up, sensed that she was being tugged along, and followed. Her bare feet froze on the icy tiles, she realized that she was walking down the red wing hallway, then the ground, as cold as before, became rough; she was walking upon flagstones, sandstone, perhaps granite. Twice the valet brought her to a halt, twice she heard a key

scrape in a lock and a lock click as a door closed. "Be careful of the steps," said Pierre, and she descended a stairway, once almost tripped. Pierre caught her in time, though, caught her round the waist. Prior to this, he had never touched her save to chain or beat her, but now here he was laying her upon the cold steps where with her pinioned hands she hung on as best she could to avoid slithering down, here he was clutching her breasts. His mouth was roving from one to the other and at the same time he was pressing himself upon her, she felt his member gradually stiffen. It was only when he was entirely satisfied that he helped her to her feet. Perspiring and trembling from cold, she finally descended the last steps, then heard him open yet another door, through which she was led, immediately feeling a thick carpet under her feet. The chain was still exerting a pull. Yet another pull on the chain and then Pierre's hands released her hands, untied the blindfold: she was in a circular and vaulted room, quite small and very low-ceilinged; the walls and vault were of unfaced stone, the joints in the masonry were visible. The chain leading to her collar was secured to an eye-bolt set in the wall about a yard above the floor and opposite the door, leaving her free to move no more than two paces in any direction. Here, there was neither a bed nor anything that might substitute for one, there was no blanket, not a scrap of covering, and only three or four cushions like the Moroccan cushions, but out of her reach and not meant for her. On the other hand, set in the niche whence shone the sole light illuminating the room, lay a wooden tray; on it were water, fruit, and bread, and these were within her reach. The heat coming from radiators which had been installed at the base of and recessed in the thickness of the walls, and which formed a sort of burning plinth all the way around her, was nevertheless not enough to overcome the damp smell of mustiness and stone which is the odour of ancient prisons and, in old castles, of uninhabited keeps. In this sultry, soundless twilight, O soon lost all track of time, for here there was neither night nor day, and never was the light turned off. Pierre or some other valet, it didn't matter which, replenished her supply of water, placed fruit and bread on the tray when none were left, and would take her to bathe in a nearby dungeon. She never saw the men who entered, because, whenever they came, they were preceded by a valet who blindfolded her and didn't remove the blindfold until they had gone. She also lost track of these visitors, of their number, and neither her gentle blindly caressing hands nor her lips were ever able to identify whom they touched. Sometimes there were several of them, most often they came singly, but every time, before she was approached, she was placed on her knees, her face to the wall, her collar fastened to the same bolt to which her chain was affixed, and whipped. She would lay her palms flat against the wall and press her face against the back of her hands so as to avoid being scraped by the stone; but it lacerated her knees and breasts. She also lost track of the whippings and of her screams; the vault muffled them. She waited. All of a sudden, time stopped standing still. In the very midst of her velvety, anaesthetic night-time she felt her chain being detached. She'd been waiting about three months, about three days, or ten days, or ten years. She felt herself being swathed in some heavy cloth, and someone taking her under the shoulders and under the legs; felt herself being lifted and borne away. She found herself in her cell again, lying underneath her black fur covering; it was early in the afternoon, her eyes were open, her hands were free,

and there was René sitting beside her, caressing her hair. "Come, dress yourself," he said, "we're going."

She took one last bath, he brushed her hair, handed her powder and her lipstick. When she came back into her cell, her suit, her blouse, her slip, her stockings, her shoes lay on the foot of the bed, her handbag and her gloves too. There was even the coat she put on over her suit when the weather began to get cold, and a square of silk she wore to protect her neck, but no garter-belt, no panties. She dressed herself slowly, rolling her stockings to just above the knee, and didn't put on her jacket, for it was very warm in the cell. That was the moment when there entered a man who, the first evening, had explained what would be expected of her. He undid the collar and the wristbands which had held her captive for a fortnight. Was she freed of them? or did she feel something missing? She said not a word, hardly daring touch her fingers to her wrists, not daring raise them to her neck. He then asked her to choose, from amongst all those identical rings he was presenting to her in a little wooden case, the one which would go on the ring-finger of her left hand. They were curious, these rings, made of iron, the inner surface was of gold; the signet was massive, shaped like a knight's shield, convex, and in gold niello bore a device consisting of a kind of three-spoked wheel, each spoke spiralling in towards the hub, similar, all in all, to the sun-wheel of the Celts. She tried one, then another, and, by forcing it a little, found that it fitted her perfectly. It felt heavy on her hand, and the gold gleamed almost secretively in the polished iron's dull grey. Why iron? and why gold? And this device she didn't understand? But it wasn't possible to talk in this room, with its red hangings, with its chain still hanging over the bed, in this room where the black blanket, rumpled once again, dragged on the floor, where the valet Pierre could enter, was going to enter, was bound to, absurd in his operetta costume and in the fleecy light of November. She was mistaken, Pierre didn't enter.

René had her put on her suit jacket and her long gloves that reached up over the ends of the sleeves. He took her scarf, her bag, and folded her coat over his arm. The heels of her shoes made less noise on the hallway floor than her clogs had, the doors were shut, the antechamber empty. O held her lover's hand. The stranger who accompanied them opened the grilled gate Jeanne had said was the enclosure gate and which neither valets nor dogs were guarding now. He raised one of the green velvet curtains and had them both go through. The curtain fell back again. The grilled gate was heard to swing to. They were alone in another antechamber; beyond them stretched the garden. They had now only to go down a short flight of steps, and there in the drive was the car, O recognized it. She sat down next to her lover who was at the wheel, and they started. When they'd gone through the main gateway, which was wide open, and gone on a hundred yards or so further, he stopped to kiss her. It was just before a peaceful little village they came to a moment or two later that O saw the signpost. On it was painted: Roissy.

From THE SLIT

Sebastion Gray

Sebastion Gray's *The Slit* is one of the stranger manifestations of the early-1970s pulp porn fiction market. Its style, with its weakness for surreal metaphor and bizarre prose-poetic neology, suggests the author might have been a bored, middle-aged lecturer languishing in the English department of some benighted Midwestern college, with little better to do than write a 'pornographic' novel. Or quite possibly, one of his students. The plot is part 'Quest', part 'Voyage and Return'. An elderly sex toy manufacturer sends his virginal daughter, Celeste, on a voyage around the world 'to taste and enjoy every conceivable form of sex'. She is accompanied by a taciturn older brother, Jok, who will act as her guide and protector and for whom, during the course of the voyage, she develops an entirely unreciprocated sexual passion. Jok is given six envelopes by their father. Each one contains a different destination: each country holds a different sexual ordeal for the inexperienced Celeste. In the following extract, we join Celeste's odyssey after she has lost her virginity in the shadow of a Mayan pyramid to six *café-au-lait*-skinned youths. She and her brother have left Central America and are now on their way to Sweden.

The envelope is blue – ice blue.

She has seen it as Jok strolls the lower decks of the creaky Belgian freighter.

They always dine at the Captain's table. The Captain is attentive to her in his royal blue and tarnished braid. He winks at her – politely. He grins with stained teeth out of a carefully trimmed Van Dyke moustache.

She wonders what it would be like to lie deep in the goose mattress of her compartment and feel the Captain's fat and hairy body envelop her like a blue fog. She can sense the ageing, bearded chin upon her breasts, the tattooed anchor of his prick sunk between her drowning legs.

But the Captain does not touch her. He spins sea yarns at table, smokes black cigars that smell like turpentine and rolls thimblesips of brandy in his mouth as if he had just tasted the freshest little cunt in Brussels.

But she is not touched.

Not by the Captain and his disciplined crew, nor by the handful of other passengers.

And not by Jok.

She is left alone in her cabin to think of the green jungles under the eye of Xipe. To remember the brown-skinned Indian boys with their fierce young cocks, hard as polished teak.

To think of that – and the ice-blue envelope.

They say goodbye to the Captain in the mist of one early morning. He winks and waves, dipping his eyes downwards like some knowing Poseidon, ready to claim the sea again.

They travel once more by air, high into madder blue clouds and icy light.

North.

Into the whiteness of cold and aerated space.

Then down again, on stiffened wings with icicles fanging the windows. Down, down they come into a torch-lighted field, a landscape blue-white with snow and frigid lakes beyond.

Sweden.

The word is like a bright bauble to her. She knows no more geography than can be found on the palm of her hand or the skinscape of her body, but she likes the world of hoarfrost about her.

No pyramids here. No superstitions under glass. No decadent fruits with fly-buzz.

Only the hard, bluish icefields swept against the hardy firs and pines, and, their faces lit by torchlight, the Nordic gods who never blush.

There are four of them – tall, long-faced and handsome, with golden hair and cobalt eyes. All young. All with bodies impatient with their coloured sweaters and thick scarves and toboggan hats. All laughing with strong and perfect teeth.

They pull her into an *akja*, with Jok beside her.

The boat-like sled begins to move under the clap of hands and the sting of whips on reindeer backs. The fragile horns toss against the snowdrift air, and the *akja* moves, slicking softly over the cadaverous earth.

A merry, rollicking tune accompanies them on the journey. The strong male voices ring like copper bells against the night. She feels warm and wanted. She even snuggles back against the warmth of Jok.

But he is cold to her touch. The cudgels of his knees are like carved pedestals of ice. The lapfur is her only comfort.

They arrive at a postcard lodge, wedged deep into a crevice of snow, a spangle of tall tree shadows behind, a ribbon of beryl smoke rising from the chimney lip. The apples of her cheeks are pulsing. Blood races sharp-hoofed through her brain. Her breath makes little wanton ghosts upon the air.

She is carried from the *akja* by the laughing, singing young men.

Inside the lodge, she finds a simplicity that amazes her. The walls are rough-hewn, unpainted splinters with the frozen splash of caulk between the cracks of heavy beams. The windows are set like fists into the walls. A fireplace – a lion's mouth of brick – bellows and crackles with birch logs. A long, oaken table with splitaxe stools. And on the table, food.

The smorgasbord is not for fragile throats. Plates laden with cheese, pickled herring, *sardellen*, anchovies, baked mushrooms, great cold chunks of meat.

To wash it down, tankards of glacier cold beer and schnapps.

They make her eat. They feel that she is thin, that she has a pallor, that to be strapping and wholesome and fit for games one must stuff.

As she eats she tries to memorise their names.

Dag, Sven, Olof and Viktor.

The names are like things under a microscope, strange and new to her. Strong names, names like their strong young bodies. She likes their hands. She can see nothing of them but their hands and faces.

The hands of each are wide enough to circle her waist. Heavy of knuckle and long of finger. Sven and Dag are younger. Viktor and Olof are very much men. There is a fine matting of golden hair on the backs of their hands. It matches the thick nape of sunyellow hair at their tarpon ears and hearty necks.

Sven and Dag are overgrown boys, an enchanting 20 apiece. They are like twin suns in an arctic sky. Steelblue eyes above high, ruddy cheeks and happy mouths.

They all drink toasts to her, shouting *skal*!

The schnapps runs down their sculptured chins, seeps into the dimpled places in their cheeks.

She wonders when they will lose their smiles, like the hungry boys under the curse of Xipe, and want to fuck her in dead seriousness. Already she has seen the poses of the male. The laugh that hides the rattle of greed. The boyish kiss that cloaks the thrusting truncheon of their lust.

She glances to the end of the long scabrous table to Jok, hoping for an answer.

He is intent on sucking the memory of a *sardellen* from his fingertips. Morose, indifferent, detached. He is eating because he is hungry.

She is being urged to eat for quite a different reason.

Her little tummy is full – packed with cheese and pickled herring, awash with foamy draughts of beer.

She wants to sleep, but Olof is unhappy with the thought.

He conveys to her in a parody of broken English that sleeping after eating is gluttony. Sloth. A sound insult to the wellbeing of her body.

One should never sleep after eating. One should exercise, churn the blood, stir the body to song.

It may all be done, however, he grins, on a feather bed.

So come!

There are no real lights in the lodge. Only thick, buttery candles set sentinel at the right places. There is one at the bottom of the crude log steps leading upstairs, and one set at the top. There are two in the narrow hallway above, and one in the room they enter.

It is her room. Her own little room, again.

No spoonbill feathers and pliant animal skins here. A flat, hard bed of uncarved wood. A pitcher and a bowl of ice-white, durable, ironstone. A rack of wooden pegs for her clothes. A stretched hide over a straight-backed chair for the sin of an idle buttock.

Olof pushes the tit-flame of his candle against the one in her room to make a double light.

No exercise worth doing should be done in the dark, he hums. It is an old Nordic custom.

The room is as chilly as a fjord.

Olof begins to undress. He is half-through with his merry task when he notices that she has not budged.

His blue eyes twinkle.

The coach must always breathe encouragement.

His large, gentle-rough hands move over the furry collar of her little coat, unbuttoning, undoing, undressing her.

At last she takes up the task herself, shuddering with cold, wishing for the sun in the jungle village. Wishing she had not filled her stomach with so much oppressive food. Wishing . . .

Olof is naked.

Vikings yet live, bold with muscle and thick of calf, horned at the head, with bracelets of hammered steel around their arms.

She cannot breathe for staring at him.

He is as clean and white as an ice floe, incredibly healthy, flawless, proud.

His prick is like the great white tusk of a walrus. It wags between his legs softly as he walks back to the bed. He sits down, a muscled gallant, to assist her final disrobing.

She is ashamed of her body. Thin as a reed with its little nippled breasts grown only vaguely bolder by the orgy at Xipe. And her arms, her legs, her pelvis – skeleton-sized beside the marvellous masculinity of Olof. She blushes, not from the cold, but from shame.

He lifts her chin with one great, firm finger. He smiles at her, his placid eyes alive with life, his teeth as strong as marble.

The look tells her that she is there to grow.

His hands go back to the task of making her as naked as he. The coat, the dress, the slip, the panties – all snowfall to the floor until she is flagrantly nude in the middle of the great white tongue of a bed.

Olof moves in beside her, the thick columns of his legs solidly in place against her own. The fat, soft fish of his cock lays broadly across the upper part of his smooth thigh.

He takes her small hands in his own and carries them down to his sex, totally without guilt.

Her fingers tremble. The prick is much larger than the largest one at Xipe. Very white and very long. The little whorl of citron-coloured hair above the root looks like a puff of spun gold.

The prick begins to grow under her feathering touch. It is a muscular prick, grown firm and hale on push-ups. It rises to the occasion and stands up, shaft-strong, pointing up at the dark ceiling of the cold room. The head reminds her of the great mushroom she choked down earlier – a pink one this time, perfectly formed, dry, spongy to the touch.

Olof leans over her. As he glides, he kisses her throat, then the fluttering nipple of each dove-like breast.

His gliding has a purpose. Suddenly he is in a position to fuck her where she lies.

A simple, gymnastic trick on his part – well-practised, competent, casual.

He adjusts the little pillows of her rear by sliding his spadeflat hands under

each buttock and lifting them into a coned and triangular target. Carefully, he parts her spindle legs until her tingling, narrow cunt is splayed apart like a pink tea-dance invitation.

Then he moves upon her with the great long javelin of his prick.

He sinks it deep into the oval cup of her cunt. Her juices have not yet rushed to aid her, it is a dry cunt, a very unready cunt for such a rakish thrust.

She cries out, a rabbit on a spit.

He ignores her purbertal bleat and grins carelessly.

Some, he seems to feel, must learn the hard way – and the harder, the better.

An hour at a time ought to be enough!

He is a rabid fuckmaster, the head of the team.

The trophies all go to Olof for such stuff. He can trot a cunt into the home stretch without a single gasp.

He's proving it with her.

His prick digs deep into her heated slit. The juices are coming for her now, oozing up out of the hidden springwells of her timid flesh.

And lubrication helps.

Helps him, helps her.

The oily slime generating healthily from her pussy coats his moving stiffness, allows him deeper passage, quicker strokes, stronger throbs.

He fucks her quite athletically.

The chill of the room becomes a myth. The place is tropical with rakehell heat. She might be a crooning lizard baking on a desert rock, a shard being stroked by flames. She opens her legs wider, lifts her happy young cunt higher, twists wantonly on the skewer of his large white prick.

Olof is all form. His beautiful body is suspended above her on gracefully stiffened, tautly muscled arms. His body is like a diver's. Long of line, small of hip, narrow of thigh. His legs are close together and distended so that the balls of his naked feet are braced against the strong footboard. It gives him leverage to swing up and down in an oddly lubricious, calmly pedantic fuck.

He is teaching her. Teaching her how to be fucked. To like strong fucking, the endurance kind. Training her as if for some future, dark Olympics.

Nothing touches her but his prick. It is a trapeze act of venery. With each downwards swoop, his long, thick cock thrusts slurpily through the gasping little wicket of her twat, submerges deeply, bluntly, to her very core – convulsing her, of course, with pleasure – then strokes out again. It never fails to brush her clit with its big, stony head. Clit-joggling is fun for her. The sport of Queens.

Her tits grow hard. Spicy little peaks, begging for a good, long suck. She has never been fucked-sucked in unison. The idea appeals to her. Olof has such a fine, brusque mouth. She imagines his huge, Laplander tongue stimulating her nipples. They burn like blister beetles for his mouth.

"Olof . . ."

The word dies on her lips. His fucking has suddenly grown stronger. Her cunt is on fire. He is jolting it with his big birthday-toy of a prick.

Deeper now, deeper with every plunge – a magic dolphin in her cunt, as if he would split her screaming thighs and fuck up high into her lungs!

She moans contentedly and curls her toes to better taste the copulatory bliss.

His citron cock-hair is tangling with the darker fur around her cunted lips. He is in her to the dregs. The soft, round hotness of his balls jounce the girlish crack of her hollowed ass. His abdomen, flat and hard as a heated anvil, kisses hers with every downward thrust.

She is coming!

Her brave little cunt tries to rally, to extend the bliss. But it's no use. She is definitely coming. Definitely!

The walls of her pussy warp around the strong invader like a dripping fist and squeeze up tight.

She comes off like a debauched harem girl. Full of throaty gruntings and shameless explosions in her thighs. Her liquids shoot in a dozen directions, inundating Olof's victorious and rigid prick.

He grins as the Caesar's head of his cock is rewarded with the laurels of her juice.

Pleasure snorts through her with swinish greed.

Still she is being fucked.

It is a marathon of lust.

She smiles and curls the little vines of her legs into a lazy cricket's pose. His large, relentless cock is giving her freshly satisfied cunt something new to think about.

She knows he will not stop until her slit is like a sewer swimming with his sperm.

It may take all night.

Forever.

She wakes under the thick coverlet on the great, strong bed.

The sun is barely pink against the windows, but there is a heavy tramping of boots on the stairs. She wonders if it is Olof or Viktor. Both have had her. Incessantly. All night long. In relays, like runners passing a torch.

She grins, knowing how she liked it.

That Viking, Viktor!

He has fucked her with the strength of ten!

As the tramping boots hear her door, she slides a fearful hand down between her legs to see if anything is left. Is it a great kangaroo pouch of flesh?

A gaping, empty, market bag of a cunt?

She is amazed to find it intact – almost the size it was, except for some obvious thickening of the lips, some sensual pouting of the humps. But inside she has changed.

She burns with emptiness.

Prickhungry at dawn!

She smiles. Perhaps the booted feet belong to . . .

The door flies open.

And it is not Jok.

Two raw young mastiffs instead. Dag and Sven. Naked except for loincloths of reindeer skin – and boots. Healthy as rams!

With shouts of youthful bravado, they pull her from the warmth of the bed and carry her like a lovely leg of lamb down the stairs and into the snow.

She screams at the fate they have in mind for her.

Naked, her thicker, heavier-budded nipples turning blue, she is swung between the laughing oafs like a sack of wheat and tossed into the wintry air.

She falls, shrieking, deep into the fleecy, freezing depths of a snow bank.

Her nipples shrivel into peas. Her cunt puckers and pulls inward, like a flap. The icy chill penetrates her bone, her very marrow.

They pull her out with hoarse shouts of joy and laugh sportily at the snow maiden they have created.

It is another custom.

A healthy one, of course.

A snowbath before breakfast. And before breakfast, something else as customary.

They carry her blue, nude body back into the lodge and back up to her bedroom. She needs unthawing, now.

She is placed, frozen and chattering, on her side in the middle of the bed. Then her two abductors become her comforters.

Ripping off their meagre loincloths, dragging off their reindeer boots, they pile into bed with her. Naked and eager, they sandwich her between them, one facing her cunt and tits, one facing her rounded buttocks and her trembling shoulder blades. The warmth of their strong young bodies begins to surge through her.

And with the warmth, erotic desire.

It is Sven who is facing her, whose hands are cupping and massaging her gelid tits, with firm, long fingers. It is Dag behind her, his hands mauling and rubbing the frigid globes of her chilly buttocks.

The blood circulates again, the slate-blue skin glows pink, the breathing pumps robustly once more.

The peas of her breasts grow into heated plums. The core of her cunt yearns to play with the two stiff prongs she feels pressing against her from opposite directions.

Both young Swedes are horny. Both have man-sized cocks between their strong, fun-loving legs.

Both obviously desire very much to fuck her as dearly as their older pals.

She becomes honey between the hard loaves of their bodies.

Sven is the bolder of the two, devilish in his gleeful jactitation. With fingers cupped, he finds her slit and spreads it open like a mouth. He probes the itching centre with his thumb and her breath is hot upon his neck.

He shoves his throbbing colonnade deep inside. Her eager cunt lips close over him and suck him deeper. The pornographic pose entices the spirit of Dag, behind. He fingers the brown bud of her anus, hurting her until the tip of his finger is wedged within. He wriggles it in a screwing motion until it is knuckle deep, until she feels that surely he will tickle the tip of Sven's upthrust cock!

When her virginal ass-hole is breached, his prick replaces his finger.

Now she has cocks galore. In cunt and crack. Only boys would think of such early-morning games!

They hold her still, welding her between them, only their shoving pricks in motion.

It is a waltzing fuck that changes to a raggedy, sawhorse screw. Their cocks expand and lengthen with each jiggle and jog. And now she fancies their cocks will meet – kiss queerly in the bowels of her flaming cunt, then spit thick semen at each other.

She loves the curiosa of it all, the salacious madness of getting humped in front and back by such bright-eyed, husky minks.

Her tits swell into balloons of hot need. The nipples pop out like burning rocks.

"Suck me!" she yells.

Sven grins and wraps his obedient mouth over each nipple in turn, sucking, salivating, licking until she is a thrashing animal of lust.

She comes for them, spitting a triple-fanged spate of juice against Sven's moving prick.

He likes it. It makes him harden more, drives him to suck her tits more goatishly.

Dag cornholes with the grace of a bull. His prick's head is like a lump of lavastone. It digs and cores her burning rear, doubling the ruttish joy of what the one in front is doing to her.

She comes again as they release their own spewing proof of lustiness and youth.

Their pricks spurt molten fire into her loins. The sticky nectar of their unleashed balls runs down her legs and theirs, down the dimpled cleft of her rump and into the gristle of Dag's snag of pubic hair.

They dismount with the laughing, healthy shouts of boys ready for recess.

And breakfast.

The days take on a regimen.

Discipline is the key to health, so saith Viktor.

She is systematically fucked by all at night. Fucked until her cunt grows as strong as the lungs of an underwater swimmer. Strong enough to last.

They take turns keeping her in practice. Viktor is the easy champion among the older pair. Olof may lag after two hours, but Viktor has not found a cunt able to defeat him. He could fuck a stone clitoris into dust, he brags.

During the day, she is allowed to play games with Sven and Dag – if they do not neglect the prescribed business at hand. That is, to make her titties grow larger by the hour.

Seven hundred strokes a day. Three hundred and fifty from Sven's strong hands, and the same number from Dag's. They are to use pulling strokes, the cow-milking kind, carefully executed so that the cupped male fingers and the ball of the thumb catch as much of the sphere as possible and pull slowly out to the peak. The gorged nipple must then be tweaked and pinched.

Such petting of the breasts produces side effects, of course. In all concerned.

Such matters, passed over lightly in whatever textbooks there might be on the subject, become an area for invention. Sven and Dag are not noticeably inventive, nor noticeably original.

They merely fuck her while they stroke.

But it seems to shoe the horse.

A footnote in the instruction suggests that, for variety's sake alone, a sucking tongue may be substituted for a stroking thumb.

Dag is the valedictorian here. He has a tongue that would drive the deepest cunt in the world to shrieking madness.

It's glad to do the same for tits.

Hers grow twice their dormant size under the punishing stroke of Dag's hot mouth. The nipples turn to inch-long, blushing nubs. He roils them until they drool with milk, then bites them with his teeth.

It is at such times that she is grateful to have Sven pumping away between her legs. If she could not come through her saucy cunt, she is sure her vaginal juices would make a safari to the tips of her tits and spit love juice into Dag's grinning mouth.

It is on the eve of her departure, on Walpurgis night, that she learns how Jok has entertained himself during her long days of conditioning.

The festival of winter's farewell brings a holiday air to the lodge. It is to be her test, her final one, and the lodge is filled with singing voices, healthy faces, male and female.

Before the long night begins, during which she will be fucked by some 20 husky Nords in all, she steals away to spy on Jok and the bosomy maiden she saw him take upstairs.

The girl has hair the colour of lemons in sunlight. It reaches to her plump waist and spills like sulphurous smoke around the huge white whale-tits that adorn her. Her cunt is fringed with brownish hair, and on the bed, healthy skater's legs thrown wide apart, her pinkish slit invites the triumph of Jok's enormous, stiffened cock.

She watches the idyll, the Swedish treat, from behind a half-closed door.

Jock fucks the girl into oblivion.

"My name is Celeste," she whispers to the door, half-hoping Jok will hear. "I exist, too. You do this for a strange cunt on a stranger's bed. Why not for me?"

He chooses not to hear. He is too busy sullenly fucking the enchanted female beast.

She turns finally from the door.

It is the winter of her discontent – and a farewell to much more than virginity.

From BEHIND CLOSED DOORS

Alina Reyes

Alina Reyes was born in Bruges, Gironde. Originally a freelance journalist, she started to write fiction after a visit to Montreal. Reyes acquired notoriety with the success of her first novel, *The Butcher* (1988), which was translated into numerous languages and adapted for the theatre. Like many of her later novels and essays, *The Butcher* revealed a concern with contemporary eroticism and how to treat it in literary fiction. *Behind Closed Doors* was published in 1994. She now divides her time between Paris and the Pyrenees.

The Golden Phallus

I entered a huge gaming room, which was so large I couldn't see the other end. The pitiless artificial lights made everything shine brightly, especially the golden, neoclassical-kitsch décor. As far as the eye could see there were dozens of rows of one-armed bandits lined up in all directions.

The casino staff who patrolled the alleys were all men, handsome young men, entirely naked except for headbands in their hair and laced-up leather sandals on their feet. And the clients were all female, women of all ages, sitting on stools in front of their one-armed bandits, gripping in their hands the long, thick golden phalluses which served as handles.

The machines rang, spat out coins here and there and, when the jackpot was sufficiently large, one of the naked croupiers would run up to the winner to congratulate her and help her stack her dollars in a rack.

This was all rather exciting but I didn't have any change in my pocket with which to to try my luck. I crossed the room, looking for the hotel desk, for this casino undoubtedly belonged to one. It was probably the twin of a similar room reserved for men, with female lovelies on hand to provide the service.

I found the lobby of the hotel; it was vast and gaudy. These establishments are always flashily luxurious, but offer modestly priced rooms, in order to seduce the mugs into the gaming rooms. I located a lift, in front of which a fat man was waiting. I entered the lift with him.

As soon as the doors closed, I said to him:

"I would like to play, but I haven't any money for my first stake."

And he looked me straight in the eyes. He seemed to have got the message. So I added:

"Twenty dollars for a blow-job."

He took the notes out of his pocket and undid his buttons. I did the deed next to the lift buttons, so that I only had to reach out a hand to get the lift to move up or down. So we went up and down like that for as long as it took, which wasn't very long, for I thought it was more fun to do it on the move, rather than block the lift, which might have brought on my claustrophobia, even if it was only for a couple of minutes. Also, we ran the risk of being discovered, which added a little spice to the proceedings.

With my twenty dollars in my hand I went back to the gaming room, found a free machine and held fast to the golden phallus, which I lowered and raised vigorously with every coin I slipped into the slot. A nicely built waiter came to offer me a drink and I looked at him with interest but didn't stare, out of shyness. Then I noticed that the other women had no qualms about exchanging compliments and pleasantries with the members of the staff, and even fondling them a bit. When the waiter returned with my drink, without hesitation I flashed him a pleasing smile while gently weighing up his balls in my hand.

At one point I won a dozen or so dollars, then I lost the lot. So I had to go back to the lifts. Once again, I chose my prey well, for my proposition was warmly received, even though I had doubled my fee. I was particularly lucky, for another guy stepped into the lift on the eighteenth floor and caught us at it. I paused only long enough to tell him:

"I'm working, sir."

So he undid his buttons as well and awaited his turn.

So I had eighty dollars in my pocket when I returned to my assault on the one-armed bandits and their golden phalluses.

This trick lasted all night, or perhaps all day, or all night and all day, for it was impossible to keep track of time in this place where there was no other life but the game and no other light but the neon.

I won the jackpot several times: the machine continually coughed out dollars and immediately the croupier would appear and, in my enthusiasm, I couldn't resist fondling him before offering him a large tip.

When I felt thirsty, I called a waiter; when I felt hungry, I went to the restaurant, where they served everything at every hour; when I ran out of funds, I went to the lifts; and, when I won, I played again until I lost everything.

When I had exhausted all the joys the place had to offer, I signalled to the croupier that I thought was the best looking, drew him to the end of my row and made him a present of the whole of my last winnings. He took my face in his hands and kissed me on my mouth, a long, real cinema kiss. As I left him, I had the pleasure of ascertaining that his member was as proudly erect as the golden phalluses. I would gladly have given him a blow-job, but my jaws were beginning to ache. We gave each other a little wave and went our separate ways.

I found the door back to the corridors and set off. Immediately the sinister ghosts came and breathed in my ears. To get away from the nuisance I opened the following door.

*

The Man at the Window

"Will I find him again one day?' I thought, as I opened a new door. Already I was unsure who this man was for whom I was searching. Wasn't he one of those I had made love to here? By following in the steps of the man who had entered the little circus, who must be wandering like me through this strange kingdom and making love to other women, was I not pursuing an illusion? Or, on the contrary, were the men I had loved here no more than mere phantasms? Would I find true love only once I had completed this quest, so full of desires, joys and pains?

How we would all like to be lucid all the time, to know what we are doing and why we are doing it! But, just as the more we gather knowledge the more we see the depth of our ignorance, so the more we progress in our understanding of ourselves and of the world the more the mystery, within us and around us, deepens. That is why, cast out in these dark corridors, we find ourselves at the mercy of fantasies which rule us more than we rule them, yet which are our allies, a sort of army which swells and accompanies us on our adventures.

I had entered a small, simple room. I went to the window which was covered by light white curtains. It faced directly into the window of another building, separated from mine by a narrow alley. And in this room, which was similar to mine, a man sat in an armchair, reading.

He was tall, well-built, mature, obviously handsome and athletic in his youth, but now grown a bit heavy with age. Was it the act of observing him through a window? Straight away I felt a strong curiosity about him.

Strangely for a man reading quietly in his room he was wearing a dark, elegant suit, a white shirt and a narrow, sober tie which he had loosened around his open collar. His hair, cut short on his thick neck, was greying, and, even though he had an intellectual look about him, his heavy head could almost be that of a boxer, with his lumpy nose, his low brow, his prominent cheekbones and square chin. The bottom of his right trouser leg had ridden up as he sat cross-legged and I could see his sock, a fine, grey cotton sock snug over his ankle. I wasn't able to make out the title of the book he was reading.

The man didn't move, yet the fact that I was spying on him without his knowledge excited me considerably. I felt that, by observing him, I was going to penetrate inside him, pierce his secrecy. It was like a rape without violence, something which filled me with a very soft, very sharp sensation.

I looked at him and wondered what his life must be like; I imagined his naked body, his way of making love, his way of life . . . What was on his mind at this exact moment? What type of woman did he like? Was he sensuous, loving and sexual? Free? Capable of fantasy? Intelligent? Fun-loving? Shadowy? Mysterious?

The man got up, went to his window and stopped, directly opposite me. I don't know whether he could see me behind my curtains. We stood motionless for a while and soon I knew, from the expression on his face, that he was looking at me. I started slowly to undo the buttons down the front of my dress.

Once I had opened my dress, I opened the curtains. He looked at my body, looked at me. I knelt down at the window and placed my mouth against the glass at the height of his penis on the other side of the alley. With my lips against the pane I started sucking, staring into his eyes, imploring him to respond to my desire. He undid his flies and took out his penis. He was erect.

I closed my eyes for a moment in sheer happiness. He was magnificent. I devoured him with my gaze, again and again. Those balls and that thick cock sticking out of his elegant suit, beneath his tie, were magnificent. I got up, took off my dress and turned around slowly, wiggling my hips to allow him to examine my anatomy at his leisure.

I pressed my breasts against the window and fondled them. He took his cock in his hand and slid it up and down. Then I pulled the chair up to the window, sat down with my legs spread over the armrests and started wanking right in front of him, without taking my eyes off him. I came as I watched him rub himself, faster and faster. At the moment when my hips convulsed and lifted from the chair, at the moment when I cried out, with my head back, I was aware that he was watching me eagerly and that I excited him as much as he excited me. I opened my eyes in time to see him ejaculate, shooting his lovely semen all over the window, where it began dripping down slowly.

Then he left the room and didn't reappear. I went to lie down and fell asleep immediately. I woke up at dusk. In bed, my first action was to look out the window. At that precise moment I saw the light go on and the man come into the room accompanied by a woman.

She was a tall, strong woman wearing lots of make-up. "A whore," I thought. She took off her coat, beneath which she was wearing a basque and stockings, her shoes had excessively long and pointed heels. Her large bosom swelled out like a pigeon's breast.

I left the light off in my room. They started making love and I told myself that he had deliberately brought her back to fuck her in a fully lit room before my eyes. She knelt down in front of him, as I had done in front of the window, and began sucking him off. Then he took her to the bed and began to grope and chew her large tits. How I wished I were in her place! How stiff he must be! I wanted him to have pleasure, even if I couldn't give it to him myself. Yet, he soon lost interest. With the help of the girl he got undressed, lay on top of her and took her.

The girl's ankles, with their pointed heels, were wrapped around the neck of my loved-one, and his broad back moved up and down steadily between her thighs. I felt both very excited and very sad to see him making love with another woman. And I wasn't sure whether it was the flame of jealousy or lust that was keeping me there behind this window in the dark, my chest tight, breathing in short gasps, making sure I caught every single detail of their copulation.

The man made the girl go down on all fours in front of the window and, kneeling behind her, he buggered her, directly opposite me. I peered intensely at his face which was contorted with pleasure. I wanted to cry out "No, no!" and "Yes, yes!", for I wanted to be her, I wanted to be him, I wanted him, I wanted this to be happening in my body . . . At the last minute he withdrew from the girl and ejaculated in the air, towards me. "That's for me," I thought, "it's my present, he did it for me." I came at the same time as him, my mouth open, as if I could swallow the come he was sending me.

I left the room, feeling a little lost. I was never able to touch the man. He had given me nothing but the sight of him, and he would never give me anything else. Yet, if I had been able to meet him, he might have been the man I could have loved most in the world . . .

I walked for a long time in the corridors, constantly seeing the same cruel and fascinating images. Was I right to expose myself like that in front of him? It was so ridiculous . . . but it would have been even worse if I hadn't been able to express my desire. What had he thought of me? Had he loved me a little? Now that I had lost this man, this man I had never had, I had no appetite for anything else.

The ghosts followed me, whispering behind my back and disappearing each time I turned round to try to see them. In the end they preoccupied me more than the memory of the man at the window. To escape from their tormenting games I decided to open another door.

From ATOMISED

Michel Houellebecq

Michel Houellebecq is a French author, filmmaker, and poet. Having written poetry and a biographical essay on the horror writer H. P. Lovecraft, he published his first novel, *Whatever*, in 1994. *Atomised* followed in 1998, and *Platform* in 2001. A publicity tour for *Platform* led to his being taken to court for inciting racial hatred, but a panel of three judges, delivering their verdict to a packed Paris courtroom, acquitted the author, ascribing Houellebecq's opinions to the legitimate right of criticizing religions. He moved to Ireland to write for several years and currently resides in France.

On Friday night Bruno barely slept. He had a bad dream. He was a piglet, his little body fat and glabrous. With the other little piglets, he was sucked by a vortex into a vast, dark tunnel, its walls rusted. He was carried by the slow drift of the current. At times, his feet touched the bottom, but then a powerful swell would carry him on. Sometimes he could make out the whitish flesh of his companions as they were brutally sucked down. He struggled through the darkness and a silence broken only by the scraping of their trotters on the metal walls. As they plunged deeper, he could hear the dull sound of machines in the distance. He began to realise that the vortex was pulling them towards turbines with huge, razor-sharp blades.

Later, he saw his severed head lying in a meadow below the drainage pipe. His skull had been split from top to bottom, though what remained, lying on the grass, was still conscious. He knew that ants would slowly work their way into the exposed brain tissue to eat away at the neurons and finally he would slip into unconsciousness. As he waited, he looked at the horizon through his one remaining eye. The grass seemed to stretch out forever. Huge cogwheels turned under a metallic sky. Perhaps this was the end of time; at least the world that he had known had ceased to exist.

Over breakfast he met the leader of the watercolour workshop – a veteran of '68 who lived in Brittany. His name was Paul Le Dantec, one of the founding members of the Lieu; his brother was the current manager. He was the archetypal old hippie: long grey beard, Indian waistcoat and an ankh on a chain round his neck. At 55 this oldster lived a peaceful life. He would get up at dawn to go bird-watching in the hills, then sit down to a bowl of coffee and Calvados, and roll a cigarette amid the human traffic. The watercolour class didn't start until ten o'clock; he had all the time in the world to chat.

"As a veteran of the Lieu," said Bruno, laughing to establish a sense of

complicity, however false, "you must have a lot of stories about this place when it first opened – the Seventies, sexual liberation . . ."

"Liberation my arse," groaned the old hippie. "There were always women who could knit in the middle of an orgy and there were always blokes who just stood there waving their dicks. Take it from me, nothing much has changed."

"But I thought AIDS changed everything," said Bruno.

"I suppose it's true that it used to be easier for men," admitted the water-colourist. "You'd find a mouth or a pussy wide open and you could dive right in – no standing on ceremony. But for that, it had to be a proper orgy, invitation only, usually only couples. I tell you, I saw women with their legs wide open, wet and up for it, spending the whole evening masturbating because no one would fuck them. They couldn't even find someone to get them off – you had to be able to get it up first."

"So, what you're saying," said Bruno thoughtfully, "is that there never was real sexual liberation – just another form of seduction."

"Oh, yeah . . ." agreed the hippie, "there's always been a lot of seduction."

This didn't exactly sound promising. Still, it was Saturday, so there would probably be a crop of new-comers. Bruno decided to chill out, take things as they came, go with the flow. He would try to get through the day without bother, and, ideally, without incident. At about eleven o'clock that evening he went down to the jacuzzi. A delicate haze rose above the gentle roar of the water, lit by the full moon. He approached soundlessly. A couple were entwined on the far side of the pool; it looked as if she had mounted him like a horse. "I have as much right as they have . . ." thought Bruno furiously. He undressed quickly and slipped into the jacuzzi. The night air was cool, the water, by contrast, was deliciously warm. Between the twisted branches of the pine trees he could see the stars, he could feel himself relax a little. The couple paid no attention to him; the girl continued to pump up and down on the guy, she started to whimper. It was impossible to see her face. The man began to breathe heavily too. The woman's rhythm began to pick up tempo; she threw her head back and, for a moment, the moon lit up her breasts, her face still hidden behind a dark mass of hair. Then she crushed herself against her partner and wrapped herself around him; his breathing was heavier now, then he let out a long moan and was silent.

They stayed there for a minute, wrapped around one another, then the man stood up and got out of the pool. He unrolled the condom on his penis before dressing. Bruno was surprised to see that the woman was not leaving with him. The man's footsteps died away and there was silence once more. She stretched out her legs in the water. Bruno did likewise. He felt her foot on his thigh, brushing against his penis. With a soft splash she pushed herself from the edge and came to him. Clouds shadowed the moon; the woman was barely a foot away but still he could not make out her face. He felt an arm against his thigh and another wrap around his shoulder. Bruno pressed his body to hers, his face against her small, firm breasts. He let go of the edge and gave himself up to the moment. He could feel her drawing him towards the centre of the pool, then slowly she began to turn. He felt the muscles in his neck give, his head felt suddenly heavy. Below the surface, the gentle murmur of the water became a thunderous roar. He saw the stars as they wheeled slowly overhead. He relaxed into her arms, his

erect penis broke the surface of the water. She moved her hands gently, barely a caress. He was completely weight-less. Her long hair brushed his stomach and then her tongue touched the tip of his glans. His whole body shuddered with pleasure. She closed her lips and slowly, so slowly, took him in her mouth. He closed his eyes, his body shuddering in ecstasy. The thunderous underwater roar was regular and reassuring. When he felt her lips at the base of his penis, he could feel the movement of her throat. He felt himself flooded with intense waves of pleasure and buoyed up by the thunderous whirlpool. All at once he felt very hot. She gently allowed her throat to contract around him; all the energy in his being rushed suddenly to his penis. He howled as he came; he had never felt such fulfilment in his life.

THE DEVIL'S WHISPER

Henri Breton

Henri Breton, a painter and writer of Anglo-French parentage, has written several short stories and articles for the *Erotic Review*. In his youth, for reasons never fully explained, he took passage on a tramp steamer from Liverpool to Valparaiso, where he remained for some years, earning a living from journalism until his return to Europe. His main love is the Mediterranean and the countries that surround it. He currently divides his time between London and Barcelona.

The Sea Captain had spotted a slim, dapper man the other side of the café and beckoned him with a wave. He waved back and came over to us, a slightly built individual, with a dark complexion and black, brilliantined hair. He gave the appearance of a nervous mouse scurrying for cover, moving in little darting rushes, and he apologised for disrupting our table. We cheerfully disabused him of this, found another chair and made room for him. And in no time at all the company had assimilated him, placed a glass before him and made sure it was full.

"How are things with you, Claude?"

"Well, not much to tell you, really," he replied with an apologetic smile, and as he said this his head inclined to the left and he shot his hands out sideways, palms up, like a maître d'hôtel announcing that all he could offer for dinner was an omelette.

We drank some more, smoked, and gradually, inevitably, the conversation came around to women. The company was exclusively male that evening, and the language we used, though full of respect for so important a subject, was both extravagant and without restraint. Later the area under discussion was further narrowed down to "disappointments in love". I thought that the Sea Captain would have something to add here, for he had often hinted at romantic failures in the past, but he was unusually silent and if he had anything in the way of comment or reminiscence, it was going to have to wait for another day.

"It's hardly something to boast about, but I think I can cap all of your stories tonight," ventured Claude in a quiet, clear voice. "Disappointments are always sad, but missed opportunities are sometimes tragic."

"About two years back, I met this girl from Gothenburg – Birgit. She worked for a small shipping business here in the city: she was lovely, really, a pretty face with everything large except her little retroussé nose: full lips, generous mouth, and huge eyes – eyes like the grey Atlantic Ocean. All framed by blonde hair that

fell to her shoulders. She was taller than me – but that was all right, I couldn't get enough of her. Even if she'd been twice my size.

"She had been married briefly and unhappily. Her husband was a drunken lout who beat her and, very sensibly, she left him, taking the first job her firm could offer her far from Gothenburg, far from Sweden. Despite her unhappy marital life, she was a domesticated soul: God, she loved to cook, or what passes for cooking in Sweden – they have very different ideas, you know – and every evening I would turn up at her place to eat. And every night it was the same thing: a sort of *smörgåsbord* – or as near as she could get to it – accompanied by ice-cold *akavit* or beer and followed by some energetic but sadly, quite unremarkable, fucking. I would usually leave before midnight, for we both found it more convenient that I should. She had a sweet, generous nature and I grew very fond of this tall, lusty Swedish blonde and her regime; she was quite the archetype of Scandinavian womanhood – or so I thought – and it seemed to me that I could do worse than settle down with someone who had so much going for her.

"But we weren't in love, I suppose, and though I'm not the most romantic man in the world, I do believe in that vital spark between two people: something more than just good sex or shared enjoyment of the sensual pleasures. I'm not sure if it was the unswervingly homely nature of the *smörgåsbord* and the sex or the thought that our relationship was essentially a sterile one, but I told myself in a rather priggish way that I was leading the poor girl on, that she would start to expect more than I could possibly give her. All in all, I managed to convince myself that I should do the decent thing and end the affair before it was too late.

"It was on a Friday, when, as you know, the mood of the city lightens somewhat with the prospect of the weekend ahead. I knocked on the door of the little apartment that she rented. It was plainly decorated, yet Birgit had somehow contrived to make a virtue of her apartment's lack of furnishings; normally I found this unfussiness refreshing, but this evening it seemed only bleak and filled me with gloomy foreboding.

"The *smörgåsbord* was set out with her usual geometrical precision, and I sat glumly as she prepared the drinks and busied herself in the tiny kitchen putting the finishing touches to the meal.

"She joined me at the table and only then did she notice my downcast expression.

"'What's the matter, Claude?' she asked, in her curious, lilting accent.

"It all came out in a rush, without any finesse. By the time I had finished I felt awful, a real heel. Birgit made me feel worse by saying bravely, 'Oh well, never mind. It was fine while it lasted. Let's eat.'

"We ate sparingly and drank rather a lot. Beer with *akavit* chasers. Then more beer. Then more *akavit*. By the end of the meal I think that we were both quite drunk. I got up to go.

"'Goodbye, Birgit. I'm so sorry it didn't . . .'

"'Don't worry. It happens this way sometimes. But listen – for goodness' sake! Why don't we have one more – you know – for good luck?'

"For some reason, knowing that this was our last fuck together made me incredibly randy and I think she felt the same way. While Birgit pulled off her clothes I watched as her breasts tumbled out of her brassiere and noticed, as if

for the first time, how beautiful the soft curve of her belly was. For some reason I remember the slight imprint that the zip of her skirt had made and, as she turned away from me and bent over to fold her clothes, the full swell of her buttocks tinted by a faint, rosy blush.

"Lord, we fell into each other's arms and soon we were at it like minks. We were oblivious to the hot night air that surrounded us like a blanket and we fucked in every position we could. I kissed, licked and tasted every square centimetre of her body. Her cunt was the real meal of the evening: its lips were pink and suffused and lay scarcely hidden by its soft, golden curls; imperfectly sealed was its secret reservoir of sweet juices like a ripe plum. I had an erection that reminded me of the ones I had when I was a teenager – I was so stiff it almost hurt. Birgit's big warm breasts swung in my face as she straddled my prone body and, holding my prick, eased herself down onto it.

"She was so wet! And then she fucked me. She fucked me almost as if she were a man, grunting and taking her pleasure, rising and falling, grinding her clit against my pubic bone. I grabbed the smooth, heavy globes of her bottom, one in each hand and squeezed and kneaded and pulled and pinched and slapped and generally punished them. I introduced a finger alongside my cock, which made her moan with pleasure; then I slipped it into her arsehole, something I had never dared do with her before, which made her moan even more. Soon we were both slippery with sweat and before either of us had come, we went to the refrigerator and got more beer to drink. I found a carrot, which, childishly, she inserted up her cunt so that the fern-like leaves hung down from her blonde pubic bush, the green and the gold together. We laughed so much it hurt and then she insisted on shoving another carrot up my arse and we laughed a great deal more.

"We went back to bed and fucked in the missionary position, then on our sides, then with her on all fours, until she came, explosively: I followed soon after. It was her 'safe' time and when this was the case, she loved me to ejaculate inside her, so I did. Then we collapsed and slept. I was woken by Birgit's hand between my legs, searching for my cock.

"While she groped around looking for my prick, my fingers flew to her cunt and got busy there: she was oozing sperm and I opened up her tight channel by slipping in two fingers. Her vagina squeezed and throbbed like some sort of animated glove, she quivered and shook every time I thrust inside her, mimicking the action of fucking; Birgit wanted to be fucked again, very badly, I thought, but by a real cock, not just my fingers, and I was not yet ready. The Devil whispered something in my ear and I passed it on to Birgit in a low, urgent voice. Her reaction was to shudder, I thought from disgust, but she said 'Yes!' in a low, passionate tone.

"I took her firmly by the arm, made her get up and, keeping my fingers in her cunt, walked her over to the little balcony outside the window. We looked down into the street below and saw no one suitable. Eventually a couple of sailor boys strolled into view. I knew that if they looked up they would be able to see Birgit's breasts and my naked chest. They looked slightly drunk, but they were at the happy stage of drunkenness. To my surprise, it was Birgit who called down to them, 'Want some free pussy? Come up here, boys . . .' and then she looked at

me and laughed. The sailors glanced up, puzzled, until they located the source of this delightful invitation, then grinned and ran for the entrance below. I felt her wriggle, as if she had suddenly had a change of heart, but I took her face in my hands and I spat at her, 'Do you want more cock or not? Make up your mind!' She sighed and I felt her body slump against me in a gesture of mute resignation. We both knew that she did.

"There were footsteps on the bare boards of the staircase outside the apartment and the sailors, resourceful lads that they were, were soon knocking on Birgit's door. I met them in the little vestibule.

"'Look – help me out here, boys,' I said in a low voice that I hoped Birgit wouldn't hear, 'I've just fucked my girl and she's still desperate for more cock – but I'm totally fucked-out!'

"The two shipmates looked at me suspiciously, then at each other, as if there were a catch to this otherwise splendid suggestion. But they could see Birgit standing behind me naked, legs well apart; they could see the dribble of semen running from the pink and bruised lips of Birgit's cunt and Sailor A, dark and swarthy with curly hair, said, 'OK, we'll fuck her for you Mister. No problem!' And they started to pull off their uniforms, their squashed hats with red pompoms sailing through the air to land in a corner. I put an arm around Birgit and realised that she was shivering, as if she had a fever. 'Are you nervous?' I asked. 'Do you want to change your mind?' She looked up at me, her eyes half-closed and she smiled at me as if I were a simpleton. I realised that she was literally shaking with lust, trembling with lust and excitement, so I pushed her back down on to the bed and parted her thighs so that her cunt was accessible to us. I stood back and realised how beautiful and powerful she was as she lay there, passive, open to the world, yet with all of us in her thrall. Sailor B, with red hair and freckles, asked, 'Does she take it up the arse?' At first I was a little cross: he was acting as if Birgit simply wasn't there, as if this had nothing to do with her. So I said, a little curtly, 'Why don't you ask her yourself. Her name is Birgit, by the way.'

"But by then, Sailor A was standing over Birgit; he already had his cock in her mouth, and she was gorging on it, as if it were some incredible, irresistible delicacy that she had to stuff as much of into her mouth as she could, squeezing his balls in time to the lunges she made with her mouth. Sailor B was sitting next to her, his erection at the perpendicular, and was pawing her superb breasts, rolling the swollen, red nipples between finger and thumb.

"I sat the other side of her and whispered to her, 'I think they'll want to fuck you in the cunt and arse at the same time. Have you ever done that? Would you *like* to do that – a sandwich? Just think . . . those two big cocks inside you at once! Incredible. I'd love to watch that . . . and maybe I'd fuck you after.' She whimpered softly with desire. My hand wandered down to the matted nest of hair below her belly. I parted the strands and found her juicy slit. There was still more juice now, a fresh supply . . . she was ready again. She was ready to fuck. Answering the three of us at once, she looked up and smiled a mad little smile – half apologetic and half hysterical – 'Yes . . . I want you *all* inside me at once.' Straight away, Birgit got up and pushed back the sailor sitting, Sailor B, and with a rather uncustomary awkwardness, gingerly lowered herself down onto his upright cock, still facing her audience of two.

"It was somehow a magnificent, moving sight, and I soon realised why she was being so careful – she was about to take the full, quivering spear of flesh up her arse. She steadied herself with one hand on his big, muscular thigh while with the other she delicately circled his cock with her fingers and swept its head along the length of her dripping cunt. Thus suitably smeared with her vagina's oily secretions, she shifted the head into the slight declivity of her arsehole and, frowning with concentration, started to lower herself. As Birgit slowly impaled herself in a way that she had never attempted before, Sailor A knelt between her thighs and started to lick at her swollen and oozing pussy.

"I stood a little to one side and caught her eye, trying to read in her expression what was going on, trying to make sense of what was happening between us. It was as if the two men were automatons that I had introduced for her exclusive pleasure, to assuage her nymphomaniac desires, but both of us knew that this was really for my entertainment as much as hers, and I could feel my cock hardening once more. All this was communicated in the gaze between us, in the slight, fleeting, grimaces of pain that she made as her anus and rectum adjusted to this new and extraordinary intrusion. Then she started to rise and fall on Sailor B's cock, slowly at first, then faster and faster until she reached a steady rhythm that seemed to suit her. Even as she bounced up and down on his cock, breasts dancing wildly, even in this slightly absurd and vulnerable position, she held my gaze and her cool grey eyes locked on mine. I became acutely aware of every new and subtle transformation in the map of her face. Soon I detected the ghost of a smile, a proud smile with just a hint of a raised eyebrow . . . now I saw the twitch of her mouth's corner and finally, there it was, a broad, jubilant grin which said everything.

"It told me that – if she ever had been – she was no longer particularly upset about our parting. It told me that I had been a fool to take her so much for granted, and never to guess that there was an exciting, sexual woman beneath her *gemütlich* exterior and her clean, tidy life. And most of all it told me that I had probably come to realise this too late. She ran her fingers through Sailor A's curly hair then clenched her fists, pulled him up to her by two handfuls of his thick, wavy locks and kissed him full on a mouth all shiny with her juices. There was a moment when she broke her gaze towards me to reach down and grab Sailor A's cock and place the head at the opening to her dripping cunt, where the usually fair hair was now completely dark and sodden with the various liquids of sex. As he entered her with a hard thrust, she gave a cry that I had never heard her utter before. It was more like an animal grunt or groan, not loud, but still I found it utterly compelling, and I was gripped by an intense pang of irrational jealousy. Again, her eyes lost mine and this time she broke our gaze entirely and I could see that she was entirely preoccupied by the activity that was taking place between her thighs. I watched as the twin pistons drove into her soft flesh, and then pulled out; the sailors had created a sort of rhythm to their thrusts and I wondered if they had done this double act before.

"I moved over to where Birgit's head lolled on the shoulder of Sailor B. I stroked her cheek and she became aware of my presence. She reached for my cock and pulled me towards her mouth. She sucked me until I was hard again. Then she pushed off Sailor A and said, 'It's your turn, Claude. Fuck me – fuck

me like you've never fucked me before.' I had never even heard her say the word 'fuck' before and it had a galvanic effect.

"The sensation was strange: I could smell the other man's sweat, the outside of my knees brushed his hairy thighs and I wondered if I was going to be able to go through with it. Then I was in and suddenly my cock was plunged deep into a fleshy turmoil, as if it were thrusting inside the guts of a squirming octopus, a strange convulsion of moving, rippling flesh. Only minutes later Sailor B groaned and yelled, 'I'm there! I'm coming up her arse!' Birgit shuddered with pleasure.

"We re-arranged ourselves so that Birgit was on top of me, and she started to fuck in earnest, pausing only for Sailor A, who had knelt behind her, to introduce his cock into her arse. I felt him drive it in, separated from my own by a millimetre or two of flesh. I looked up at Birgit and she stooped to kiss me; as she did so I saw Sailor A's seemingly disembodied hands come around to seize her breasts and torment her turgid nipples with callused fingers, causing her to moan into my mouth with the pleasure born of pain. 'Come inside my cunt!' she murmured. 'Let's come together!' But it was Sailor A who came first, cursing and gasping and shuddering: so close were we to our respective crises that this act poured petrol onto our already blazing lust, and we followed suit immediately.

"The sailors took off as soon as they decently could; perhaps they sensed that we didn't really want them around any longer. The room stank of sex and the bed looked as though there had been a battle fought there, which, in a way, there had. Birgit looked at me and smiled wanly.

"'Would you stay the night? I think I'd like that, if it's not too much trouble for you . . .'

"'Of course,' I replied and we held each other as we fell into a deep sleep.

"The next morning I left early even though I didn't have to go to work that day. Apart from our almost formal goodbyes, there was not much said and I knew what I had suspected the night before – that something irrevocable had taken place. I looked into her sea-grey eyes for a last time and saw that there was definitely no going back. Some weeks later I heard that she had returned to Sweden.

"That, gentlemen, is my sad story, and hardly a day goes by that I don't think of setting off for Gothenburg to find Birgit, but somehow I know that I lost her for ever, back then, when the Devil whispered in my ear."

THE PERFECT W

Michel Faber

Michel Faber was born in The Hague, Netherlands, before his parents emigrated with him to Australia in 1967. He attended the University of Melbourne. He worked as a cleaner and at various other casual jobs, before training as a nurse. In 1993 he emigrated to Scotland. Faber declined to become a UK citizen in order that his book, *The Crimson Petal*, be submitted for the Booker Prize as he disagreed with the UK government's foreign policy. He identifies himself as no particular nationality, and the themes, scope and style of his literary work are not characteristically British, Australian, or Dutch, but broadly European.

Acting on doctor's orders, the nurse peered down the neck of Claire's surgical gown to check that Claire was naked underneath. Satisfied, she whipped the little gauze veil off the green plastic kidney dish. Inside was a disposable hypodermic and some square white sachets that looked like condom wrappers.

"I'm here to give you your pre-med," said the nurse. "It won't put you to sleep, but you'll feel relaxed and dreamy."

The word 'dreamy' discomfited Claire like an unwelcome touch; sweat prickled through her underarm anti-perspirant at the thought of dreams. Once again she imagined herself having her recurring nightmare, screaming uncontrollably, then being rushed to some sort of mental institution – doctors would sign the necessary forms while she was drugged or irrational, and the doors would slam shut on her... Years and years later she would finally be released, middle-aged, dull-eyed, and disgustingly fat... Her girlfriends would look at her in shock and pity, she who always used to be a size 10. In fact, her girlfriends probably wouldn't recognize her at all – how could they, if her normal appearance was lost?

But no, Claire reminded herself: none of this would happen; she mustn't give in to fear. Hadn't she spent last night in the hospital, and not dreamed the dream? And surely, in a sleep that was anaesthetized, she'd be even less likely to? Oh God! How ironic that in deciding to do something to empower herself, she should risk such powerlessness...

The nurse ripped open one of the sachets, revealing a pure white alcohol swab that smelled surprisingly like a spirit you might drink if offered. At this exclusive clinic, even the alcohol swabs were luxury quality.

"This won't hurt," murmured the nurse as she dabbed Claire's arm.

Claire stared at the nurse's hands as the needle went in, not really hurting. The

hands were perfect, right down to the manicured fingernails. The face was flawless too: no doubt with the help of Dr Nadir or one of his talented colleagues. Claire tried to picture the nurse in a one-piece swimsuit, wondering if she had what Claire would soon have: a perfect W.

W denoted the shape of vulva that every woman wanted: clearly defined, perfectly symmetrical, pubescent in its smoothness and solidity, plump but pert. All the most beautiful women in the world had one, though not all of them were 100% honest about where they'd got it. There were rumours, for example, that Marielle Coxon had had a simply repulsive cunt before she'd had it surgically reshaped, but she wasn't admitting anything. In fact, Claire had read an interview with her just recently in FEMME magazine, where Marielle was saying that it really was a little bit invasive, all this interest in her private parts. Of course, there she was in the glossy photographs accompanying the interview, modelling the latest contour-hugging swimwear and panties, her perfect W sticking out for all it was worth. Which was probably about £8,000. That was what Dr Nadir was charging Claire anyway.

As if sensing himself thought about, Dr Nadir walked into Claire's room and approached her bedside, shooing the nurse away with the density of his arrival. He was dressed, as always, in an Armani suit, unbuttoned to allow for his paunch, and he carried a leatherbound folder holding Claire's papers. He glanced at these briefly through the bottom half of his bifocals, and nodded to Claire.

"Now, you understand what's going to be done to you today?" Despite his rich brown skin, he had that English-academic-type voice that all successful doctors in private practice seemed to have, as if he'd been left, a black infant foundling, on the doorstep of a prestigious medical university. "Yes," she said at last.

"And what's that?" rejoined Dr Nadir. His tone was still lazily authoritative, but with a subtle highlight of playful condescension. Was he enjoying this? Or simply checking he had the right patient in front of him?

"Um... You're going to give me a... a new vagina..." she stammered.

She knew as soon as she'd said it she'd branded herself contemptibly ignorant in his eyes. The word that had come to her first was cunt. The word she should have used was vulva, but she'd had a mental block on it and instead used the one she'd been taught at school, in the quaint pre-New Woman days.

"Hardly," sighed the doctor, with a little grimace of offended pedanticism. "Your vagina has nothing to do with this procedure. I am going to surgically reshape your vulva, involving some reduction and compaction, and possibly some implants. This is the procedure you have requested and for which you have signed these consent forms. Yes?"

"Yes," said Claire again. It seemed the only vaguely intelligent thing she had to say to him.

"Good," he murmured, consulting his watch. "I'll see you in theatre, then, in about twenty minutes."

He said it as if they were rendezvousing at a restaurant of mutual choosing; so much so that, for a moment, Claire was anxious about how she'd get to this theatre – how would she find it, never having been there before? But of course, the clinic staff would fetch her when the time came. "Thank you," she said, and he was gone.

She settled back against the pillow and turned her head to the great bay window, because all of a sudden her room was weirdly dim despite the electric lights. Outside, a soundproofed blizzard of snow was whirling past the glass, vagueing out the world. Next summer seemed a long way away, and Claire had a sudden flush of anxiety that by then, a different cunt might be in fashion. Wouldn't it be terrible if there were some sort of fashion revolution, and suddenly Ws were considered gross? But no, it must be the pre-med fuddling her judgement: Ws were an eternal standard. There'd been a retrospective in US & THEM magazine, showing all the drop-dead-gorgeous women in history, from babe-of-the-moment Arlette Binchois right back through Livvy Warren, Steffie Kerr, Kiki Farouf, even really ancient ones like Pamela Anderson – all Ws. Plus of course, all very young girls were naturally Ws, and that just proved that being anything else was giving in to the creeping deterioration of age.

Belatedly, she became aware that she was sweating so much that she had soaked the underarms of her theatre gown. Was her cunt really so bad that she had to... do something... drastic? Sluggishly she threw off the bedcovers and pulled the gown up onto her abdomen, trying to examine herself, but of course she couldn't see anything. Cunts were for other people to see.

At home, using mirrors, she'd examined hers endlessly though, hadn't she? It was definitely not right. It wasn't a W, wasn't even a vee. It was heading in the direction of something horrible and flaccid and old, like limp cabbage or lettuce. She should have got it fixed in her early twenties, not waited until she was about to turn thirty.

It wasn't as if Claire was a surgery junkie like some women. She hadn't even had her breasts done, which all her friends certainly had. It just so happened that her breasts were OK, she thought. In fact, they were so good that everyone assumed she'd had them done anyway. She almost felt like a fraud. Whenever she unhooked her bra, she always feared that a man's gaze would droop slightly in disappointment, but this had never happened. Not that she'd had a man for ages now. She didn't want anything to do with them for a while: she'd been hurt too much.

This operation, in fact, was her way of reclaiming lost self-esteem. Relationships with men flagellated her emotions, until she was mutilated, out of shape, bits of her hanging out everywhere. Surgery allowed you to become streamlined again; it planed back the damage.

This wasn't her first cosmetic surgery, though. She'd dabbled. As an assertion of adult independence, she'd had some microsuction done on her cheeks two days after her eighteenth birthday. She hadn't even needed a general anaesthetic. The doctor had inserted the long needle behind her ear and hoovered it into her jowls, slurping away some of what her mother had always fondly (but repulsively) referred to as puppy fat. Cheekbones had materialized before her very eyes. A few years later, following endless grief with her parents, she'd noticed a premature frown line forming above the bridge of her nose, and had that fixed with a wee implant.

But nothing major until now. She hadn't had the money, for one thing. Plus there was the problem of sleeping in a strange place, and the dream.

Her best friend Chloe had had almost every cosmetic operation imaginable,

but then she'd always been wealthy, or at least attracted the wealth of others. And, of course, she was pushing forty.

Chloe was a great friend to Claire, though. She'd visited her last night, right here in the hospital, even though it was a Friday night and The Aquarium wasn't reserving tables for anyone anymore.

Chloe had arrived looking like a sixties icon, sprung from the pages of YOU ME US. She had, after all, been born sometime in that decade, the high point of the previous century, and liked to claim she remembered it well, despite looking a whole generation too young. To emphasise the point, she also liked to wear original sixties clothes, not modern copies; she bought them at Sotheby's or paid hard-up students commission to find them for her at street markets.

In Chloe's opinion, wearing mass-produced clothes was no different from eating at McDonalds or drinking coffee from a vending machine, but she was tolerant enough to forgive her friends for apparently disagreeing. Now here she was on Claire's bed, sporting an ankle-length, wing-collared dress worn by Nico in La Cicatrice Intérieure, the slit neckline swaying over her bra-less breastbone. Claire's nightgown, by contrast, was a Harvey Nichols number. The two women's eyes met; understood; and let it go.

"Chloe, you shouldn't have," Claire had protested, so relieved to have Chloe's miraculous body perched at the end of her bed.

"Oh, there are other places to eat than The Aquarium," pooh-poohed Chloe with a flick of her hand. "Not many, though," she added with a knowing cocktail shake of the eyeballs.

Pleasantries over, Chloe got down to what really mattered. "Are you scared?" she asked concernedly, leaning close.

"Maybe a bit," said Claire. It was a guess. She was too scared about the dreams to know how scared she was about the surgery.

Chloe gave her the low-down on the operation, at once frank and reassuring. She'd had vulvoplasty herself, though not in Britain, but on one of her trips to Paris with Brett. It was an impulse thing: she'd just saved herself thousands of pounds in VAT and whatnot, by buying clothes at source, and then she'd actually met a darling of a surgeon at a do, and next day she was in a clinic having her cunt done. It was only really sore for a week or so afterwards; after that the big problem was boredom. You had to lie on your back all day waiting for your perfect W to heal enough for you to be able to sit down on it.

"It also depends," elaborated Chloe, "whether you have your clitoris worked on or not."

"N-no," breathed Claire, oddly squeamish. "I... He'll leave that alone, I think. I mean, we didn't discuss anything about that. I certainly haven't paid for anything to be done."

"Oh, good," affirmed Chloe. "Some women get the hood trimmed and the clitoris enlarged a bit, but I think that's a bit tacky, quite frankly. I suppose it would suit sex maniacs who want to be turned on all the time."

"No, I've opted for the... ah... classic look," said Claire.

She had, too: smooth, rounded pubis and outer labia, firm rosebud inner labia, the untidy flaps tidied up, splayed out symmetrically and fixed in shape with plastic underwiring. She had been offered a variety of styles like different collars

of a jacket; Claire knew that Geraldine Walsh had had hers fashioned into an exact replica of Marilyn Monroe's mouth (sideways, presumably) but that was so crass and unnatural and so American. Claire had chosen a classic cunt, a cunt which would keep its value, a cunt she could wear forever. In the end, there was no arguing with the soundness of the decision, and Chloe ran out of reassurances. Instead, she became abruptly playful.

"So," she smirked. "What does your surgeon look like?"

"Look like?" echoed Claire.

"You know," prompted Chloe. "Is he dishy?"

"No way!" Claire exclaimed, then immediately wavered. "Well... maybe in a rugged way. He's kind of... fat." She shrugged non-commitally, not wanting to be caught out. There'd been a real fashion for ugly men recently, sparked off initially by a fad for French stars of the 1950s and 60s – Jean-Paul Belmondo, Serge Gainsbourg, Jacques Brel – and Claire wasn't sure if it was all over. She preferred Adonises herself. Or actually, she wasn't certain anymore: men were increasingly alien creatures and nobody seemed to agree on what they were really supposed to look like.

Chloe wound up her visit by presenting Claire with a gift: a little something, she said, to celebrate the new cunt with. From an elaborately wrapped cocoon of crepe paper, Claire extracted a pair of Pierre Artisse leggings, the last word in chic for Ws. They were black with a spidery grey brocade woven down the sides, loops at the waist for a belt (leggings with belts were the absolute latest thing) and of course cut very tight in the crotch and thighs, to separate the legs and show off the cunt contours. Tears sprang to Claire's eyes, at the thought of having a friend who would buy her something like this. She embraced Chloe impulsively, their first-ever physical intimacy, and Chloe made her embarrassed excuses and left.

Alone again, Claire slumped back and looked at the window. She couldn't tell what the weather was like outside, as it was pitch dark now and the glass reflected, with fluorescent-strip clarity, Claire's own body in the hospital bed. She wept some more, clutching the Pierre Artisse leggings, then got worried she'd damage them with her nails.

She consulted the digital clock on the DVD player under the dormant television (yes, this place had everything!) and was surprised how sleepy she was at such an early hour. Though it hadn't been so very long since dinner, the dream – the nightmare – was already peering through the spyhole of her consciousness. She shut her eyes tightly, which of course only made it worse.

It was always the same dream. She had no others anymore. As a child, she'd been all kinds of things in her sleep; her dream self might be a princess, a warrior maiden, a sports champion, a detective, a witch. She'd even dreamed of not being human anymore: a bright young fish exploring the limitless ocean, a seagull cruising over misty clifftops. Once, when she'd been very young, she'd seen a TV show about the weather, and that night had dreamed about being a snowflake, spiralling gently down through the sky. Each snowflake was different, the show had said. Another time she'd dreamed of being a bat – furry, tiny, ugly and infinitely self-satisfied, flying around at the speed of a flashlight, then folding up to sleep with thousands of other bats in a warm cave somewhere.

Nowadays in her dreams – in the dream, singular, because it was the only one left – she was exactly the same person as when she was awake. The dream would find her lying in bed, starving hungry as usual after another long day of staying size 10. A man had promised to come in the morning and take her away from her loneliness: all she had to do was be good and stay beautiful until he came. But always she would get up out of bed, helplessly, and she would walk through the tasteful emptiness of her house until she came to the kitchen. There she would kneel at the refrigerator, in the pale light of its opened door, and examine its contents. Everything she ever yearned to eat was there; no one treat in particular, just food in all its different forms. With a squeal of rage and desire she would lurch forward, plunging her hands inside the luminous metal torso in search of its soft and perishable heart. Everything she pulled out she ate, like an animal, clawing meat off polystyrene trays, guzzling milk and custard, scooping fatty gunge out of plastic tubs with her fingers, ladling up gravy in the palms of her hands, swallowing hard on leaking mouthfuls of the raw and the cooked. This would go on for hours and hours, until finally at dawn she would glance aside, and suddenly see a pair of grey-trousered male legs standing right next to her, and, below them, polished black shoes half-submerged in a glutinous moat of spilled food. Then she would scream, and the scream would wake her, and then she would rush to the kitchen in a panic to check that she'd really been dreaming, and that the fridge was neat and clean and contained only what was supposed to be there, untouched, with plenty of chilly space around it.

Claire tried to tell herself that she couldn't possibly have the dream in hospital – there was no kitchen, no fridge to go to. Yes, that's what she had to keep reminding herself, as a way of immunizing herself against the dream. But then she realized that there must be a fridge somewhere nearby – for drugs and urine samples. Queasily, she glimpsed the possibility of having a cruel hospital variant of her nightmare, where she squatted in front of some clinical icebox, greedily consuming human waste.

However, when the time actually came, on that first night in the hospital, she hadn't dreamed the dream after all. She'd slept like a lamb.

Now it was tomorrow already, and here she was full of pre-med, waiting for her turn under the blade. She was relaxed and dozy, enchanted by the snow swirling silently outside, compliant as the orderlies scooped her childishly light body off the bed and transferred it onto a trolley.

Even Dr Nadir, when he saw her minutes later, seemed pleasantly surprised by how close to unconsciousness she already was, on a drug so weak.

"Now," he said, as the anaesthetist was injecting her with the real thing. "I want you to think of what year it is, and count backwards from it."

"2009, 2008, 2007... 2006..." began Claire, thinking she would probably make it as far as the 1960s. But by 2003, she was already under.

HANNAH'S TALE – FLAT

Lucy Golden

Lucy Golden is an intensely private person: she is unwilling to publish her biographical details, considering the intimate revelations in her books to be more than adequate. She says, 'My books and stories are extremely personal. They are drawn from the very deepest parts of my mind and if you don't know me after reading them, you never will.' Her fiction is based both on her own experiences and those of friends; these people are not impossibly rich, nor are they cardboard cutouts. They are real people, with real families, real lives, real careers, who all have a keen interest in sex which they have shared with the author. This populist element in her writing could explain why Lucy Golden has built up such a devoted following.

It wasn't the day Mike left. That had been a day of betrayal and bitterness; of loathing him and loathing everything he stood for and everything he had ever owned or touched (including me). It was a few weeks later, the day Mike came back, with that smarmy little cow waiting outside for him while he went through the flat in a carnage of bin bags and cardboard boxes packing up all his stuff. But that was all it was: just stuff. And yet he was tearing our life apart: not our lives (plural), not separate lives, but that one indivisible wholeness which had made us one thing, drawing together the clouds and the trees and the earth and the whole universe into a single being which was us and meant eternity.

Tearing up the long slow Sundays when we wouldn't leave the flat for a single minute, because that was the one day we cooked a meal together, pulled out the table and laid the cutlery and glasses. Real food – cooked food – that we took turns to prepare and spent the rest of the day quietly enjoying and digesting as we flopped out in front of videos or read books. Tearing up those warm days walking out into Ken Wood or Hampstead Heath. Or further, to real countryside and forest, to places where there was only sky and birds or insects to watch us curl up together, sliding hands inside the clothes that had been so carefully selected to be unobstructive. On other days, the shorter days, it would just be the Common, where the limitations would be tantalising but the danger of discovery would be greater and the lovemaking more intense, a magic that rather than being spoiled had actually been enhanced by the two occasions when that danger became reality.

Ripping into those Friday evenings when – sometimes – we could both finish work on time and would meet in that disgusting smoky little pub where we drank too much. And that often led to a film, but certainly a takeaway pizza

devoured in our bed with a bottle of wine, drunk straight from the bottle, or from each other's mouths or stomachs or Mike would – well Mike had options I didn't. Until the whole bed was a disgusting mess of spilt wine and smears of tomato sauce: slices of greasy mushroom on the sheets and on our skin; slivers of cheese laid in a trail down my front where I bribed his mouth to follow. By now the ice-cream would be half melted but still cold: goose-pimpling, nipple-hardeningly cold when he scooped fingerfuls into my mouth and across my body and I wrapped handfuls round his cock; instant deflation that I quickly repaired when I turned the sticky cold to slippery cool between steady stroking hands. And afterwards we slept like that, wallowing in the disgustingness of it all and waking in shamefaced delight at our squalor. The bath together was the best bit before the sheets were stuffed into the washing machine and we remade the bed, smirking, each taunting the other with how decadent we had become and drawing strength from the security of having shared such private and unspeakable delights.

She'd never do anything like that: the vacant-headed little bitch with the E cup bra who was waiting for him in his ugly little car. I bet she'd never even let him touch her without washing first, and then washing again afterwards. I glared down at her from the bay window, challenging her to have the courage to look up at me, while keeping my back to the destruction that he worked through every room and cupboard we had shared. Every door that he opened and closed I recognised. Every sound invaded my head.

From the bedroom – no longer our bedroom – he called through that he was taking his alarm clock ('Please do!' I whispered back, wishing it wasn't still waiting so cosily, so tellingly, beside my bed); then that he'd leave the sheets, so that I wondered whether those same memories had been running through his brain, but possibly not; maybe the words were meant only to underline his generosity, to mark out what had originally been his. I yelled back that he could take them, that I didn't want them. But he said no, they'd bought new ones, fresh ones. He wanted to wound me, to distance himself from our coupled past but when I tried to answer that I would be getting new ones too, it just sounded petty so I shut up.

And all the while she sat there, gazing down the street with scarcely a twitch: purity itself. She'd never lie there in the sweat and the stains and the glory of it all. She'd never pin him down on the bed and slap a handful of double chocolate-chip across his chest and then kneel astride him to sluice it off, drenching him in a flood of her own piss, just because she could and because it was the one thing they'd never done. She wouldn't. Not little Miss Perfect. She was so fucking pure that she'd step out of the shower to take a piss.

Okay, I was angry. I admit it but I think I was entitled to be. I'd introduced them for God's sake, because Mike had left 4-Deque by the time she arrived: fresh from the agency, new to London, and not knowing anyone. I invited her to supper, cooked for her, just trying to be friendly because it wasn't an easy place to settle into, 4-Deque: all testosterone and sports injuries, with she and me the only females.

She managed well enough, was fine as a receptionist, could manage the phones and a bit of typing, although you wouldn't ask too much more of her. "Eye candy", the lads called her, but Rob from Marketing was the first one. He

reported that she really was as dumb as she looked, quite a cuddly little bimbo, he said, but lips like a suction pump. So then Steve said he'd have some of that. And he did. Then someone else followed and before long they had all been there. And still she showed up the next morning in a fresh clean dress with a fresh clean smirk on her puffy red lips, those lips between which they were all dribbling their smug mark of possession. Until Mike was the only one who hadn't.

And then I discovered that he had too.

We rowed, and didn't speak and made up and I might have forgiven him that one slip, except that he went back for more. And how do I know? She told me.

All the lads were invited to Steve's stag-night, except it wasn't going to be a night, it was to be a weekend in Amsterdam starting on Friday evening. So Ruth and I were left behind, and not to be outdone went to a silly Oscar-contending weepy film, where we duly cried and brought a bottle back afterwards – here, into this very room because my flat was closer than hers – and as we emptied the bottle, and then a second one, so we unloaded our consciences. Things we'd done, including her confession about Mike, when she cried and said she hadn't meant to hurt me, and mine of what I'd done -- but she had never done but sometimes wanted to. And then we both went quiet.

They had been right about her lips. She kissed with a power that you wouldn't believe from so delicate a figure: long kisses with a tongue that swept round inside my mouth as if it were covering every bit of me with a caress. Wine flavoured, but milder and interspersed with tiny nips from her lips that grabbed mine and held them while a tiny pointed tip of tongue pattered against me. And hands which I longed to feel touching me so when they didn't, I lifted them myself: laid them on my breasts where they just rested for a second before beginning a slow gentle massage that produced an effect I was unwilling even to try to ignore. A hardening here: a moistening there. Reactions that came as readily as if she had been Mike, and I couldn't wait for more. I took over then, leading her through into our bedroom and there, with her willing help, we settled down together to start uncovering her.

First a dress which I'd seen often enough skimming through the office but whose colour – she now admitted – she wasn't sure about; inside it, a stretch of skin so smooth and clear I was jealous of the finding. I trailed my fingertips across the neat ridges of her ribs and the soft warm dimple of her tummy button. And my lips followed where my fingers had been, across the gently rising velvet of her stomach, over all the skin that was available to me. Next her bra: a giggly and very sensible bra from the same chain that I use which lifted away to reveal pale golden nipples on a creamy white bosom that tumbled down both sides of her chest in a way mine never does. I sank straight down and first kissed but then simply licked: sweeping my tongue across her as I grinned into her face and her eyes grinned back. So round and inviting that I could not leave them alone but held them, moulded between my hands like bread dough, cradled as gently as an injured bird, supported squeezed and kissed again, just lightly round her little nipples as their paleness grew less pale and the little tips curled up ever tighter and more eager. Tights: ordinary, but leaving sweet indentations like rows of tiny teeth round her waist, and I kissed those too, before I tugged the tights out from under her bottom and down her legs. At last

her knickers: big, purple and sweetly unfashionable. "Sorry. I hadn't . . ." But I kissed what nestled inside them and her apology died. A neatly shaped golden bush, trimmed short, but not aggressively so, that she ruffled nervously in her fingers as soon as it came in sight.

"Now you," she said, although I think it was shyness more than eagerness that moved her, but her hands were very tender in unbuttoning, unzipping, unhooking me. She stroked my nipples where they poked up through the thin bra, kissed them, and kissed them again after the bra was gone. She moved quickly to my knickers, tugged them off, threw them away and then stopped: kneeling beside me with her lip bitten in her teeth.

"Can I . . ." she pushed back her hair, "can I look?"

"Look?"

"Only I've never seen another girl, you know properly."

She looked, as I gave myself up to her, opened myself out wide, offering myself to her inspection and her fingers, to play with my folds, work along the creases and pull at the lips.

"You're different."

"What?"

"There's much more of you. I'm not like that."

"Let me see."

"Wait!" and she pushed me back down, continuing to explore: separating out the lips, peeling back the hood, touching, playing, stroking.

"Let me see!" and this time she relented, and I looked, and she was right: she was different. Whoever trimmed, and, I could now see, shaved the underneath, had done a very good job: professional, I imagine. Closed up like a bud, but a vibrant brilliant pink bud, that glistened already, whose scent was already teeming. I touched her: slid one finger down the tiny pink ridges and inside. She sighed and trembled, her legs twitched a little more open and I was welcome. She tasted different, too. Sweeter than me and, as I lapped at her, wetter. Oh, but she was responsive: almost at once she began to squirm, her golden thighs twisting and her heels dragging up either side of me before her legs shot out straight again with a low wail of contentment. I reached up for her breasts, groping for the shy little nipples that seemed so lost in the expanse of creamy white, and found her own hands already there, although she surrendered one to me and that hand came down to my head, tangling through my hair as I worked. The moans were longer now, faltering and stammering, but louder too. Her heels came up to ride onto my shoulders, beating on my back when crying was not enough, keeping me there, spurring me on, and finally lifting her hips up to push even harder against my face as one strangled scream finally stilled her.

She lay there, grinning, gorgeously naked, her legs slowly relaxing back to a more demure togetherness, her soft bosom, warm and wide, rising and falling with each breath. And I reached over and planted a kiss on each nipple.

"Well?" I asked her, and planted another, and then one on her lips too.

"That was . . ." but I kissed her mouth again, enjoying the way her scent was wafted back to me on her breath.

"Well?" I repeated and kissed her nipples again, and then again because they were so irresistibly soft: so pale and innocent.

". . . interesting."

"Interesting?" I sat up.

"Yes." She must have caught sight of my face. "I mean it was very nice and everything. I'm glad I did it, but I wouldn't want to do it again. It's just that, well, I guess I'm not a dyke."

I forget the precise sequence after that. I know the scene wasn't pretty, and that she left fairly quickly, scrabbling for her shoes which I had flung out into the hallway. And how it developed from there I don't know either, but by Monday lunchtime all the lads at 4-Deque knew. By the evening, Mike knew. He spent that night on Steve's couch and started moving his clothes out on the Thursday. And now this: a remembered "That's everything. I'll be going" still echoing in the hall as I watched him walk to the car. There had not been one night in the last six weeks that I hadn't spent alone. Not one morning that I hadn't woken up alone. I could barely even remember the feel of Mike's cock in the morning. Hard? Yes, naturally, but how hard? Leather? Wood? Iron? I could no longer quite recapture the detail. Or the smell. Or the taste. All these sensations which had once been so familiar and been part of what we were but which had now been whipped away: packed up with his clutter into cardboard boxes; hustled down the steps and out of my life, leaving my memory as empty as our flat. The flat.

GLOVE STORY

Geoff Nicholson

Geoff Nicholson is the author of sixteen novels, including *Bleeding London*, and most recently *The City Under the Skin*. His non-fiction titles include *Sex Collectors* and *The Lost Art of Walking*. He lives in Los Angeles.

I work in "women's gloves" in a large London department store. It's not a job that every man would be happy with, but for me it's just about ideal. I get to meet a lot of women with very beautiful hands. I get to see these hands at close quarters, and quite often I get to touch them. I talk to the women who possess these hands, and then I sell them beautiful leather or kidskin or suede or silk or satin or velvet gloves. Then, later, in the privacy of my own mind, I start thinking about what these women could do with their hands and their gloves, and how they might use them on me.

It's not a dirty job unless you think about it the right way, although of course that's precisely the way I like to think about it.

Inevitably in this job I also get to see a lot of women with very ordinary or even downright ugly hands. This is not a pleasure in itself, obviously, but ultimately it's not so terrible, because it's still my business to sell these women beautiful gloves which will hide the ordinariness or ugliness of their hands. This strikes me as a valuable service.

Now, you could argue that gloves, by definition, hide beautiful hands every bit as much as they hide ordinary or ugly ones. But that's not a problem as far as I can see. Knowing that there's a beautiful hand sheathed in a beautiful glove is just fine. It's better than fine. Or if it's problematic at all, it's more like a Zen paradox. Is a hand still beautiful, still an object of erotic fascination, even when you can't see it? Well, of course it is.

I always tried not to be too obsessive about these things. I suppose I'd always have found it impossible to go out with a woman who had ugly or fat or stunted or spatulate hands, or who bit her nails or who had chipped nail varnish or who – oh God, please, no – wore false nails. But apart from that I'm not foolish enough to believe there's any such thing as the perfect hand, or indeed the perfect glove. Nevertheless, that fateful day when Vanessa first came into the department, peeled off the black leather gloves she was wearing and revealed the gorgeous, long, slender, articulate hands beneath: well, if that wasn't perfection it was near enough for me.

These were hands to die for: taut, pale and lean enough that the intricate lacings of bone and vein were visible through the pure white skin. The fingers

were finely jointed, the nails not too short, not too long, well seated in their symmetrical nail beds, shaped like almonds and painted a colour that I recognized as Bronze Chianti.

I'm sure I gaped, and very possibly I gasped, but apparently it was a reaction Vanessa was accustomed to.

"Yes, I know they're more or less perfect," she said, and it might have sounded arrogant or narcissistic coming from somebody else, but she said it in a matter-of-fact way, as though she was discussing a natural phenomenon, like a sunset or a cloud formation, something that had nothing to do with her. Need I say, this wasn't literally true. Nature may have given her potentially perfect hands but she had clearly taken great care of them, nurtured them, made them realize their full potential. You had to admire that.

"Are you a hand model or something?" I asked.

"No," she said. "I could be, obviously, but you know, I think that would be debasing my gift, like prostitution. I don't want to show them to all and sundry. I want to save them for someone special."

It seemed obvious to me that I was indeed that very someone. I took a bold step. I saw that Vanessa was eyeing a pair of red, cabretta leather gloves, so I let her buy them at an enormous discount and then I asked her out. We may not have been strictly compatible, but we did have one very important thing in common. I adored Vanessa's hands and so did she. Relationships have been based on less. The first evening went very well, and so we started dating.

In lots of ways it was an entirely ordinary relationship. We did all the usual things that people do when they date. The only thing that was a little unusual was our sex life. Vanessa didn't really want to have sex with me, at least not what most people would call sex, at least not conventional sex. The hand-job was her preferred form, in fact the only form she was prepared to consider with me. And you might think a hand-job from a woman with perfect hands wouldn't be so bad. But Vanessa would only give me a hand-job if she could keep a pair of gloves on. And again, that wasn't absolutely terrible.

The touch of glove on penis felt pretty good, and knowing that a perfect hand was inside the glove certainly added to the pleasure. And Vanessa had skills. A few minutes, brisk manipulation and I was gushing messily, although I noticed she was as dexterous as a card shark when it came to making sure that none of my goo ever went anywhere near her precious gloves.

Was I happy with this arrangement? Well, yes and no. A part of me felt I had no right to complain, but another part felt utterly dissatisfied. I wanted more. Not an unreasonably large amount more either, it seemed to me; I wanted the touch of her flesh on mine, her perfect hands touching my (admittedly all too imperfect) cock. Was that too much to ask?

I tried to do the grown-up thing. I expressed my needs. Frequently. I would say to Vanessa, "How about a proper hand-job, you know, as in with the bare hand, skin on skin?"

And she would say, and this was obviously pretty hurtful, that she couldn't. She didn't feel that way about me. She didn't deny that I was a decent man, appreciative and attentive and so forth, but my penis and I weren't sufficiently

exceptional to receive the gift of contact from her exquisite bare hands. In the beginning she'd thought I might be special, but now she knew I wasn't nearly special enough. Sometimes my self-esteem was low enough to believe she might have a point here, but that didn't make me any happier.

Naturally Vanessa didn't wear gloves every single minute of the day and night. She didn't wear them to sleep in for example, though that was something of an irrelevance since we never slept together, nor did she wear them when she was eating or in the shower. And obviously she didn't wear them when she gave herself a manicure; and there was a lot of manicure work that went on with Vanessa, a lot of rubbing and massaging, lots of lotions, anti-ageing creams, penetrating oils, paraffin wax and so forth. I watched as she performed these arcane and beguiling operations, and I liked what I saw, but it only made things more tantalizing and frustrating. I began to hatch a plan.

We were at her flat one day, it was the afternoon, and I would be long gone before the night, and I was watching her paint her nails an intense shade called Rusted Cerise. After a while I said, "When you're finished, can we have sex?" and she said sure. It wasn't that she lacked enthusiasm for sex, just that she only had enthusiasm for one kind.

"Which gloves?" she asked.

"Oh, I think the red cabretta, don't you?" I said.

While she was finishing her manicure I did a terrible thing. I mean it wasn't so very terrible in the greater scheme of things, but quite terrible enough in Vanessa's scheme, I suspected. I went into the bedroom, took one of the red cabretta gloves, the right, got out my cock, slipped it inside and started to masturbate. The soft interior of the glove felt terrific, even if the stitching of the seams was a mite scratchy, and before long I ejaculated into the innermost folds and cavities of the glove. Then I zipped myself up and waited for Vanessa to join me in the bedroom.

She came in, and without any preliminaries, slipped her freshly manicured right hand into the glove I'd been using. Instantly her face showed surprise, confusion, distrust, alarm, realization and distaste. She pulled off the glove and revealed her beautiful bare hand, now smeared with strands and globs of my semen. Her hand had never looked better, if you asked me, and in my fantasies she would have shared that opinion, and this would have been a moment of transformation. She would suddenly have understood, she'd have smiled at me lasciviously, licked the sperm off her hand with excited delight, and we'd have moved on to a brand-new and exciting phase of our relationship.

In the real world it didn't work that way. In the real world she was furious and disgusted, and utterly untransformed. She said I could take my disgusting desires, my disgusting penis and my disgusting sperm and I could leave her life for good. She said I could also take her now sullied red cabretta gloves since she would never touch them again; which I duly did.

It was the inevitable end of a relationship that had always been far from perfect, despite containing certain elements of absolute perfection.

I tried not to mope. I threw myself into my work, grateful that I still had that. I did my best to get over it. Nevertheless there were many times, in the middle of long, feverish, lonely nights when I found myself brooding about Vanessa

and what might have been. At times like that, I gazed at the red cabretta gloves, touched them, sniffed them, and sometimes – almost against my will, it seemed – my hand would slip inside the right glove. It was a snug fit at first, but cabretta is wonderfully yielding. Before long, I would find myself masturbating, bringing myself to a wet, messy climax, and if I got some sperm on the glove, well that was all part of the experience. It wasn't the same as having Vanessa do the job for me, of course, but you know, there were certain ways in which it seemed much better.

MEAN STREAK

Christine Pountney

Christine Pountney is a Toronto-based writer, teacher, and Core Energetics practitioner, whose work has been published to great critical acclaim in Canada and the UK. Her first novel, *Last Chance Texaco*, was long-listed for the Orange Prize in 2000. Pountney has since published two more novels, *The Best Way You Know How* and *Sweet Jesus* – which Irvine Welsh and Barbara Gowdy both chose as one of their 'Best Books of 2012'.

They'd been married without children for eight years and she loved him with a love that was fierce and true, but he had a mean streak and she sometimes wondered if she loved him more or less because of it – and often suspected more. He sat on the board of directors at the Royal Opera House in London and they frequently attended black-tie events. She was tall and Egyptian and carried herself with a regal grace, though with a flare in her manner of dress that sometimes offended his strict sensibility. He would have liked her to dress more conservatively, but enjoyed the attention she received because of it, especially from other women, whom he often caught eyeing her with an envious admiration bordering on lust.

This evening, when she came down the stairs like a princess from the Raj, dressed in a red and gold silk gown, he shook his head and said, "What in Christ's name are you wearing?"

He said this to crush her, but only succeeded in crushing her a little. She was well schooled in deflecting his comments and accepted them as a prelude to praise. As cruel as he could be, he could be just as repentant.

He placed a velvet shawl around her shoulders and, lifting her hair, kissed her on the back of the neck. Then they walked out to the car that was waiting for them in the street.

Just before they entered the ballroom at the hotel where the reception was to take place, he took hold of her with such an urgency that it belied any indifference he could pretend, and whispered, "You're so fucken gorgeous. You make me horny. I'm gonna go crazy if I can't fuck you soon."

She lowered her face and, peering up at him from under her dark brow, said haughtily, "You've always taken me when it suited you. I don't see what the difference is now. Nobody's stopping you."

This kind of taunting infuriated him and she liked to infuriate him just before they entered a room full of people. She could see the redness of his neck flare up against his white tuxedo collar and felt an erotic supremacy over him. She liked

to mock him. It provoked the right reaction from him, an angry retaliation that she enjoyed.

Sometimes as they moved around the room, mingling with the other guests, he would squeeze her arm painfully. The pain was such that it gave her a sultry, breathless, heavy-lidded look that men found stimulating in an animal way. As if she was in a perpetual state of sexual arousal, she had the look of a big cat, seemingly languid and insolent before the kill.

After they've been there a little while, they run into a couple they've met only once previously and don't expect to see much of in the future.

"Well, if it isn't Jim and Jacky Fluckerty," the man says sarcastically.

"It's Flaherty, actually," Jacky corrects him.

"Of course it is," the man says.

There's a pause between the four adults, then Jim says, "It's a pleasure to see you again," and nods at the man's beautiful wife, glancing down at her breasts.

"Seems the pleasure's all yours," her husband says.

"Pardon me?" Jim asks.

"I can see you're gagging for it," he says.

"Come on, honey," Jacky says and pulls her husband away.

"What a pathetic bunch of people," the man says looking around the room and finishes off his whiskey. Then he pulls his wife towards him and says, "I want to fuck you now. I'm gonna ram you hard with my cock. Is that what you want?"

The woman nods and, holding herself with unwavering dignity, follows her husband to a side exit leading to a concrete stairwell. They walk down two flights of stairs and he pushes her back against the wall.

"My God," he says, dropping to his knees and wrapping his arms around her waist and pressing his head against her stomach, "you're so fucken beautiful. What would I do without you?"

"Don't bore me," she says, yanking his head back by the hair. "Try behaving like a man, for a change."

At that, the man stands up and slaps his wife on the side of the head. He's learnt where to hit her so that he leaves no mark. She turns away from him and winces, raising her arms to defend herself. He hits her again and says, "You're such a whore."

"No, babe," she says. "I only ever do what you tell me to."

"And have I ever told you to suck another man's cock?"

"No, babe."

"So whose cock do you suck?"

"Yours, babe."

"And whose cock fucks this pussy?" the man asks, grabbing her crotch.

"Just yours, babe. Only yours."

"That's right," he says. "Now turn around and bend over. I'm gonna drill you from behind."

The man's beautiful wife bends forward, pushing her ass towards him. He lifts the hem of her dress and drapes it over her head so that he can't see her face. He puts one hand on her lower back and wrapping his other fist around her underwear, rips them off.

Then he drags his well-manicured fingernails up the outside of his wife's thighs

and over her hips, scraping into her flesh, drawing blood. She tries to straighten up, but he holds her down, the pain like a white spear through her brain, the abraded flesh already rising in four red furrows along her legs.

The man spits on his hand and gets ready to ram his cock into her. "I'm gonna ram you now, baby."

"Okay, babe," she whispers. "You ram me."

"I'm gonna bang you so hard."

"Make it hard, babe."

But just as she feels the hard soft hot tip of her husband's cock at her pussy, there is a noise on the stairs, a woman's laughter and then silence. The man turns and sees a young couple, hotel employees, the man a waiter probably, his girlfriend a chambermaid, heading out for the night.

"Sorry," the young woman says, brushing past and scurrying down the stairs. The young man takes longer and, as he's passing, the man, still holding his wife draped in red silk and bent at the waist, takes hold of his arm and says, "Listen son, I need your help here."

The young man glances down at his girlfriend. She jerks her head as if to say, Let's go, but he pauses, and in that split second of reluctance, the man knows that he's got him.

"It's something else, isn't it?" he says, standing up and tucking his cock back into his trousers. "My wife's got a beautiful pussy, don't you think?"

The young man doesn't look at it.

"Look at it," the husband says. "It's the most beautiful, muscular pussy you'll ever see in your life. Do you want to touch it?"

The young man swallows and looks down at his girlfriend. She opens her hands and says, "This is sick, James. You don't want to get involved in this."

"Look at her legs," she hisses, under her breath. "Come on. Let's go."

When he doesn't comply, she makes a disgusted noise at the back of her throat and runs down the stairs.

"Your girlfriend's a bit squeamish," the older man says and James looks back at him.

Again the man nods towards his wife's exposed vagina. "Go on, cop yourself a feel. Chance of a lifetime, boy."

James runs his hands through his hair and licks his lips and glances down the stairwell in the direction his girlfriend went, then he looks at the woman's beautiful ass and her long legs in their expensive stockings. As if pulled by gravity, he lifts a hand and moves it slowly towards the woman's pretty wet pink cunt. He touches it lightly with a finger and the woman moans, arching her back. He looks at the husband who nods again, and pushes a finger in. The slippery hot skin of her pussy makes his cock grow hard.

"Try another finger," the man says, and so he does, each finger eliciting a stronger reaction of pleasure from the man's half-concealed wife.

James becomes so entranced by the woman's fleshy cunt that he doesn't notice the husband position himself behind him, until he feels a hand on his elbow. The man's voice is right at his ear.

"Put all your fingers in, boy."

Obediently, James makes a beak of his fingers and eases his whole hand into

the woman's body. When he is in to his knuckles and feeling the tightness of her flesh, the husband tightens his grip on James's elbow and eases his hand in further.

James can feel his fingers pushing against the soft inner walls of the woman's body. His hand is completely inside her now and the man is right behind him. He's got his left arm around James's chest, holding him there, and with the other he starts ramming James's hand into his wife's body. She lets out a moan, a painful noise, and James's instinct is to pull his hand out but the man won't let him. The man pushes his hand in, up to the wrist, and James curls his fingers into a fist, afraid of poking something vital inside her, of catching something with a fingernail.

With every rough punch of his fist, the woman cries out now. She starts flailing her arms, pushing against the wall. Her husband leans forward, putting all his weight into it, and James can't help but transfer this weight to the woman until, eventually, she collapses, her head in the corner where the wall meets the floor. James uses his free hand to brace himself, kneeling over her, her husband kneeling behind. It is at this point that James realizes his arm is in half way to the elbow.

"Stop," he says, breathlessly. "Stop it, you're hurting her."

"I'm not hurting her," the husband says. "You are."

"Please stop," James says. "I'm begging you."

The man's wife is quieter now, but still breathing heavily, whimpering in pain.

"Please," James implores the wife now. "Please tell him to stop." There are tears on his cheeks, falling onto the woman's back.

"Okay," the woman says eventually, from underneath her red silk veil. "That's enough. The boy's right. It's time to let him go."

The man gets off the boy and stands up.

The boy withdraws his hand, wet and glistening like a newborn calf, and cradles it, relieved to be in possession of it again.

"Get out of here," the husband says and the boy takes a quick look at him, then tears down the stairs.

"Come here, sweetheart," the man says, taking his wife in his arms, rearranging her dress, then stroking her face. "You okay, baby?"

The woman nods.

"I didn't hurt you too much?"

She shakes her head.

"I love you, babe," she says.

"I love you too, baby. I love you so much. What would I do without you?"

"Well, you'd have to get used to squeamish girls, for one," his wife says and they both laugh.

He pulls his wife to her feet and they head back towards the party in a sated silence that is so commonly mistaken for love.

THE CAT THAT GOT THE CREAM

Christine Pountney

Christine Pountney is a Toronto-based writer, teacher, and Core Energetics practitioner, whose work has been published to great critical acclaim in Canada and the UK. Her first novel, *Last Chance Texaco*, was long-listed for the Orange Prize in 2000. Pountney has since published two more novels, *The Best Way You Know How* and *Sweet Jesus* – which Irvine Welsh and Barbara Gowdy both chose as one of their 'Best Books of 2012'.

It's not like I don't get paid for this shit. But I knew Latif Eljadidi as a friend. He was known as The Sheik, though he probably wasn't even Arab. I think he was from Libya. He ran the local convenience store and had always been nice to me. He knew me way back in the days when I was just a street waif, when I was still a junkie and nothing more than a bad-ass streetwalker, lady of the night, doggone hooker. Now he knows I only go out when I get called. That I make upwards of $1,000 an evening. That I only have to fuck one client at a time, and at a leisurely pace. I say this because anybody who knows a thing or two about what goes on in my neighbourhood knows that making one end meet another as a bad-ass junkie hooker, you've got to be turning a helluva lotta tricks. And that can wear you out. Not to mention the heart and soul.

I guess the thing I did with Latif was a nostalgia kick for me. Something perverse to remind me that I still had a long way to go to a healthy lifestyle. But let's get back to Latif.

Sometime pretty soon after Latif immigrated to this fair land of ours with his family, some 28 years ago, so soon that his mom was too busy hanging hijabs in her brand-new walk-in closet to notice that he was gone, Latif wandered away from the house. He was only nine years old. As the sun began to set over Liberty, our ice-cream lady of the harbour, all sorts of pagan, nightmarish creatures began to appear. Ghosts, goblins, witches, cowboys, super heroes, robots. Latif didn't know what the hell was happening. He became terrified. He started to cry. He got chased down a dark alleyway by a sinister group of boys in rubber President Nixon masks. He peed his pants. They punched him in the eye. They laughed at him. Welcome to America.

Ever since that childhood experience, Latif vowed to set some kind of annual sabotage, a trap for unsuspecting trick-or-treating brats. And even though

things turned out pretty well for Latif – he never married, but he did become the successful owner of a rather successful business – there was something about Halloween that still rankled his Eastern sensibility, still brought out a vindictive streak. Children begging for candy, imagine that. He found the whole idea of Halloween offensive.

So this is where I come in.

For the last six years, Latif has hired me for the night and the drill has always been the same. He would pay me handsomely and I would arrive, equally handsome, in a one-piece black lycra catsuit and heels. A cat mask and whiskers, two pointy cat ears and a long, rather stiff, black velvet tail. He would greet me with a kiss on the cheek and once inside, he would pull the blind on the door, the only window in his shop. He would then produce four leather restraining straps and a saddle blanket, which he would lay across the counter beside the cash register. He would then ask me to bend over it and rest my belly on the counter with my arms hanging down on the other side. Arched just like one of those black cats in the Halloween ads that are always standing on the witch's broom as she flies in silhouette across an orange moon.

With my legs straight and slightly parted, and my stomach on the counter, I could just about touch the floor with my palms. In this position, Latif would begin to fasten me. He didn't talk much at this stage, and come to think about it, we rarely said a word to each other on these nights. It's as if we had to adopt a false formality to avoid the embarrassment. I thought it was all rather discreet.

Latif had four hooks drilled into the floor along the bottom edge of the counter, two on either side. They were barely noticeable, and it was to these hooks that he would attach the restraining straps, fastening me securely by my ankles and wrists.

"Beautiful," Latif would sometimes whisper at this point, standing behind me with his hands on my hips. He flicked my tail one way and then the other as if playing a private game. He leaned forward and put his head on my back. He got up and walked around the counter and took a small pair of nail scissors out of the money drawer of the register to my left. Walking around the counter again and standing between my legs, Latif cut a hole in the lycra of my catsuit. From a sudden cool sensation, I could tell that the elasticized material had peeled back of its own accord as if eager to reveal what it had, up 'til now, been concealing.

Sometimes, at this point, Latif would take me from behind. Just a dozen or so quick thrusts, maybe less, but always forceful, as if he was denying himself some greater pleasure that he wanted, but wouldn't allow himself to take. There was a hint of violence in the power of his thrusts, but it never lasted long. If he did fuck me then, he did so expediently. And as surreptitiously as he began, he would desist, tucking his cock back into his pants and setting about his business.

Latif took a carton of milk from the fridge, which he put in the microwave for a minute to warm up. He placed a saucer on the floor in front of me and filled it with milk. He held it to my lips and watched me lap at the milk like a big, black, arched-back cat, while he stroked my head. Then he got some olive oil from the shelf, filled a cup with oil, cut the top off the carton and crouching in front of me, slowly pulled the warm milk into the throat of a turkey-baster. Then he dipped the mouth of the turkey-baster in the oil and, standing up, bent over me

and gently inserted it into my ass. He squeezed the rubber pump and filled my rectum with warm milk.

This he did until the two-litre carton was empty.

"Hold on," he said tenderly, as I admitted having an irrepressible urge to empty my bowels. He unfastened my wrists and got me to sit down in a chair which he'd placed behind me, into the seat of which he'd cut a hole and attached a bucket. I unclenched my sphincter and let my bowels void (ah, what relief!) in a great rush of shit and milk.

"That's great," he said after a while, helping me to stand and refastening me once again. Latif stood behind me and wiped my ass. "Clean as a mother's tit," he said quietly to himself while pushing a finger in. Again he seemed resistant of his own desire, but took me anyway, and fucked me quickly in the ass without coming.

He pulled out and I heard him sigh with his hands on my bum. Then he walked to the back of the store and returned, lumbering under the bulk of his Halloween Machine. The Halloween Machine was an old refrigerator box that he had painted to look like a robot years ago. There were dials and digits and small holes cut into the box through which poked several small christmas lights, which blinked and flickered when the extension cord was plugged in. On either side of the box, Latif had cut large squares to fit the counter, so he could place the box over the counter and me, and you'd have no idea that I was there.

On the inside of the box, at the same height as my ass, was a plastic funnel, angled down towards an opening painted on the outside to look like a miniature stage. Latif had even fashioned some red velvet curtains and glued them to the box. Level with my hips was another window on the side, also with a curtain, where the puppet master could reach in and insert a boiled sweet into my ass. Latif would do this and see if everything was working. Then he'd yank on the blind and send it spinning up and flip the "closed" sign to "open" and we would wait for a child to come along.

When the door opened to a little chime of bells, Latif would welcome the children into his shop and instruct them to hold their loot bags up to the little stage and repeat the magic words. "Trick-or-treat!" they would sing, and when I heard that signal, I was to squeeze my buttocks and pop the boiled sweet out of my ass and into the funnel, where it would roll down and out the cardboard box and into the child's candy bag.

Latif would often roar with laughter when the candy popped out, and by the sound of their rapidly retreating footsteps, it must have spooked the children. I don't really blame them. It's a sinister holiday at the best of times. But sometimes I liked to hear him laugh, too. I liked the fact that we were scaring the kids. It seemed right. It seemed like a warning. I got some kind of conspiratorial satisfaction out of what we were doing. I guess it was my own little vendetta against the neighbourhood. It was sweet revenge for both of us.

THE SNOW LEOPARD

David Henry Sterry

David Henry Sterry's parents emigrated from Newcastle to the United States just before he was born. While attending Immaculate Heart College in Hollywood, he was employed as a sex worker. This became the subject of his first memoir, *Chicken: Self-Portrait of a Young Man for Rent*, which has been translated into a dozen languages and is being made into a film. He graduated in 1978 from Reed College, where he studied existentialism and poetry. After training in England, he was offered a professional soccer contract when he was twenty-one. He has worked as a building inspector, a chicken fryer, a limousine driver, a telephone solicitor, a soccer referee, a marriage counsellor, and as the Master of Ceremonies at Chippendale's Male Strip Club, which is the subject of his second memoir, *Unzipped*. He is the author of fourteen other books as well, and has been featured in (among many other places) *The Times*, on the cover of the *New York Times Book Review*, on the BBC and National Public Radio. For more information than you'd ever care to know about David Henry Sterry, go to his website: DavidHenrySterry.com

When I first saw the bulge in the crotch of her panties I was frankly disappointed. Don't get me wrong, I got nothin' against a hot trannie, I'm just not built that way. Or maybe it wasn't a bulge. The black of the moonless night shed no light in the nasty room. Did she/he semi-flash me? I couldn't be sure. You're not here for that anyway, I reminded myself. Just get the package and be on yer merry way.

Chinese Willy said midnight, there was no room for confusion when Crack Harry delivered the message. Room 43, 11 pm. Felipe's Massage Parlour. There was no Felipe. No one was here for a massage. Occasionally a man would squeal in pain, and a female voice would berate him.

The Snow Leopard. When Shiva Shiv said that was the contact name, I laughed out loud. I stopped laughing when Shiva Shiv said, "What the fuck you laughin' at?" in a voice dripping of curry and murder. I couldn't stop thinking about that name. Snow Leopard. That night I had a dream. I was with the Snow Leopard. She was half-cat, half-woman. And she was in heat. I could smell it. She kept changing back and forth, from cat to woman and back: whiskers, lips, fangs, tongue, claws, breasts, fur, hair, but all crazy hungry jungle feline sex. She was tearing me to shreds, blood and guts ripped open, even as she was pounding me strokingly into submission. I was dying and coming at the same time when I woke up with a cold sweat and a curtain rod for a Johnson.

And now here she was. The Snow Leopard. And when she got up she flashed me. Or did she? Maybe it was just me. Wishful thinking. Wish fulfilment. Not getting laid nearly enough for a man in my line of work. Call it what you like. Long black straight hair. Barely-there black skirt. Black jacket with white spots. Camouflaged. Moving in the dark of the shabby unchic body-fluid-smelling room, I couldn't pin down exactly what she looked like. Asian? African? Mexican? Italian? Spanish? Long nails painted black. Coal eyes. I started to ask if she was the Snow Leopard, but as I rolled it around on my tongue, it sounded like something only a rank rookie would say, or someone who watched too many bad cable movies. I smelled that smell from my dream. The smell of heat. An animal in heat.

Shut up and get the package. Where's the package? She didn't have a bag, the skirt wasn't big enough for pockets. Maybe that was the bulge. Or was it a bulge? I fondled the ten grand in my secret jacket pocket. Why doesn't she say something? She paced like, well, frankly, like a big cat in a cage. And I could hear the beat of the jungle drum. Or maybe it was just Busta Rhymes booming from the next room.

I try to explain to people who aren't in the business why it's such a fun and rewarding line of work. It's exciting. I was excited. The blood was pumping. Adrenaline working overtime, I was jacked to the max and stone cold sober. Often when I'm on the job I get what I can only describe as an evangelical feeling, like this is what God wants me to do, like God is watching me and smiling. And today I felt like He, or She – I'm not gender restrictive when it comes to my deity – had brought me to the Snow Leopard to change my life. I can't explain it really, except to say that this job felt like one of those jobs where you look back from the future and you say, "Wow, that was some job." Or maybe not. Maybe this was one of those jobs you look back on and say, "I started day-dreaming and let my guard down and that's how I got this scar."

The more we didn't talk, the more charged the air got, like two saturated clouds bumping and humping and rubbing, the rumbling building as the lightning gathers. I wanted to see her. I reached for the light. This is what prompted the first word we ever spoke. Inevitably that word was: "No." And she was the one who said it, in that chilled voice of a frosty predator. And so we stood in the dark. "I need your help," she purred. This was not in the script. When Chinese Willy is expecting delivery of his package at midnight, and it's 11:13 pm, and ten grand is flaming in your secret jacket pocket, you need to keep your priorities straight. This is an excellent score, and sets up the next score, which is the big score. My dance card is full. Or is God calling me? "Hello, my name is Michael Bradshaw," I said, trying to cool my way through, "but people call me Mikey the Monkey. And you must be . . . ?" "I got no time for bullshit," she shot back, those coal eyes glowing. "Any minute now two big guys with automatic weapons are gonna burst through that door . . ."

Before she could even get through the sentence, two very big guys with automatic weapons burst through the door. She dropped straight down, behind the bed frame, and pulled out a tiny little pistol. I unholstered, then ducked and rolled, firing as fast as my fingers would fly. I took down the big guy on the left, first shot in the right shoulder, second in the belly, third in the right leg. As he fell he started

firing his Glock, bullets spraying around the room like the gun was prematurely ejaculating. When he hit the floor, eye level with me, I got off the shot I'm truly proud of. Plugged him just over the nose. That's when the big guy's lights went out. The Snow Leopard had killed quickly, cleanly, effortlessly, with style and grace. As is her wont. One dainty shot. With her tiny gun. Through the left eyeball of the big guy on the right. I was starting to fall hard for this cool kitty cat.

As gun smoke hung heavy, and two very big guys sprawled dead, the sounds of panicked screams from Felipe's clientele filtered into the room. I kept rolling, pulled myself under the bed, and had my gun at her head in the flash of an instant. Suddenly I was face-to-face under the bed with the Snow Leopard, staring into those cat eyes. I felt something hard poking into my ribs. Lo and behold it was her little gun. Maybe it was the blood splashed on the floor. Maybe it was the thrill of the kill. Maybe it was God. But suddenly my lips had minds of their own.

Our hands ravished each other, and before I knew what was what she had me out, fully in hand, then swallowed me whole. A cold metal pressed into my balls. Her little gun. Made my nuts hop like a couple of Mexican jumping beans. As she gorged on me, she dug those long sharp black claws into my chest. That smell of heat, she was animal-wild growling from way deep inside her throat. I had to be all the way in her. That's where God is, I remember thinking. I reached down between her legs. The bulge. In all the excitement I had quite forgotten about the perhaps-imaginary bulge. But there it was. The bulge. Before she knew what was happening I was in her knickers and I pulled it out. It was my package. I pocketed it. Thought of Chinese Willy looking fat and happy when I handed it to him. I rubbed my gun between her thighs and she sighed. My nozzle flirted with her fleshy folds, opened and explored the tip of her. I pulled the cash out of my inside jacket pocket, and as I slipped the money into her hand I spilled into her. She was fierce, biting, clawing and scratching, drawing blood. She put the tip of her little gun on my lips. I never wanted anyone or anything more. I rubbed my gun across her nipples, stroked her throat slow. She kept manoeuvring around so she could get at me better, bucking and howling, fast cuz we knew any second that bigger larger trouble could very well walk in. It was in-heat fucking, insane fucking, where time is no more and the mind is no more, and there is nothing else in the universe, even as the universe flows through you and into her then back through you, and then you skydive together off the top of Brooklyn Bridge together. We floated shaking and speaking in tongues together, as we landed back on earth. Breathing fire into each other we panted, this close, glowing in the after-rapture of it.

Funny how fast the brain can work when it has to. Do I walk away? Do I take her with me? Do I run away with her? That's when she shot me. Through the left eyeball. With that dainty little gun. Now that I'm dead I can honestly say I'm grateful the Snow Leopard did it so quickly, cleanly, effortlessly, with such style and grace. In the end, when you get into this line of work, that's all you can really ask for.

MOONBURN

Mitzi Szereto

Mitzi Szereto, an author and anthology editor of multi-genre fiction and non-fiction, has her own blog, *Errant Ramblings: Mitzi Szereto's Web-blog*, and is creator/presenter of the Web TV channel, *Mitzi TV*, which covers quirky London. Mitzi has pioneered erotic writing workshops in the UK and mainland Europe, teaching them from the Cheltenham Festival to the Greek islands. She has also lectured in creative writing at a number of British universities. Her anthology, *Erotic Travel Tales 2*, is the first anthology of erotica to feature a Fellow of the Royal Society of Literature.

She rarely goes out in the daytime. This is not because she doesn't like the sun, but because she likes the moon better. It seems wiser and more economical to store up her erotic energy for the night rather than squandering it by day. Besides, pretty much anyone can be out during the day; there's nothing special about baring your flesh to the sun. And, if anything, she is special.

One might expect her to look pale and sickly from this self-imposed retreat from natural light, but it's exactly the opposite. Her skin possesses a rich shimmering glow similar to the kind earned from an expensive Mediterranean tan, although this glow comes from her exposure to the moon and cannot be compared to any identifiable shade of summer bronze. Even her hair appears to have been created from the night – as if the darkness has been pulled from the sky, then combed into silky filaments to frame her face and cascade like silvery-black water down her gracefully arched spine.

She is neither young nor old. It would even be difficult to say whether she can be defined as beautiful, since nobody bothers to focus on her face. The knee-length khaki trench coat that doesn't quite conceal her customary uniform of seduction remains unbelted and open in the front, placing on deliberate display a pair of long, black-stockinged legs with diamond-patterned seams snaking up the calves, which stay shapely from so much nocturnal walking. Midway up the thighs the tops of these stockings terminate in the hooks of a red garter belt, the elastic straps forming a lacy frame for the meticulously manicured crossroads of her vulva. She likes the feeling of being closely trimmed. It enhances the subtlest sensation while retaining an element of mystery a complete divestment of hair would have sacrificed.

With every step, her rounded breasts undulate proudly against her out-thrust rib cage, the dainty, peach-coloured nipples pointing an invitation at passers-by. The extravagantly tall heels on which she manages to balance her slight weight

look like weapons designed to be driven into an unsuspecting foot and have on occasion served this purpose. As these sadistically spiked heels sound their call-to-arms against the luridly lighted sidewalks that make up her battleground, their wearer's clitoris swells with need, stiffening to a nipple-like point in the cool night air. Fortunately the khaki coat performs its intended function of cloaking both her nakedness and her desire from those walking behind or passing to the sides. After all, she doesn't wish to cause a stir.

The streets, sidewalks, and doorways of Soho are filled with people, particularly at night when those seeking to burrow into the sexual underbelly of London emerge from their lairs. Hence there is never a shortage of prospects for anonymous encounters – and that suits her just fine, since she likes quantity as well as variety. A dread-locked young busker strumming a cheap out-of-tune guitar and singing an off-key Beatles melody can be as satisfying as the proper middle-aged businessman skulking guiltily from a gentlemen's club, his enjoyment of the evening's high-priced entertainment stiffly evident in his tailored trousers, which still retain the pert imprint of the aerobics-honed buttocks of a lap dancer. Hopefully he can brush away this sexual stigma before returning home to his sharp-eyed missus.

Although summertime is best for these urban peregrinations, she doesn't curtail her activities in compliance with the fickle English weather. Obviously lust cannot be put away in a closet like a pair of wellies, only to be taken out when it rains. It's just that in the milder months of summer the city offers the greatest variety of people. American students with their shabby backpacks bursting with traveller's cheques and condoms, foreign tourists on the lookout for forbidden adventure, staid and tweedy Englishmen stepping out with their wives – the possibilities seem endless, as are the manner of the encounters. If you ask her whether she has a favourite, she couldn't say. Each experience has something to offer – a pleasure to be tasted and savoured for that particular moment, then set aside as the next pleasure moves in to replace it. And she wouldn't have it any other way.

He tells her that he performs as a mime in Covent Garden, a stepping stone to what he believes will be the professional stages of the West End. His hopeful young face is painted in the mime's traditional whiteface, with a sorrowful, down-turned mouth edged in black and matching eyebrows in a state of perpetual surprise. Yet even with this theatrical and comical camouflage she can see that he's very good-looking. He smells of greasepaint and the more subtle and tantalising scents of youthful male sweat and budget cologne. This excites her and prompts her to rub her pulsing clitoris against his blue-jeaned thigh, creating a distinctive wet spot on the fabric. The rough denim provides a satisfactory surface on which to pleasure herself, and she thrusts her tongue between the mime's eagerly parted lips, sighing her climax into his throat.

By now, the young busker's green-flecked pupils have become dilated with desire, and he leads her hand toward the cylindrical bulge straining the front of his jeans. His movements are clumsy as he stuffs her slender fingers inside his unbuttoned fly, his desperation for relief nearly thwarting him from his goal. She will not need to work very hard, for no sooner does she grasp the spongy head of her partner's prick and proceed to squeeze it than a warm, creamy liquid fills

her palm. She wipes the familiar stickiness away on the white cotton handkerchief she keeps ready for such eventualities in the pocket of her coat, her clitoris still fused like a melting flower against the young man's denim-clad thigh. A pair of fingers finds their way inside the slippery channel of her vagina, and they search about with fledgling urgency, making moist smacking sounds in the traffic-choked evening.

"Come home with me and let me fuck you," the mime cries hoarsely into her ear, sucking the lobe in invitation.

But she never goes home with anyone. There is never any reason to.

With the night still in its infancy and the moon yet to reach its zenith, she tosses back her head and shakes out the tangles from her dark tresses. They shine silver-black as they catch the waxing London moonlight, providing a striking contrast to the glowing petal of pink protruding from her precisely trimmed pubic mound. Touching the mime's expectant face, she kisses him a kind farewell, allowing her tongue to lap over his lips to taste his fleeting youth before she continues on her way. She knows better than to drag out these things, since that can lead to something more involved.

The forlorn young busker will be left alone with his fantasies of what might have been throbbing in his jeans, the only evidence of his encounter with the dark-haired woman in the khaki coat drying to a perfumed powder on his fingers. Within minutes he will be a memory as a man several years his senior attired in a handsomely cut three-piece suit and swinging an expensive black leather briefcase advances toward her, his expression one of dreamy distraction. She has seen his type before. With the emergence of so many gentlemen's clubs in the area, it is not uncommon to find up-and-coming executives and their high-powered bosses wandering the streets of Soho long after the office has closed. As the man's footfalls bring him nearer, she checks to make certain her coat remains open in the front, exposing her nakedness and her need to their fullest. Never yet has this startling image failed to entice a man – or, for that matter, a woman – into her sexual sphere. Although the more timid of these Soho pedestrians might pause only long enough for a whimsical exploration with their fingers, the bolder of her male and female quarry have no compunction about giving free rein to their genitals, or their tongues.

In the darkened doorway of an Indian restaurant whose staff and patrons have gone home hours ago, the rear flap of her trench coat will be flung up to expose her garter-striped buttocks so that the man in the three-piece suit can bend her over and fit the desire-slickened head of his prick into her hindmost entrance. She prefers to take it this way, finding it a less vulnerable thoroughfare than the traditional one, which can easily become sore in the span of a busy evening. The louder the grunts made by the well-dressed businessman stationed at her protruding buttocks, the more vigorously she cries "Harder!" as people pass along the sidewalk, either unaware of this hindward coupling transpiring a few feet away or too jaded by the sexual excesses of Soho life to care.

Still lodged firmly inside her, the man pulls her disarranged figure into the narrow alleyway that runs alongside the shuttered restaurant, his need for privacy undoubtedly stronger than her own. Here the guttural sounds of masculine lust emanating from his throat will be drowned out by music from

an adjacent nightclub, the thunderous pounding matching his strokes beat for beat. Grabbing the rusted iron bars lining the littered alley to support herself, she hikes a spike-heeled foot up onto the man's briefcase in order to be penetrated more effectively, his amused snort of "Darling, you'll never walk again!" urging her toward greater abandon, at which point she grasps her ankles and bites her moon-burnished lower lip, waiting for the inevitable filling. With each eviscerating thrust, her sharp heel scrapes across the fine, buttery black leather of the briefcase like the tip of a knife. She smiles at the damage she has unintentionally inflicted upon the innocent and very expensive case. Every time its owner looks at it, he will remember her.

The likelihood of this alleyway encounter's going unnoticed is not to be, however. For no sooner does the gentleman in the three-piece suit clench his teeth in climax than a male figure of markedly rougher exterior pauses at the mouth of the alley to light a cigarette and be treated to a performance he concludes is considerably more up-market than the one for which he has just paid good money. His rugged features twist themselves into a lewd grin as he witnesses the other man's shudders, the grin changing to a raucous chuckle as the stealthily hidden target to which his better-dressed counterpart has been aiming his strokes makes itself apparent on withdrawal. The newcomer steps forward so he will be seen by his rival. Although not above using force to get what he wants, he has found that his rough-hewn appearance is usually a sufficient form of persuasion.

Stuffing himself back into his tailored Savile Row trousers, the man in the now-rumpled business suit makes a hasty and undignified exit through the far end of the grimy Soho alleyway, but not before pulling his lacerated briefcase out from beneath the dangerously spiked heel of the woman whose posterior has just squeezed a lifetime of come out of him. He would not have minded sticking around for another go, only he doesn't want any trouble. And the unshaven brute with the cigarette smouldering between his thick fingers definitely looks like trouble.

With his partially smoked cigarette clamped between his lips, the newcomer moves into his predecessor's place, forcing the khaki-coated woman's ankles farther apart with a mud-caked work boot. He acts quickly before the moment is lost, his razor stubble scraping her silky neck as he wedges himself against her buttocks. In his world it's rare to find a woman willing to volunteer herself so freely in this fashion, and he fully intends to take advantage of his windfall. However, he must first bow to tradition, the hot, slippery opening his fingers meet when they search between her thighs proving too irresistible a lure for his prick. By now her lower half has turned liquid, the rigorous activity she just indulged in prompting this wetness to spatter her nylon stocking tops. Therefore she doesn't even flinch when her new partner launches the entire length of himself into her vagina. Nor, for that matter, does he flinch when she jabs a spiked heel onto the toe of his work boot at the moment of her climax.

"We'll have to do this again sometime," he replies afterward, zipping up his dampened fly. She offers him an empty smile, knowing such a scenario is unlikely to take place a second time. She takes a deep drag from his freshly lighted cigarette, the acrid rush of smoke to her lungs steadying her and readying her to move on. He had been exceptionally rough when taking her in the rear, dragging out the process longer than she's accustomed to. She could tell it was a treat for

him – although that's often the case with the men she meets, which might explain why they appear so reluctant to let her go after they have finished. She touches her neck where the man's facial stubble has scraped it raw, hoping this one won't get it into his head to follow her. This has happened in the past with others, especially these rough types who are used to getting their way.

To be on the safe side, she takes a circuitous route past the pubs and strip clubs and thinly disguised bordellos of the neighbourhood, the juices from her two alleyway lovers trickling down the insides of her thighs and fusing her buttocks together. Certain she has not been followed, she pauses in the shadow of a doorway, using the handkerchief in the pocket of her coat to wipe herself clean. She has already forgotten the men whose fluids stain the crumpled white square of cotton, although the image of a muddied work boot forcing her feet apart will abruptly reawaken her passion and keep her walking these moonlit sidewalks for a little while longer.

As she rounds another Soho corner, she collides with a pair of pillowy lips as red and glossy as those of her vagina after a busy night of anonymous couplings. Eyes lined black with kohl stare unflinchingly into hers, seeming to have the ability to see inside her. Their exotic owner might be a dancer in one of the clubs, or a woman stood up by her date, or a prostitute. She might even be like herself: a kindred spirit prowling the night in search of nameless, faceless pleasure. But none of this matters when their lips meet and her tongue melts like caramel in the other woman's mouth. Her clitoris still burns from its encounter with the young mime's blue-jeaned thigh and its ruder chafing by her work-booted lover, who kneaded it relentlessly between his coarse fingers until she climaxed twice in his hand, gracing his palm with a wet and fragrant souvenir of his big night out in Soho.

The fleshy fire surging from her closely groomed vulval lips is momentarily cooled by the saliva-moistened softness of the other's mouth, only to flare up again as two shiny red lips wrap covetously around it. With the ankles of her spike-tipped legs gripped so that they remain flush to the pavement and widely splayed, she finds herself held captive by the kohl-eyed stranger's painted mouth, which sucks the syrupy wetness from her like liquid siphoned through a small opening. Her ecstasy will be swift in coming and when it does, it leaves her pleasurer's lips even glossier than before. When she glances down to admire herself – something she likes to do after an erotic encounter – she is greeted by a clitoris glowing bright red with lipstick. She shivers with pleasure, this altered landscape almost as pleasing as the act that brought it about.

"Can I see you again?" asks the woman, the kohl having streaked beneath one eye.

The only response is the sound of a khaki trench coat snapping sharply in the night breeze as she walks away from the kneeling figure of her female lover. She doesn't mean to be rude. There is simply no other way.

Her body still humming with sexual electricity, she debates whether to continue with these nocturnal wanderings or belt up both her coat and her nudity against the misty elements. A damp chill has begun to blow in off the river and a watery sun is due to replace the moon in a few hours. Perhaps the time has come to go home.

BURNING DESIRE

Harriet Warner

Harriet Warner began her career as a journalist writing for *The Times*, *Independent on Sunday*, *Loaded*, the *Erotic Review* and *GQ*. In 2003, her focus switched to writing for television, writing and creating her own shows with the likes of the BBC and TNT in the US, as well as working on a variety of programmes including *Sinbad*, *Mistress* and *Call The Midwife*. One of her episodes of *Call the Midwife* was nominated for a Mind Media Award in 2014.

I just got out of jail. And I'm standing by the door of the Deptford Mission crying in the rain. I'd been given bad love and I made sure it never happened again. Jamie Delaney had turned me over and I fixed him so the only thing he turned over again was a starter motor. And the only place he turned it? In his grave.

Jamie and me went back. All the way to south-east London's wet, black streets. Since I was 22 he'd pick me up at night in his fuck-me Merc and take me driving: one hand on the wheel and one hand in my pants, squeezing my cunt and straining himself to slip a finger up there. And I'd grip myself around that finger and drag it deeper up there, 'til his hand was nearly breaking, and he'd have to swerve to miss a kid.

Then one night he told me to dress up good and stick me finery on: he'd pick me up at eight. When eight rolled round he rocked up: in a cab, with a rose, and a ring in his hand. "Bridie," he says, from the back of the cab, "you and me are getting wed. Jump in girl, we're off to the Met."

So the cab throbs on through a dark, damp night and it ain't that long before Jamie Delaney pulls me over. It's a curling, cupped, strong hand and it reaches for mine and pulls me across to him. He bites at my ear and says he wants to fuck me. I tell him, "Jamie – we can't in a cab, it ain't right."

So he shouts to the driver, "The long way mate," and he reaches his hands right under my arse and lifts me up and on to his lap and my legs go down astride his and I'm looking at the back of the cabbie's head. "I don't think we should," I say but he ain't listening. And his hands shove up my dress and I can feel his shaft getting thick and hard as it rises up against my arse. One hand slips inside my kecks and he fishes around with his meaty fingers 'til he finds my clit and back and forth and around it he goes, and all the time he's jerking at me from behind. And I know how much he wants it because he tells me all the time, "I want to get inside your cunt." And when he talks to me like that I find that that's exactly where I want him: big and thick and up my chuff.

And so I cast an eye to the cabbie's mirror and he's casting his right back at me: you dirty bleeder, I mouth, and he winks.

Jamie Delaney's other hand is working under my cheeks to drag down his fly and I step up a bit as I hear the zip. He pulls aside my pants and leans me forward. His other hand grips his cock and he eases it in and it feels like a plunger is stuffed up my box. I let out some breath and he pushes some more: and he's in. Then he pulls me back down as hard as he can and I'm taking the whole of his dick, right there in the cab. The cabbie is driving with only one hand.

One hand's on my cunt, still flicking my clit and the other is gripping my tits, pushing them together. I like it with Jamie, he don't treat me nice, he's hard and he's brutal and it's over quite fast. I'm a girl that's built more like a fella, I like it in hard and I come in a tick.

And all the time he's up inside me, London closes in and closes down around us, the sound of shutters banging down over spartan shops. Ultraviolet lights and screaming euro blue lamps flash up at us as traffic pounds along our highway, and always sirens, always alarms, wailing through the night.

So he's pumping away at me from behind, and my hands are pushed up to the sinking rubber of the ceiling so I can lever myself further down on his cock. And he's forgotten my clit and just working my tits. Two monkey's hands pushing my baps together so he can feel what a pair and a cleavage I've got.

And as he comes he splutters that he wants to fuck me through every day and every night that we're together, from behind, lying on my back, from the side, sucking him off, and he ain't got no more imagination because he just says it all over again. But don't worry, Jamie, because I've got a book at home. And as he trickles out of my box in creamy little drips he gives another couple of weak thrusts and then leans back, his head on the headrest.

The cabbie grimaces and jumps a red and it's a while before both hands are back on the wheel. Then Jamie pushes me up and slips himself out of me. He pokes his cock back in his pants and zips up his fly.

"You're at the Met." The cabbie wheezes like he's short of breath.

And we stroll in like we're the King and Queen of London. The black trousers of his suit are wet around the groin and my hair is curling from the damp and sweat. Our faces are red and shiny but we're a regal pair and we breeze it.

"Jamie Delaney!" someone calls, and we turn and she's beautiful. Tall with stockings with a seam and carrying a cigarette tray like she's out of the Fifties. "I don't feckin' believe it." And her mouth chews harder on her gum and she sways over to us, looking right through me like I'm glass. "It must be fifteen years since you were in Ireland."

And Jamie's frowning and then he's grinning like there's something more than the Old Country that they shared. "Georgia?"

And she nods.

I grip onto Jamie's suited arm and squeeze him tighter, but he wriggles to be free. "Be a doll and order us some drinks, toots." He rolls off a dirty fifty and slips it down my top.

"I ain't thirsty yet, Jamie," I try, but he looks down at me with a darkening face. "I said, get some drinks. Now beat it, kid."

And I go to the bar. And in every mirror that coats the room, I see an old flame licked into life, and a fire is growing, right there in the Met. She leans into him as they talk and he puts an arm against the wall and cups her in his shadow. And he talks to her with his other hand in his pocket and I can see his groin pumping in the slightest of ways, and I know what that means.

And she's in her dress of red shining lycra, with her stockings and heels. And she reaches up a hand and touches my monster's cheek. And I can see that it's the touch that he's missed. There's a tenderness to him that he ain't never shown me and he smiles and he closes his eyes and leans down to her and kisses her head.

And that gets me stoked.

"Oi, Jamie. Ever seen me? I'm the bird what you fucked in the cab on the way. Do you remember this ring?" And I stand there with my ring in his face and I cast her a dirty but she just gives a laugh and she slips a hand in his and says, "Come for a walk with me J."

And Jamie Delaney turns with a shrug. "Sorry old girl – but she's the one of me dreams. I never imagined I'd meet her again." And he turns and they go and I'm left at the bar. And the music plays on and the crowd swallow them whole.

But Bridie McLean is tougher than that – so I light up a Benson and order a drink. And I drink that and five others and then make a plan.

At a table in a corner I find them both later, she's on his lap, his hands on her tits, it's the same old routine. So I drop my fag on her lap: I'm clumsy like that. And she goes up in flames. And he catches it too. He was right, she was the one of his dreams and together they made a really hot couple.

DEAD GIRLS

Anne Billson

Anne Billson is a film critic, novelist and photographer. She has lived in London, Tokyo, Paris and Croydon, and now lives in Brussels. Her books include *Suckers* (an upwardly-mobile vampire novel), *Stiff Lips* (a Notting Hill ghost story) and *The Ex* (a supernatural detective story), as well as several works of non-fiction, including monographs on the films *The Thing* and *Let the Right One In.*

"You're fucking insane," I said.

It just slipped out. I apologised immediately, because the remark hadn't been professional, and Nutman would have been well within his rights to take his custom elsewhere. But his options were limited, and he knew it. Our agency was unique.

Nutman shrugged. "Maybe I am. But I have to try it. Just once. Because I've tried everything else."

He was exaggerating, of course. Because there *were* types of sexual congress he *hadn't* tried, at least not recently. Missionary position with a normal woman, for instance – he hadn't tried that one in a long, long while. Male-on-male sodomy was another option that hadn't appealed. But then Nutman's proclivities were like none we'd ever encountered before, even in our line of work. His tastes were . . . I suppose you could call them rarefied.

He'd come to the right place. Our agency prided itself on meeting unusual demands: Siamese twins, tattooed girls, girls with three or four breasts, girls with beards, girls with clitorises in their armpits, girls with vaginas so muscular they could make a man ejaculate just by constricting their fleshy inner coils around his penis, like an anaconda squeezing its prey. Our books were full of fabulous freaks and beautiful mutants, and we did a roaring trade. I like to think we performed a public service for the girls as well – where else could a one-legged hermaphrodite with multiple piercings find such gainful employment?

Nutman was something else, though. When he first walked through our doors we had him pegged as a common or garden thrill-seeker, but it soon became clear that his requirements were anything but run of the mill. Once upon a time, he told me, he'd been a regular guy with a healthy libido. Perhaps too healthy. He'd never been short of mistresses. The problem was that he'd been forced to find a new one every week. They always parted on the best of terms, but he simply exhausted them, giving them orgasm after orgasm until they begged for mercy.

Nutman discovered his unusual proclivities by accident one day, while rogering a Polish countess in a suite at the Ritz. He'd vaguely noticed, while

pumping away with his usual enthusiasm, that his partner had become strangely passive. At the time he thought little of it – he'd already given her half a dozen climaxes, cresting her increasingly violent convulsions like a surfer riding a tsunami. When at last she stopped convulsing, he simply assumed she was taking a breather, husbanding her forces in preparation for the one last shattering mutual spasm of satisfaction that lay in store.

It wasn't until after a good ten minutes of thrusting that he realised she was dead.

In that instant, Nutman experienced a heady cocktail of conflicting emotions. There was guilt in there, and sadness, and regret. But he also felt a burgeoning excitement as blood rushed to his already swollen cock. The upshot was that he'd continued to ram his rod into the corpse for several hours, and his orgasm, when it had finally occurred, had been of an earth-shattering intensity, the like of which he'd never experienced before. There had been a moment of panic when he'd been unable to extricate himself immediately, but a combination of copious spunk and cock-shrivelling fear had finally enabled him to withdraw.

He swore to the medical examiner he hadn't noticed his partner's plight until it was too late, and that he'd stopped banging her the instant he'd become aware of it. Eyebrows were raised during the inquest, which he'd dutifully attended, but it was established she'd been suffering from a rare heart condition. Even the Countess's relatives, who'd jetted in *en masse* from Kraków, shook him cordially by the hand and whispered their gratitude that at least she'd died happy. It probably helped also that Nutman gave no indication of intending to make a claim on any part of her inheritance.

From that moment on, he was a man with a mission. Living, breathing women just didn't do it for him any more. And because he was neither sadist nor murderer, he turned to us. As professional caterers for peculiar tastes, it was our biggest challenge to date, but one to which we'd happily risen. At first, we supplied him with corpses that still bore signs of recent life, their flesh still relatively wholesome and occasionally even pliable to the touch. But then there'd been a mix-up over dates, and before anyone had spotted the error Nutman had found himself locked in congress with a cadaver that was no longer, shall we say, in the first flush of death. To cut a long story short, he had discovered that his cock was not the only living thing in the corpse's vagina, only to realise almost instantaneously that a certain maggoty presence was only adding zest to his pleasure. After that he begged us for bodies that were bloated and rotting and heaving with all manner of creepy-crawlies.

It didn't stop there, of course, because Nutman was no bog-standard necrophiliac. I remember the first time he tentatively inquired about the possibility of fucking a zombie. With my customary *sang froid* I managed not to react as though this were the sickest request I had ever dealt with. Instead, I entrusted the relevant research to Lapotaire and Gulliver, who had yet to return from one of their field-trips empty-handed. And lo, Nutman arrived at our establishment one week later, all aquiver with anticipation, and found himself sequestered in the Yellow Suite with the finest specimen of the walking dead that you could ever hope to muster – a lovely young thing with greyish-green skin (some but not all of it hanging off in flaps), expressionless eyes wreathed in crepey mauve circles and an insatiable craving for human

flesh that made it necessary to chain her to the bed so that Nutman could get his jollies without her teeth tearing chunks out of him. He swore to me afterwards that he'd made her come, but this was a claim I took with a large pinch of salt. I mean, with all that snarling and thrashing around from the start, not to mention a natural tendency towards deliquescence, how could he tell?

After that his demands grew ever more recherché. The banshee wasn't too much of a problem, though we'd had to issue earplugs to everyone on the premises, and a number of dead rodents with bloodied orifices had to be cleared out of the cellar afterwards. But the ghost had required an inordinate amount of preparation. We'd been obliged to set up temporary shop in an old manor house on the Norfolk coast, since the shade of the maidservant who had died there some two hundred years earlier was unable to leave the room in which she'd been murdered. Nutman had declared the experience so exhilarating – "like plunging my penis into shrieking quicksilver", as he put it – that we'd gone out of our way to provide him with further refinements on the theme: a phantom governess who'd been hanged for poisoning the two children in her charge and – our *pièce de résistance* – a spectral French aristocrat who'd been guillotined during the Terror. This last one had required a field trip to Paris, but Nutman, as always, paid handsomely and declared it the most exciting sexual experience of his life, albeit one tinged with frustration at his partner not being in any condition to give satisfactory head. He evidently put the stump of her neck to good use, though.

But I could tell he was beginning to grow weary again. It was increasingly a case of been there, fucked that. We'd heard rumours about a female werewolf on the loose in Dorset, but Nutman just wasn't interested. A werewolf wasn't *dead*, he said. They had to be *dead*.

And then he came up with another idea.

"A vampire," he said. "I've *got* to have a vampire."

I stared at him open-mouthed and said, "You're fucking insane."

I tried to explain that zombies and ghosts were one thing. Zombies were flesh-eaters, but slow-witted and easily restrained. Ghosts were too ethereal to offer much in the way of physical threat. But vampires were something else entirely. Vampires were seductive, cunning . . . and invariably lethal.

He shook his head. "I'm prepared to take the risk."

So we set it up. Lapotaire caught the plane to Bucharest – and was never heard from again. Gulliver followed his trail into the Carpathians, but was better equipped than his missing colleague and managed to strike some sort of deal with the gypsies he encountered there. When he came back, it was with a heavy wooden box.

I examined her (during daylight hours, of course. I may put on a show of being devil-may-care, but I'm no fool), and have to say – she was beautiful. Skin almost translucent, lips succulent and red, just a hint of pearly-white tooth, breasts ripe and luscious, just begging to be licked and sucked. The only thing missing was a heartbeat.

And Nutman was enchanted. He came back night after night, disappearing into the Azure Suite at sundown and emerging exhausted at dawn. For the first time since we'd met, I sensed he was becoming emotionally as well as physically

involved. We'd urged him to take precautions and instructed him in the correct use of garlic, but I couldn't help noticing that he'd taken to wearing his collar up so we couldn't see his neck. I began to fret – and not just because I didn't want to lose one of our most valuable customers – so Wyvern and I cooked up a scheme that would enable us to examine his throat. It involved the simultaneous presentation of a Dry Martini and removal of Nutman's overcoat, and we pulled the manoeuvre off without a hitch, the absurdly elaborate ring on my left hand catching on Nutman's shirt collar and dragging it askew, just as we'd planned.

Wyvern and I, stationed on either side of him, murmured our apologies and straightened the collar before catching each other's eye and, in that very same instant, letting out a barely perceptible sigh of relief. The neck was intact, unbitten. Nutman, who seemed not to have noticed our inhabitually close attentions, knocked back the Martini in a couple of gulps, thanked us and hurried, as usual, into the Azure Suite.

But the noises that issued forth that night were anything but usual. They began with convivial laughter, but presently changed to a groaning so unearthly it sent chills down my spine. As time wore on, the pitch of the groaning rose until it sounded more like screaming. But this was nothing like any of the screaming I'd ever heard – and I hear a lot of it in my job, as you can imagine. Something had gone horribly wrong, I think we all realised that. Even so, I waited until sunrise before venturing into the Azure Suite. Better safe than sorry.

The vampire lay asleep on the bed, plump and replete, cheeks flushed and lips even ruddier than normal. Nutman, or what was left of him, lay naked in her arms, a desiccated husk of a human being. I looked at his neck again and saw the flesh there was still unpunctured. The man's penis, on the other hand, was a shrivelled-up seed pod covered in tooth-marks. It was obvious what had happened. The vampire had been giving him the blow job of a lifetime, night after night, sucking the life-blood out of his cock along with his sperm, and he hadn't been able to resist.

And so we lost our most faithful and lucrative client. But at least I can say with certainty that he died a happy man.

We kept the vampire on our books.

THIS YEAR AT MARIENBAD

Angelica Jacob

Angelica Jacob is the pseudonym of S. G. Klein. Having worked as a book editor in London for fourteen years, she moved to Cornwall before returning to her native Scotland where she now lives and works. Her first novel, *Fermentation*, was published in 1997. Her second novel, *Confession*, was published in 2013. It tells of a two-year period in the life of Charlotte Brontë when she met and fell in love with her French tutor, Monsieur Constantin Héger. S. G. Klein has also written numerous short stories.

Greta and Niklaus had been travelling two months when they arrived at NovoGrand Central Station Marienbad. They'd already visited all the run-of-the-mill countries such as Holland, France, Spain and Italy, but the Czech Republic was the destination both had invested in so heavily – or, to be more precise, the Mariánské Lázně spa, where *Last Year at Marienbad*, a film they had a passion for, was set.

For Niklaus, it was the culmination of a year's careful planning. *Last Year at Marienbad* was one of the most erotically charged films he had ever seen, and he hoped to inject some of the same noirish depth into his relationship with Greta. But for Greta the film (and therefore the trip) was little more than an intellectual exercise, something to be reviewed and discussed, but not necessarily indulged. Nonetheless, as soon as they arrived, Niklaus stepped from the train and the game began.

"Excuse me," he said, "but I believe I met you here last year, didn't I? You were travelling en route to somewhere, but you stopped off here on the way."

"I don't remember," she replied. "No, I can't recall such a meeting. You must be mistaken."

"Oh, but we did," continued Niklaus, as he picked up his suitcase and began following her down the platform. "Of course, it could have been in Karlstadt or Friedrichsbad or perhaps Baden-Salsa, but wherever it was, it was springtime, all the blossom was out – apple, almond, cherry. You said it looked like pink and white snow. You were wearing a pale yellow dress with a choker of pearls at your neck. I remember touching them, how cool they felt and how smooth."

Ignoring Niklaus, Greta held out her hand and hailed a cab.

"The Mariánské Lázně spa," she said, hoping the driver would understand where she meant.

Speeding through the town, with its crumbling façades and legendary bridges, Niklaus continued his tirade of memories, insisting that he and Greta had met the previous spring, while she for her part continued to act as if what she was hearing were ludicrous. It wasn't until they caught sight of the hotel that both fell silent.

The building was more than they had expected: vaster, more baroque, more mysterious. Standing in acre upon acre of garden, it rose four-square from the ground, an edifice replete with turreted walls, interior courtyards and tiered marble staircases.

As they entered the foyer, Greta took a sharp intake of breath. The reception area was cavernous, furnished mostly with mirrors and chandeliers – exactly as it had been in the film. She could already hear her footsteps echoing down endless corridors, feel herself drifting from room to room, catch herself looking at the reflections in the million-and-one gilded mirrors.

"You do remember now, don't you?" Niklaus whispered into her ear. "This is the hotel in which hallways cross hallways, this is where we met that troupe of performers. There were midgets and a woman who balanced chairs on her feet and a man who ate fire. They performed for us in one of the ballrooms. There was a girl with tattoos on her body, snakes entwined with roses – you insisted she was the most beautiful creature you had ever set eyes upon."

But Greta shook her head, displaying not one iota of interest and disguising her puzzlement at Niklaus's digression from the game – since when were there circus entertainers in the film? "You're mistaken," she replied, sticking to the script as she knew it. "I remember nothing of the kind. This is my first visit to the Mariánské Lázně."

Unperturbed, Niklaus continued.

"You were wearing a red dress," he said as they walked up the central staircase towards their room. Their footsteps echoed against the cold stone. "It was midnight, and we were standing at the roulette table. The whole place was crowded, but there was a woman wearing a top hat and coat-tails – you said she looked magical. You said you wanted to make love to her and that I was to watch you."

Greta shot him a glance.

"I doubt I said that. No, I wouldn't have said that."

The porter opened the door to their bedroom and, once inside, Niklaus went and stood by the large French windows overlooking the garden. Below him, people, couples mainly, moved in unison: some held hands, others were deep in conversation. And there, a little ahead of a tiered patio, were the serried ranks of familiar shrubs, each one tortured into a dark geometric shape with barely a leaf out of place. Gravelled pathways ran in straight lines across manicured lawns, just as it was on celluloid. It was strange, stepping into this movie scene, strange – and oddly exciting – to fabricate whatever you and your partner might have experienced the previous spring.

Suddenly, he began to imagine a whole gamut of things he would like to have done to Greta, things they might have enjoyed had she not been so reticent. He'd like to have blindfolded her, like to have spent hours playing with her cunt, like to have experienced a threesome, like to have had her suck him off in a public place.

He turned from the window.

"Do you remember?" he asked. "This is the same room we stayed in last year. You must remember. You were wearing a black dress and diamonds here." Niklaus touched his neck. "You took the dress off and you asked for the woman croupier to be brought from downstairs. When she entered the room, you told her to sit on the bed with you. I was to remain in the shadows: I wasn't to talk, I was only to watch. You made the croupier – her name was Marietta, remember? – you asked her to undress, which she did, and then she lay down beside you. The light from the chandelier played on your skin, white diamonds and rhomboids of colour, and your sighs echoed through the silence, whispers of air. I watched the two of you kiss, your mouths looked softer than egg yolks, your legs were entwined around each other's backs. I like to think my presence made your passion more intense. You were groaning and I could see your hand beginning to rub Marietta's thighs, delving between her legs. I could see it all, your two oystery cunts glistening and wet, and then how you began to lick down Marietta's stomach, between her legs. Your back arched and at that moment I moved from where I was sitting, silently crept up behind you. The instant I touched your skin, your whole body tensed, but I leant forward, told you to keep licking Marietta or I'd snap your neck. You cannot have expected me to keep to my corner, to watch and not participate. That would have been unkind."

"Stop!" said Greta. "This didn't happen. We've never been here before. I don't like this game any longer. Niklaus? This wasn't part of the film!"

But Niklaus's "memories" were too vivid to halt.

"I forced your head between her thighs; you were on all fours, like an animal, beautiful, besotted, bestial. I pushed myself into your cunt, I had my hands round your throat, you wanted me inside you, you were enjoying yourself with Marietta, I wanted to spit and split you in two and I held my hands tighter – you remember that – you could hardly breathe, you were struggling under me –"

"No," whispered Greta, with more determination than she had done before. Her cheeks burned with humiliation. "None of this happened. I've never been here, we've never been here. Niklaus, none of this is true. I wouldn't allow it."

"You have been here," said Niklaus. "This is the bed where I strangled you, where you died. We were making love, I put my hands round your throat, you couldn't breathe and when I came I finished the job, squeezed my hands tighter. Marietta got dressed and left the room. You looked so beautiful, lying there on the bed. I combed your hair away from your eyes, put perfume on your wrists –"

Greta stood up and went to stand by Niklaus at the window. Outside, the light was fading fast, but even so she could still see shadows passing between the trees, the dim outlines of couples parading up and down the neat gravel pathways.

"This is only a game, remember?" she said, but Niklaus shook his head in denial.

"It's you who does not remember," he replied, then once again started in with his memories: how they had played hide-and-seek within the hotel's immense network of rooms, how she had been wearing an emerald-green dress and how she had finally surrendered to him in one of the drawing rooms. They'd made love on the floor while the other guests watched from the far side of the room.

"You were so beautiful," he said. "They all admired you, all wanted you, you held them in the palm of your hand. You sucked me off in front of them as

though it were the most ordinary act in the world. You paraded me before them like I was prize meat, made me stand in front of the women while they inspected my body . . . Some of them laughed: they said I was too thin, too fat, they ran their fingers over every inch of me, made me bend over, slapped me . . ."

Niklaus's words continued apace. Greta could hear them, picture the images he was conjuring up and, despite herself, contrary to everything she had vowed, slowly felt herself being drawn in. "Perhaps we should lie down," she said, slipping out of her dress. "Perhaps I'll remember more clearly if you explain these things to me again."

Niklaus was happy to follow her lead. Scenes were played and replayed, blood drawn, skin stretched and welted. Greta took a handful of Niklaus's hair and dragged him round the room on his hands and knees, made him lie prostrate while she trampled his spine. She forced him to lie spread-eagled, face down on the bed, while she whipped him with leather, then revelled in the sight of the blood that stained the sheets. Life and love, memories, dreams and reflections, everything merged into one.

"You won't forget this now, will you?" Greta whispered as she touched his wounds, licked blood from her fingers. "You're not going to forget this, not after what I've done to you, tell me you won't. This is one memory you'll never obliterate. Say it, say you'll never forget what I've done to you, how you begged me to stop . . ."

But Niklaus did not want to acquiesce to Greta's demands. Instead, he wanted to forget all about being treated so shamefully.

"I can't recall," he stuttered. "Nothing's occurred, has it? I don't know what you're talking about."

"Last night," Greta said, "when I punished you. You remember, I know you do. You're still bleeding – if I touched you, you'd wince."

"As usual, you're talking rubbish," he said, after which he closed his eyes, rolled away from his lover.

"Maybe," she said, "but I'll always remember. I'll never forget for as long as I live."

At dawn, the couple rose, packed their bags and left the spa. Speeding down the driveway, Niklaus took one last look back. The hotel glimmered in the morning light; a bend in the road and the whole place disappeared.

CALIFORNIA STREAMIN'

Geoff Nicholson

Geoff Nicholson is the author of sixteen novels, including *Bleeding London*, and most recently *The City Under the Skin*. His non-fiction titles include *Sex Collectors* and *The Lost Art of Walking*. He lives in Los Angeles.

At first, all the movies made by Gold-on-Gold Productions were pretty much the same. An attractive woman, a California girl to be sure (though California girls are a surprisingly diverse group), is discovered reclining beside a sparkling, sunlit swimming pool. We're high in the Hollywood Hills, the city nestling below us in the blue haze. Palm trees and Spanish-style bungalows are visible in the near distance, but we're not really interested in the scenery. We're focused on the girl. Her bikini is tight against her flesh, and we suspect she's going to be taking it off quite soon. And we're right.

The sun beats down. She feels the heat, removes the bikini, drinks deeply from the big jug of water conveniently placed beside her. She's likely to spill a little of the water on herself in the process. That's OK. She begins touching her body, stroking it, playing with herself in a lazy, Californian sort of way. Before very long at all she comes to an intense if (let's face it) not all that convincing orgasm.

Then she gets up and takes a pee.

All right! This is what we've been waiting for. This is the unique selling point of a Gold-on-Gold movie. The girl squats down, the camera zooms in, the girl opens herself up, holds her pussy lips apart so you can see right inside, through the folds, right into her body, into this truly secret place. And as you, and the camera, stare in tense fascination, the pure pink flesh of the vulva twitches a little, tautens, pulses, and before you know it pure, hot golden urine makes its appearance.

The girl does it right there beside the pool, on the pale terracotta tiles, which darken as they get wet. The pee is just a trickle at first, then a stream, then a growing puddle that spreads out like a deep reservoir of gamily scented sexuality. OK, I exaggerate, but I'm trying to convey my enthusiasm here. Eventually the girl finishes peeing, looks straight into camera, winks, blows a kiss, and that's the end of the movie.

You have just seen a Gold-on-Gold Production, conceived, produced, directed and shot by Pat Reynolds. "Golden Showers from the Golden State" was their motto. Still is. And as you see, it was pretty harmless stuff back then. No humiliation, no peeing on other people's bodies or faces or genitals, no drinking the damn stuff. That would have been disgusting.

The story starts, as many do, in a bar in LA. That was where I met Pat Reynolds. I was working there semi-legally as a bartender. When I'd arrived in Tinseltown, six months earlier, I thought I'd have no trouble exploiting my breezy English charm and my two years at film school to get some cool job in the movie industry. Well, you can imagine how that panned out. I found myself working in a dive off Hollywood Boulevard (so much less cool than it sounds), doing my best to mix martinis, manhattans, cosmopolitans and all those other all-American painkillers.

On this occasion I was also trying to be a good, genial bartender and I was reading out a news item from some tabloid. It was about a town in Sweden where they have an annual "pee outdoor day". I think it had something to do with saving water by not flushing toilets, which is a big concern here in LA, too.

A woman sitting at the bar listened and laughed and said in a deep, dry twang: "Where I live, every day is pee outside day."

I was already aware of her, because I'd served her a couple of margaritas. She was a good-looking older blonde, tough, tanned, only lightly tweaked by plastic surgery.

"How's that?" I asked.

"I'm Pat Reynolds," she said. "You've probably never heard of me."

But I had. Of course I had. It had just never occurred to me that Pat Reynolds was female.

"I know your work," I said. "I love it, but I never knew . . ."

"Yeah, I'm all woman," she said, and she was mocking both herself and me. "Make me another margarita, will you honey?"

I admit that when I said I really loved her work, it had less to do with her film-making skills, which were modest, than with my passionate interest in the subject matter. What's the big attraction of water sports, golden showers, piss play, toilet sex, whatever you want to call it? Oh, I don't know, I'm sure it's got something to do with watching the forbidden, with naughtiness, dirtiness, the breaking of a small taboo. You're publicly seeing something that's supposed to be very private. Whatever. Basically I don't analyse it too much. I just enjoy.

So Pat Reynolds and I got talking and we got on pretty well. I guess she didn't meet too many people who knew who she was and treated her like a celebrity. And we talked about me, and how I wanted to be in pictures, and she said: "All right, be at my house on Thursday morning. You've got yourself a job."

Even then I don't suppose I thought this was going to be the big movie break I'd been waiting for. I always knew she'd be employing me as a gofer, a dogsbody. On that first day, for instance, I learned that one thing I had to do was keep the girls well supplied with fluids – you only get out what you put in. There was beer and wine if they wanted it, but most of these girls were surprisingly clean-living. They only drank water, gallons of the stuff, and they could be very bitchy if they didn't get precisely what they wanted. It had to be the right brand, at the right temperature, still or sparkling, with or without ice, with or without a slice of lemon or lime. I did my best to make the girls happy, told myself it was important for a would-be filmmaker to know how to deal with difficult performers.

But that was only part of the job, and not the most important part as far as Pat was concerned. The really vital thing I had to do was mop up the pee and

make sure none of it went into her precious swimming pool. It was a dirty job and I was really quite pleased to be the one doing it. I liked the girls. I liked their pee. I had my bucket and my sponge mop and I did what was required of me. Pat liked my work. I was efficient, enthusiastic, unobtrusive. I became a more or less permanent employee.

This went on for some time, and then one day I had my big idea. I'd just cleaned up after a beautiful Valley girl called Bobbi, and I realised I had a whole sponge full of nothing but her pee. Instead of squeezing it out into my bucket, thereby diluting it, I squeezed it into the now empty water jug. Then later I poured it into one of the empty water bottles, and I took it home with me.

I did it furtively so that nobody saw what I was doing, but I really needn't have worried. I was just the guy with the mop. I was invisible as far as Bobbi was concerned. And Pat was far too busy to pay attention to what I was doing. The next day I did it again, and the next and the next.

I suppose I've always been a bit of a collector: books, magazines, DVDs, the first 50 movies released by Gold-on-Gold Productions, but I've never collected anything with the enthusiasm and passion that I brought to urine. From that day on, every time I cleaned up after one of the models, I did the old mop-jug-bottle routine, and before long I had quite a little collection of samples of female urine. I labelled them carefully with the date and the girl's name, and then I kept them in my fridge so they wouldn't deteriorate. They looked great sitting there in neat rows on the shelves. You'd be amazed at the subtle variations in colour, from dark amber to the palest yellow, from soft wheat to saffron blond, and all the shades in between. The women, just like the urine, came in all types too; a huge range of ages, looks, ethnicities: classy older women, tattooed punks, Goth-chicks, Latino babes, co-eds. Some nights I'd just go home and gaze into my fridge and get horny as hell. For a while I was a very happy boy indeed.

I didn't spend much time hanging out with Pat. Ours was a strictly professional relationship, and director/producers really don't fraternise much with their urine-moppers. But from time to time she did ask me what I liked about water sports and I told her pretty much what I've already told you: secrecy, intimacy, taboo. Nothing very original. And in any case, I thought, what could I possibly tell her that she didn't already know?

"You're Pat Reynolds," I said. "You make the best water sports movies on the planet. You know what it's all about. Why are you even asking me?"

"Because I *don't* know what it's all about, honey. Basically I just don't get it, and it kind of disgusts me if you really want to know. I'm just into making the movies. And I'm into making money. Which is harder than it sounds. Sales have been pretty flat lately. Something's going to have to change around here."

That's when Pat had *her* big idea. She decided she'd have pairs and trios and groups of women in her movies. They'd pee in series, in sequence, alone and together. Gold-on-Gold Productions seemed to be mutating. Some of it, of course, was pretty hot. Women being dirty together is always good. But as far as my collection went it was a dead loss. All the various urines got mixed together, like badly thought-out cocktails: two parts Geena, one part Lexis, five parts Tawnee. What was the point of that? It offended my sensibilities and my collecting instincts, but I tolerated it.

And then Pat came up with another idea, a really bad one. She introduced men to her films, and that changed everything. Now there was humiliation, peeing on breasts and faces and genitals, pee drinking, the works.

I was really offended. Worse than that, I was still expected to do the mopping up. Wiping up women's pee was one thing – a nice, sexy, appealing thing; wiping up men's pee was just plain revolting. I was really angry with Pat. I felt like she'd let me down, betrayed me. She'd been telling the truth. She really didn't get it. I worked on one shoot featuring men, did some perfunctory mopping, and then I quit.

Pat said she understood. "Hey, we've all got our limits," she said. "See you around. Have a nice life."

"Yeah right," I said. "I'll always have my memories," but what I didn't say was that I also still had a fridge full of urine samples.

My great career in the movies was over and I went back to working in the bar. After a while Pat even started drinking there again. She behaved like there were no hard feelings, but I had plenty of hard feelings. I'd had the perfect job and she'd ruined everything.

I used to go home at night after my shift at the bar, open up the fridge and stare at my collection. Where once it had been a vital, living sexy thing, it now seemed inert and finished. Then one night I did what anyone might do in the circumstances. I opened up one of the bottles, from a Korean girl who called herself Sapphire, and I filled an ice cube tray. Before too long I had enough, slightly yellowish, ice cubes to make quite a few margaritas. Next day I took them to work in a cool box.

When I first served Pat Reynolds with a urine-enhanced margarita I expected her to choke and spit it out. I really did. In reality she knocked it back and didn't even notice. She still hasn't. She comes in all the time, drinks margaritas, and more often than not she compliments me on the way I make them.

And you know, the funny thing is, whenever I see her drinking those margaritas, it's the sexiest, dirtiest, most arousing thing I've ever seen in my life. Go figure, as we like to say in LA. Of course, my collection is gradually being depleted, but under the circumstances, I think it's well worth it.

LUST

D. B. C. Pierre

D. B. C. Pierre is best known for his work, *Vernon God Little*, which won him the Booker Prize in 2003. Pierre used the prize money to repay his debts, which he incurred during his twenties while suffering from psychological issues and drug abuse. In 2007, *Vernon God Little* was adapted for the London stage. To date, the work has been translated in more than forty countries worldwide, and produced as a play by at least four theatre companies. More recently, Pierre returned to Mexico, where he spent his youth, to explore and document the downfall of the Aztecs.

In my room there's a woman I can't see or speak to. But I can taste her. Taste her coming my way. My ragged little snotbox. I entice her with my mind, scrape a dirt clearing on its floor for her to blare sticky and languid like melted brass music dripping genital sweat. My chutney bacchanal.

My sin, but like all sins she poisons me slowly, insufficiently. So I love her. To possess her I've only to scrape the right sounds from my tongue. The buff gasps, the stinging red cheeks we'd enjoy if only I spoke, but I don't, can't speak to her at all. So I pelt kernels of aching smut from my mind knowing that one of these, ingested, will explode through her, spit her ribs in bloody splinters like sperm from a gun. I'll fill her with my fury.

She knows this. She feels me call to her. And I know she'll come to me. In time.

So here you find me. My life of carefully matched socks, awkwardness with family, my reliance on stand-ins for my mother, has been reduced to this rude throbbing thing, admitting no other thought than the dew on this woman's pouch, no other plan but to live like a worm in her nectar.

She's close by me now. I sense her as she bends forward beside me, oyster bed pleated into damp marmite silk beneath nylon beneath cotton, a taste of nuts chewed with butter burnt in blood. Then footsteps. Now voices.

"Are they ready?" asks a man from the door.

"I've prepared them as best I can," says the woman. "They should be all right."

"Sort out that hose before they come in, will you? I've checked the pressure twice, but it's given different readings."

The routine in my room is different today. I don't know why. I don't dwell on it either, being more concerned with her seeming detachment from me. I ache with her detachment. Her voice gives no hint of this fever, the cholera set to seal us in an aspic of burst veins and drumbeats when I'm hers. Instead she slides tidily around the room, not moaning with succulent anticipation, but serving words as crisp and ordinary as cups of hot tea. Wasted little trout. She always

plays this game, battering me with the swish of her boyish gait, fetching me an odd chirp of plimsoll on lino, or a breath of dark air from the ruptured rose cloud of her sex. She moves lightly, humming, sometimes singing softly and tunelessly, always pop hits of the kind designed to stimulate blood flow in the very young. It drives me insane for her. She's fucking life itself. I rage to reach out and smack her gap with the flat of my hand. But I can't.

"Oh, and – signatures?" the man asks from the door.

"Uh-huh," she says.

"All yours then. Let me know if you need a hand with him."

"Thanks, I'll be fine."

She'll be fine. She'll be fine when I suck the fucking womb out of her. I track the man's steps as they move away up the corridor. Then we're alone.

She moves closer still. Her taste overwhelms me, I hear her sleeves concertina to blow the hint of cheap deodorant that so embodies her rangy presence. This is a girl from the suburbs, a could've-been-a-lawyer who lost her early twenties to romance, holiday repping, anything to avoid life with her parents. A liberal, if not bohemian young woman who's baked a conservative crust around her steaming wet drives and now delights in the effect of their vapours escaping. My little pheromone barb. Her breath blows me pictures of her drenched in our sweat, losing sobs from her mouth with delicious, deliberate inadvertence.

I hear her thighs. Actually hear them softly meet as she leans over me to prise open one eyelid, then the other, even though she knows the game by now. I see her clearly, even with my eyes shut. Savour her, sense the accidental mambo between her legs, scissoring to send taut ripples through the globes of her bottom, apricot pestles poised for our spice.

I'll have her just now, take her by the scruff with my teeth and slam her like a frenzied dog, burst her, fuck her dead. As she leans close I beg one of my hands to fly to her, cup her moist heat then furrow a wake between lips of toasted brown before she can blush. But no hand obeys, save the hand of my mind, or perhaps it's my soul, this knotted rag alight with forgotten pudenda; snatch I could've, should've, never did have, save this one engulfing fish, wriggling frantic with life around me.

Another voice rings through the door, a foreign voice. "Do you want them now?"

"Give me a minute," says my girl. "I'll tidy him up."

The tips of her fingers flick through what's left of my hair, she straightens the sheet across my chest, smoothes it with the flat of her hand. Then a warm, wet flannel scrapes over my face like a babe's mother's tongue. My body lays quiet, but I can't contain the dream in which my soul arches glistening above the bed, crackling with shock. Oozing screams, it rips open her skirt from behind and parts her legs, breaks them like halves of a wishbone, daring the glossy whites of her eyes to flash abandon. Soft as air, the fingers of my hand develop tentacles every bit as soft and mossy as the fronds of her writhing sex, they attach to it and try to suck, suck her near, suck her onto the bed until she kneels astride my chest, takes the head of my cock into her mouth, but I feel nothing. I yearn for a fresh spike of heat, but having transformed into her own texture I feel nothing at all.

At the height of my dismay, more feet shuffle through the door. Familiar perfumes approach. A whimper pops over my bedside.

"Will he feel anything?"

It's my wife. Her voice is strained, and comes announced by the tinkle of 43 tiny charms on the bracelet made of years I assured her were golden. My son shuffles beside her, a sensible man charged, like all children, with dismantling a musty net curtain of family lies.

"He won't feel a thing," says my woman, "you can be quite sure of that."

"But I read somewhere that they can still hear, and think . . ."

My woman hesitates. "Although it's unpleasant, this is quite a routine process. Our best knowledge is that there'll be no change in his reception of stimulus."

There's a pause. I feel another hand on my forehead, my wife's. My woman steps to her side with a soft kind of briskness that serves to set the moment in a mould of everyday necessity. She speaks.

"I'm so sorry. It might help if you accept that the person you knew has already passed away – he hasn't responded to stimuli in over a week now. I assure you his vital signs will die within a minute of being unplugged. I'm afraid his injuries were just too serious. We've done all we can."

"He's had a good innings, mum," says my son, stepping closer. "Thank you, Nurse, we don't need to stay any longer."

Nurse gives them a moment before speaking. "Let me walk you back to the lounge. Doctor Bowman would like to see you, and I'm sure we can organise some coffee."

As their footsteps recede, my soul stiffens with the guilty resolve of a nine-year-old plotting trouble. Throbbing flanges erupt from my body with a sticky screech, dirty wings with arteries and organs unfurl like fetid petals to gather and twist around a smoking purple tower of flesh, a cock raging, already in spasm to discharge my life's dreams.

Nurse's footsteps approach.

I wait, alone between life and death, and burn rabid with lust for them both.

MEN AND MOTORS

Helen Walsh

Helen Walsh was born in Warrington, England. Her debut, *Brass*, won the Betty Trask prize in 2005, and her follow-up, *Once Upon a Time in England*, won the Somerset Maugham Prize in 2009. Walsh writes with purity and precision, skewering contemporary constructions of race, class and motherhood while unintentionally encouraging the robust use of reliable contraception.

It's a quarter to five in the morning. I can't sleep. Again. So, for the fourth night running I find myself on 19th, hanging with the city's insomniacs, cruisers and hustlers in the smouldering dregs of clubland. I'm in some all-night sex shop, wired on the free lattes, eyeing up the double-enders. Business has been slack this last month or so. A couple of femmes opened up a rival agency on Polk and recruited the meanest butches around – real mechanics with real stubble. I'm damn good at what I do but I'm not so devoted I'll start shooting up testosterone like these other crazy bitches. However, the thought *did* drop into my head around three this morning, that if I want to hold on to my regulars I should at least upgrade my tools.

I can't quite decide between this sexy little stainless steel number and the standard rubber. The workman in me is browbeating me into the latter – the more durable, flexible and altogether more reliable model. Not to mention a whole $70 cheaper. But my aesthetic side won't hear any of it. "Fuck reliability," it's saying. "If Hugh Hefner had've ranked reliability where the hell would he be now?" I kind of have to agree.

I'm still trying to talk myself out of love with it when this big-breasted sales assistant rushes over, arms flailing wildly.

"My God! It is! It's you! I fucking knew it was . . ."

I try to place her breasts. I never forget a set of breasts – least not a set as staggering as hers. This kind of thing happens all the time you see, clients accosting me, usually down the mall or the filling station. It's true to say some of them seem genuinely betrayed when they see me out of my overalls. One crazy bitch even threatened to sue!

"I'm sorry. Have we met?"

"This is awesome! I can't believe you're in our shop!" she shrieks. "Can I just tell you that you completely rock! I like, totally dug your film. It's my favourite of all the *Men and Motors*. Along with that one where they're fucking in the truck? And that old lady from next door calls the cops 'cos she thinks she's witnessing, like, a rape?"

I wonder if some crazy club kid has spiked the lattes. I slap my cheek and blink my eyes real hard. She's still there.

She extends a slim brown hand.

"Marie-Anne," she says, grabbing mine and shaking it aggressively. "Big fan. Biiig fan."

A dozen eyes burn into me. I start to palpitate.

"Look, I think you've mistaken me for someone."

"Ohmiggod!" she interjects. "*Oh-my-fucking-God.* You can sign them."

She scurries off, then returns seconds later with a clutch of videos. I just stand and stare. Shellshocked. It's me. That's fucking me – splashed across the jacket of a DIY porno. It's me alright – or one of me. Lucky Strike hanging from my lips. Oil-sodden overalls unbuttoned to my waist. She plonks them on the counter and thrusts a pen in my face.

"Jeez! This is, like, really starting to freak me?"

And then it slaps me in the face. Hard, wet and fast.

Hank . . .

"Hank," I glower into the rear mirror. "Nice to meet you, Ma'am."

I turn down the corners of my mouth, snap the vowels wide open and give it my best Southern drawl. God knows why, but these women go crazy for a bit of redneck.

"Haaank. Nice to meeet you Maaam."

I pull over on the hard shoulder, slap the hazards on, extract a battered street directory from the dashboard and try to figure out which end of Portola she lives on. South of the avenue, it's all thirty-something soccer Mums who are neither sex-starved nor closets. They're just looking for a quick, safe slam to break the monotony of school runs and housework. North Portola's a lean stretch of cool lawns and long drives – sniffy old dames who don't even like you taking a leak in their goddamn bathrooms, but who sure as hell do tip. Mrs Piccioti – *Ma'am* – lives right spank in the middle, it'd seem.

I check my teeth and gums for stray flakes of oatmeal, wink back at myself, then flip a U-ee onto the freeway.

The assignment came at 7.00 this morning. Well, 6.30 if we're being picky – that's when my laptop hollered "You've Got Mail!" and wrenched me from my slumber just six yards from scoring a homer. But it was only when my cell phone started kicking off around 7.00 – some aggressive new kid from the agency threatening to take me offa their books – that I dragged myself out of bed to see what the story was.

The job seemed easy enough and I figured I should be out of there and tucking into a big, dirty fry-up in time for the game. Some dames you see, they'll send you these big crazy scenarios. They go way beyond fantasies some of these – they're full-blown porn scripts. Some of them expect you to be word-perfect. Take crazy Mrs Cole up Nob Hill, for instance. I'm slamming her full force from behind with this big leather strap-on? It's like tearing my goddamn snatch to pieces? And she signals with a wink just like it said in her script, so I start to crank the pace up, slap her ass and what have you, and I growl:

"This how you like it, bitch?"

And next thing you know she's lunging a fist at me:

"That's not what it said!" she's yelling. "The script is specific! It's, 'Is. This. How. You. Like. It You. *Cock*. *Sucking*. Ho!'"

And then there's the ad-libs, which most of the time is really just dames wanting to be raped or roughed up, but they're too shy to say so. And I guess, when I'm spunky and upbeat, when I'm not nursing a hangover, I kind of get a kick out of the ad-libs. Yeah, those'll definitely be my favourite gigs.

Ma'am, though, I gets the feeling she just wants plain old Stanley Kowalski. The agency gave me the following brief:

"She'll address you by the name of 'Hank'. You'll address her as 'Ma'am'. You'll attend to an imaginary oil leak. She'll invite you in to wash your hands. You'll fuck her. No goddamn strap-ons, no rape heists. Nothing. Just good clean fucking, God love her."

She's perched on a veranda swing – all honey-hued limbs and corn-coloured locks. An inch of skirt. My hangover just leaks away. Most of the time you see, it's just a means of keeping the landlady off my back. Graft. Goddamn messy graft when you've got some arthritic old dame jamming your head between her legs, trying to coax an orgasm from her stubborn snatch. But, every now and then, some little slice of eye candy will sway into your life and punch the air from your tummy. And boy, just the sight of her naked calves swinging to and fro sets my loins reeling and my heart thumping. The realization that I'm going to touch her and taste her and carry her scent all the way back to my apartment – it's enough to send a girl crazy.

She walks over and I'm suddenly conscious of the stench of metabolized liquor on my breath and I'm wishing I'd used a mouth rinse. But BO and late-night breath, that's how these dames like it, crazy bitches.

I slide the window down.

"Hello Ma'am," I say, my eyes burning moodily in a classic James Dean grimace. I stroke an imaginary patch of stubble.

She leans right in and dunks her cleavage on the ledge.

"You must be Hank," she purrs.

Her voice is all husky and smoke scorched. It gets me right between the thighs. She steps back and opens the door for me. I jump down onto the gravel and light a Lucky. Our eyes crash above the flame. She rakes a hand through her locks and grins.

"Okay Ma'am, let's take a look at her."

I drop to my haunches and run a hand across the bonnet. I take a conclusive pull on the half-smoked cigarette and stub it out on the wheel. She smiles.

"I'll be in the kitchen if you *need* anything, Hank."

She repositions herself, widening the distance between her feet and dragging my gaze up her legs and under her skirt. She's wearing no panties and her snatch is all neat and shaven, just like the broads down at Lusty Lady.

"Well, I'll be in the kitchen I guess . . ." she says, then turns on her heels and floats off, leaving the sweet scent of pruned Portola snatch lingering in the breeze.

"All done, Ma'am," I say when I step into the kitchen. She's sitting at the table, naked, rolling a rubber onto a big, mother-fuck of a strap-on. It still kills me whenever I see a woman bagging up. I suppress a smirk.

"You can wash your hands now," she says and gestures with her eyes to the sink.

I fill a bowl of hot soapy water and plunge my hands in. Outside, her gardener is driving a mower up and down the lawn, and on the pavement beyond, good decent folk are walking their dogs.

She comes up behind, pushes her tits into my back and begins rubbing my crotch just like I'm a guy.

"That feel good Hank?"

"Yes Ma'am."

"This what you've been hankering after all morning?"

The quip's there, sitting up and pointing its chin at me, but I let it go.

"Yes Ma'am."

"Yeah, I seen the way you been looking at me, you dirty son of a bastard."

She unfastens my overalls, wrenches them down to my knees and prises my thighs apart. A brief pause, the sound of spitting, and of spit being smeared onto her cock, and then she enters me. Up the ass. Hard and fast.

"That'll teach you, Hank," she gasps. "That'll teach you, you goddamn son of a bitch."

"Yes Ma'am," I say and, steadying myself against the lurch of the ride, smile politely at the gardener who has paused to wipe his brow.

I guess I never did find out just why Hank was being taught a lesson. She came in me real quick, offered me some wet wipes and a piece of fruit cake, then sent me on my way with a bow leg and a $20 tip. She never mentioned no goddamn skin-flick though.

"Hey listen," I say to the star-struck sales assistant. "So just how popular are my videos?"

"Hell, these are selling like crazy. This is our sixth re-order in two weeks."

I sign all twelve of them, then exit the store with a couple tucked under my arm and the germ of an idea fluttering about my head. When I'm certain I'm out of earshot of any of my fans that may have followed me out, I get right on the phone to an agent friend of mine over in Santa Monica.

"Hi. Cameron. How's it going?"

"How's it fucking going? It's five in the fucking morning!"

"Yeah I know, but listen. D'you have any contacts in the skin trade? I'm thinking of branching out."

YOU'VE BEEN FRAMED

Helen Walsh

Helen Walsh was born in Warrington, England. Her debut, *Brass*, won the Betty Trask prize in 2005, and her follow-up, *Once Upon a Time in England*, won the Somerset Maugham Prize in 2009. Walsh writes with purity and precision, skewering contemporary constructions of race, class and motherhood while unintentionally encouraging the robust use of reliable contraception.

Charlotte stood in the centre of the living room sizing up the new woman in her husband's life. She eyeballed her for a long, bold instant, dragging her gaze across her breasts and along her thighs which spilled out of violent green stockings. Her legs were parted in such a way as to suggest dissoluteness, yet her eyes looked upwards from heavy sunken orbits and hinted at compliance, servility even. Charlotte felt conflicting emotions – hatred, jealousy, pity. She raised an eyebrow at her, sighed, then left for work.

It was a birthday present from his mother – a Schiele print she'd "tracked down" in Vienna. She'd encased the poster in a ludicrous gold splintered frame and presented it as though it were an original canvas. Charlotte shook her head as she remembered the roguish grin her mother-in-law wore as she watched Jack plough through the intricate layers of wrapping.

"It's a sharing present," she simpered. "You know, a house-warming and a birthday thing?"

Jack had been pathetically pleased. He had sat there for a long time, beaming at the woman and then at his mother.

"She's . . . It's striking!" he gushed, squinting at the signature.

"It's a Schiele," his mother declared, then turned to Charlotte: "You're probably not au fait with him, darling. A bit before your time. He was an Expressionist. Fiercely anti-Classical. Renowned for giving his women great bulging vaginas, and truncating the penises of his males. Such a tormented soul, God bless him."

Charlotte bit hard on the flesh of her cheeks and forced a smile. She contemplated pointing out that every gauche undergraduate at St Martin's had a Schiele tacked to their wall. That that wretch appeared on more of her students' T-shirts than Che Guevara. But instead she said thank you, and erected it centre stage above the fireplace.

Jack was a junior doctor working the graveyard shift at Bart's. Each morning, when he arrived home, he'd crack open a beer, switch on the TV and digest the dregs of yesterday's news. And only when the drama and discord of the hospital had leaked from his head would he retire to the bedroom. Often Charlotte would

be waking as he was crawling into bed and they would meet in a hazy fumble of adolescent groping and delving that nine times out of ten blossomed into full-blown intercourse. Since the woman had arrived in their living room though, Jack had found himself body-swerving their pre-dawn bedroom gymnastics and devoting himself wholly to the solitary and selfish vocation of masturbation.

It started the day after his birthday. He'd stumbled through the door, snapped on the TV and drifted off. When he woke it was past midday. The curtains were drawn and a blanket had been thrown over him. The first thing he saw was the woman's alabaster thighs, lit up in a lash of colour from the TV. Lying flat on the sofa afforded him a new vantage point of the woman, and he noticed for the first time the gentle swell of flesh between her legs. Instinctively, he unzipped his trousers, took out his cock and luxuriated in a slow, languorous wank.

He laughed at the recollection later on that night at work, and for a moment felt faintly absurd, but by the time he was driving home he was eager to repeat the whole thing.

Jack was disappointed to find Charlotte awake when he got in. She called him through to the bedroom. She was lying on the bed, naked, a wolfish glint flickering in her eyes. His heart plummeted and his disappointed dick sank back into his balls. She gestured for him to lie down, then tugged his trousers to his knees. "How long?" she teased, and with the tip of her tongue attempted to revive his thwarted penis through the fabric of his shorts. Jack tried to get into it, to get into her, but his thoughts were consumed only by the woman in the next room – her brilliant thighs, the earthy jut of her breasts, the promise of sex skulking between her legs. When Jack could stand it no longer he yanked his wife's undulating head from his lap and dragged her through to the living room. He ordered her to her knees, pushed her head to the floor, then fixing his gaze on the woman's stockings, fucked his wife with an alarming brutality. Charlotte was too stunned, too excited to protest as the carpet clawed at her cheeks and her husband's angry member slammed full-force into her arse. She came quickly, seconds before Jack. She giggled, hoisted herself up, cupping her arse and cunt with both hands and scurried off to the bathroom. Jack lay prostrate on the floor, staring up at the woman. He felt a pang of something, but wasn't sure what.

Jack's crush soon ballooned into an all-consuming obsession. He simply could not stop thinking about her. He drove home each morning stupidly excited, his balls churning at the thought of another liaison. He hadn't masturbated so much since he was a teenager and the pang of something he'd felt that first morning had unveiled itself in a shocking detonation. Jack Gresty was in love. He was as good as having an affair with a portrait. What was more, Charlotte was on to him. Her jibes about his sudden loss of libido took on an accusatory tone. She ransacked his pockets and briefcase, opened his phone bills and, when she found nothing, sought retribution in the form of an all-singing all-dancing vibrator. In the weeks that followed, Jack would often return home from work to the sound of metronomic plunging. When she called him one evening at work and asked if he'd join her on *Trisha*, Jack knew his time was up. The Schiele had to go.

As Jack peeled left out of the hospital car park the next morning an almighty pall descended over his world. It was silly, unfathomable that he should be feeling this way, but as he pulled into his drive he felt an astonishing sense of loss.

He decided he would console himself with a valedictory wank.

He poured himself a large scotch, lit some candles and lay flat on the sofa with his aching cock in his hand. She looked spectacular by candlelight and within moments he was bang into a greedy rhythm and a flight of disgusting sex scenarios. He was shuddering his way towards a magnificent climax, when he noticed a gradual shift of her legs. He froze. She shifted again, this time exposing the glistening matted well between her legs. Jack's fingernails cut into his cock. He could barely breathe. He got up, slapped himself hard in the face and snapped the light on. Christ! She'd moved again. Gingerly, he approached the portrait. She opened her legs a little wider then shifted her arse forward so her cunt was right up in his face. Migod, he could smell her! Jack took his trembling fingers to her mound. Her arse jarred forward another inch and she swallowed them whole. More aroused than frightened, he leapt over to the dining table, grabbed a chair and positioned it in front of the fireplace. He climbed up, then placing his arms either side of the portrait to steady himself, entered her with a violent urgency.

"What on earth . . . ?"

Jack spun round to find his wife in the doorway dressed for work, her face buckled in terror at the spectacle of her husband dry-humping the wall.

A tearful confession vacillated on his lips, but before he could speak Charlotte was rushing over to him, her arms outstretched, her face etched in concern.

"Christ! You're sleepwalking! Shhh. Don't be alarmed . . ."

"Uh?"

Jack swung back round and confronted the portrait. It was exactly as it always was. He dropped his gaze to his deflating dick – blood red and chafed at the tip, and screamed. When Charlotte got in from work that night she noted that the portrait was gone. She was quietly relieved. It was assumed that Jack's erratic sleeping habits had been the cause of his recent misdemeanors and the "portrait incident" was not mentioned again. Jack spoke to the hospital superior, transferred over to a day shift and things returned to normal in the Gresty household.

Later that year, Jack's mother announced she would be visiting. It was the first time they'd thought of the voluptuous portrait in eight months. What would they tell her? Jack suggested they just say it was stolen, but Charlotte, fearing this might give the tawdry gift more prestige than it deserved, insisted on retrieving it from the attic. Jack was in the garden when she went up for it. He heard a loud yelp and then the sound of a body slapping the ground. He rushed indoors to find Charlotte supine on the floor, wide-eyed and gibbering. She gestured to the portrait lying face downwards at the other end of the hall. Jack advanced slowly towards it, his mind starting to whirr and sputter. He flipped it over, took one look at the woman's heavily pregnant belly and fled the house.

FINNY'S TALE – THE CREATURE IN THE GARDEN

Lucy Golden

Lucy Golden is an intensely private person: she is unwilling to publish her biographical details, considering the intimate revelations in her books to be more than adequate. She says, 'My books and stories are extremely personal. They are drawn from the very deepest parts of my mind and if you don't know me after reading them, you never will.' Her fiction is based both on her own experiences and those of friends; these people are not impossibly rich, nor are they cardboard cutouts. They are real people, with real families, real lives, real careers, who all have a keen interest in sex which they have shared with the author. This populist element in her writing could explain why Lucy Golden has built up such a devoted following.

I'd never seen a stripper before Rosie's party. That's not to say that I'm a complete innocent, but it's not a normal part of a girl's everyday life, is it?

I've known Rosie since heaven knows when. In fact it was from her that I heard about this contract devising the new Census Data Collection Forms in the first place. Through her, I joined the contract team, and we shared a flat from the outset. Malcolm joined the team about eighteen months later, and although they hit it off straight away, it was one of those on-again, off-again kind of relationships, that you know will never get anywhere.

I was on my own at that time and feeling sorry for myself: Rosie was not the only one to fancy Malcolm. I had managed a few gropes and snogs, but beyond that it never really got going and when his work on the contract came to an end and he announced he was going back home to South Africa, I knew I was going to miss him. Then it emerged that Rosie was going with him and that they were going to get married at some stage, and I knew I was going to miss her. In fact, I was jealous. I mean I was pleased for them, and I am fond of Rosie, but it brought home to me that it could have been me looking so happy and about to get married and it wasn't. And I had been working on this one contract for three years and I was no nearer knowing what I wanted from life, let alone finding what I wanted, than when I started. I was beginning to feel old.

So I approached their party, a combined going-away, stag party and hen night, determined to have a good time. I knew that most of the contract staff would be

there so I was expecting to get lucky even if it didn't last for ever. Sunday morning is the loneliest time of the week if you wake up to an empty bed, particularly when you can hear voices – or more – coming from your flat-mate's room.

It was early July, gloriously hot, and the party was being held in the old Victorian house that Malcolm and the other lads rented out along The Avenue. We held most of our parties there because although the house was nothing special, it had an enormous walled garden and a wide lawn lined by thick trees and bushes. Alan, Malcolm's best man, had organised "His and Hers" strippers: a Portuguese girl called Marenia for Malcolm and a gorilla man for Rosie. I drank quite a bit, probably more than I should, and made a last doomed bid for Malcolm which got nowhere; I'm not sure he even fully realised what was on offer. Anyway Alan dragged him back to the living room where, despite Malcolm's pretence of objection, he was made to sit in a straight-backed chair in the centre of the floor. Marenia came down from where she had been hiding somewhere upstairs, the music started, and she began to do her stuff.

Now I am not a lesbian, and I have no wish whatsoever to become one, but she was pretty, well no, more than pretty and not exactly pretty. She was stunning; glamorous, tall and elegant, but strutted with determination and pride in herself. The music was just right. She did two tracks, first a dance number and then a really old slow one called "Je t'aime", and she danced really well to both of them. As I said, I had never seen a girl do a strip before, and I didn't realise that she would take everything off and I didn't realise that once she had done that she would drop down into a low squat on the floor and that her legs would be spread wide apart and we would all be able to see her, all of her. Nor that on some girls there could be so much to see.

And I didn't realise that she could do all that in someone's house in front of forty or fifty people she had never seen before, and do it openly, unashamed, uninhibited with total confidence in herself, with grace in her movements and pride in the silent attention from all of us, male and female, her audience.

And I didn't realise how erotic all that could be, how deep an effect it could have when someone, who could be male or female, comes out and does something so exclusively and deliberately sexual in front of a crowd of people, and mostly how much of an effect that could have on me. She had a torrent of black hair which, all through her dance, swooped from side to side so that even after she had taken her top off, when we knew she was only wearing her little knickers, even then this thick wild mane kept tumbling forwards over her front. Her hands would disappear under the curtain of hair and then she would spin and the hair would spread out and suddenly we could see her breasts and her nipples and they would be hard and erect and I knew that mine were as well.

And maybe it was because she was Portuguese, or maybe just confident, or maybe that was just how she preferred it, but she hadn't shaved under her arms so there was thick luxuriant hair there and a sort of soft dark down running along her arms. It was all quite animal and untamed and I felt myself wanting to touch her, stroke her, and not just the hair but the skin too.

So when – finally, after an age of teasing and waiting – she slid her tiny black knickers down her long dark legs, I expected another thick bush of that glorious hair, but she shocked me again. There was none: she was immaculately shaved,

revealing thick ripe lips almost pouting at me with another pair of lips pushing out from between them and even her clit poked out too. Everything was being offered to us, visible and available. She looked so ready, so complete a woman like some kind of erotic fertility goddess. Everything that she had done, every gesture she had made (and all the little gaps which our minds had filled out), had built to this. Her whole body was primed, totally ripe and ready for sex. And I think I was jealous again. When she was naked she carried on writhing sensuously over Malcolm, resting one foot on his knee then sliding it up his thigh, completely opening herself up for him to see every fold, every glistening crease, every shining pore, everything. Her foot rested in his lap and the toes wriggled around, massaging him gently. At one point she slipped her hand inside the waist band of his shorts and for a few moments, as we all giggled with embarrassment, we only saw the fluttering of fingers beneath the thin cotton. And I was jealous of that too, of the attention that he was paying to her, of the sneaky gropes under her thighs and across her bottom, and of the way she was able to grope him. I wanted it to be me who was doing something so manifestly sexual, me who Malcolm was watching so intently and my body that he was casually caressing. And I wanted to be the one who kept running back to his lap, who could feel his erection, who could hold his head to my breasts and feel his lips nuzzle at me, pretending he was just pretending when we all knew he wasn't.

And at last, as the song sobbed to its wailing end, it should have been me who came up to wrap their arms round him, and me who pressed his face hard against my belly. It should have been my body, my scent, my arousal, he inhaled in those deep slow breaths. Me, he finally kissed.

But it wasn't me and my arousal was wasted and it all seemed so unfair, specially when he already had Rosie who would be good and loyal, and now he had this girl too, offered in front of all of us, simply as a pleasant diversion. I knew I could have filled either role and I wanted to fill both and I was denied either.

I stayed in the doorway, outside the cheering and the laughter, watching from a safe distance behind the door as she took her bow and collected her clothes. As she left, passing close in front of me, her clothes bundled under one arm, she flashed an excited, jubilant grin and then was gone, a smooth naked bottom scampering up the stairs to get dressed. I wanted to follow her, but for what? To complain that Malcolm didn't want me? To tell her I was jealous? That I wanted her life? That I wanted people to stand round watching me, admiring me, the way they admired her? That I wanted to be her? It would have been stupid and I skulked back into the living room as people were preparing Rosie for her turn.

She too had to take her place on the chair in the centre while a man in a gorilla suit, looking frankly rather silly, came out and started prancing around her. At least, it started silly, but that changed. Again, there was some music and he pulled her up so that he was sort of dancing with her but his huge hands, all moulded plastic and nylon fur, kept groping all over her, over her bottom and up the front of her tee shirt, and his wrinkled plastic nose sniffed and snorted, pushing under her arms and between her legs and making obscene animal grunts of joy at the smells he was pretending to find. It was well done, and was very funny. Rosie laughed as much as everybody else, but following the girl before and with

the thoughts that she had put in my mind, well I am sure in all our minds, the gorilla's game was not entirely innocent. His blank disregard for her attempts to restrain his hands, the complete lack of any expression on his artificial face, his refusal to give any indication that he understood speech, all these together gave it a sinister edge. Like a ventriloquist's discarded dummy, it was both human and inhuman: familiar and dangerous; playful and frightening. Overall, it made him even more uncontrollable and intimidating and yet, somehow, alluring.

He was a big man – and Rosie is five foot nothing in the tallest of her spike heels – so when he picked her up bodily he could turn her upside down ignoring her struggles to keep her skirt from tumbling down and showing her knickers. He simply cuffed her hands away and eventually she gave up, letting the skirt fall down over her head while his unfeeling plastic fingers scratched at the taut material between her thighs, jabbed at the damp crease and plucked at the elastic, threatening always to pull her knickers right off. Then he pulled her up higher, gathering in the skirt but now tugging at her tee shirt where it was tucked in at the waist and finally releasing it. Amid her squeals and giggles, she tried to keep him at bay, but again he ignored her protests and finally pulled it out so the shirt tumbled down to her armpits and her bare breasts were revealed to us all, excited, erect and full. Turned back again, he tucked her under one arm and she made only token resistance when he began to pull her top right off. Once that had been tossed away, she tried to cover herself with her hands but he shoved them aside and scratched around her breasts, flicking at her nipples and pulling, pinching at the real flesh with synthetic, unyielding claws.

With his curiosity apparently satisfied, he laid her down on the floor, but still kept snuffling around at her and preventing her getting up, grunting and then rubbing himself and sort of humping at her. Finally he hauled her up again, threw her over his shoulder and in a half crouch ambled off out of the circle, pausing briefly next to one girl who squealed in real fear the instant he put his face against her. The cheers and laughter with a big round of applause drowned all this as he put Rosie down again, took his mask off, kissed her and took his bow.

When a game of "Pig in the Middle" started – the lads refusing to let Rosie have her tee shirt back – I refilled my glass and slipped out onto the terrace to get a little air, to sit down and allow my thoughts to calm in the stillness of evening. They had put candles around, little tea-lights mixed in with bigger candles stuck on plates and in bottles so the whole area twinkled. The sun had disappeared behind the gigantic Cedar trees which marked the bottom of the garden, but it was still light and the smell of barbecues and the sound of other music from other parties drifted through the night.

"Lovely garden! Lovely night!" The gorilla man was standing behind me, now in shorts and a striped shirt, gripping a beer can in one great fist and a slice of pizza in the other.

I hated to be so transparent. "I suppose so. I hate gardens."

"Oh," he said. "That's rather a pity." His voice came low and deep from inside his chest and sounded wounded so that I was ashamed of my scorn and tried to make amends.

"But no, you're right. It is lovely."

He grinned. "I'm Jeff" and drank most of the beer down in one and then grinned again, mischievous and enticing. "Bloody hot in that suit."

I smiled, or something. He did not look any smaller now that he was out of the gorilla suit but he did seem friendly and his slightly dishevelled fair curly hair seemed almost boyish. I was really fairly drunk by this stage and when he moved on to some vacuous comment about the pizza (he was only making polite conversation after all) I said I thought gorillas only ate bananas. What a stupid thing to say!

"Oh well," he said determined to maintain his jovial mood, "I like them too."

"Mmm," I answered, and to this day I have no idea what on earth I can have been thinking about, but I lifted my eyes to him and then down to an obvious stare at his crotch. "Mmm," I said, "so do I."

He looked at me for a few seconds, taking in my open sandals, my thin cotton dress and bare legs, and the empty glass in my hand and he smiled at me.

"Can I fetch you another drink? I'm getting myself one."

"Thanks, Jeff."

When he brought them back, we leaned on the wall side by side and drank in silence. Inside, everybody else was playing a game, I think it was the truth game with matches because Rosie came to shut the patio doors to stop them being blown out. It seemed private out there, in half darkness, his face – and mine too, I suppose – in shadow from the lights of the house behind us and I asked, just casually: "You live with Marenia?"

"Well we share a flat, but we're not, you know, 'together'. I'm not really her type."

"Ah." I tried to make the sound into an invitation to continue.

"Her partner left her rather unexpectedly and she was looking for someone to help her with the gorilla stuff and I was looking for somewhere cheap to stay for a few months."

"I see." There was another pause.

"You're Finny, someone said."

"Yes, short for Fiona."

"So, what did you think of it? The gorilla routine?"

"Different!"

"Ah." He sounded sad. "You didn't like it. I saw you were hiding at the back."

"Well I liked it, but it was kind of unnerving. Is it all planned out in advance, I mean always the same?"

"No, I discuss beforehand with whoever has arranged the booking to see how far they want me to go, and then I play it by ear, depending on the reaction. Alan had said Rosie was a good sport, that she would not mind if I pulled her top off."

"No. There haven't been many parties in this house where her boobs have not made an appearance at some stage."

"I see." He was interested and after a minute's thought. "And yours as well?"

"Occasionally, maybe; from time to time."

"I am sorry I missed them. Still, I suppose the party's not over yet."

I did not respond and then he dropped his voice, confessing suddenly to the quiet truths that can only come out between strangers in the secure silence of a little shadow world. "I am exaggerating. This is only the third time I have ever

done this; I only left drama school six months ago and there is bugger all proper work about."

"Well, it seemed good to me. I mean it! But to be honest, I have never seen one of these before so don't really have anything to judge it by. In fact, don't tell anyone, but I had never seen a stripper before tonight."

"And was it exciting?"

"Which?"

"Both."

"Yes."

"Good." He paused and his voice came through very gently. "But would you like it to have been you?"

"Which?"

"Both."

"Yes." But that was too glib and I needed to wipe away the words I had nearly said. "Yes, I would. Come and do one for me when I leave here." I offered it as a throw away and he knew better than to let on that he knew it wasn't.

"Are you leaving?"

"No."

"Then I had better do it soon."

I laughed at his lack of logic without accepting or refusing the offer but when I shivered in the little breeze, he put his arm around me and I snuggled in close. He may have discarded the gorilla suit, but he was still big and comfortable and secure to rest against. I felt him turn, knew he was looking down at me, considering options, but I did not respond. A gorilla ought to be able to make its own decisions over a mate.

His hand came back onto my shoulder and gently pulled me to him and when I turned this time he kissed me, first a peck, then a nibble and at last a full, entirely breathless kiss. His hands roamed over my back and down to my bottom and then back up, made the usual circle which is supposed to be so innocent but which we all know is checking for a bra strap. Finding none, one hand worked its way round between us and held me, moulded me, sliding across the front and raising the appropriate peaks of interest.

And then we were surrounded. Half the party poured out onto the terrace announcing that Rosie was leading the hen night down into town where there was supposed to be a Chippendale-type male strip show on. Alan, Malcolm and several others had offered to do their own but since this was conditional on the girls reciprocating, their offer had been rejected. In response they were going to watch a porny video. I didn't care for either option, but Jeff was new and when Alan kept pestering him, he relented: he did not understand how to refuse people he did not know. The girls were all childishly excited and enthusiastic and that just annoyed me. I said I wasn't interested although Rosie and even Marenia urged me to come along but the more they pleaded, the less I was tempted until finally, in something of a strop, I told them to piss off and leave me alone.

They did.

I sneaked back into the kitchen, ignoring the few voices (all male) in the living room, refilled my glass and made my way back out to the garden, through the shrubs and railings down to a small ornamental pond surrounded by low stone

walls. Here I settled myself down on the paving, my back leaning against the warm stones, and kicked off my sandals. The night was clear, starlit and open and there were still sounds of cars and people and music somewhere up behind me, but in the little hollow round the pond, it was quiet and private. It looked like being another lonely night, and although I really wanted something less familiar than my own hands for comfort, if they were to be the only hands available, I would make do. I wanted to start straight away in the cool of the open sky with the wide world around and above me, so I tucked the cold beer can between my legs, up high against the bare skin of my thighs and the thin cotton of my knickers where the coolness was needed and where the condensation from the can could refresh me where my own moisture was working exactly the opposite.

All around me the contented rustling of a thousand night creatures made the quiet that bit more comforting until a twig snapped behind me; not close, but close enough. Too loud, too big a twig, to have been a bird or a hedgehog, and I froze. The last thing I wanted was sympathy, someone else coming to tell me to cheer up and come and enjoy the fun and I pulled my knees up to cover the bare skin and make me less conspicuous. After a few minutes with no further sign or sound of anyone, I peered round the corner of the wall, relieved to find no one there. I relaxed back into my place, slipped a hand back under my dress and in a sudden silence, heard behind me regular low breathing, not quite panting, more like somebody deliberately trying to make no noise. I carefully put down the glass, peered round the other side of the stones and was confronted by a wall of black fur. I screamed before I saw what it was, I screamed again when it reached out and grabbed my hair and my shoulder and then the huge gorilla pulled me over to its chest, its thick long arms enfolding, engulfing me in the tangle of hair. It spun me around so that my back was against its chest and one long arm reached down over my shoulder and clamped me fast.

My first reaction was simple relief at realising what – who – it was and that I was safe, but when I stupidly said "Hello, Jeff!" the figure stopped in a terrible ominous stillness and then reached out and deliberately cuffed me with the back of its hand, hard across my thigh. I screamed out a protest, suddenly unsure it was Jeff, wriggled and tried to push him away, but the clamp tightened and the free hand started to creep across me. It did not respond to my struggles, and too strong for my grasp, too uncaring of my protests, it continued to drag over me, pulling at my clothes, rubbing over my chest. It virtually disregarded my breasts, simply ran over my front in a series of big circles that reached down to my waist and up my side and across both breasts. I grabbed his wrist but he was much stronger than me and I could not restrain him; the more I pulled, the more he pushed. The arm encircling my shoulders tightened and the other arm stretched, reached down the front of my dress until the hard pointed claws rasped along skin, hooked under the hem and pulled. Up my legs, up my thighs, my knickers suddenly came into view, white in the dusk, and the dress was pulled higher still. I was now fully encased in his crossed arms, pinioned and captive. Even if I had tried to resist, even if I had wanted to resist, I would have been powerless.

But it was then that things changed, for slowly edging round the far side of the stone wall came someone – something – else; also in a suit of black fur, also ambling, grunting and then, when it reached me, nudging with its nerveless nose at

the exposed crotch of my knickers before its moulded hands slithered up my legs, right up under my dress to my breasts. Not quite as big as the first one, it was no less menacing, no less alien and equally uncompromising in its unchanging stare. There was little flexibility in the stubby fingers as they clawed at my nipples, scraped across and over them, but the complete lack of delicacy did not in any way reduce the effect: if anything the opposite. I was helpless in their grasp: held tight by one; accessible to the crude and insensitive maulings of the other. I was frightened, but with the exhilarated terror of the fairground. I didn't actually believe I was in real danger, but neither was I in control. The ride had started and I was committed until it ended, but the ending was not at my bidding. They had chosen to scare me for their amusement, and their next choice could be anything else they desired. For now I was theirs, a captive, alone with them in a deserted garden under the stars.

In retrospect, I do not know why I didn't just laugh. It seems so crazy, two figures in ridiculous party costumes pinning me down in the garden of a suburban house. What threat was there? But we don't live our lives in retrospect and the course of the evening had led me to see these creatures only as they appeared, as wild untameable animals, uncaring and dangerous. More than that, it all seemed vital and passionate and an invigorating contrast to the sterile predictability of the life I had been living. I despised the safe artificiality of the show that the girls had gone to see, trooping off to gawp from a secure distance at immaculate coiffured elegance. I was cramped on the ground with two huge black hairy monsters. It was glorious.

From behind, the first creature pushed me forward up against the new arrival where all I could see was a pair of deep black eyes staring back at me through the mask, moist eyes, shining, full and excited at the knowledge of its power, at what it was doing. The scent of this one was, if anything, stronger, slightly more sweaty and animal than the other so I could not be sure if this was really Jeff, or if the other was; and if this was Jeff, who was the other, the first one? Who was it now behind me, arms embracing me, hands reaching down and pulling insistently at my knickers? Pushing down inside to claw at my own inadequate covering of hair? The front one also joined in, digging at the elastic waistband, scrabbling at the top and trying to get inside or get them down or somehow, anyhow, to get rid of their flimsy protection. Finally it grew impatient and with a sudden yank, the material was simply ripped, torn almost in two and pulled away. For a moment he held the pink clammy remnant up at eye level between us, then clasped it to his nostrils and snorted before it was tossed up high into the air where it flapped once before it disappeared.

I turned back, my eyes drawn to the luminance of my pale thighs shining out in the half-light, to my dress which had been pushed right up during the battle for possession of my knickers and to the point just below the hem where was visible the tip of the slightly darker shadow of my neatly trimmed triangle. The one in front of me now held my shoulders while the other fumbled at the back of my neck. Its claws were struggling to grip the tongue of the zip and hot gasps of increasingly frustrated breath came onto the bare skin of my neck. Finally impatience took over again and with one hand in the neck band it simply pulled the dress apart, enough to start the zip running down, enough for it to continue

and work it down to the bottom where the dress was rucked up around my waist. The other one now took over, pulled at the torn neckline to tug the garment down my arms, simply dragging it completely inside out, over my hips and legs and off. It bundled the cloth up and tossed it away into the shrubs.

That was all I had been wearing, so I lay back, naked, a nakedness made even more complete by the contrast with the heavy masses of animal hair. I was gripped and cradled in the arms of the first one while the second stared at me. My arms were clamped down by my sides and my legs pushed out in front of me leaving me so available, utterly ready for them to take charge.

The one in front of me brought himself up into the same low crouch and taking hold of my wrist pulled me out of the other's grasp and forward onto hands and knees. He released me and we stared at each other while I waited; there was little doubt what was the next step in the game.

They wanted me: they had found me.

They had caught me: they had stripped me.

I dripped.

Suddenly I felt a stinging slap across my bare bottom which made me gasp and turn on the attacker behind but immediately I turned, I was slapped from the other side and when I tried to protect myself from this, a long black arm reached out and the cold rigid fingers, like pre-formed claws, pinched my nipple, pinched me hard. Caught between them like this, I was entirely vulnerable. I jumped to my feet and tried to make a run for it, but as soon as I was up, I realised that I was visible to anybody still left in the house, or on the terrace or even in any of the adjoining houses.

I darted behind the fruit-cage but immediately one of them appeared at the corner and although I kept my back to the wall, I was slapped on the thigh, then on the bottom again and then right across the breast, and it hurt. I slipped out between them and across the damp grass towards the shrubbery and heard them lumbering after me as I ran. It was the unpredictability which made it so hard to bear, which undermined me. When they had first appeared, I had been frightened, then complacent; now I was scared again. Sitting in the comfort and safety of a living room surrounded by friends, it may have been stirring to watch the charade of an amorous gorilla dancing to music. It was entirely different to be utterly alone, stripped naked by two creatures who did not respond to any command or any word spoken to them, who reacted only as animals, whose intention was solely their own pleasure, a pleasure which clearly included playing me like a mouse, and causing me pain by slapping me and pinching me whenever I came within range. I managed to reach the shrubbery, but while I picked delicately across the rough earth between the twigs and thorns, they simply shoved their way through behind me and as soon as I stopped, another stinging slap across my bottom sent me further on.

And still I could not be completely certain who they were. I was almost certain that one was Jeff, but I had no idea at all about the other. It could possibly be Alan but Alan should have been taller. If not Alan, then who? Malcolm? I would have liked it to be and it seemed the right height, but I could not know for sure. For a minute I considered trying to head back to the house, but there was nowhere there to hide and with no chance to recover my clothes, I could hardly

go back to the party. At the far side of the garden, where the side of the garage ran very close to the wall of the garden, there was rather more shadow and it did look as if it might offer more cover than was available among the shrubs. I scampered across the lawn and found a tiny area where, with my back to the garage, nobody could creep up behind me and, squeezed between the two walls, I was almost invisible.

I crouched down into the corner and drew my knees up to my chest. The sudden pressure of warm skin on my breasts, even though it was my own warm skin, sent a little ripple through me and, without thinking, my thighs opened a fraction and my hands reached down to cover me, to protect and to comfort me, and my fingertips stroked gently at the little damp protrusion. As soon as I pressed it, the dampness increased markedly, betraying how readily my body responded to the attention and stimulation it had already received, and in anticipation of the more there would be to come.

It happened quickly. I heard the unmistakable sound of shuffling feet and the light in front of me was blocked by the black mass of one of the animals. It reached in, grabbed my ankle and started to haul me out and although I tried to pull back, it was so much stronger than me that unless I was willing to be dragged across the stones on my back, I had no choice but to concede and worm my way out.

As soon as I emerged, they each grabbed one arm and I was dragged backwards across the lawn and up the steps onto the terrace. As we arrived, a roar of muffled laughter came from inside where the others were still watching their stupid film.

At the top of the terrace steps, they laid me down on the warm flagstones, one taking my wrists, the other taking my ankles, and I was spread like a sacrifice. The sky was still bright and with the candles all around, I was plainly visible, a pale virgin star, their plaything.

Now I was shared; brittle plastic and soft fur scuttling over me, artificial hands to squeeze and paw at my breasts, hands whose cold unnatural hardness made their blunt caresses all the more stimulating. Had anyone else groped me so roughly, I would have protested, or left, or both. This was different. They had changed me: I was as animal as either of them. I could smell their sweat and could feel my own running down me, and it was not just sweat I was leaking. My legs were spread wide, my pussy peeled open and that smell too drifted up to me.

The game was over and I was impatient. After all that had happened, I could not wait for any long slow foreplay; in reality the foreplay had begun hours ago when the Portuguese stripper first stepped out onto the floor; maybe that afternoon, when I had taken a shower and changed ready for the night. Now I was entirely ready.

One of them half stood up and shuffled over to the low parapet wall, where it selected one of the candles, not one of the neat elegant, dinner-table types in their finely painted candlesticks, but a cruder one, a thicker one: an altar candle; one whose length and width could not help but stir images in my brain, and – obviously – in the creature's brain too. It snapped the candle free of its saucer, shaking loose the molten wax and extinguishing the flame in the process, and

turned back to me, settled onto its haunches between my legs, staring at the deep shadow between my thighs, shuffling up further, closer, pressing down on my thigh and with the candle clamped tight in its hand, reaching forward to pull at my pussy lips, opening me, running the candle once, twice along the side and then – with no preparation beyond a low grunt – simply twisting it in, deep, deep in. I moaned.

Its free hand was still rasping over me, up my thighs, across my stomach and raking through my pubic hair, but the sharp point of the thumb nail kept returning to ride my clitoris, running spirals up one side, across the far too sensitive top, and back down the sides. At the same time, the candle never stopped: sliding in and out of me in a brutally careless piston, relentlessly lifting and exciting me however much I tried to dismiss it all as sheer mechanics.

What attracted their attention, the men who had stayed behind to watch stupid films? A sound that I made, although I had tried to be quiet? A sudden movement from one of the beasts? The erratic flickering, part obscured, of the row of candles? I heard a single low call, just the one, and then the patio door was being pushed open and as I looked up from the ground, they poured out, fifteen, twenty maybe, excited grins already flooding over their faces. They formed their own circle around us, a ring beyond the two creatures (who had anyway entirely ignored them) but where they could watch me, watch what was being done to me, and I could watch them watching me.

If I hadn't called a halt before, this should have been the moment to stop the game: I knew many of these men, worked with them, would meet them in the office again in two days' time. I would have to face them while we both remembered the sight I now presented. I should have stopped then.

But it was too late. Powerful hands were still scraping and pinching at my breasts: a cruel and relentless assault, exquisitely painful. The smaller one stayed crouched between my legs, intently focused on its thumb nail rasping at my clit and its fist driving the candle, a constant unbearable rhythm that was irresistible. I no longer cared that I was so publicly exposed and humiliated: I just wanted them to go on. I heard myself moan, looked up to see the mocking reaction of my spectators – yes, Malcolm among them: now he could see how much better he might have done if he had chosen more carefully – and saw the concentration on all those faces as they watched the crude simplicity of the candle pounding in and out of me. I moaned again and this time it was just a single wail as the intensity of it all became too much and the stimulation of watching, of being watched, of being so simply and unambiguously treated, all of that finally pushed me over the edge into an extended sobbing orgasm that washed away any other thoughts or feelings, that obliterated all thoughts of the people around me and I no longer cared for what any of them saw or thought as long as the feelings would just continue for ever.

It wasn't for ever; it was all too brief. But it wasn't completely over.

The candle was pulled away and the two animals spun me round, hauling and twisting me to the position they wanted until I was clamped against the second one's chest while it was the first one, who had been behind me, who now shuffled up close to take his place squatting between my legs, gripping one ankle in each huge fist, lifting and spreading me wide again.

And he didn't want the candle: he was fiddling with the crotch of his costume, awkwardly, almost comically, but I was too impatient. I needed more and brought my knees up, the better to open myself to him, lifted my hips to offer myself to him and reached down to squeeze my clit to make sure I would be fully ready when the time came. I separated my lips and, dipping a finger deep inside, smeared the abundant wetness across both swollen sides and up the whole length of my crease. He was trying to concentrate on his costume, but distracted by watching me, and even the hands across my breasts froze as both of them paused to watch the spectacle; at last I had taken back control. I heard the expectant silence from the outer ring of spectators and was tempted to carry on. Now I was the centre of attention: that stripper had not dared to go this far. I did; I dared. Lying naked in front of all of them, I had let myself be fucked by a candle. In a minute I was going to be fucked by a man. Before that, I might, if I chose, if I felt they deserved it, I might let them watch me masturbate.

Even the thought was almost enough to make me come a second time, but I was on a plateau and I had been waiting long enough and needed something more so I did not protest when my fingers were pushed aside by a long claw which slithered down my front, came to rest in my lap and started to dig its way inside me. It dug at the moisture it found there and brought it out and up to smear it over my nipples.

At last the other creature eased his costume open and a glorious erection appeared, pink and slightly incongruous surrounded by the sea of artificially black hair, but I didn't care. It was there, visibly hard, erect and ready; the ultimate compliment to my offering. He moved up to squat over me and as my own hands were pinioned by the other creature, he swung his huge erection across my face, slapping my cheeks with it, teasing and prodding at my mouth, but quickly pulling away every time my tongue reached out for him.

As soon as he crawled back down between my thighs and I felt the tip of his cock nosing around me for entrance, I reached down, took hold of him in my fist and fed it in. I was so wet he almost slipped straight out again so I grabbed tight handfuls of hair on his sides, locked my ankles behind him to make sure he could not escape. His hips lifted back and then dropped as he slid far in and the first beautifully vicious thrust knocked my breath out; I heard and felt a gasp as the shock drove me back further against the figure behind.

The black mask loomed over me, and it was that which I was most aware of, that which I still recognised as my lover. Ridiculous, yes, but still powerful, still strong and intimidating. As well as that, the mask prevented any kisses or tenderness, so that his grunts, coming muffled through it, were not of love but of animal passion, of lust. He was clearly as ready as I was. Before another steady dozen bruising thrusts had driven me back still harder into the arms and the caresses of the figure behind, I was lost, the trembling beginning somewhere way down deep and mushrooming up through me in a flood. I clamped his hairy black shoulder in my mouth and lifted my bottom to meet him, pushing back with my hips as hard as I squeezed in with my thighs to force every atom of pleasure out of him and into me and hearing my own voice screaming obscenities of encouragement out into the night air, encouragement which he didn't need for he was already pressing ever more savage thrusts at me, animal grunts from both

of us and somewhere above me, chanting from our watchers. It was short and rough and brutal and wonderful and nothing since has even come close.

When finally it had been enough, and I realised that he had stopped his thrusts, in fact that my slot was now as full of his wetness as of mine, I slowly relaxed my grip and let him ease away, nursing his bleeding shoulder where my teeth had bitten right through the costume. We sat back, panting, both shocked by the force of the encounter, by the way we had been entirely taken up in the parts we were playing. He eased the mask off and for the first time I could see Jeff's face as he leaned back down to kiss me. He reached his arms around me and hugged me up to him and this time it really was Jeff, not some wild creature that was embracing me, kissing me, whose tongue at last met mine, whose breath mixed with mine. But such subtlety was lost on our cheering circle of spectators whose laughter and clapping embarrassed me so that we broke apart. I remembered the other creature and immediately looked round for him, but he was gone, no sign beyond a black shadow pushing through the grinning circle which closed up behind him.

So I still don't know who that other person was. I have a few suspicions and a couple of clues. I never saw them stand up straight so I cannot judge the height and I never heard them speak so I cannot judge the voice, although that may be a clue in itself. I do know two things. Three things.

First, when I looked into the mask, and even allowing for the whole face being entirely unlit, the eyes looking back at me were a very dark brown, almost black. I don't know any of the guys I have considered who have eyes quite that colour.

Second, thinking back over the sequence of things, at the end I was lying in their lap and in spite of everything that had happened and was still happening, in spite of it all I could feel no bulge, no erection under my back. But I was cradled against a very soft chest.

Third, the two of them never spoke, as if words were not needed for a game which they had played together before. And Jeff only knew one other person at that party.

I don't know what to think.

LET'S PUT THIS TO BED

Katie Kelly

Former contributor to the *Erotic Review* and secret writer of rude stories, Katie Kelly is currently lurking in the rolling Pennines. When she isn't spending time thinking and writing about things she probably shouldn't be, she distracts herself by making nutritious family meals her children refuse to eat, gambolling through rain-sodden, cow-pat-strewn hills and persuading her friends to join her in her pledge to discover the perfect gin dry martini.

This is not a story of romantic love. This is the tale of my first (last? Better not be hasty) foray into bad love, a so bad it's good love, resplendent in its many guises. I intend to focus on the physical one you'll be relieved to hear. I'm writing this down for two reasons. The first is self-indulgent. I don't talk about those few months spent embroiled in you any more, so by writing this I get to relive those amazing moments without having to relive our messy demise. The second is simple. I want to, I need to forget you. Memories of you have, for too long, saturated my thoughts and as frequently my knickers. So I shall write this down, read it one last time and then burn it and kiss you goodbye, beautiful man.

Where to start? Should it be in your bed, where we ended up after two years of restrained, polite conversation? Pants were yanked down, t-shirts discarded and mouths hungrily explored. "We shouldn't have sex," I whispered in your ear. Forty-seven minutes later you were fucking me on all fours on the floor in front of the full-length wardrobe mirror. My knees were glowing for days afterwards. So too, unfortunately, was my nose, which took the brunt of your 3 am stubble. What I've glossed over though in my recollection of that night, is how rough we were. I scratched up your back; you repaid the favour by digging your fingers into my ass with impressive fervour. You bruised my mouth with your kisses, pulled me off the bed onto the floor and laid me on my front.

"I want your ass in the air."

I faltered for perhaps, hmmmm, a second and then, pulling myself to my knees, arched my back and gave you an unrestricted view of my soaking wet, pink pussy. Spreading my cheeks apart you sank your face right in and devoured every drenched bit. Then, for want of a more romantic phrase, you fucked me really hard: on my back with my feet on your shoulders, against the wall with my legs wrapped around your waist, and bent over the bed, clinging onto sex-sodden sheets as your cock hit that spot over and over. In the morning, by which I mean after perhaps an hour of sleep, we did it all over again, adding some shower action to our repertoire. Later, as I meandered in a dazed and confused

state towards the station, I felt for the first time an unfamiliar but indescribably sweet ache in my pussy.

Pain maintained a shadowy and persistent presence throughout our time together. I was self-obsessed, caught up in dramas; you had no choice but to take a second place too. You'd take your revenge later, when you had me naked in your room. Instinctively we knew how to hurt each other and not just verbally. Perversely though, the nastier we were, the better the sex was. It was only a matter of weeks before you were taking your frustrations at our failing relationship out on my ass.

A white-wine-induced tirade (mine) was halted abruptly when you pulled me over your lap, yanked down my knickers and spanked me until my shrieks of rage faded into a muffled apology. An apology, which quickly turned into a stifled sigh of wanting, as your fingers sank between the slick heat between my cheeks and worked my pussy into such a state of excitement, I was soon feverishly grabbing for the remnants of the bottle of Pinot Grigio stashed by the bed. But you got yours too, didn't you? We were always equal when it came to playing the bitch with a whip routine, and I had you over a pillow once, remember? I was playing with your ass, a finely gym-honed vision of suntanned pert firmness. I gently nipped your cheeks with my teeth, grinning as you wriggled. Then edging your thighs apart I ran my tongue deep in between from the base of your cock, to your ass hole which is where I lingered, gently flicking over this most sensitive place. With each measured stroke of my tongue, a shudder ran through your body and you'd squirm, only to be stilled by a stinging slap to your ass. Your ass was tongued and spanked until I reached underneath and felt you ready to explode. Murmuring "turn over", I slid happily onto your hard cock and rode you like an over-enthusiastic pony club virgin.

Though it was already blatantly clear now that this was going to be a love of the self-destructive variety, destined to end in therapy not marriage, I couldn't stop. Alarm bells should have triggered the first time you pushed me down onto my knees, by my hair, and told me to suck your cock. I stared up at you incredulously. "Suck my cock," you ordered again and then, using your fistful of curls, forced my head towards your groin. As I struggled to pull away, your other hand reached between my thighs. I was soaking and got more so as you spread me wide and spanked my pussy. Gently at first, then a little harder. I moaned and with one fluid movement, you took advantage of my distracted state and slid your cock deep into my mouth. There was no gentle love for us, no lazy early--morning spooning whilst you kissed my neck and stroked my hair, not when there was a sofa to be bent over, a table to be fucked on, handcuffs to be used, a ruler to be brandished, an argument to be had, a cutting comment to be made and retribution to be delivered.

The end came as violently as I always did. We'd been bouncing barbed emails back and forth all day. I was wearing a skirt you thought was inappropriate for the office. One that looks deceivingly respectable lying on the bed, but entirely not so when wrapped around a well-shaped female behind. A black pencil skirt that touched my knees, but was tight enough to transform my walk from a confident stride, into a languid saunter. You used to love this skirt. Happy you were not, and you got less so when I decided to join my team for a few drinks

after work. I knew I was taunting you but I didn't care. I went out to the bar next to the office and ignored your texts and phone calls. Particularly when they became increasingly frequent after ten. Midnight, and as I made my way towards your apartment, my defiance was steadily losing a battle to nerves. I had been an utter bitch and you were not known for your patience under such circumstances. Unfortunately I couldn't slip in unnoticed. The entrance to your building was through an underground car park and I had to call for you to buzz open the main doors. The phone rang and rang. You picked up only to hang up immediately, cutting off my hello. Looking up I saw the light from the lift flick on, signifying someone was on the way down. I leant uneasily against the bonnet of your car, and waited. The entrance doors opened and there you were, still wearing the suit you'd had on that morning, standing a few metres away from me and not smiling. I tried a hesitant grin. It elicited no response. If anything your jaw clenched shut an extra millimetre or so.

"OK, I'm sorry!" I exclaimed, "I'm sorry for ignoring your calls, I'm sorry for not . . ."

"Turn around," you interrupted, "put your hands on the bonnet of the car and please just shut the fuck up."

Now would have been the time to shake my head in offended disbelief and walk away. But having heard the story so far and witnessed my somewhat positive response to imminent chastisement, I'm sure you won't be surprised to hear that I didn't take that course of action. Instead I obeyed, turned around and placed my hands on the car.

"Now pull up your skirt."

Jeeeeeeeesus. I looked over my shoulder, were you joking?

"Pull it up, don't make me come over there." It would appear you weren't.

Flushing slightly and whispering an apology to my feminist sisters, I inched my skirt up. Not an easy task but with a bit of strategic wiggling it crept upwards, navigated my undeniably round ass until it rested, belt-like around my waist. My knickers were displayed to you in all their scanty glory, sheer and black, hugging my cheeks. Nervously I shifted from one foot to another. I heard the gentle hiss of a belt being pulled through trouser loops. Footsteps brought you closer to me. I could feel your stare, moving heatedly up my legs, resting on my ass. I wasn't expecting to feel, though, your hand rest on my hip. Your palm felt cool against my skin. Your fingers curled around the waistband of my knickers and slowly, slowly pulled them down to beneath my ass, then down to my knees. Your hand moved back up, cupped my left cheek and gently squeezed it, assessing the fullness. Did you mean for your finger to brush over my pussy as you did that? It sent a jolt through me, my hands slipped over the polished surface of the car and a small moan escaped, cutting through the silence. Moving away from me, I looked back and saw for the first time the belt in your hand, folded over. Having enjoyed many an Indiana Jones fantasy ever since watching Harrison brandish a whip in *Raiders of the Lost Ark*, the jolt of fear I felt as I saw that belt took me by surprise. Feeling the flood of wetness to my pussy, however, did not. Would you really do it? Surely not. My deliberation was rudely interrupted by the whistle of a belt in flight followed by a sharp crack as it connected beautifully across my ass. You barely gave me time to gasp before delivering the second stroke, which

landed perhaps a centimetre above the first. Tears prickled insistently. It hurt; you were hurting me and I still wasn't moving. Again I turned to look at you; your arm was raised, the belt loose in your hand and as it fell once again, hitting the very top of my thighs, that tender skin beneath the swell of my bottom, I bit my lip and you saw a tear slip out, slide down my face and splash onto the surface of the car. Angry, I twisted my head away so didn't see you move until you were against me biting my neck, whispering that I had to learn my lesson, that I was a bad girl. Your hands travelled to my ass, traced the hot marks the belt had left, then in between, enjoying the slippery warmth and the force with which I pushed back onto your fingers. Deftly, you opened your trousers. Your cock sprung out, thick and hard, and then you were blissfully deep inside me. You fucked me with all the anger you had, months of it hoarded and now tinged with regret. But it felt so good and though we both knew we were, in our own fucked-up way, saying goodbye, we savoured every last second, every last thrust, every last caught breath. Bruised you left me. I watched you walk away.

So that's how it ended. Ended? I'm wincing as I write that. I did love you my beautiful man and I wish I'd been nicer, but I'll take my "what-ifs" with me and let you go.

Now where are the matches?

Maybe I'll read through this just one last time.

THE BOYS

A. F. Harrold

A. F. Harrold was born in Sussex, but subsequently moved to somewhere less aesthetically pleasing. He is best known as a comic performance poet (*Postcards from the Hedgehog*, 2007) – 'original: weird and wonderful' Brian Patten; comedian – 'made me cry' Leonard Cohen; and straight poet (*Logic and the Heart*, 2004) – 'brave and compassionate' *PN Review*, even though he does any number of other things as well. Both the poetry books are published by Two Rivers Press. He has frequently contributed to the *Erotic Review*.

One of the nicest things about being a human being (I suspect it happens to all of us, now and again) is being able to give unsolicited advice about situations we have no expertise in to people who would be much better off sorting things out themselves. As a species we are nothing if not helpful. So it was last Christmas that a friend of mine was bemoaning her troubled love life – out loud in a purely rhetorical manner. She loves a man who lives the other side of the country and has had an off and on relationship with him for years, in the meantime she's living with another chap who she is very fond of, who has all the characteristics lacking in her true love – he's artistic and brilliant. Her first man doesn't know she's moved in with this second chap, even though they talk regularly and at length on the telephone. She can't decide who to be with, or how to untangle the situation without injuring someone . . . and so on and on.

The solution seemed fairly obvious to me – well, a solution at least, and probably not one likely to actually work, but which it seemed to be remiss not to at least mention out of the kindness of my heart, and so I sketched out the following plan for her – an unexpected little Christmas present, if you will.

When you find yourself at that point in life when there are two men who long for you and for whom you long, between whom you can't quite make up your mind, recognising in each of them certain essential qualities (kindness, creativity, madness, eagerness, loyalty, unexpectedness, enthusiasm, maturity, surprise, immaturity, indefatigable passion, fire, ruthlessness, power and searching, stretching, lusting hands, eyes and lips . . .) . . . qualities that between them, when added together, would make the contradictory, but remarkably and peculiarly perfect, homunculus you'd like to own. Added together they would never survive the unlike stresses of their combined personality, but what a moment it would be, what a thing to see.

You find yourself living with one of them, after the other, who came first, has

vanished from the scene. He left you opened and unlocked, unsure and uncertain of the direction you had been travelling before he'd arrived, unable to quite pick up the trail again, to head along happily, and so you fell in with the second one, the one who had lurked on the outside, who'd always still been around. He's the one who's loved you for years, he's the one who is the artist, who's the crazy, forever leaping up to paint another abstract, to jot another poem. He fucks expressively and unexpectedly, like his art.

But living with him you find you're thinking of the first one again; there is dissatisfaction in the home. And then he calls up. He's been an idiot, but you knew that, and you know you're an idiot to think of listening to him, after what he's done and what he did. But three hours pass by in one phone call and later you go back to your artist, climb into his bed, eat his food, sleep beside him and dream of places, people and solutions that don't exist.

One day you arrange these two unlikely men in one room. You bring them together to talk, to listen, to try to find an answer for yourself. Strange, because they know each other and hate each other. Their natures are contradictions, their world-views are diametric. But they're here for you, for the one thing they have in common: a certain beat of the heart.

You've cleared the furniture away, moved it out to the edges of this space, this room, and the three of you stand in the centre, the men side by side and you facing them. They don't look at each other, hands at their sides, feet a little apart, shoes scuffling. It's almost funny how carefully they don't look at each other, as if one glance would set fire to a fuse that would prove impossible to douse; as if there could only be one survivor, and neither one is sure it would be him.

And as if you hadn't had a plan when they arrived, something wakes in you now. A sudden realisation lifts its head, swings its gaze, licks its finger and slowly strokes it between your legs. Your heart-rate has risen, your mouth has opened a half inch of its own accord.

As you stand there, feet apart, one hand on your hip, the other waving airily and masterfully in the air, you tell your two golden boys to undress. That seems the simplest way to get this started.

They hesitate, of course. They look at you, begin to speak, but your raised finger is the finest weapon you have and it hushes them immediately. There's no arguing today, there's no brooking disagreement, there is nothing at work here but your will.

The one on your right, number one, begins to unbutton his shirt; number two shrugs off his jacket, reaches down to unlace his shoes. Ah, they're doing what you want, you think. The surge of joy that competes with the nervous realisation that there's no step back thumps in your mouth, dries you up just as it moistens you. You shift your legs, move your weight from foot to foot as slow, loose items of clothing are tossed aside. You squeeze your thighs together, revel in the sudden heat.

With embarrassment and with the still absolute refusal to look at one another, your two men pull off the last of their clothes, let them fall on top of their respective piles and stand naked in the warm room, facing you, side by side. You know they long to look at each other, you know they do. Neither is worried who

has been the best lover, who has performed better or more often in your bed – those are the concerns of teenagers, of the insecure, of the foolish. No, these two are mature enough to know there are very few things in life that are simple calculations of "better" and "worse", that sex, like all things, runs the gamut, a full spectrum of experience. They both know that you love them, for what and who they are.

But, at the same time (because nothing is simple), you know they long to compare themselves, to know, statistically, who is bigger, who is thicker, who is leaner, who is stronger, who is . . . who is . . . These things are quantitative and are easily charted, and although they'd prove nothing, it would be a set of data they could take away at the end of the day. And you know both boys secretly like statistics, however creative or blasé they claim to be.

While they don't look, you do. You note the difference in height. Number one is broader in the chest, but hairless. Number two, narrower, with a dark wispy cirrus that fades away as you head south, before beginning pointedly below his navel and rising like a storm cloud around his dangling, half-hard, dark cock. Number one keeps himself shaven smooth and his cock, thicker, rounder, is also harder.

You walk around them, between them. As you pass behind them you wonder what they do with their eyes. Those eyes (blue and brown) that have been locked on you. Do they meet? Do they stare ahead as if they were lined up for an inspection, waiting in a cold waiting room for the cup and the cough? You graze your eyes across their backs, across the lovely spinning globes of their buttocks, one pair plumper, one pair furrier than the other. You think of how often they've pistoned away between your thighs, sometimes engrossingly, sometimes dully, sometimes ineffectually and often noisily. You try to see your ankles locked in their lower backs, picture the differences, see your hands on their shoulders, gripping their ribs, pulling at their buttocks. Oh, how you long for one or either to leap you now, to pull you to the floor, to tip you, to tup you. But that's not the plan, neither one's to be left out.

Standing between them, an inch in advance of them you reach down to grip those meaty rods. Each hand fills with hot, hard-soft cock. The texture's a delight, that skin that shifts over the stiffening iron slug inside, the strange mechanics of the thing. A blood-filled sock, locked off by a biological tourniquet at one end. You wonder whether, if you were to cut into a fully erect, tempestuously hard, bubbling with vim, prick, whether the blood, maintained under such pressure, would reach the far wall; whether it could injure, hit the ceiling, take a small child's eye out.

You squeeze, rub your hands along, feel the rods grow hard, antithetical to a forge: as these get hotter they get harder; but later, when they reach their hottest, they too, will wilt, beaten.

They look at you, both of them turn to look at you, their eyes travelling from their own cocks, up your tanned arm, to your face, and you know that in their peripheral gaze, out of focus, is an image of the other. You know if you were to lean back, take one step back, their opposite's face would snap into focus, spring out at them, this image of the hated other, the unlikely and unliked rival. And you also know that would ruin what ambitions you have.

You let go of their cocks, leaving them to bounce and bob in the air (like pricks must bob in the International Space Station, you think unexpectedly) before them. And without looking you reach out for their own hands, and pull them down to their own cocks. As much as you'd love to lay their hands on one another, to see these two boys of yours act in concert, in combination, you don't do it. But you leave them to hold themselves and walk forwards, spinning on the ball of your foot a few yards away.

The picture you see when you face them is so hot that your heart skips more than one beat taking it in. These two naked lovers, these two loves, are stood, feet apart, hard cocks in hand, staring into your eyes. Embarrassment evaporates. Your cunt throbs, leaks, gapes for filling. It mouths longing into your ears, asking and asking for either one of those sweetmeats to eat: it's not that fussy, when it comes down to it. But this isn't the plan.

You move your feet apart and touch the crotch of your jeans. Push the seam into your cleft. You're surprised the juice hasn't soaked the denim. You squeeze yourself, rippling good feelings into your belly, into your spine. You tell the boys to wank and they slowly begin, each eyeing you closely as you push harder at your smooth, rich, dark delta.

You wish you had the attention to pay equally to each cock, to eye them both simultaneously, to watch each poking head, each blue-purple vein, each slow down of strokes, each pause, each new rapid jerking, the next pause, the long squeeze that begins at the balls, the little fingertip squeezes across the eaves of the head. Each little variation should be recorded, deserves to be noted and remembered, to be archived as being a unique moment. But it's all gone on the wind, half of it unwatched, half of it forgotten.

As they stroke their eyes change, from you, from watching your eyes focused on them, to watching their own cocks (always a marvel of sorts), to being closed and then gone, who knows where.

You forget yourself for now and kneel in front of the boys, a hand held out under each pounding cock and you wait. And wait.

In time the inevitable happens: a shut eye, a sigh, a whimper and a final, squeezing jerk fills each of your palms with the strange mucous that begins life and over which lives are lost. A small puddle of the clear-white albumen slops in your palm, strings on your wrists, on your sleeve, on the floor, but the majority pools just where you want it.

The boys are aching, are weak in the knees and you command them to kneel with you. They obey, slumping to the wooden boards, their deflated cocks looking sheepish, sticky and so very human between their thighs, balls hanging toward the floor, as if sweetly overcome by gravity.

You lift each palm in turn to your nose, breathe deep of the heady aroma, the glorious, gorgeous aroma of come, that salty loving scent, somewhere near Brie, somewhere near persimmon, somewhere far out to sea. All through your life the most unexpected things have reminded you of this smell, in the most unexpected of places. But now you have the original, pooled and soon cooled in your hands.

But now you hold your hands out to the boys, one each, but swapped over, so your arms cross at the elbow, and you tell them to lap, to lick like a cat, to sup on the seed, and to your excitement they each lean forward and dip the dab-end

of their tongues into the viscous mess – that surface tension hard to break, but the tart flavour quickly absorbed.

You lift your hands, push the palms into their mouths, smear their lips with come, with the sticky stuff. Watch them gag, spit, and lick it up. Each ashamed, but unable to not eat their lover's lover's come, neither one willing to wimp out, to be seen to be the lesser.

Soon it is impossible to know whether your palms are still sticky with come or with saliva and you wipe them, uncaringly, on the hips of your jeans as you lean forward, kiss one man after the other after the other. Savouring the smell, the taste even, the knowledge most importantly of what has happened here. These two loves, these two hates merged for a moment in three mouths – viscous, bloodless blood-brothers of a sort, for a moment, for a time.

Your face comes away sticky and wet and the heady aroma stays with you as you stand, turn and leave the room, unsure exactly what will happen next, what can happen next, but smiling like the cat that got the prize carp out of the pond onto the land, wondering if you'll ever manage to get it home intact. Wondering if this evening will ever come up in conversation, whether either boy will remember it in the morning, or whether it will just remain one dream among many that bring a much needed, knowing smile to your life but which, in the end, turns out to not be the simple solution you were seeking after all.

But for now, you just smile.

As far as I know she never took my advice.

SHANDEE FINDS DAVE'S ARM

Nicholson Baker

Nicholson Baker is the author of nine novels and four works of nonfiction, including *Double Fold,* which won a National Book Critics Circle Award, and *House of Holes*, a *New York Times* Notable Book of the Year. His work has appeared in *The New Yorker*, *Harper's*, and *The New York Review of Books*. He lives in Maine with his family.

Shandee's sister gave her all her makeup because she was going off to Guatemala. That night Shandee spent about two hours trying on lipstick. Then, the next morning, she went to a quarry with her Geology 101 class. The quarry was called the "Rock of Ages." It was vast and they dug granite there, mostly for tombstones. The tour guide was kind of cute although his hair wasn't good – he was maybe twenty-seven. Pretty drastically cute, though, she thought. They were standing on the brink of a space that looked like something from another planet, and he said, "There's enough granite here to last us four thousand five hundred years." My gracious goodness, thought Shandee, that's a lot of tombstones. She turned away from the edge, and that's when she saw a hand poking out from behind a rock.

While the others listened to the tour guide, she went over to the hand. The hand was attached to its forearm, and there was a clean torn cloth wrapped around the end that would have been attached to the rest of his arm. There was no blood on the cloth. Shandee picked it up and felt it. It was warm; the fingers moved a little. The hand pointed urgently at her bag, so she stuffed it inside and went back to the group and listened to the rest of the tour.

When she got home she pulled the forearm out and laid it on her bed. It was strong, with sensitive fingers and a blue vein traveling up along the muscle on the underside. She lifted it and whispered, "Arm, can you hear me?"

In answer the arm caressed her cheek with two fingers. It had a gentle touch.

Shandee said, "Are you comfortable? Do you need anything?" The arm made a handwriting gesture. Shandee found a pen and handed it over. The hand wrote, "Please unwrap the rag and feed me some mashed-up fish food in an electrolyte solution."

"Where?" Shandee asked.

"Funnel it into the little hole with the green rim," the arm wrote. And then: "I'm glad you found me."

She unwrapped the towel and saw that the arm was capped with a sort of power pack made of black rubber. There looked to be a place for a battery and a place for waste to be discharged, and a place for nutrients to enter.

She had an intuition. "Are you Italian?"

"Half Italian, half Welsh," the arm wrote. "I'm known as Dave's arm."

"Well, Dave's arm, I'm very pleased to meet you." They shook. Then she noticed the clock. "Oh dear. Can you sit tight here for an hour?" she said. "I promised someone I'd go to his party and I can't bear to hurt his feelings."

Dave's arm scribbled something rapidly. "Sure, but – let me put on the lipstick for you," he wrote.

"Okay, you can try." Shandee grasped the arm firmly and held him so that his hand was in front of her mouth. He touched all the way around her lips, feeling the exact shape, and then, with very fine almost vibrating movements, he applied the lipstick. It was extremely red, a color called Terranova.

"Good job," said Shandee. "You're good. And this color is great." Her lips looked really luscious. "Thank you, Dave's arm."

He made a little nod with his hand and then, lifting the pen, reminded her that he needed to have some of the fish-food mash and to be relieved of his chemical wastes. She took him to the toilet and popped open a little vent on his cap. A tiny trickle of gray water dripped out. Then she fed him some fish-food gruel, and he seemed quite revived. He asked her to place him on the windowsill, because he had a solar panel for energy. She did, and then she went to the party and danced and had a wonderful time, but she came home early because she felt she had a new friend that she had to take care of.

When she got back her roommate Rianne was there. Rianne's lips were very red – she'd been sampling the new lipsticks, probably – and she was holding on to Dave's arm. The hand end was in her shirt, obviously doing something tender with one of her breasts. Rianne hurriedly drew him out. There was a pad of paper with lots of hasty writing scrawled on it next to where she was lounging on her bed.

"So, you've discovered my arm," Shandee said, with an edge.

Rianne nodded. "He has a lovely touch."

"That he does," Shandee agreed.

Rianne said that she'd found out quite a bit about the arm and where it came from. "It belongs to someone named Dave," she said.

"I knew that," Shandee snapped.

"He went to a place called the House of Holes. There Dave had requested a larger thicker penis. Apparently you can do that. But at a price. The director, this woman named Lila, said to him: 'Would you be willing to give your right arm for a larger penis?' Dave said no at first, because his right arm was necessary for his work. But Lila said that it was only temporary – only till someone found the arm and took it back and stuck it on him. Dave said, 'Oh, if it's temporary, sure.' So he underwent a voluntary amputation right near the elbow, and his arm had the self-contained life-support pack grafted on."

"You sure did find out a lot," said Shandee.

"I must say his touch is extremely sensitive," Rianne went on. She threw herself back on the bed and laid the arm on her chest.

Shandee watched the hand push aside the sides of Rianne's shirt and find her breast again.

"Hmm," Shandee said. "I don't know about this. I found him, not you." She felt finger-snappings of jealousy.

Rianne's lips parted. "Oh my gosh, his fingers know what to do," she said, flushing. The hand was gently rolling her nipple like a tender round pea. And then it surrounded her whole breast and shook it once. After that it turned and began crawling over her belly toward her pajama pants.

"Are you just going to let that happen?" Shandee said, riveted.

"Um, yes," she said. "Could you dim the light?"

Shandee turned off the overhead light and watched the arm undo the knot of Rianne's pajama bottoms. It disappeared. Rianne went "Shooooo."

Shandee turned away. "He's found it," Rianne said, "and, boy, he's got the touch of a master." Then her voice changed and she said, "Oh my god, two fingers. Haw. Haw." Shandee glanced at her. Rianne's knees had fallen apart and her eyes were slitted closed. "He seems to want to make me come, oh god, oh shit." Then: "Ham, ham, oo, oo, oo, oo, oo, oo, ham, ham, HAW!"

She lay still and held up the arm. He made an O with his fingers, which glittered with her sex juices.

"You want me to go with you?" Rianne said. "Okay, I'll go. Bye, Shandee, I'm going!" With that, her face and body began to blur, and she swooshed into a long thin shape that went through the finger-O of Dave's hand.

She was gone. The hand lay on the bed. It began crawling toward Shandee. It reached her thigh.

Shandee handed it a pen and folded back the yellow pad to give it a fresh page. "Where did my roommate go off to?" she asked.

"The House of Holes," the arm wrote. "Would you like to come, too?"

"Maybe," said Shandee. "How?"

"If you let me touch you," he wrote.

"Touch where?" said Shandee.

"Where it aches."

"It aches in my head," she said. "Never enough sleep."

"Let me help," the arm scrawled.

She held it, and the hand surged through her hair, and when she steered it around to the back of her neck it massaged the stiffness away.

His fingers were mobile and trembly now. She gave him back the pen. "Isn't there another place that aches?" he wrote.

"Yes," she said, "there is."

He wrote: "TWAT?"

"Mhm," Shandee said. "But I really don't think I can let you do that until I know you better. You need to be more than an arm to me."

"Take me to class tomorrow," he wrote.

The next morning she fed him some fish paste and drained his waste and wrapped the cloth around his life-support addendum and put him in her bag. In the middle of her nineteenth-century novel class she felt his fingers very gently brushing her calf. She reached down and held his hand and loved how it felt.

When she got home that afternoon, she washed the hand carefully in the sink

and then took him back to her room and dimmed the lights and put on Appleseed's "When Are We Going (to Do It)." She said, "I'm ready for you to hold me now, any way you want."

His hand brushed over her lips – she was wearing Terranova again – and she opened her mouth and tasted his fingers, and he circled her tongue and tweaked it, and then as she steadied him he crawled down. She put her feet together and let her knees fall open. His hand found her stash and she looked down and saw his fingers half buried in her folds, and then she felt a warm filling feeling as first one, then two of Dave's fingers slid inside.

She held his arm and helped him angle his fingers in and then pull them out. Then she pulled him up to her clitty and he circled it. "Oh, that's nice," she said. Just before she came, he stopped and held his hand up to her mouth.

"What is it, baby?" she asked.

His fingers made the O and then he pushed the O shape to her mouth. She put her tongue through it, and her mind and neck and body stretched until they were very long and flowed through his fingers, and then his fingers flowed with her. She was pulled in a whoosh of wispiness, and she landed and condensed. Before her was a sign in the grass: "Welcome to the House of Holes."

She looked down at her hands. They were still holding Dave's arm.

THE PHENOMENOLOGY OF THE WHIP (PORN MIX)

Fulani

Fulani is the author of erotica, much of it with content of a fetish and bondage nature. His work is published by Xcite Books, Pink Flamingo, Renaissance Sizzler, 1001 Nights Press and Sweetmeats Press. His stories often seek to explore how fantasy and the subconscious link to our everyday lives.

Even when lying coiled on the chair, it looks alive. The braided leather, thick by the Turk's-head knot, gradually tapering, calls to mind the scales of a snake. The fall and cracker, the rattle of a rattlesnake, the sting of a scorpion. The leather glistens gently where it catches the light, a sheen that says it's used, but not worn with use, a working animal. Yet when he holds it, moves his hands over its length, it is also a pet. If it had memory, speech, it would chuckle dryly, crackling, over stories of bodies it had stung, flesh it had pressed itself into until the welts came.

When he cracks it, there is a moment of equipoise; a point at which it lies in the air, invisibly suspended, motionless, in repose. Then the tail licks out faster than the eye can follow, a blur of red/purple as the cracker accelerates across the room.

The physics of it is something you already know. The energy delivered to the handle, its cross-section the thickness of a thumb, is passed progressively to the other end of the whip, tapering at the cracker to no more than a few strands of cotton. As the energy is concentrated, the end of the whip accelerates. The cracker meets, exceeds, the speed of sound. Hence the crack.

Even so it sounds like a pistol shot, a promise of concentrated violence, searing pain.

You are, as normal, spread-eagled, standing, wrists pulled up and outward on the frame, ankles placed wide apart so that your heels are not quite on the floor, and your weight is taken on the balls of your feet. You are, as normal, naked. Vulnerable, open, accessible to caresses, to suffering, to agony.

A whip can caress. Did you know this? He flicks it out and the fall wraps twice around your outstretched forearm. It's gentle, sweet almost. The other whip, the one with the nylon fall, wraps, but the nylon slides off your skin. This whip, having a leather fall, grips more easily. The wrap isn't tight, the sensation is akin to the process of bondage – something circling a limb, cinching just enough to feel like a restraint, a slight pull back on the forearm, enough that you can feel

your balance challenged and need to stretch your legs just that little bit wider apart, exhale and pull on the muscles of your stomach that little bit more, to return to equilibrium.

The wraps move from right forearm to right upper arm, left forearm to left upper arm, right calf to right thigh, left calf to left thigh, a lazy pattern, dulling your senses yet making you focus on your own body and the massage-like repetition of a foot or so of leather being wound around it.

When he moves to wrap your waist it bites just a little more, the greater speed required making you aware of the knot that joins the fall and the cracker as it makes contact with left or right hip.

Around your breasts. This time the knot lands on the outside arc of your left or right breast and the breast itself is made to bounce gently. The skin is more sensitive here, erogenous; and the tautness of braided leather across your breasts – because such a wrap requires half the length of the whip – makes you catch your breath at each stroke. The repeated impacts are light, refined, almost affectionate, yet somehow dangerous. They contain the promise of something stronger.

When he cracks the whip again, to your right, you feel only the wind of its passing yet the sharp retort makes you gasp involuntarily. It reminds you that the whip is a technology for tearing and mutilating flesh. For encouragement. For training. For ensuring compliance. For punishment. For what offence, even whether guilty or innocent, will not matter to the whip. Perhaps even the punishment of the innocent is a purer, cleaner, application of its capabilities.

Are you innocent?

And, imagining yourself as he sees you – nude, exposed, and with just enough freedom of movement to twist and dance on the end of the whip – it occurs to you that it has one further purpose.

Entertainment.

The whip can tease. He stands back, allowing the entire seven-foot length of the instrument to extend, and flicks it out. The cracker is comprised of fine cotton, about twenty double strands, twisted tightly together and held with a knot. Beyond the knot, the very tip of the beast comprises forty or so short lengths of cotton, unbraided. You can feel, on your shoulders and arse, the subtle thwack of those cotton lengths, the last quarter-inch or so of the whip. It is sensation, not pain, because although the force is there the strands are very light. It feels a little like threading, where a single strand is used to abrade the very top layer of skin. The sensation is so odd it makes you laugh out loud.

There is only one place on your body that causes a different reaction. When the tip of the cracker finds the very centre of the shoulder blade, the scapula, there is a nerve, a pressure point, that is unexpectedly sensitive. With your arms outstretched and bearing half your weight, the sensation is magnified. It hurts, but it is not yet pain.

And you know that the whip, while licking at you, is being held back, controlled, like a wild animal on a leash. It's saying to itself: tender flesh, tempting flesh, clean unmarked flesh, let me write on you. Let me write a story in angry welts on this cool, blank flesh.

What it really wants to do is bite.

Is there a confusion here between the whip and its wielder? The wielder, the man standing behind you, out of your vision, who you know only as "he", is like an orchestral conductor. He moves his wrist. The whip, given motivation, extends its own interpretation to the movement. It can, like the bow of a violin, glide gently – or attack. It can switch from *andante* and *piano* to *staccato*, *forte*, *con forzo*.

But not yet. Nearly, but not yet. A stroke comes up between your legs, the fall lying precisely between the lips of your cunt, the tip nuzzling hard a few inches above your clitoris. This is new, unexpected. It is still gentle, yet has the promise now of sexual viciousness, exacting cruelty. Again, the knot of the cracker has sought out a pressure point, a chakra. There are nodes there that in shiatsu, in acupuncture, are held to relate to the kidney, the liver... and what in Chinese terminology is sweetly called the "conception vessel".

The blow makes you jump, makes your breath jump, reminds you of your helpless state. And it is undeniably sexual. The strike serves to remind you of your sex, in all its meanings.

Again. Again. The repetition, the emphasis on your sex, your passivity, is mesmerising.

Then the whip takes your arse in its jaws and tears at your flesh.

This is not pain. Not at first. It is so much more than the word "pain" encompasses. The sensation is sharp, clear, overwhelming, almost transcendental. To call this "pain" would be like calling a Leonardo da Vinci drawing, perhaps the *Study for the Head of Christ*, a quick working sketch.

It has several components.

First, the energy transmitted by the whip must go somewhere. It flings you forwards in your bonds. The shockwave travels up your body and you bounce against the cuffs holding wrists and ankles, every muscle jerking taut. You'd yell if you could, but a sudden spasm grips around your lungs, making noise impossible. And, truth be told, you feel that sudden spasm deep in your belly also.

Second, there are the thoughts in your head. The whip has an animus. It has, of course, its own identity, but it is being wielded by him. He hit me. He hit me hard. He hit me with malice. He enjoys my helplessness, my suffering, it amuses him. This level of violence and cruelty, directed and controlled, is a rare thing. It is outrageous – more so than if he'd slapped your face in a fit of temper, an argument.

Third is the fact, that all this energy was forced through a piece of skin perhaps a quarter of an inch wide and eighteen inches in length, across the buttocks. Four and a half square inches. An amount of flesh considerably smaller than the palm of your hand. The outer layer of skin, the epidermis, is only a couple of millimetres – let us say one-sixteenth of an inch – thick. The stroke must have bitten in, pushing deeper, perhaps half an inch. Now the line taken by the lash threads out, nerve endings squealing and cells reacting to the sudden shock. A tracery of poker-hot flame runs across your arse, as if a thin stream of molten lead had been streaked across it, marking the line of what will shortly become a raised abrasion and a band of bruised muscle. You can feel every single hard diamond-shaped mark from the braid of the leather.

And fourth. . . fourth is the realisation that this was the first stroke. How

many more will there be? How many do you think you can take? How much need will this stoke between your outstretched thighs?

There's no hurry. Anticipation is a hungry, tension-making pleasure. And there is a great deal more of this particular human canvas to paint the colour of weals and welts.

PARK ANTICS

Danielle Schloss

Danielle Schloss loves being with friends, baking cakes, and hiking in various places, including exotic tropical forests, volcanic islands and mountain pastures. A fan of cows, for their deep dark eyes and placidity, she avoids pastures with calves, as cows lose all placidity and charge trespassers, sometimes causing injury. She is currently working on an anthology of her short fiction, as well as her first novel about sex, intrigue and sudden death in the corporate world.

Jorge, a young Spanish jogger, paced himself to the song. "Lady P, Lady P, Lady P, Lady P . . ." he hummed in his mind, listening to McCartney's song on his iPod. He had learnt that it was in fact "*Let it be*" since his English had improved, but he rather preferred his own version with a mysterious Lady P, so still mouthed it as he had when he had first heard the song, some years ago. The park was dark and he enjoyed the solitary act every evening. It was a ritual of his, a cleansing of his soul after a hard day's trading in the financial markets. All things considered, he was happy to have a job in a cushy office with high pay in a country that was stable politically and had a low unemployment rate. His salary supported not only him, but also his parents back in Spain and his sister who was still studying. He had every reason to be pleased. He had for the first time met his new neighbour, a strikingly beautiful Russian girl, Ivanka, who had just moved into the flat opposite his own.

They had begun by nodding at each other across the balcony. Then they had bumped into each other in the lift. Ivanka had greeted him in heavily accented English, assuming that the *lingua franca* of the modern world would serve its purpose. They had progressed far enough to have a few Sunday brunches at the local tea room. He was of course hoping that it might evolve further, and his fantasies about her often helped him to sleep at night, by providing solitary release in the depths of his large but empty double bed. He had moved from Spain to follow a girlfriend, who had recompensed by dumping him one month into his new job. Perhaps, after all, it had been a good thing. The future looked hopeful.

As he ran he reviewed his day, then planned out the morrow. His deals had been successful for the past few weeks and as the year drew to a close he could expect a hefty bonus. He would give half to his parents, but he would keep half to spend on some luxury for himself. Perhaps a weekend in a five-star hotel in Gstaad with his neighbour. He would offer her champagne and caviar, and they would spend the weekend drinking and fucking. It seemed like a pretty good plan.

As he ran he noticed out of the corner of his eye a movement in the trees. The autumn was closing and the grey November skies augured several months of a grey lid over the city, till the snow fell and the wind swept through. For the moment, it was chilly, but still bearable. Wearing black clothes to be invisible in the dark as he ran round the park, he made no noise, a lone shadow in the dark. He circled round quietly and went to see what had caught his eye. He stopped short and only just prevented himself from exclaiming out loud.

Ivanka, wearing a thick fur coat, was tied to a tree. Her legs were splayed and her ankles were chained to the tree. A rope was wound twice around her neck and tied to the branches behind her. Her arms were pinned to her sides by a man, whose posterior Jorge could see with startling clarity: a sagging bottom, with a patch of ginger hair just above the bottom crack. The man was stark naked. Clearly rather heavy, he half turned and picked up a scarf from a pile of clothes at Ivanka's feet. He stuffed the scarf into her mouth with one hand, keeping her pinioned with the other. Then he slowly unbuttoned her fur coat, revealing a startlingly white naked body decked with only a string of diamonds at her neck.

Jorge wondered what to do. Normally he would have intervened, but the particular attire of Ivanka suggested that she had been prepared and that this was not a random attack. He decided to wait and watch.

Ivanka remained glacially immobile. Her fur coat kept her arms and back warm and prevented the tree bark from chafing her skin. Ivanka spat out the scarf and moved her head sideways. The man slapped her. She did not react. He picked up the scarf again and this time tied it over her mouth. As Ivanka's arms were free, she reached down to the man's sex and started pumping it. The man hissed, "slower, slower". She slowed down. Jorge changed position, feeling his own sex rising. He could see that the man was well hung: an enormous pink penis swollen and engorged profiled itself in the dark. Ivanka murmured, "I can't lick you, you have tied me up too tight. Let me go, let me go."

The man grunted and moved forward to Ivanka. He put his hand over her pubis, then slid two fat fingers into her sex. "Take this bitch!" She arched her back as he explored her innards, and then began to stroke her clitoris with more force. Her strokes on his penis became more rapid.

"No no, slow down. I want to fuck you first" and simultaneously he pulled his fingers out, swept her hands away and lunged forward and up, thrusting his penis into her. Jorge heard her intake of breath as the large member slid in.

"Feel me?" Ivanka didn't react. "Do you feel me bitch?" She stayed silent and immobile. He got more frenzied, stabbing at her ferociously, using the tree's strength to make his jabs more forceful. Jorge could see his buttocks clenching and unclenching and the swing of the ginger-haired testicles as he thrust and danced in front of his ice queen. "Tighten up you bitch. Your cunt is too loose. Grip me. Tighter."

Jorge didn't know whether to laugh or cry. Should he intervene or should he pass on by? Ivanka did not look as if she were suffering, nor did she look as if she were enjoying it. If he intervened the other man might get violent. He decided to wait and see. The man was accelerating his movements. Ivanka managed to free one of her arms and pushed him back violently. She twisted against the tree, baring her behind. The man assaulted her posterior, punching her stomach as he

dipped into her from behind. "Take this, and this. You are a bitch. You will kiss my feet afterwards. I'll fuck you. I'll fuck your mother and your grandmother."

The language was coarse and the man was getting more and more het up. Jorge could not see his face, but could see that the man was more and more excited by the fact that his scrotum was getting tighter and higher. Ivanka gave a violent counterthrust of her gracious hips and the man fell back, his glistening sex retreating from her cunt with a sucking sound. Jorge made a note to himself that she was wet, so perhaps she was enjoying it after all. The man threw himself at her, pulling on the rope that held her neck. "I'll kill you for that."

He yanked her head up and, as he did so, penetrated her with a groan. He slumped forward, convulsing as he came.

Jorge fingered his own sex. He was hard and throbbing. He had never seen anything like this. He pulled his penis out of his shorts and started stroking himself. His penis felt really sensitive, almost as if the violence Ivanka had experienced had been transferred into his own dick. He stroked himself softly, pressing on the thick central vein, cupping his balls with his other hand. The Beatles were singing *Strawberry Fields* in his earphones. He felt the orgasm coming just as the man pulled himself up and untied Ivanka, forcing her onto her knees, her fur coat draped around her. She swore at him. A stream of filthy words came out of her sexy mouth and, to Jorge's amazement, he could see the man's sex rising again. She flipped up the back of her coat, crouching on all fours. The man mounted her from behind. She moved into him and they lurched together drunkenly till they climaxed, this time together.

Jorge looked around, suddenly realizing that he was not alone in the observation. Several other men were dotted around the bushes, each one with a hand deep in their own trousers. Suddenly he felt ashamed, caught in a voyeuristic pose that others had shared, each taking solitary pleasure from a coitus that was not theirs. He padded off, feeling disgruntled and dirty. Ivanka could go to hell. He would have no further truck with her.

The next day he was coming in from work when Ivanka stepped into the lift with him. He blushed furiously and mumbled a greeting. She looked him straight in the eyes and said hello. She was wearing a scarf round her neck and there was no sign of her fur coat or any jewellery. "Would you like to come to my place for a drink now?" she asked.

"No, thanks, I'm . . . well no I can't really."

"Oh," she sounded disappointed. "Another day?"

"We'll see." He stumbled out of the lift in front of her, turning his back on her while he unlocked his door. He could feel her puzzling after him. Normally he was the one who suggested they met, had a drink, chatted. He had been fumbling and inadequate, but perhaps she would just put it down to a hard day's work. He hoped so.

A little while later, the doorbell rang. He went to open the door and found Ivanka dressed in her fur coat standing in front of the door.

"Care to join me?" she asked.

He blushed again. Perhaps she had seen him after all. He stammered "To do what?"

"I am going for a walk in the park. I know you jog at night, so perhaps you

can jog with me. I don't feel safe." She put on her most winning smile. His heart missed a beat. Perhaps she would do those things to him.

"Wait a second, I will just put on my jogging gear."

He dashed back into his room and quickly changed, joining her once again on the doorstep. They sauntered down to the park, chatting amiably about their respective days and how the weather was getting worse – banalities that enabled Jorge to overcome his unease. Once they got onto the path in the park, she urged him to jog ahead, saying that he could catch her up on his second run around. He slipped on his earphones and the Beatles' voices occupied his eardrums. He got his pace right and ran round the park. As he got to the tree, he saw Ivanka standing against the tree with her fur coat open. He slowed down and ran to the tree, stopping in front of her.

"Ivanka, what are you doing?" he asked.

"Let's have sex here," she replied.

"Here? Why?"

"For the fun of it." He stepped closer. He could see blue bruises where the other man had punched her.

"What happened?" he asked, as if he didn't know.

"Oh nothing special. Come, let's have some sex."

Jorge could not believe what he was hearing. It was such a turn-off. This woman who had caused him wet dreams, been the object of his idle fantasies, and who he had built into an ice goddess was some vulgar little tramp who needed to satisfy her own insatiable appetite.

"I . . . I don't think so," he stuttered, backing away.

"How do you think I earn my living you stupid boy?"

"No, I . . . I mean I never thought about it . . . I . . ." Jorge stumbled away, tears in his eyes. He heard her laughing behind him. He gathered up speed and turned the volume of his iPod up. He would have to change his jogging patterns now, to avoid the park entirely. Lady P was so much more elegant and infinitely more faithful, she would follow him wherever he went.

TOKYO

Ortensia Visconti

Ortensia Visconti was born into the world of Italian cinema, and has spent her life in the arts. She studied French and Comparative Literature at the Sorbonne and at the London School of Photojournalism. In 2000, Ortensia travelled to Algeria as a reporter for the *Washington Post*, where she covered the civil war that had plagued the country for nearly a decade. After Algeria, Ortensia travelled to Palestine where she began reporting as a journalist for Italian newspapers. Her career as a war reporter took her to Afghanistan in 2001, where she travelled with the Northern Alliance, documenting the fall of Kabul and the American military response to 9/11. Ortensia spent seven years reporting on Afghanistan, crossing into Pakistan's tribal areas and northern borders, writing not only on the constantly unfolding war, but also on the plight of Afghan women. Her first novel, *Stregonesco*, was published in Italy in 2004. 'Tokyo' is taken from her short story collection *L'Idée Fixe* (2013).

Ma, the pause between two notes.

The space between the lines of a haiku, the silence between one drop and the next, running down Eve's leg.

Ma, the empty space full of meaning.

Eve is sleeping. She floats on the large branch of a dead camphor laurel, her kimono loosened at the waist to reveal her adolescent breasts and falling open over her thigh, which dangles in the air, the drops running down it into the still surface of the ocean.

Ma.

The interval of each instant.

The Tsukiji fish market is drenched with a fine rain. The fog is clearing in the grey dawn, under the neon tubes that flood the auction with dazzling light. The bodies are lined up, like the aftermath of a massacre. Frozen white, the thick slabs of meat are gutted, labelled, marked, sold. The gills are punctured and the fins cut off. They lie in rows on the ground, in a trail that leads the way out of the vast, ugly market. Outside, the trail continues, but here the fish are thawed, grey, shiny-salted, mouths open in grimaces, fins sticking out as though they are still at swim in the sea. The men don't notice anything. They drive the loaded forklifts, darting between the polystyrene aisles, paying no attention to the obstacles. There is no more sea in the sea. Blood drips through the cracks in the wooden trestles, trickles down and fills the vats below to the brim. The present stretches out like a worn elastic band and the blood gurgles and bubbles.

Tentacles emerge, their stiffening suction cups like blossoms, reach out, grip the edges. *Tako*, *anago*, *ika* – octopus, sea eel and squid. The shells clack like jaws, mark the rhythm of the waves in their polystyrene containers. Scallops, limpets, oysters, clams.

Scales, still slimy, slide against shards of ice, gills breathe in air, dull eyes turn shiny again. *Hamachi*, *hirame*, *kanpachi*, *saba*, *tai*, *Suzuki* – amber fish, halibut, Japanese yellowtail tuna, mackerel, snapper and sea bass.

Swollen with poison, the *fugu*, the pufferfish, glide up to the dock, roll into port; for a few moments, before diving, they float like excrement.

Past and future converge on the present. Now. The moment has come. The earth is stone and sand, lava and ash, caked among the roots of semi-tropical vegetation. Below it there is a monster, as big as the island, who thrashes about. There is only one point in Japan that is inactive: it is the handle of the fan, the join of four tectonic plates. The rest is earthquakes, typhoons, tsunamis, cyclones, eruptions, tremors, fires, nuclear action.

Now the monster heaves its scaly back. The concentric circles from the drops that run down Eve's leg and into the sea, the silence between them, drive him crazy. *Ase*, *chi*, *zamen*? Sweat, blood or semen? His long, scaly head approaches, his nostrils dilate, his forked tongue quivers. He lifts the sleeping girl's body, and she lets him caress her as she gracefully raises a hand: her slender fingers clasp the two ribbons of tongue like creeping tendrils. The monster's eyeballs bulge, his claws shoot out from his reptilian body, sink into Eve's childish knees and spread them apart. *Nicha-nicha*, the slick secretion of his scales, sticks to Eve's skin; he slides over her. The kimono rips and shreds of silk drift to the flat surface of the sea.

Eve screams. "Please, I beg you, no!"

The sea begins to churn. *Pocha-pocha*. Tentacles surface. Eight huge arms, with two hundred and forty suction cups, attached to three hearts and a brain that lusts. *Muku-muku*. Up close, its eyes are opaque, inky globes. The camphor branch snaps, the dragon's head is caught in a knot and Eve is plunged into the sea. The suckers aspirate her, drawing her blood through her skin, while a tentacle explores her mouth. *Tsupa-tsupa*. Eve cannot cry out. The viscous arms spread her thighs open, bind her arms, pin her head back; her throat is swollen, she cannot breathe. Then the octopus's mouth finds her sex and begins to suck. He drains her fluids and goes on sucking. Tears blind her as a tentacle reaches her anus and finds its way inside her.

The dragon has cracked the handle of the fan and shrugged Japan off his back, leaving it floating in the ocean like a walnut. He is flushed and furious, and his fire melts the octopus's suction cups, while his claw tears through its head, splitting into two purple slabs.

Eve screams. "No more, enough." The sea spills over, submerges, engulfs. *Muka-muka*. Its surge sweeps away the Tsukiji market, now empty of fish. It washes away Tokyo the way a gust of wind scatters the petals of a flowering cherry tree.

Ma.

Tokyo burns, lit by a reddish light, covered by a cloud of chemical vapours. The men are dead and the alarms go on wailing.

BRINNG
"*Baku*."
BRINNG
"*Baku*, eat."

"Yes, hello?"
"Were you sleeping, Ichiro-san?"
"Who is this?"
"The concierge. I'm sorry to wake you."
"Has something happened?"
"Yes, something serious."

BRINNG

What the hell. Ichiro slides over the futon to reach his alarm and hits the off button.

"You said something serious?"

"I was sweeping the entryway between the cherry tree, which started blooming this morning. I overheard a conversation between these two guys – gangsters, I promise you. They were talking about breaking into 17F – by Friday."

"Oh . . ."

"Everything okay, Ichiro-san?"

Ichiro is sleepy, but even so he looks as though he's concentrating intensely. It's his expression – as if he were taking an exam or piloting an airliner. When all he's doing is getting up from the futon. He runs his hands through his short-cropped hair, trying to take in the information he's just been given. The shreds of a dream mingle confusingly with the concierge's story. *Watch out*. He pushes a button and the shutters all rise at the same time. The view of Tokyo, dazzling and dense with concrete, calls up another feeling from his dream, vague and alarming. He puts his slippers on and slides open the rice paper screen. The flat is cluttered. It wouldn't be such a mess, but it's too small to hold a television, stereo, computer, cello, chairs – and a large, lacquered, inlaid wooden chest that looks like a coffin. And then there's the Buddhist altar. Ichiro opens the cabinet doors and bows a greeting to his mother's photograph. He nods, satisfied; he'll see to the offerings later. He leaves his slippers outside the bathroom and slips on his *geta*. When he looks at his reflection in the mirror, he relaxes the frown on his forehead. *Gangsters, I promise you*. He has a habit of doing this before he brushes his teeth. *They were talking about breaking into 17F*. With the toothbrush whirring, he returns to the living room, stepping out of his *geta* and back into his slippers. He goes over to the wooden chest, which is lined up between the TV and the Playstation 3. He frowns again as he runs his hand over the lacquer, between the inlay and the precious seals. He shakes his head. By Friday! He heads back into the bathroom, taking off his slippers, slipping into the *geta*, and spits the toothpaste into the sink.

The train is overflowing with salarymen. As rigid as though undergoing group hypnosis, all of them in neckties, their expressions like those of *karoshi*, men dead from overwork. By a stroke of luck, an elderly man – who appeared to

have fallen asleep two stations ago – suddenly rises and gets off the train. Ichiro, incredulous, takes his seat. He gains a few inches of space. He leafs through the manga he always keeps in his inside jacket pocket, but something stops him. He stares straight ahead, concentrating like a child sitting on the toilet. *Ma*, he thinks, *is where the art begins*. *Ma* is the length of silence between two sounds. Music values the interval of each moment, at the expense of the overall structure. It is on *ma* that he must compose if he wants to make the next Sony campaign succeed. A loud brand like that should use the elegance of silence to sell even more. *Higengo komyunikeshon*.

Suddenly a cloud of pink tulle brushes against his ear. The edge of the gothic Lolita's tutu is level with his face. Ichiro peeks down: she's wearing pale blue lace-up shoes with a round toe. Her stockings stop just below plump knees that curve slightly inward. Her panties are visible, at least to him: a series of small flounces that remind him of cherry blossoms. Ichiro stretches his neck to see over the cloud of tulle and look at her face. The blonde curls that fall down over her chemise are caught up by a blue ribbon tied tightly in a bow. Below her bangs, her face is covered with rice powder, impassive, like a porcelain geisha. Her gaze is fixed, with the lifeless expression of a *shojo*.

When Ichiro sits back, his eyes below her dress again, his heart pops in his chest like an air rifle. Something is shaking the cherry blossoms, a frenetic movement among the gothic Lolita's ruffles. Ichiro sinks down in his seat, lowering his gaze a few more inches. Slender, almost feminine fingers grab the elastic edge of the girl's panties and move them aside, revealing her smooth, hairless mound. Ichiro is so confused that his vision fogs over; impulsively, he moves his hands, as though he were using his Playstation console. But the controls don't respond and the fabric of his suit stretches, tugging between his legs. He quickly places the comic book from his pocket over his crotch, but he can't stop himself from watching. He wonders if the girl waxes, or if she's really that young. The fingers slide into her sex like the tentacles of an octopus. *Tsuru-tsuru*. Ichiro straightens up in his seat: the gothic Lolita's face is doll-like in its innocence. Ichiro's eyes travel from the jerking wrist, up along the culprit's arm, and stop at the man's pelvis. He too has an erection, and he doesn't cover it with a book of manga, but drives it between the girl's buttocks.

At this, the gothic Lolita opens her school bag. She extracts a metal tool, inches from Ichiro's face. The man's fingers are still groping inside her when the *shojo*, with a skilful movement, places the tool on the molesting organ, curls her finger and squeezes. When Ichiro hears the *clack* it's too late to do anything. *What would I do?* The man's scream is shrill and womanish. The staples fired from that particular model of staple gun are almost half an inch long.

Ichiro leaps to his feet. Panic closes his throat; he can't breathe. He can feel the pain of the staple pass through the light fabric of his trousers and pierce his hardened sex. He leaves the train, cradling his genitals, protecting them for as long as it takes to get away. This is not his stop. But then he had no intention of going in to the office in any case. Not today. And definitely not now. *By Friday!* He forces himself to breathe deeply. There's not much time left to make his preparations. Tokyo Hands is where he must start.

The big department store is almost empty at this hour of the morning. Ichiro follows the signs up to the third floor. They have almost anything you might want there. The shelves go on and on, offering all that the human imagination has managed to come up with, from the Stone Age on. The music pounds out the same deafening notes over and over again, in contrast to the childish voice of the female singer: *Everyone says, girls are so pretty when they're in love. Is it true? How I want it to be. Even the shy one, even the ugly one, when she's in love her eyes shine like stars. Mamemimumeno, mamemimumeno!* Ichiro's hearing is very sensitive and this music bothers him. He tries to tune it out, tightening his jaw, making his ears buzz. But his phone is vibrating now. He counts four rings and answers. His colleague's voice is so frantic that he holds the phone away from his ear.

"Where are you? Did you forget our morning meeting with the boss? It's not like you, Ichiro. An empty desk, at 11 a.m."

"I had an idea, for the Sony campaign. I'll write it up and send it to you."

"Send it to me? You have to come in to the office now, Ichiro."

"Can I help you, sir?"

Ichiro ends the call and turns to the clerk. "I need some . . . knives, please."

He follows the young man through the department, his eyes glued to the roll of fat that hangs over the clerk's waistband, along with the top of his pants. *American food every day*, Ichiro thinks. He used to have a roll like that. But it wasn't the Big Macs. After his mother died, Ichiro lost all the fat that once blanketed his body. When did she die? He can't seem to make time into something tangible. It's a sequence of images. Sometimes long, sometimes short.

The young man is pointing to a wall of steel blades. Twelve horizontal rows by nine vertical ones. One hundred and eight knives, arranged by their five different sizes. Ichiro runs a finger over the blade of the one the clerk hands him, and shudders. It would slice through a two-hundred-foot-plus tentacle of a cephalopod as though it were a piece of sushi.

". . . Unless you're interested in ceramic knives?"

"No, steel is fine. I'll take five – the biggest ones."

The young man nods and takes down the knives, leaving a gap on the wall. The pause between two notes. The empty space full of feeling.

"Anything else, sir?"

"Yes – security systems."

The clerk sniggers, snorting and making a barking sound like a seal. "A *bakemono* attack?"

Ichiro scratches his head. He doesn't know how, but it seems this guy has guessed the truth. He imagines the burglars, like colossal lizards and squid fed by nerve gas and atomic nuclei, surprised by the concierge. Sea monsters determined to break into his flat and steal the only thing of value there besides the cello. He says, "It's a premeditated crime."

"Oh . . ." The clerk pulls his trousers up over the roll of fat and underpants. "Come with me." And he darts between the shelves. Ichiro has to quicken his pace to keep up with him, and to hear what he's saying. "You want a system that prevents false alarms – even if the cat is in the house. Simple to install, effective, not too expensive, easy to maintain and above all easy to use."

Ichiro nods in agreement. To tell the truth, he has no idea what he wants.

"You want a practical system, wireless. A set-up that will signal the approach from well outside the area. To give you time to prepare yourself." The clerk waves at the shopping cart with the knives and winks, conspiratorially. "You have to use your wits if you want to win the battle. You have to be creative with these devices . . ."

At last he comes to a halt. They are in the security systems department. Outdoor surveillance cameras, hallway monitors, sensors, antitheft smoke bombs and fog dischargers, directional microphones, fibre optics, access control . . .

". . . you have to focus on the deterrent level of the system, create simulated presence, obstacles and other automated functions that are designed to scare the intruder away."

"Is there something that connects to the police via satellite?"

The clerk snorts like a seal again. Through the choking sounds, he keeps talking. "The police, sure, but when will they turn up? And what will they do when they get there?"

When Ichiro goes down to the first floor, his cart is full of stuff. He moves his lips almost imperceptibly, totting up the bill. But then he stops in front of the wig counter. The wigs come in all different colours and lengths. He reaches out and, casually, picks up a red one, with long, waist-length curls. A few feet before the checkout counter he grabs a pair of fluorescent pink fishnet stockings, and eye shadow of the same colour. The last thing he picks up are false eyelashes, purple as irises.

Eve is the main character. The rising star. All it takes is a wave, the press of a button and her reputation begins to grow; she gathers consensus. Everything is set. There is no margin for error. In a few months, Eve will be every man's fantasy, every woman's ideal; she'll be in the girls' latest styles and between the sheets of every teenage boy.

She has a strange, dangerous air – it's her role. Even when her personalities multiply as a function of the number of her spokespeople. Her round face, sickly pale, narrows below prominent cheekbones towards her little, heart-shaped mouth. But it expresses neither sadness, anger nor joy. It's a transparent face, a mirror that reflects the emotions of those who gaze at her. Like Buddha, Eve is love, death, beauty, all at the same time. She must help those who play with her, those who treat her like an object, and help discover what lies in their souls. A *ningyo*, bound to cause catastrophes before saving Japan from destruction.

The video game in which Eve is the main character will be released at Christmas. At least, for those who are concerned with her virtual being. What is already alive, however, is crafted from choice morsels. Her limbs are articulated around spherical balls, her ligaments are made of rubber; the vagina is made of Liquid Silicone Rubber, interchangeable and washable. Her pale colour comes from powdered shells; her teeth are ceramic, her eyes are plucked from a stuffed cat. The product of more than twelve months of work from Nobuyuki Kodama's team at Orient Industry, Eve embodies perfection – a flesh and bone manga heroine.

"She's a promotional creature," Fuco Shima mutters, as he tucks his shirt into

his trousers, tosses his passport and wallet onto the tatami mat. "They gave her to me hoping I'd fall in love, because they wanted me to write about her. She's worth five million yen."

Fuco Shima suffers from Paris syndrome. Ichiro himself has never had the travel bug. Travel is dangerous. The unpredictable reigns. When his commands from the virtual world in which he's used to living have no effect beyond the walls of his house, he has panic attacks; "outside of Japan" is something he has never even considered. There was a time, though, when Fuco Shima had a thirst for adventure. Though he too belongs to the culture of *otaku*, and grew up around manga and avatars, though he writes articles on video games, up until two years ago he was drawn to the real. More precisely, he was drawn to Paris.

What does Paris represent for a Japanese man? It's the question that underlies all Fuco Shima's troubles, which are many. He displays an impressive number of psychiatric symptoms: feelings of sharp disappointment, hallucinations, a persecution complex, depersonalisation disorder, anguish and the loss of a sense of reality (ironically, a warning of the danger of being around him, Ichiro thinks). And then there are the psychosomatic illnesses: tachycardia, excessive sweating, vertigo . . . Ever since he came home, two years ago, Fuco Shima has been a shadow of a soul.

What happened to him in Paris? Another pertinent question. But all that Ichiro can get out of his neighbour at 17G are confused answers, which clearly make their rare conversations a source of palpable agony. Fuco Shima flushes and begins to tremble. Especially when he speaks of a certain French taxi driver, who, if you can believe it, told him to "*bouge ta merde*" before crushing his computer bag under a Pirelli tyre. As far as Ichiro can make out, Fuco Shima had felt like the victim of some prejudice – against the Japanese? Against Asians? Or for some other, more personal, reason? But it wasn't only that. The real insult, which manifests even now in trembling and in childish behaviour, appears to have been the general French attitude of aggression and hostility. Paranoia, for sure. And it's the same with this story of the boulevards around the Bastille being blocked by tractors full of angry peasants. According to Fuco Shima, when he tried to decipher the words on the side of one of these vehicles, they had bombarded him with lumps of manure. He read, *This tractor belongs to my bank.* Too late: for the next hour he stank of manure and the men mocked him. But Ichiro is suspicious of these stories, twisted as they are by Fuco Shima's illness. Paris, as everyone knows, is one of the most refined cities in the world.

After two years of nightmares and hallucinations, Fuco Shima's psychoanalyst decided to combat Fuco Shima's misery with something even worse. He reminded him that his case was not an isolated one, and that he had no excuse: twenty victims a year, out of the six million Japanese who go to Paris. Fuco Shima's last hope, given the gravity of his case, will be to relive his trauma. He must arrange a trip to Paris, as quickly as possible, no time to waste, without any planning whatsoever.

He didn't take it well. The first few days, he couldn't write a word, let alone write the article for the video game magazine he worked for. Even playing seemed impossible. He stayed in his apartment, in the dark, barely moving.

And then one morning, a few days later, he rang Ichiro's doorbell. He was shaking like an electric muscle stimulator, pale but determined. He said, "I'm ready to go back."

And then he entrusted Eve to Ichiro.

Ichiro sits cross-legged on the tatami in his living room, surrounded by remote controls and pieces of alarm clocks, microphones and smoke alarms. Open instruction booklets are scattered around him like petals and, in a deep voice, he is imitating the fat guy from the store: "What you need is an easy-to-install, easy-to-use wireless system!" The screwdriver slips along the head of a bolt and embeds itself under the nail of his index finger. Ichiro leaps to his feet, squeezing his hurt finger in his fist. Holding in a cry, he hurries to the bathroom, without doing up his *geta*, and runs cold water over his finger. Once the pain dies down, he comes back in and stares at the red lacquered box. *She costs five million yen.* Is it her they want, those thugs? What else could be in there that they'd be interested in? *A cello.* Who would risk prison to steal some shabby instrument from some failure of a musician, a failure because . . . *Because he's addicted to videogames.* No one. In his tower block there are hundreds of flats, and they spoke specifically of flat 17F. "Look after it," Fuco Shima had said, "it's safer here – I trust you more than I trust myself." *It is Eve they want.* Ichiro picked up the screwdriver and walked towards the box. The idea of opening the box hadn't crossed his mind, when his friend was confiding in him. *Or had it?* A doll worth five million yen, designed to make Japan dream, sitting in his living room for a whole week. And Ichiro? He'd been playing. Every since your mother died, you haven't played a note, let alone auditioned for an orchestra. Him, he does nothing but play. Impulsively, he slots the screwdriver between the steel edges of the seal, and lifts it. The wire jumps like a tightly wound string. The cover of the box opens with a sound like teeth grinding together. Eve is attached to the box like a Barbie doll. *Almost.* The cord holds her just below her breasts, constricting them, pushing them up around the sugar flowers of her nipples. A finely wound *shibari* ties her up as though she were a roast, cutting into the octopus tattooed on her chest and pinning her wrists behind, then reappearing at the cleft of her buttocks and wrapping around one thigh, pulling it up. Her dark-angel's face looks detached from the rest of her body, in spite of the strip of bamboo that she is obliged to hold between her teeth, and which is secured behind her head. She is luminous, even with one leg forced up to expose her sex, hairless and pink, spread for Ichiro, the *kuritorisu* twisted a little to one side above a perfectly rendered *kitsukitsu*. And Ichiro, in the grip of a violent erection, suddenly feels her fear, the arousal, the error; she offers herself to him and she is ashamed.

Ichiro grabs one of the knives he bought from Tokyo Hands and, with a few careful cuts, slices her free of her harness. Then he lowers her leg, to conceal her sex, resisting the temptation to touch her warm skin. When that's done, he goes in search of his mother's red kimono. Once she's finally covered, he feels better. The kimono's pattern is of pink herons taking flight from the smooth surface of the sea; it is the most precious thing his mother left to him.

Her absence.

Ma.

Eve seems conscious. Her cheeks turn pale as shells. The anger in her eyes fades.

Ichiro stretches out on the ground and begins to masturbate slowly. He tries to peek under the kimono at the cleft between Eve's legs, but it is hidden within the folds of silk and he cannot catch sight of it.

He wakes with a start. Something metal has struck the outside wall of his flat. Ichiro hears the elevator door closing. He jumps to his feet, buckling his belt, and grabs the knife. His heart beats wildly, his breath reeks. He presses his eye to the spyhole and waits. Behind him, on the other side of the window, the sun sits just above a chimney like a scoop of orange ice cream in a cone. It will soon go down behind the snows of Mount Fuji. The city is still and silent, at this height. But then the screen of his mobile phone blinks, and rings without stopping. Nine missed calls.

At last something enters his field of vision. It's an aluminium shopping trolley, filled with carrots and celery roots. Pushed by the old woman at 17 B.

Ichiro presses his forehead against the door, tries to slow his breath. When his pulse returns to normal, he unlocks the door and steps into the hall. No one, just the bent back of the old woman, who hobbles slowly towards her apartment.

"Ma'am?"

She turns, sees the knife, takes a step back.

"Ma'am, tell me, please, is today Wednesday or Thursday?"

The old lady scuttles quick as a rat into her apartment. Ichiro goes back to his tatami, glances at his mobile. The work day is over; they'll leave him alone for the night. He'll have just enough time to install the security camera and the smoke detector outside his door, in case he falls asleep. He picks up the alarm fixture and the screwdriver that gave him a black nail, and the installation guide. Now and then he looks up at the silhouette of Eve in the red kimono. She emits light, warmth: something that might disappear along with her. He says, "No one will take you away, Eve!" His words resonate in the silent flat and the sky grows dark above the city as the neon lights blink on.

By 19.35, Ichiro has woken a dozen times, going to the spyhole with the knife in his hand, expecting the thugs to be there, his heart banging in his chest. He has seen so many new faces going in and out of the seventeenth-floor apartments, heads he doesn't know though he's lived here for ten years. His neighbours. Strangers who, for an instant, become assailants, sending his heartbeat into a frenzy. He hopes the coming and going will slow down soon; it's nearly dinner-time. He leans the knife up against the door and goes to the toilet. He keeps his *geta* done up. He has done none of the things that usually mark the rhythm of his days. He hasn't even played on his Playstation. Now he pisses without lifting the seat. "I'm going mad, Eve," he says. And at that moment someone buzzes his door. His bladder freezes. He tries to swallow but his saliva too has dried up. As he zips up his trousers, he sees his hands are trembling. He catches a glimpse in the mirror of some survivor from the Kobe earthquake. He doesn't recognise

himself, but it doesn't matter. He picks up the knife and, holding his breath, moves to the spyhole. Instinctively, he jumps back. The face is deformed by the curve of the glass, and very close.

"Hey, Ichiro, I know you're in there."

It's Ryuko Mori's voice. His colleague is not going to admit defeat. She even looks like a man.

"I've called you at least ten times. You're not the kind of guy who misses two important meetings. Open up, come on. Everyone at the office is saying you're turning into a *hikikomori*." Ichiro stands still, a metre from the door, breathing slowly. *Hikikomori*. He hadn't thought of that. It's true he has no desire to leave his flat, but then he has a good reason to stay. It wasn't as though he'd had a breakdown or anything like that. That doll, right there, cost 5 million yen, and she's been entrusted to him. If she were stolen, he'd be responsible. He looks over at Eve, sees that she is emitting a light just like the moon, which is rising in the sky, its own light dimmed in the lights of Tokyo. Ryuko Mori is still chattering behind the door, but Ichiro no longer hears her voice. He walks towards Eve, raising one hand towards this source of energy, and sees that the kimono has fallen open over her chest. Below, her Mount of Venus is smooth and bare. Once again Ichiro is disturbed, and feels the need to cover her up. An absurd idea comes to him: Ryuko Mori's knickers! He smiles and nods his head. She doesn't come near Eve's perfection. His mother had, but unfortunately she'd never worn knickers.

Women's underclothes had tormented Ichiro from a very young age. His grandmother hadn't worn any either, and she wasn't even a geisha. She'd worn a *koshimaki* or a *naga-juban*, like the "real Japanese". Wearing knickers meant you were imitating the Americans. She used to say, "You, Ichiro, *you* know what those Americans are like!" And it had sounded like a threat. As though Ichiro had had something to do with women's matters. As though he could somehow bring his grandfather, blown to bits by the atomic bomb, back to life.

And so he grew up among women with no knickers. And, the only man in the house, he bore all the responsibility for Little Boy and for Fat Man, as though he were every man in the world.

Ever since he was a teenager, it's been the little cotton panties, especially the white ones, the ones for children, that have driven him crazy. They are pure rebellion. Not to mention manga, where you learn what a pussy is through the pleats of panties that are rolled up, stretched, torn, pulled askew. Even so, and even though in Tokyo it is pretty common, Ichiro had never tried to procure a little girl's little white panties. It was a line he'd never dreamed of crossing – until now. It would be like . . . opening Eve's box and playing with her. Ichiro pushes the Playstation 3 away with his foot, to make some space. He asks himself, as he does, how he could ever have spent so much time glued to *Final Fantasy*. Now, just the idea of turning it on gives him a sick feeling, like the smell of food after having indigestion.

The sound of the elevator interrupts his thoughts. "Is it them, Eve?" Ichiro slides the knife into his trouser pocket, opens the door and peers outside. The concierge is coming down the hall towards him with a questioning look. Ichiro nods his head.

"Still nothing, ma'am. But I'm waiting!"

"Is there someone in there with you?"

"Yes . . . or, nobody, I mean. Look, I'm just putting these up." Ichiro lifts the security camera above the doorway. "Could you help me? When I'm up on the chair, pass this to me."

"*Banzai*! You're talking about a knife, Ichiro *san*!"

"I can't hear you. Now, hold the drill."

"Like this?"

"Very good, hand it to me. There – from now on, everyone who walks by will appear on my computer screen, and an alarm will sound."

"Well, you won't sleep at night!"

"It's just until tomorrow, ma'am."

"Don't do anything stupid, Ichiro *san*."

An hour later, Ichiro's computer screen glows in the dark flat. At the top right, the image of the hallway. In the middle of the screen, the online catalogue for Suera, the original *burusera* shop, which does 24-hour home delivery. "So long as they don't send an actual child, Eve. I don't think I could . . . today, in the metro, there was an awful thing. A monster with fingers almost like tentacles, who threatened a— Fuck, they're sick, these guys, listen to this:

Knickers stained with excrement: 5,000 Y

Very filthy G-string: 6,000 Y

Tights worn for one month: 7,000 Y

And this can't be for real, listen:

Tampon worn during a period: 3,000 Y

Knickers worn during a period: 10,000 Y

Expensive, I'm telling you. And then there are the refrigerated items:

Urine: 5,000 Y

Saliva: 5,000 Y

They're sick, people who buy actual shit. I just want a pair of panties to cover you. Eve?" Ichiro looks at her. "You're so pretty, you don't need anything." Then he smacks his forehead with his hand. "I forgot!" He turns on the lights and, a few seconds later, he comes towards her with the red wig. He covers the pale skin of her head, sticks on the purple eyelashes, pulls the fluorescent pink fishnets up her legs.

"Me, I prefer a fiction, Eve. The distortion of the real. You see, to play like this, without anyone . . ." As he moves her, a little golden book falls to the floor. Ichiro flips through it. He looks troubled. After a few minutes, he drags the cello case in front of Eve, and opens it. Placing the book at his feet, he begins with a few chords. Then he plays. *Play for mama*. He shakes his head and keeps playing. The melody is dramatic, a siren song. Tokyo is flooded, burned. The neon explodes. A black, chemical smoke envelops the tops of the skyscrapers. His fingers press the strings, the bow sets them quivering and Ichiro breathes in the destruction that Eve has brought with her. One single wave, one single orgasm and Tokyo is submerged. All the men are dead and the alarms go on wailing.

Ichiro smells danger. From his nostrils, it insinuates itself into his skull, into

the ankylosed mechanism of desire. He wants to bite her full breasts, still flushed from her bindings, tear off the fishnet stockings that mark her flesh. Suck at her pussy. She is real, Eve, and she drives him mad. His penis is pressed up against the back of the cello and it makes the body of the cello resonate every time he moves. His tie is undone, his shirt is unbuttoned over his smooth chest and his sleeves are pushed up, leaving his forearms bare, their swollen veins, tendons and tensed muscles.

How long does he play? It's hard to measure time objectively. It is a succession of notes. At last he rests his bow and stands. He collects up the little gilded book and flips through it frenetically.

The user's guide to Eve.

Eve's fingernails are made of the real fingernails of schoolgirls.

"No, not this." He turns the pages as though they are burning.

To undo the knots of Eve's shibari, which is inspired by the grand master of bondage of the twentieth century, Denki Akechi, pay close attention to the following illustrations . . .

"Shit, where is it?" Ichiro tries to be calm. At last he finds the page:

The Liquid Silicone Rubber elements are the product of a reaction between two different gelatinous components. The process of reticulation, comparable to vulcanisation, can be accelerated or slowed depending on the temperature. Eve's organ is perfectly adaptable for all sizes and can withstand temperatures of -60 degrees to +280 degrees.

Ichiro does not dare. But his member, swollen like a pufferfish, throbs. So much so that he lets the book drop to the floor before he finishes reading down to the bottom of the page: *WARNING: Read these instructions carefully.* "Excuse me, my sweet," he says. Remembering the drawings in the user's guide, he introduces one finger into Eve's sex, the fleshy part of his finger turned up. And he feels it – the G spot, the ejection button. When he finds himself with the whole organ in his hand, he trembles with impatience. "I only need a few millimetres," he tells himself.

In the kitchen, he puts the vagina in the microwave. He sets it for 30 seconds. And then he hears a long beep from the next room. He runs to the living room, convinced that there are thieves. But he trips over a slipper and lands on his arse on the tatami. There's a stab of pain, and, paralysed for a moment, he looks outside. Daybreak, an artificial blue, transforms Tokyo. Between night and day. He rises, rubbing his tailbone. The screen flickers on his mobile: *If you don't make it into work today, he'll sack you. Ryuko.* "Fuck, Ryuko," Ichiro whispers, between his teeth. He goes back into the kitchen and switches off the microwave. And then the burglar alarm begins to ring.

There are three of them. A commando unit.

They fill the computer screen. They're coming down the hall, kitted out in chemical protective gear, brandishing funnels that look like hoovers. Ichiro is seized with panic. He grabs the knife, laughs, but it sounds more like a moan. He lets the knife fall to the floor. "It's sarin, Eve." He turns towards every corner of his flat, but there's nothing that can protect him. They are only a few metres away when he hears the explosion. The smell of burning rubber fills the flat and

Ichiro covers his mouth with his hand. His serious eyes fill with tears. He knows that that sound was Eve's vagina exploding, but he says nothing. It's all over. The men are at the door. Ichiro seizes the cello and throws open the door, howling like a samurai. The men step aside, and Ichiro trips over one of the funnels and glides into the air, his cello under him like a flying carpet. When they hit the ground together the body of the cello cracks like a nut, and splits open. Ichiro rolls over, encased in the instrument. He wants to see them, but the men's faces are covered by masks.

He says, "Do whatever you want, she's burned. Can't you smell it?"

The three men look at him.

"What are you talking about?"

One of them offers him a gloved hand. "Stand up, sir – are you all right?"

"Perhaps you weren't notified."

"It's weird, the concierge was just there . . ."

"Mr Uku, we're here for the annual disinfection."

But Ichiro can't hear them, his ears are ringing. And it's almost as though they ring with the song of a *ningyo*, a doll, a malevolent mermaid . . .

Glossary

ma – "between", the time between two events, a space between two things, the relation between two people or two moments within the same story
pocha-pocha – a lapping, a swishswashing
muku-muku – a man's excited grunt
tsupa-tsupa – a sucking, a slurping, the sound made between two mouths
baku – an eater of dreams, an imaginary being rather like a tapir. On waking from a nightmare, you must say, "Baku, eat my dream"
Higengo komyunikeshon – non-verbal communication
geta – thong sandals
shojo – a delicate girl-woman
tsuru-tsuru – the sounds a finger makes as it moves in and out of a wet vagina
bakemono – monsters in human form, such as vampires, werewolves and the like
ningyo – a doll, but when pronounced slightly differently, a siren, a malevolent sea creature
shibari – the art of erotic binding
kuritorisu - clitoris
kitsukitsu – a tight vagina
hikikomori – a voluntary recluse. Someone who shuts himself away, refusing any social contact; a symbol of the failure of a society
koshimaki – a skirt with a sash
naga-juban – a kimono you wear like a slip, below your clothes
banzai – an exclamation meaning "long life"
burusera – play on the words "bloomer seller", seller of undergarments, and also of "bloomer sailor", the name for schoolgirls' knickers

Translated from Italian by Anne Milano Appel and Norah Perkins.

From THE SAINT

Tiffany Reisz

Tiffany Reisz is the author of the internationally-bestselling and award-winning *Original Sinners* series for Mira Books (Harlequin/Mills & Boon). Tiffany's books inhabit a sexy shadowy world where romance, erotica and literature meet and do immoral and possibly illegal things to each other. She describes her genre as 'literary friction', a term she stole from her main character, who gets in trouble almost as often as the author herself. Reisz is a Romance Writers of America (RITA) Award winner, as well as a Book Reviews Award nominee. She lives in Oregon.

Søren lingered at her mouth, he kissed her and she returned the kiss with equal and even greater fervency. Their tongues mingled and she drank of the wine on his lips, swallowed the heat of his mouth. Eleanor winced as Søren nipped her bottom lip.

Søren dusted kisses across the sensitive skin of her chest. Under his mouth her heart pounded, her blood throbbed. She ached to touch him but every time she tried to move her hands the bonds held her. Kingsley had warned her about the bondage. Søren needed to stay in control as much as possible. The more helpless she was, the more he would feel compelled to protect her.

She inhaled as Søren licked the tip of her right nipple. He brought his mouth down on her breast and sucked gently as he teased her left nipple with his fingers. Tied down as she was, she couldn't do much but arch her back to offer more of her breasts to him. He moved his mouth to her left nipple. Heat gathered in her breasts and melted through her stomach, settling into her hips. She wanted him inside her. No, not wanted, needed.

"Please, sir . . ." she begged.

"Please what?" He raised his head and cocked his eyebrow at her as if amused she would even dare beg for anything.

"I want you."

"You have me."

"I want you inside me."

"I'm always inside you, Little One."

Eleanor entertained a brief fantasy of stabbing him in the neck. But then he moved his lips to her mouth again.

"Patience," he whispered against her skin. "I have waited years for this night. I won't rush it."

"Did you really want me from the day we met?"

"So much it scared me."

He ran his fingertips down the center of her body until he rested his palm against her clitoris. It pulsed against his hand.

"I want you to come for me. I need you as wet as possible before I enter you. Understand?"

"Yes, sir." She started to breathe heavier as Søren pressed the heel of his hand in deeper. He dipped two fingers into her vagina before pressing his now wet fingertips against her clitoris. Desire engulfed her as he made tight circles on the swollen knot of flesh.

Her hips rose off the bed and she went still underneath him. Her entire body locked up before exploding with pleasure. Her vagina clenched and released rapidly, fluttering inside her and pressing against nothing. She couldn't wait to come around him, to let him feel her own pleasure on his body.

"Good girl," he said, brushing a lock of hair off her forehead.

He kissed her nipples again as she recovered from her orgasm. He sucked leisurely, lazily, at them as if he intended to spend all night lying between her breasts. She had a vague memory of Wyatt kissing her nipples like this. When he had done it she'd watched him and felt tenderness toward him like a mother to a child. They might have been the same age but she felt so much older than him. But with Søren she felt like the property of a king, like Esther in a harem, captured and conquered. And like Esther, she knew she had conquered the conqueror with the greatest of all powers – love.

Søren kissed the valley between her breasts and his lips traveled down her stomach and over her hips. He nipped her hip bone with his teeth and the moment the pain registered, Søren moved between her thighs. Eleanor stiffened as he licked her, kissed her, made love to her with his mouth.

"Fuck . . ." she groaned, unable to contain herself. She hadn't expected him to go down on her. He'd said he would pleasure her but this act seemed almost submissive to her as he knelt between her legs. But then he increased the pressure on her clitoris with his tongue and he pushed in two fingers and rubbed that soft hollow on the front wall inside her. He mastered her with his mouth. With his fingers he spread her folds so wide, exposing the entrance to her body. She couldn't hide from him. He saw all of her, all her most secret places. He licked her clitoris again and again, and when she came, she clenched at his lips and fingers.

He rose up and kissed her. She tasted herself on his mouth and couldn't get enough of it. Had she imagined anything so erotic before? His hand traced a line down her body from her collared neck to her thighs. He slid his thumb into her and she winced at the strange sensation. The wince turned into a gasp of pure pain as he pressed down hard against her hymen, not hard enough to tear it but hard enough that tears sprang to her eyes. He inhaled sharply as if he registered her pain inside his own body. He experienced her pain as his pleasure. Let him hurt her, then, so he could feel the pleasure of it. Let him destroy her so she could be reborn.

The pain passed and Søren settled in between her thighs, the tip of his length pressing against her clitoris. She pushed her hips hard into his, opening herself to him, offering herself to him.

She looked up and saw Søren's eyes were closed. His long, unnaturally dark eyelashes lay against his cheeks. The veins in his strong arms and shoulders quiv-

ered as he held himself over her. He started to speak but not in English. It was Danish, his first language. She knew some Danish, enough for her and Søren to tell each other "I need you, I want you" without anyone understanding them. But in her fevered state she could recognize nothing he said, not at first. He murmured the words like a prayer. She raised her head and pressed a kiss against his throat, her most favorite part of his body, the part hidden by his collar. The final words of his prayer she understood.

Jeg elsker dig.

I love you.

"I love you," he said, in his first language, and the words rose like a banner over the bed.

With her eyes half-closed, she felt the world falling asleep around her. She heard music somewhere in the distance, a haunting solo voice almost inhuman in its beauty. Did she hear this? See this? Or did it all come from within herself like a dream half remembered only hours after waking? She buried her head in the hollow between Søren's chin and shoulder. She breathed in and inhaled the scent of snow, new snow, clean and cold. And then she knew the truth.

Søren didn't smell like winter. Winter smelled like Søren.

Jeg elsker dig.

She heard Søren's voice through the mist.

With one thrust, he pushed inside her.

Pain like she'd never imagined rent her in half. Rent her in half, split her in two, burned her like fire, tore her like paper.

Beneath Søren she struggled and cried, her face buried against his chest. He cradled the back of her head as she wept tears of agony and surrender. He didn't pull out of her, didn't apologize. He held himself still, but inside her he pulsed as her vagina stretched and strained to take all of him into her. This was the price she had to pay for the kiss that couldn't be unkissed, for the apple that couldn't be unbitten, for the road she had taken. They had gone too far now. They could no longer go back.

She never wanted to go back.

The pain suffused her entire body. It burned like the hottest fire and if she had the use of her arms she would have tried to push him off her. One word could stop her suffering. She said nothing.

Slowly she emerged from the haze of pain and heard Søren's ragged breathing in her ear, the slightest catch of his breath, the subtlest moan in the back of his throat. Had there ever been a more beautiful sound than this – the sound of the pleasure he took inside her?

Instinct told her to shrink from him, to pull away. But she fought that urge and instead raised her hips again into his. He penetrated her until it seemed as if his entire body filled hers to the breaking point. Each slow, controlled thrust stretched her open wide, tearing the gate that would keep him out of her. She wanted it gone, wanted everything between them gone forever. His hand found her hand and he locked their fingers together as he rose up and pushed in again. She braced for pain but instead felt a deep stab of pleasure. Her eyes flew open at the shock of it, so carnal, so animal. With a cry she pushed her hips into his again and again. A rush of fluid between her thighs eased his passage even more.

Blood, perhaps? Her own wetness? It didn't matter. All that mattered was that he impaled her, invaded her, took ownership of her with every controlled yet merciless thrust.

She focused on his face, on the long dark eyelashes resting on his cheeks, on his partly open lips, on his blond hair that she ached to run her fingers through, on the sheen of sweat that covered his forehead, his shoulders and the vein that pulsed visibly in his neck. It must have taken all his strength to hold back and not lose himself inside her. Sixteen years since he'd last done this. His self-control could shatter at any moment. She wanted it to shatter.

Raising her head off the sheets, she kissed his shoulder. She whispered, "You own me."

Søren opened his eyes and gazed down at her.

He thrust so hard into her she stopped breathing. He thrust again just as hard and she exhaled once more. It had to be like this, it had to be brutal. It wasn't enough to take her virginity – he had to obliterate it.

For an eternity she could do nothing but breathe through the pain, breathe it into her and breathe it back out again. But as he moved in her, the pain waned and something else took its place. Something . . . desire, hunger, greed for more of him. Søren slid a hand between their bodies and kneaded her clitoris, stroking it as she ground her pelvis into his hand. A deep and primal need overtook her. She writhed underneath him, writhed and thrashed. Her inner walls throbbed against him. He pulled out and pushed in again as he teased her clitoris, dragging her close to a climax again.

The moment she saw him the first time all those years ago, she'd felt as if a golden cord had encircled her at the sight of him and tightened with each step toward him. Now she felt the cord again tight around her hips and her heart. As he pressed deeper and deeper into her, she felt the cord lifting her, carrying her higher and higher until her heart scraped the sky. The cord broke at its apex and she crashed to earth. She came apart, crying out as her climax crashed through her. This was it, the moment she had lived for and longed for since she'd first seen him. Communion was theirs at last.

Søren pushed faster against her and with a final thrust that left her gasping, he came inside her, driving into her, pouring into her endlessly as she shuddered around him and shattered beneath him. He lingered inside her after coming, devouring her mouth with his. At last he pulled out and blood and semen rushed out, pooling underneath her.

Once more Søren knelt between her thighs. He lapped at her sore inner lips, at her still throbbing clitoris. She rose up again and crashed once more. When Søren kissed her this time, she tasted blood.

He pushed his fingers into her tender opening. Soon he mounted her again, entered her again, fucked her again. Their first time might have had pretensions of lovemaking. The second time he didn't bother with any of the niceties of civilized sex. He fucked her brutally, unapologetically, fucked her like he would never have another chance to fuck her again this side of heaven and hell, and he would make the most of it even if it killed them both.

After he came a second time inside her, he pulled out and stared down at her naked, bleeding body. Welts and bruises scored her back. Cuts covered her feet.

Her vagina felt lacerated from his thrusts. She'd come four times tonight and knew one thing for certain from the look in his eyes.

He'd only begun to hurt her tonight.

The cane came out again. Then the flogger. He unlocked her from the bonds and brought her to her hands and knees and entered her still bleeding body as she steadied herself with one hand on the headboard, one hand digging into the sheets. His hands roamed over her bruised back, her thighs and hips. He grasped her by the back of the neck and held her still as he rammed into her from behind. She felt like property in his hands, owned, possessed and enslaved.

She lost herself in the night, ceased to be Eleanor, ceased to be a person with a mind or a will of her own. She was His and *His* became her only identity. If someone asked her who she was, "I'm His" would be the answer. He pushed four fingers into her, more than she'd ever dreamed she could take. And yet she took them and then him again because he gave her no choice in the matter.

"How much more can you take?" he asked as he pushed her down to her stomach.

"I can take anything you want to give me," she said. The sex and the beatings had sent her into a near-ecstatic state of peace and bliss. The pain had anesthetized her. She barely felt her body anymore. It was as if she floated above the bed. The hardest strikes of the flogger only tickled. The most vicious blow of the cane barely stung. Søren put her on her stomach and pushed into her again. For sixteen years he'd abstained from sex. He seemed determined to make up for lost time all in one night. Let him. Let him fuck her until neither one of them could move anymore. She begged to drink from this cup. She would drink until she choked on the wine of his body and his sadism. She would drink until she drowned in it.

Søren fucked her a fourth time, pausing every few minutes to bite her back and shoulders. Then he knelt on her thighs and struck her with a thin reed cane that left a line of fire on her skin wherever it landed. Never had she dreamed he would beat her while inside her. She should never have doubted his sadism. She would never doubt it again. As he rode her with long, hard thrusts, he spoke to her and told her how proud he was to own her, how she was his most precious possession, how she pleased him more than she could imagine, how he would love her always and never let her go.

By dawn she could take no more from him. By dawn he could give no more to her. He gathered her body, bruised from shoulder to knee, front and back, and held her in his arms.

They didn't speak of what had happened between them. What could they have said to each other? He had shown her his soul. She had given him her heart. They had joined their bodies and an immutable bond now sealed them together. And nothing could break them apart because nothing could break them.

When she awoke the next morning, the sun had joined them in bed.

Eleanor flinched as she stretched against the sheets. The bottoms of her feet throbbed. No doubt she still had shards of glass embedded in her skin. Her shoulders and back ached as if she'd been stretched on a rack. Her breasts and nipples were sore and swollen. Inside she was bruised and raw. She couldn't recall ever being in this much pain.

It was the best morning of her life.

Søren opened his eyes and gazed at her like he was trying to remember where he'd seen her before. She kissed him. He kissed her back.

"So now what?" she asked.

Søren smiled and something in that smile told her she was in the biggest trouble of her life.

"Everything."

ROSE MADDER AND THE SILKEN ROBE

Jo Mazelis

Jo Mazelis is a novelist, short story writer, poet and essayist. Her collection of stories, *Diving Girls* (Parthian, 2002), was shortlisted for the Commonwealth Best First Book, and Welsh Book of the Year. Her second book, *Circle Games* (Parthian, 2005), was longlisted for Welsh Book of the Year. She was born in Swansea, where she currently lives. Originally trained at Art School, she worked for many years in magazine publishing in London, as a freelance photographer, designer and illustrator, before receiving an MA in English Literature. Her novel *Significance* (Seren, 2014) won the Jerwood Fiction Uncovered Prize in 2015. Her latest book, a collection of short stories, is *Ritual, 1969*.

The classroom is modern and large, a rectangle of concrete and smooth featureless plaster bounded on two sides by glass windows. There is a long counter along one wall with locked storage cabinets under it, and at one end a sink that is usually splashed and stained with rose madder, Payne's grey, burnt sienna and yellow ochre; the surprising palette that when skilfully applied to paper make up a body's flesh and heft and shadows.

Tessa notices this only in passing, she hasn't used the sink; hasn't stood there rinsing out brushes or filling a container with fresh water. She only sees the vibrant daubs on the white porcelain out of the corner of her eye, as she heads for the screen at the back of the room. She sees the sink week after week and it seems that each time is noticing it for the first time. The crimson splashed on the white lip of the sink always particularly affects her and she wants to grab a cloth and scrub it clean, but knows she mustn't.

Instead she slips behind the screen and begins undressing.

It is ten minutes to eight on a Wednesday night. Philip dropped her off outside the main gates a few minutes ago, but he can't be there to collect her. Not tonight, as he's going to a stag do. Justin's stag do and tomorrow is Justin's wedding.

Tessa puts her shoes on the floor and puts her socks in a rolled-up ball in one of the shoes. Then she unzips her combat trousers, slides them from her body and folds them, before laying them over the shoes. Next she pulls off her sweater, then her t shirt, and adds these to the pile. Finally she takes off her bra and knickers and slips these under the t shirt. According to her method of undressing and dressing, the bra and pants should go on top, but that seems indecent in some weird and undefined way; too exposed, too obvious. As if by

concealing these last two small scraps of lace-trimmed cotton, she might yet conceal her nakedness.

Beyond the screen she hears the voices of the students as they greet one another. They all seem to know each other so well, enquiring about planned trips to Monet's garden at Giverny or to the Tate, or asking after husbands and wives or children. Chairs and stools and desks and easels are scraped over floors, the tap at the stained sink is turned on, water gushes and gurgles, the pipes rattle, then silence begins to gather. It is not the silence of an empty room, but one of expectation.

"Tessa?" she hears Christopher say. "Are you ready?"

This is her cue. She takes a breath and steps from behind the cover of the screen, walks to the centre of the room. Hardly anyone looks at her. Indeed they almost strain not to look; there is always something terribly important to be found inside a pencil case, or a bulldog clip to be adjusted on a drawing board or a date to be pencilled in at the top of a fresh sketchbook page.

Most colleges supply a dressing gown for this transitional stage in the process; a means of covering the locomotive nude between here and there. But the last model took a fancy to the silk gown that Christopher had supplied and stole it. No one noticed it had gone until the first night Tessa worked here and she had only discovered its absence after Christopher had directed her to the screen and promised that there was a robe she could slip on back there.

"I can't see a robe," she'd said.

"It should be there," Christopher had called back. "Maybe it's fallen. Is it on the floor?"

When it became clear that there was no robe, she was offered Mr Logan's mackintosh, a damp, grubby at the collar coat with a tartan lining, and there had been awkwardness and embarrassment when she'd refused it.

"It doesn't matter," she had to say loudly, seemingly addressing the entire room. "Honestly. It's fine!"

She'd stopped the mutters of protest and concern and apology then, by stepping out and brazenly, if a little briskly, crossing the room to the place where a bare mattress was laid out on the floor like some inexplicable example of fly tipping.

Christopher had promised to bring in another robe, but kept forgetting. Tessa didn't even own a dressing gown, though sometimes she'd see a fairly nice one in a charity shop, but always resented paying the three or four or five pounds they were asking. Besides which she always thought the robe was worn for the benefit of the students and the teacher, not for her, and now that they had seen her parading around naked for six weeks, it would be absurd to get all pernickety about it now.

Sometimes she thought about the robe the other model had stolen. She'd overheard two of the ladies in the class discussing it; it had been pure silk, antique, no doubt valuable, with exquisite embroidery and vibrant colours, ultramarine and magenta. Indeed the robe was so beloved that the dishonest model had been asked to pose wearing it and when Mrs Taylor exhibited her watercolours at the craft fair, it was only the two paintings of the model wearing the robe which sold, which just went to show didn't it?

The other model's name was Laura. Laura had longer legs, smaller breasts; her nipples were pinker than Tessa's. Tessa knows this because Miss Finch who studied at the Slade just before the war explains aloud how she has to mix a little burnt umber with her rose madder in order to get the correct shade for Laura's nipples.

The students love to talk about technique, to discuss the benefits of real sable as opposed to synthetic brushes, to name drop with surprising familiarity Cézanne, Picasso, Bonnard, Matisse and Degas.

Miss Finch is the best draftswoman among them and is treated with reverence and awe, but she despairs at her failing eyesight, her poor memory and the tremor that sometimes afflicts her pale bony hands.

Mr James favours the surrealists, de Chirico in particular, and despite Christopher's protests, likes to paint imaginary streets in the background of his nudes, grey vistas with geometrically uncertain colonnades and brooding, storm-ridden skies.

Tessa stands, or sits, or reclines amongst them, the invisible focus of all their attention. Invisible because she is nude; because she is a wash of Payne's grey shadow, a dry brush of raw sienna pubic hair, the almost perfect triangle of space between her bent arm and her back. Or she is the foreshortened example of contorted anatomy in Hans Baldung's woodcut Bewitched Groom or so she hears Christopher inform William Burnside who has positioned himself at a low donkey easel just south of her outstretched feet. Mr Burnside claims he enjoys the challenge of the difficult angle but Tessa suspects he's hoping for a glimpse of her cunt. She could take pity on him and let her legs drop open when she's told it's time for a rest, but modesty, or rather what remains of her modesty, prevents her.

As she poses the conversation dies away leaving only the sounds of pencil or charcoal on paper, or the vigorous splash of a fat brush head being shaken in a jam jar of water, and then Tessa begins to think of the world beyond this room.

She remembers Philip at the wheel of the car, distorting his face into a scowl at the mention of the stag do.

"It's just not my thing," he said. "It'll just be a drink with the boys, that's all. Might go for an Indian after."

She pictured herself entering the house they shared, its interior darker than the street, the awful black silence of the hallway and the stairs reaching up into an even more impenetrable darkness.

And Philip still hadn't got around to changing the light bulb in the hall so she'd have to grope her way to the middle room, all the way imagining terrible things lying in wait for her; the cruel and calculating predator of the movies. The fear would unsettle her for hours, she knew; the mere thought of it made her shudder.

"Are you cold, dear?" said the red-haired woman whose name she always forgets.

"No, no. I'm fine."

"Oh, she's cold."

"What's that?" Christopher asked.

"She's cold."

"Oh, you should have said, Tessa." And with that he gets an old-fashioned two-bar electric fire, aims it at her and plugs it in.

The heat radiates toward one flank of her body, making the other feel colder in comparison.

She could call at a friend's; Michelle's, or Judy's place down by the harbour, or she could go to the pub on her own. Or the cinema, though she has no idea what is showing.

Curiously she realises that if she had been at home and Philip had gone out she wouldn't feel afraid to be there; as if his presence carried over, extended itself, as if he had marked his space, left his scent on the house, on her, on the front path and the garden gate, and this would see off any intruders. But once the house had been left cold and empty, when the TV was off and the radio in the kitchen was silenced and there was no music, whether CD, cassette or record to be heard. When all the lights were off and the washing machine wasn't running and the toilet wasn't being flushed, and no one answered the phone, then his protective scent went cold.

Which was nonsense of course, she was no more vulnerable when he had been gone minutes or hours or even days. And darkness and silence were just darkness and silence. Risk was arbitrary; it was fear that was selective.

Tessa felt a fine mist of sweat developing on the side of her body which faced the fire. Being naked and being still focused the mind on the skin in a way that was unique and sometimes, as now, unpleasant.

Tessa was only mildly interested in art. She has however absorbed certain items of information about it from the conversations she finds herself overhearing. She knows that one artist, Renoir she believes, is said to have once claimed that he painted with his cock. Having a slightly literal mind, she had pictured this as a rather messy and not very accurate endeavour. Other artists were rather cruel to their models and mistresses and wives, forcing them to pose hour after hour in baths of chilly water. Giving them pneumonia. Killing them for art.

What we do for love! she thinks. But I do this for money. For this rather mild and well-heeled group of retired school teachers and secretaries and librarians, and yes, even one dentist, Mr Burnside.

And what do I do for love? For Philip? In the privacy of our own little rented terrace house? If I did it for money it would be vile, but as I said, I do it for love.

"Okay," says Christopher and he claps his hands twice. "That's ten minutes. We'll have two more quick poses then tea break."

Many in the class cluck their tongues and grumble in protest. They do not like the quick poses, but prefer the laboured long haul so that they can be fussy with shading and erasers and minutely recorded eyelashes. The others, like Miss Finch, see the process as work; as exercise for the hand and eye that must be kept up, lest they; it; art withers.

Tessa manoeuvres herself into a sitting position, being careful to keep her thighs clamped shut, which has become almost second nature. She stands and stretches, pointing the fingers of both hands at the ceiling and flexing her feet so that she is balanced on tiptoe.

"Ah," Christopher breathes. "That's beautiful! Could you hold that pose at all, Tessa?"

She stays where she is, balanced, ridiculous, but apparently beautiful.

What she does for love. In order to be told she is beautiful.

Thirty seconds and her ankles, her toes, her knees are quivering. Another thirty seconds and she's wobbling wildly.

Actually only a fifth of the class are even attempting to draw her. Christopher has his pocket sketch book out of his pocket and is working furiously, as are Miss Finch and the red-haired lady.

Tessa manages to hold it for two minutes, then Christopher puts his little black book back in the pocket of his corduroy jacket.

"Alright, Tessa," he says. "That's enough."

She lowers her heels onto the comforting flatness of the floor, lets her arms slowly carve the air as they drop and relax, and rolls her head to ease the tension in her neck.

"Oh, what's that?" says Miss Finch and she is pointing at Tessa's neck.

"Dear me," says the red-haired lady. "That's nasty. It looks like a burn."

She comes closer to Tessa, bearing the unstoppable concern of the school teacher, the mother, the social worker, the nurse.

"How on earth . . ." she asks and reaches for Tessa's neck.

Tessa ducks her head, tucks in her chin, pulls her hair down to cover the mark.

What we do for money is limited, but love, as Tessa knows, is another exchange.

"It's nothing," Tessa says. "It's fine."

Given the chance and the time the class would carefully squeeze red paint from their little metal tubes, use the tip of the finest brush, and artfully record this mark upon the model's neck.

She is invisible until the moment they have some evidence of her suffering.

He had promised to leave no mark, but the games were getting more elaborate. More painful.

What she does for love?

In the little rented terrace house.

With Philip who says he loves her as he fetches the rope from the box in the wardrobe, who says he won't hurt her.

She knows at this moment more than any other she should have a robe to cover herself with, and her heart burns with hatred for the thief.

THE MAN ALSO RISES

Christopher Peachment

Christopher Peachment worked as a stage manager at the Royal Court before turning to journalism. In the 1980s, he was a film editor for *Time Out* in London, later becoming Deputy Literary Editor and Arts Editor for *The Times*. More recently, he edited the specialist magazine, *Book and Magazine Collector*. He has written two novels: *Caravaggio* (2002) and *The Green and the Gold* (2003). For a long time he contributed a column to the *Erotic Review* that many feel represents the magazine's spirit and ethos, and which provided material for a book: *The Diary of a Sex Fiend*. He lives on the island of Crete.

"Animal rights activists protested against the annual Running of the Bulls in Pamplona yesterday. They branded the event 'barbaric'. The group is planning to hold a 'Running of the Nudes' alternative. Wearing only red scarves, horns and sturdy footwear, hundreds of nudes will run down Pamplona's streets." *Independent*

"Tell me, old man," I said, "what is this thing with the nude girls of the Pamplona run."

The old man looked at me and looked at the drunk, slumped in the dust against the wall of the bar.

"My throat is dry," he said.

I poured him a *tinto*.

"This *tinto* is good," he said. "It is rough and it is strong, the way a *tinto* should be."

"The girls," I said.

"This thing with the nude girls of Pamplona," he said. "It is a good thing. When you rise at dawn, and the sky is streaked, and the coffee is good and strong and the eggs are done the way you like them. And you eat before you set out to run before the girls. That is a good thing."

"Tell me about the girls," I said.

"The girls," he said. "They are not like other girls. They are specially bred for the run, in the rugged foothills of Andalucia."

"What do they look like, old man?" I said.

"Not like modern girls, the skinny ones with the small *tetas*. No. These girls are bred to have the big *tetas*, and that curve which real women used to have. And they have thighs like women used to have thighs. They have thighs that can squeeze the life from a man."

"And what do they wear in the hour of glory?" I said.

"They wear the suit," he said. "The special suit. It is a good suit."

"What suit?" I said.

"The suit that God gave them when they were born."

"You mean they are . . ."

"Nearly," he said. "Except for the thong."

"I have heard of the thong," I said.

He took another drink of the *tinto* and spat into the dust of Navarra.

"This thing with the thong," he said. "It is a good thing."

"The thong thing is a good thing," I said.

"Yes," he said.

"Some say that they have new ways," I said. "Some say they shave the parts of which we do not speak."

"I spit on this shaving thing," said the old man. "It is a new way, and it is not a good thing."

"Things change old man," I said.

"A woman's hair is her pride," he said. "It should be thick and dark, like the hair on her mother's upper lip."

An American came into the bar. He had a beard and was built like a barrel. He looked at the bar and he looked at me and he looked at the old man and I thought for a moment that he was going to hit me, they way they do, but he saw my weapon, and then I saw in his eyes that he would not. I keep my weapon concealed, but he saw it through my special suit.

"Will you be running, *Americano*?" I said.

"No," he said. "I have a wound. From the last time."

"That is a bad thing," I said. "Where is the wound?"

"I am wounded in that place we do not speak of," he said.

"I am sorry for your wound, *Americano*," I said. "It means you are not one for the run."

"No," he said. "I am not a run one."

"Still, you can watch," I said.

"*De nada*," he said. "I will watch."

"Have a *tinto*," I said.

"I will have a *tinto*," he said. "Though the *tinto* makes me *tonto*."

He turned to the old man.

"Does he know what to do?" said the Americano.

"All men know what to do," said the old man. "It is in the *cojones*. It is in the blood. It is a good thing, this thing with the *cojones* and the blood. All men have it, and they know this thing. And if they do not have it, they are a *maricon*."

And then from around the far corner I heard the sound. It was a terrible sound. I looked at the old man.

"Is that the sound?" I said.

"That is the sound," he said. "The sound that calls you to be a man."

I stood up and brushed the dust of Navarra from my special suit. The sound of beasts grew louder as they stamped and ran and trampled the dust and trampled down all before them.

"They are coming," I said.

"*Vaya con Dios,*" said the old man. "Come back a man. Or do not come back."

I stood up. That is all a man can do at this time. A man must stand up.

Round the corner they came, the nude girls of Pamplona. They were proud and they were fierce and I could see from their eyes that their blood was up. There was nothing for it but to see this thing through to its rightful end. There would be the spilling of the fluids of bodies on the sand before the sun would set. And this spilling of the fluids would be a good thing.

Already the young bucks were scattering before the charge. They were young and they were full of bravado, and they wanted the world to see that they were men. But they were not men, not yet. The nude girls of Pamplona bore down on them, their massive *tetas* swinging in the afternoon heat, their thick thighs pounding the dust of Navarra and their thongs . . . Words could not describe their thongs. Their thongs were unspeakable.

Then one man went down before the run, and in an instant they were on him. He went down in the dust and that minute was the last he knew. They were on him and they were doing what the old man warned me they would do.

"When they are on you," he said, "they will toss."

"This toss," I said, "is it a good thing?"

"It is not a good thing," he said. "If you go down, and they toss you, I will put you out of your misery." He patted the holster at his side.

"You would do that for me?" I said.

"You will thank me for it," he said.

I looked across at the young man. The nude girls of Pamplona were tossing him and tossing him. He cried out, just once, and then it was over. They left him there in the white dust of Navarra, a spent and broken husk.

And then the leading nude girl of Pamplona looked up at me.

"It is the moment of truth," said the old man.

I drew my weapon. It is a good weapon. Not as good a weapon as the old man's, which was worn and polished with use, and only a little rusty. But my weapon has been honed in the rugged houses of love in Toledo and it is a good weapon. The old man had told me how to hold it, and how to polish it for the nude girls of Pamplona.

The girl of Pamplona looked at my weapon and her nostrils grew wide and I could hear her sharp intake of breath. Her feet pawed the dust as she gathered herself. She looked into my eyes. I looked into her eyes. She charged.

She charged like no girl had charged before. When she charged the earth held steady for a moment and then it shook with the pounding of her feet. The earth moved with the weight of her thighs. Her body in its special birthday suit was thick with sweat and dust, and I knew that I must stand firm and wait.

There is a moment, just one brief moment, before she is upon you. And that moment is when a man must strike. A man must strike at this moment if he is to be a man. Knowing where to thrust the weapon is the thing to know. Standing tall, I cried out to her, twice.

"*Senorita*. Come," I cried. "Come. Come, *senorita*."

And I thrust my weapon in at the spot. It went in deep, the way a weapon should go in, and I held my ground and thrust it harder. And briefly, very briefly, the nude girl of Pamplona and I were one.

She struggled after that. But it was over. My weapon sank deeper and it was all over for her. She sank to the dust. Her eyes were glazed and her breathing slowed. And the lips of her mouth were pulled back over her teeth and she was happy in her fate.

I looked over at the old man. He nodded just once. He walked over, drew his knife, and cut off the ragged remains of her thong.

"It is yours," he said, handing the thong to me. "You have earned it, *El Hombre*."

Extended Copyright

Nicholson Baker: 'Shandee Finds Dave's Arm' from *House of Holes* by Nicholson Baker. Copyright © Nicholson Baker, 2011. First published by Simon & Schuster UK.

LaShonda Katrice Barnett: 'The Art of Losing' by LaShonda Katrice Barnett. Copyright © Katrice LaShonda Barnett, 2014. Reprinted by permission of the author.

Louise Black: 'Grammar Lessons' by Louise Black. Copyright © Louise Black, 2003. Reprinted by permission of the author.

Georges Bataille: 'The Antique Wardrobe' from *Story of the Eye: By Lord Auch* by Georges Bataille (Penguin Books). This translation copyright © Penguin Books Ltd 2012. Reproduced by permission of Penguin Books Ltd.

Anne Billson: 'Dead Girls' by Anne Billson. Copyright © Anne Billson, 2004. Reprinted by permission of the author.

Primula Bond: from *The Silver Chain* by Primula Bond. Copyright © Primula Bond, 2013. Reprinted by permission of HarperCollins Publishers Ltd.

Henri Breton: 'The Disappearing Island' and 'The Devil's Whisper' from *The Devil's Whisper and Other Stories From the Captain's Table* by Henri Breton (Erotic Print Society, 2002). Copyright © Henri Breton, 2002. Reprinted by permission of the author.

Veronica Cancio De Grandy: 'Pears and Silk' by Veronica Cancio De Grandy. Copyright © Veronica Cancio De Grandy, 2016. Reprinted by permission of the author.

Angela Carter: 'The Bloody Chamber' and 'The Company of Wolves' from *The Bloody Chamber* by Angela Carter. Published by Vintage, 2006. Copyright © Angela Carter. Reproduced by permission of the Estate of Angela Carter c/o Rogers, Coleridge & White Ltd., 20 Powis Mews, London W 11 1JN

Alex Chambers: 'The Selfish Giantess' by Alex Chambers. Copyright © Alex Chambers, 2009. Reprinted by permission of the author.

Rebecca Chance: 'Gluttony' by Rebecca Chance. Copyright © Rebecca Chance, 2003. Reprinted by permission of the author.

Helen Cross: 'Pull' by Helen Cross. Copyright © Helen Cross, 2004. Reprinted by permission from the author.

Andrew Crumey: 'Vox Vulva' by Andrew Crumey. Copyright © Andrew Crumey, 2004. Reprinted by permission of the author.

Roald Dahl: 'The Great Switcheroo' from *Switch Bitch* by Roald Dahl (published by Penguin Books) Copyright © Roald Dahl Nominee Limited, 1965, 1974

Emma Donoghue: 'The Tale of the Rose' from *Kissing the Witch* by Emma Donoghue (copyright © Emma Donoghue, 1997) is reproduced by permission of CDLA on behalf of Emma Donoghue

Justine Dubois: 'Torn Lace' and 'Dorchester Evening' by Justine Dubois. Copyright © Justine Dubois, 2003. Reprinted by permission of the author.

'San Sebastian' by Justine Dubois. Copyright © Justine Dubois, 2002. Reprinted by permission of the author.

Neville Elder: 'The Red House' by Neville Elder. Copyright © Neville Elder, 2016. Reprinted by permission of the author.

Michel Faber: 'Bed & Breakfast' by Michel Faber. Copyright © Michel Faber, 2004.

'The Perfect W' by Michel Faber. Copyright © Michel Faber, 2003.

Edward Field: 'Forbidden Arias' by Edward Field. Copyright © Edward Field, 2012. Reprinted by permission of the author.

John Fowles: from *The Magus* by John Fowles. Copyright © John Fowles 1966, 1977. Published by Vintage, an imprint of Random House Group.

Dean Francis: 'The Elegant Duchess' by Dean Francis.

'Hannah's Tale – Flat' by Lucy Golden. Copyright © Lucy Golden, 2003. Reprinted by permission of the author.

Kass Goldsworthy: 'Commute' and 'This Is What It's Like' by Kass Goldsworthy. Copyright © Kass Goldsworthy, 2014. Reprinted by permission of the author.

A. F. Harrold: 'The Boys' by A. F. Harrold. Copyright © A. F. Harrold, 2008. Reprinted by permission of the author.

Arlene Heyman: 'The Loves of Her Life' from *Scary Old Sex* by Arlene Heyman. Copyright © Arlene Heyman, 2016. Reprinted by permission of Bloomsbury Publishing Plc.

Patricia Highsmith: from *Carol* by Patricia Highsmith. Copyright © 1951 by Patricia Highsmith. Copyright © 1993 by Diogenes Verlag AG Zurich. Reprinted by permission of Virago, an imprint of Little, Brown Book Group.

Alan Hollinghurst: from *The Swimming Pool Library* by Alan Hollinghurst. Copyright © Alan Hollinghurst, 1988. Published by Vintage, an imprint of Random House.

Michel Houellebecq: from *Atomised* by Michel Houellebecq. Translated from the French *Les Particules Elementaires* by Frank Wynne. Copyright © Flammarion, 1999, copyright © Frank Wynne, 2000. Published by Vintage, an imprint of Random House.

Angelica Jacob: 'This Year at Marienbad' by Angelica Jacob. Reproduced with permission of Curtis Brown Group Ltd.,

on behalf of Angelica Jacob. Copyright © Angelica Jacob 2004.

Luke Jennings: 'Serena' by Luke Jennings. Copyright © Luke Jennings, 1999. Reprinted by permission of the author.

'Small Talk' by Luke Jennings. Copyright © Luke Jennings, 2000. Reprinted by permission of the author.

Katie Kelly: 'Let's Put This to Bed' by Katie Kelly. Copyright © Katie Kelly, 2006. Reprinted by permission of the author.

'Summer' by Katie Kelly. Copyright © Katie Kelly, 2007. Reprinted by permission of the author.

Laurence Klavan: 'The Witness' by Laurence Klavan. Copyright © Laurence Klavan, 2016. Reprinted by permission of the author.

Roberta Latow: from *Three Rivers* by Roberta Latow. Copyright © Roberta Latow, 1980. Reprinted by permission of the author's estate.

D. H. Lawrence: from Lady Chatterley's Lover by D. H. Lawrence reprinted by permission of Pollinger Limited (www.pollingerltd.com) on behalf of the Estate of Frieda Lawrence Ravagli.

Anna Maconochie: 'What Have I To Do With You?' by Anna Maconochie. Copyright © Anna Maconochie, 2015. Reprinted by permission of the author.

Adnan Mahmutović: 'Fatima' by Adnan Mahmutović. Copyright © Adnan Mahmutović, 2008. Reprinted by permission of the author.

Jodi Ellen Malpas: from *This Man* by Jodi Ellen Malpas reprinted by permission of The Orion Publishing Group Ltd, London. Copyright © Jodi Ellen Malpas 2012.

Nnenna Marcia: 'House Keeping' and 'Mrs Salad Woman' by Nnenna Marcia. Copyright © Nnenna Marcia, 2013. Reprinted by permission of the author.

Ali May: 'When It Gets Hot In Tehran' by Ali May. Copyright © Ali May, 2013. Reprinted by permission of the author.

Jo Mazelis: 'Rose Madder and the Silken Robe' by Jo Mazelis. Copyright © Jo Mazelis, 2015. Reprinted by permission of the author.

Ruby McNally: 'The Midwesterners' by Ruby McNally. Copyright © Ruby McNally, 2014. Reprinted by permission of the author.

Henry Miller: from *Quiet Days in Clichy* by Henry Miller. Reproduced with permission of Curtis Brown Group Ltd, London on behalf of The Beneficiaries of the Estate of Henry Miller. Copyright (c) The Beneficiaries of the Estate of Henry Miller, 1956.

Roger Moineau: 'Coming Swimmingly' by Roger Moineau.

Christine Pountney: 'Mean Streak' and 'The Cat that got the Cream' by Christine Pountney. Copyright © Christine Pountney, 2003. Reprinted by permission of the author.

Pauline Réage: from *Story of O* by Pauline Réage. Copyright © 1965 by Grove Press, Inc. Originally published in France as *Histoire d'O*. Copyright © 1954 by Jean-Jacques Pauvert. Reprinted by permission of Georges Borchardt, Inc., for Editions Jean-Jacques Pauvert.

Tiffany Reisz: from *The Saint* by Tiffany Reisz. Text copyright © 2014 by Tiffany Reisz. Permission to reproduce text granted by Harlequin Books S.A.

Alina Reyes: from *Behind Closed Doors* by Alina Reyes. Copyright © Editions Robert Laffont S. A, Paris, 1994.

Anne Rice: from *The Claiming of Sleeping Beauty* by Anne Rice, writing as A. N. Roquelaure. Copyright © A. N. Roquelaure, 1983. Reprinted by permission of Sphere, an imprint of Little, Brown Book Group.

Danielle Schloss: 'Park Antics' by Danielle Schloss. Copyright © Danielle Schloss, 2013. Reprinted by permission of the author.

Paullina Simons: from *The Bronze Horseman* by Paullina Simons. Copyright © Paullina Simons, 2000. Published by HarperCollins Publishers Ltd.

Elizabeth Speller: 'Thought Waves' by Elizabeth Speller. Copyright © Elizabeth Speller, 2000. Reprinted by permission of the author.

Charlotte Stein: pp. 99–127 from *Intrusion* by Charlotte Stein. Copyright Charlotte Stein, 2014. Reprinted by permission of HarperCollins Publishers.

David Henry Sterry: 'The Snow Leopard' by David Henry Sterry. Copyright © David Henry Sterry, 2003. Reprinted by permission of the author.

Garry Stewart: 'Off the Road' by Garry Stewart. Copyright © Garry Stewart, 2003. Reprinted by permission of the author.

Alessandra Rivalta: 'The Perfect Italian Wife' by Alessandra Rivalta. Copyright © Alessandra Rivalta, 2014. Reprinted by permission of the author.

Mitzi Szereto: 'Moonburn' by Mitzi Szereto. Copyright © Mitzi Szereto, 2003. Reprinted by permission of the author.

Ortensia Visconti: 'Tokyo' from *l'idée Fixe* (Naive, 2013) by Ortensia Visconti. Translated from Italian by Anne Milano Appel and Norah Perkins. Copyright © Ortensia Visconti, 2012. Reprinted by permission of Janklow & Nesbit Associates on behalf of the author.

Helen Walsh: 'Men and Motors' and 'You've Been Framed' by Helen Walsh. Copyright © Helen Walsh, 2004. Reprinted by permission of the author.

Harriet Warner: 'Burning Desire' and 'A Bed for the Night' by Harriet Warner. Copyright © Harriet Warner, 2003. Reprinted by permission of Casarroto Ramsey Associates Ltd on behalf of the author.

Louise Welsh: 'The Worm on the Bud' from *The Cutting Room* by Louise Welsh, Copyright © Louise Welsh, 2002. Reprinted by permission of Canongate Books Ltd.

'Belle and Sylvie' by Louise Welsh. First published by the Erotic Review, 2004. Copyright © Louise Welsh. Reproduced by permission of the author c/o Rogers, Colderidge & White Ltd., 20 Powis Mews, London W11 1JN.

Every effort has been made to trace copyright holders and to obtain their permission for the use of copyright material. The publisher apologizes for any errors or omissions in the above list and would be grateful if notified of any corrections that should be incorporated in future reprints or editions of this book.

About the Artwork

The cover image of the book, *World of Interiors*, is by British artist Jonathan Yeo (b. London, 18 December 1970) and part of his collage series which dates back to 2007. Yeo is one of the world's leading figurative artists with portraits of Tony Blair, Malala Yousafzai, Kevin Spacey, Cara Delevingne and Damien Hirst amongst his best known works. He is represented in many public and private collections internationally and has been the subject of major retrospective exhibitions at the National Portrait Gallery in London, The Lowry in Manchester and the Museum of National History in Denmark amongst others.

World of Interiors is an experiment in making designs from pornographic magazine cuttings which mimic the style of traditional wallpaper patterns. The work is a continuation of Yeo's Porn Collage Series, which started with an ironic portrait of former President George W. Bush in 2007, made from cuttings of similarly explicit material. By disguising the adult content as something innocuous and decorative, the viewer is invited to make the connection with the increasing pervasion of explicit imagery in advertising and contemporary culture.